CANADIAN
Ingersoll-Rand
COMPANY LIMITED

HEAD OFFICE: MONTREAL, QUE.   PLANT: SHERBROOKE, QUE.

MONTREAL

TORONTO

SUDBURY

WINNIPEG

CALGARY

EDMONTON

VANCOUVER

MR. G. E. AST

COMPRESSED AIR AND GAS DATA

Compressed Air and Gas Data

Charles W. Gibbs, *editor*

SECOND EDITION
(First Printing)

PRICE $12.00

Ingersoll-Rand Company

11 Broadway, New York, N. Y. 10004

PREFACE

In 1919 the first edition of Compressed Air Data came off the press. The following is quoted from the preface:—

> "These pages are the result of an effort to collect, under one cover, formulae and data on the subject of 'Compressed Air Engineering', essential to an understanding of its theory and practical application."

The intervening years have not only shown a tremendous growth in the use of compressed air, but have also seen the development of the process industries involving the compression of other gases.

This edition of what was known as Compressed Air Data has been given a new name—Compressed Air and Gas Data—signifying its broader coverage. This volume is specifically designed for all those at the engineering level who are involved in air and gas compression, transmission and use. Theory and its application presupposes some knowledge of thermodynamics but does not omit the basics. Certain special phases of theory involved in the compression and use of air and other gases are included. An objective approach has been taken to guide the reader in the selection of compression equipment through an evaluation of the economic factors.

It is the sincere wish of the editor and publishers that this book will serve manufacturers and users alike in an industry so essential to the total economy of the world.

Acknowledgements

So many people have cooperated in the preparation of this book that it is impossible to give credit to all. However, the Editorial Board and a few others should be mentioned. These include Messrs. W. T. Alderson, A. W. Loomis, A. G. Clark, L. M. Hunt, Jr., A. A. Lomar, J. A. Reed, R. C. Rogers, H. A. Wiegand, all with Ingersoll-Rand Company, and to Mr. S. M. Parkhill, Editor of *Compressed Air* magazine. To these and to friends in other industries, we wish to express our sincere appreciation. Their counsel has added materially to the scope and value of this book. I would be remiss if I did not also acknowledge the great assistance of my wife who typed all the written material in this book, most of it several times.

CHARLES W. GIBBS, *Editor*

TABLE OF CONTENTS

TABLE OF CONTENTS

COMPRESSED AIR AND GAS DATA

Chapter 1

An Introduction to Compressors

Caption Index   **Page**

Purposes of Compression

Compression of gas has one basic goal — to deliver gas at a pressure higher than that originally existing. The original pressure level may vary from very low absolute pressures (fractions of a micron) to several thousand pounds. The pressure rise may vary from a few ounces to many thousand pounds and the volumes handled from a few cubic feet per minute to hundreds of thousands.

Compression is undertaken for a variety of purposes:

1. To transmit power, as in a compressed air system for operating pneumatic tools;
2. To provide air for combustion;
3. To transport and distribute gas, as in natural gas pipelines and city gas distribution systems;
4. To circulate a gas through a process or a system;
5. To produce conditions more conducive to chemical reaction; and,
6. To produce and maintain reduced pressure levels for many purposes, accomplished by removing from a system unwanted gases either leaking or flowing into the system or initially present.

Methods of Compression

Four methods are used to compress gas. Two are in the *intermittent* class, and two in the *continuous flow* class. (These are descriptive, not thermodynamic or duty classification terms.) These methods are to:

1. Trap consecutive quantities of gas in some type of enclosure, reduce the volume, thus increasing the pressure, then push the compressed gas out of the enclosure;
2. Trap consecutive quantities of gas in some type of enclosure, carry it without volume change to the discharge opening, compress the gas by backflow from the discharge system, then push the compressed gas out of the enclosure;
3. Compress the gas by the mechanical action of rapidly rotating impellers or bladed rotors that impart velocity and pressure to the flowing gas (velocity is further converted into pressure in stationary diffusers or blades); and,
4. Entrain the gas in a high velocity jet of the same or another gas (usually, but not necessarily, steam) and convert the high velocity of the mixture into pressure in a diffuser.

Compressors using methods 1 and 2 are in the intermittent class and are known as *positive-displacement* compressors. Those using method 3 are known as *dynamic* compressors. Compressors using method 4 are known as *ejectors* and normally operate with an intake below atmospheric pressure.

Compressor Types

The principal types of compressors are shown in Fig. 1-A and are defined below. Cam, diaphragm, and diffusion pumps or compressors are not shown because of their specialized applications and relatively small size.

Positive-displacement units are those in which successive volumes of gas are confined within a closed space and elevated to a higher pressure.

Reciprocating compressors are positive-displacement machines in which the compressing and displacing element is a piston having a reciprocating motion within a cylinder.

Rotary positive-displacement compressors are machines in which compression and displacement is effected by the positive action of rotating elements.

Sliding-vane compressors are rotary positive-displacement machines in which axial vanes slide radially in a rotor eccentrically mounted in a cylindrical casing. Gas trapped between vanes is compressed and displaced.

Liquid-piston compressors are rotary positive-displacement machines in which water or other liquid is used as the piston to compress and displace the gas handled.

Two-impeller straight-lobe compressors are rotary positive-displacement machines in which two straight mating lobed impellers trap gas and carry it from intake to discharge. There is no internal compression.

Helical- or spiral-lobe compressors are rotary positive-displacement machines in which two intermeshing rotors, each with a helical form, compress and displace the gas.

Dynamic compressors are rotary continuous-flow machines in which the rapidly rotating element accelerates the gas as it passes through the element, converting the velocity head into pressure, partially in the rotating element and partially in stationary diffusers or blades.

Centrifugal compressors are dynamic machines in which one or more rotating impellers, usually shrouded on the sides, accelerate the gas.   Main gas flow is radial.

Axial compressors are dynamic machines in which gas acceleration is obtained by the action of the bladed rotor shrouded on the blade ends.   Main gas flow is axial.

Mixed-flow compressors are dynamic machines with an impeller form combining some characteristics of both the centrifugal and axial types.

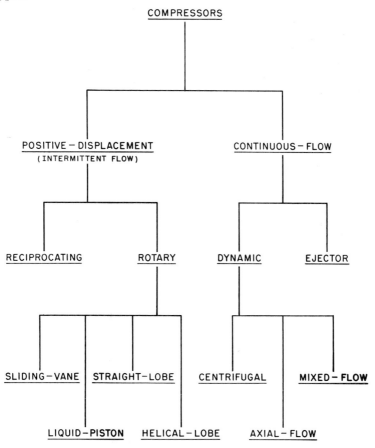

Fig. 1-A.   Chart of principal compressor types.

Ejectors are devices that use a high velocity gas or steam jet to entrain the inflowing gas, then convert the velocity of the mixture to pressure in a diffuser.

Principles of Operation

Every compressor is made up of one or more *basic elements*. A single element, or a group of elements in parallel, comprises a *single-stage* compressor.

Many compression problems involve conditions beyond the practical capability of a single compression stage. Too great a compression ratio (absolute discharge pressure divided by absolute intake pressure) may cause excessive discharge temperature or other design problems.

It therefore may become necessary to combine elements or groups of elements in series to form a *multistage* unit, in which there will be two or more steps of compression. The gas is frequently cooled between stages to reduce the temperature and volume entering the following stage.

Note that each stage is an individual basic compressor within itself. It is sized to operate in series with one or more additional basic compressors and even though they may all operate from one power source, each is still a separate compressor.

The following simplified and introductory outlines show the principles of operation of each principal type of compressor. Certain types are discussed further in later chapters.

The Reciprocating Compressor

The basic reciprocating compression element is a single cylinder compressing on only one side of the piston (*single-acting*). A unit compressing on both sides of the piston (*double-acting*) consists of two basic single-acting elements operating in parallel in one casting.

The reciprocating compressor uses automatic spring loaded valves that open only when the proper differential pressure exists across the valve. Inlet valves open when the pressure in the cylinder is slightly below the intake pressure. Discharge valves open when the pressure in the cylinder is slightly above the discharge pressure.

Fig. 1-B, diagram A, shows the basic element with the cylinder full of atmospheric air. On the theoretical pV diagram (indicator card), point 1 is the start of compression. Both valves are closed.

Diagram B shows the compression stroke, the piston having moved to the left, reducing the original volume of air with an accompanying rise in pressure. Valves remain closed. The pV diagram shows compression from point 1 to point 2, and that the pressure inside the cylinder has reached that in the receiver.

Diagram C shows the piston completing the delivery stroke. The discharge valves opened just beyond point 2. Compressed air is flowing out through the discharge valves to the receiver.

After the piston reaches point 3, the discharge valves will close leaving the clearance space filled with air at discharge pressure. During the expansion stroke, diagram D, both the inlet and discharge valves remain closed and air trapped in the clearance space increases in volume causing a reduction in pressure. This continues, as the piston moves to the right, until the cylinder pressure drops below the inlet pressure at point 4. The inlet valves now will open and air will flow into the cylinder until the end of the reverse stroke at point 1. This is the intake or suction stroke, illustrated by diagram E. At point 1 on the pV diagram, the inlet valves will close and the cycle will repeat on the next revolution of the crank.

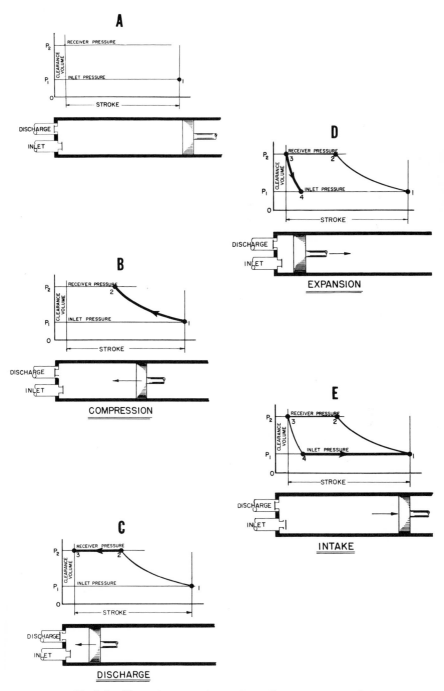

Fig. 1-B. The various steps in a reciprocating compressor cycle.

In a simple two-stage reciprocating compressor, the cylinders are proportioned according to the total compression ratio, the second stage being smaller because the gas, having already been partially compressed and cooled, occupies less volume than at the first stage inlet. Looking at the pV diagram (Fig. 1-C), the conditions before starting compression are points 1 and 5 for the first and second stages, respectively; after compression, points 2 and 6, and, after delivery, 3 and 7. Expansion or air trapped in the clearance spaces as the pistons reverse brings points 4 and 8, and on the intake stroke the cylinders are again filled at points 1 and 5 and the cycle is set for repetition.

Multiple staging of any positive displacement compressor follows the above pattern.

Reciprocating compressors are further discussed in Chapter 6.

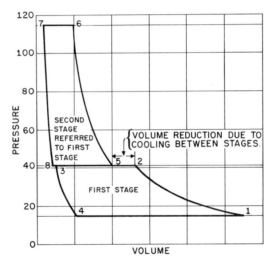

Fig. 1-C. Combined theoretical indicator card for a two-stage two-element 100 psiG positive-displacement compressor.

The Sliding-Vane Compressor

The rotary sliding-vane compressor has as its basic element the cylindrical casing with its heads and rotor assembly. When running at design pressure, the theoretical indicator card is identical to the reciprocator. There is one difference of importance, however. The reciprocating unit has spring-loaded valves that open automatically on small pressure differentials between the outside and inside of the cylinder. The discharge valve, therefore, opens as soon as point 2 (Fig. 1-B) is reached and the inlet as soon as point 4 is reached, even though there may be some variation in the discharge pressure from time to time.

The sliding-vane machine, however, has no valves. The times in the cycle when the inlet and discharge open are determined by the location of ports over which the vanes pass (Fig. 1-D). The inlet porting is normally wide and is designed to admit gas up to the point when the pocket between two vanes is the largest. It is closed when the following vane of each pocket passes the edge of the inlet port.

The pocket volume decreases as the rotor turns and the gas is com-pressed. Compression continues until the discharge port is uncovered by the leading vane of each pocket. This point must be preset or built-in when the unit is manufactured. Thus, the compressor *always* compresses the gas to *design* pressure, regardless of the pressure in the receiver into which it is discharging.

A

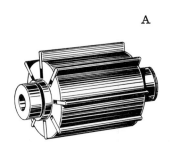

ROTOR WITH NON-METALLIC
SLIDING VANES.

C

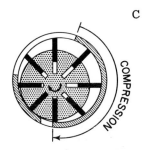

GAS IS GRADUALLY COMPRESSED
AS POCKETS GET SMALLER.

B

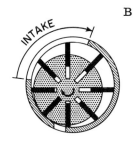

AS ROTOR TURNS, GAS IS TRAP-
IN POCKETS FORMED BY VANES.

D

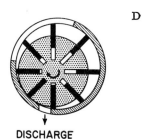

COMPRESSED GAS IS PUSHED OUT
THROUGH DISCHARGE PORT.

Fig. 1-D.   The steps in compression for a sliding-vane rotary compressor.

This results in a distortion of the *pV* diagram when the discharge pressure is higher or lower than design. To make this clear, Fig. 1-E shows, in a slightly exaggerated form, the operation of the rotary unit respectively with discharge at design pressure (top), discharge above de-sign (center), and discharge below design (bottom). These apply to *any* rotary unit with fixed ports, internal compression, and no valves.

Whereas the reciprocator will have a card similar to Fig. 1-E (top) regardless of discharge pressure changes, the fixed port rotary will re-quire slightly more power at off-design pressures as represented by the small triangle at the end of the compression line.

For high compression ratios or greater economy, multiple staging also is necessary here. As with the reciprocating compressor, the second stage is another basic compressor designed to operate in series with the first stage with a higher intake pressure and having smaller capacity. The combined indicator card for design pressure would be similar to Fig. 1-C. For further discussion, see Chapter 7.

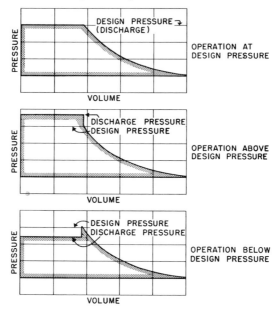

Fig. 1-E. Types of theoretical indicator cards obtained by any rotary compressor having built-in (fixed) porting.

The Liquid-Piston Compressor

The rotary liquid-piston or liquid-ring compressor uses a rotor with multiple forward turned blades turning about a central cone containing inlet and discharge ports, the blades driving a captive ring of liquid around the inside of an elliptical casing. The basic element is the casing, heads, and rotor assembly (Fig. 1-F).

A certain amount of liquid is trapped between adjacent blades and as the rotor turns, the liquid face moves in and out of this space due to the casing shape. This creates, in effect, a liquid piston. Porting in the central cone is built-in and fixed. There are no valves.

Two eccentric sweeps usually are provided to form the elliptical casing. These are opposed diametrically and thus balance out radial thrust loads. For every revolution, two compression cycles are completed in each rotor chamber.

There is compression within the pockets or chambers between the blades before the discharge port is uncovered and the theoretical indicator card will be similar to Fig. 1-E (top). Since the port location must be designed and built for a specific compression ratio, it will tend to operate as in Fig. 1-E (center and bottom) when the actual discharge pressure is above or below the design pressure.

The cooling of liquid-ring compressors is direct rather than through the walls of a casing. The required additional cooling liquid is fed into the casing where it comes into direct contact with the gas being com-pressed. The excess liquid is discharged with the gas.

The discharged mixture is passed through a conventional baffle or centrifugal type separator to remove the free liquid. Because of the in-timate contact of gas and liquid, the final discharge temperature can be held close to the temperature of the inlet cooling water. However, the discharge gas is saturated at the discharge temperature of the compress-ing liquid.

The amount of liquid that may be passed through the compressor is not critical and can be varied to obtain the desired results. The unit will not be damaged if a large quantity of liquid inadvertently, or by intent, enters its suction.

Lubrication is required only in the bearings which are generally lo-cated external to the casing. The liquid itself acts as a lubricant, sealing medium and coolant for the stuffing boxes.

Two-staging is possible by putting two machines in series.

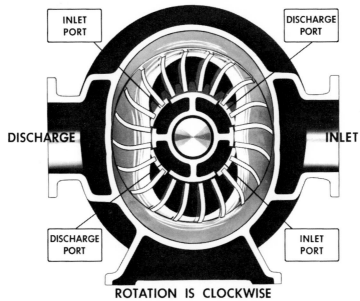

ROTATION IS CLOCKWISE

Courtesy of Nash Engineering Company

Fig. 1-F.   A typical liquid-piston rotary compressor.

The Two-Impeller Straight-Lobe Compressor

A two-impeller straight-lobe positive-displacement compressor element consists of a casing containing duplicate symmetrical rotors or impellers usually having a figure eight cross section. Some have three lobes. These intermesh, are kept in phase by external timing gears, and rotate in oppo-site directions. The term *cycloidal* often is used for this type even though the impellers may have other than cycloidal form.

There is no compression or reduction of gas volume during the turning of the rotors. The rotors merely move the gas from the inlet to the discharge. Compression is by backflow into the casing from the discharge line at the time the discharge port is uncovered. Displacement of the compressed gas into the discharge system then takes place. There are no valves.

There is no contact between the impellers or between impellers and casing. Sealing is by close clearances and lubrication is not required within the gas chamber. One impeller is driven directly while the other is driven through phasing gears. Since both impellers do the same amount of work, the gears handle 50 percent of the total power input.

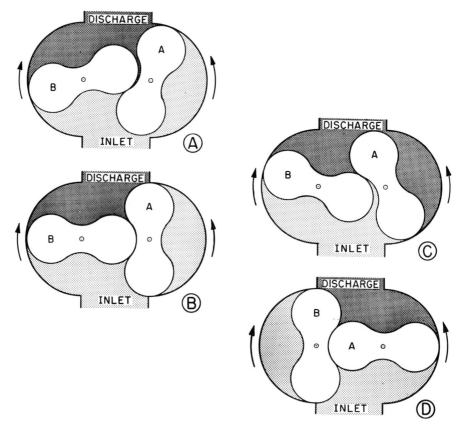

Fig. 1-G.   The operating cycle of a two-impeller straight-lobe rotary compressor.

The operation can be visualized from the diagrams of Fig. 1-G. Light shading shows gas at inlet pressure. Dark shading shows gas at discharge pressure.

Diagram A — The chamber of lobe A is full of gas at inlet pressure and further intake will soon stop. Lobe B is delivering gas at discharge pressure.

Diagram B — Lobe A has closed the intake but has not yet passed the edge of the discharge port. Lobe B is still discharging.

Diagram C — Lobe A has passed the discharge port permitting discharge gas to flow into the chamber, compressing the gas therein. The other side of Lobe A is starting the intake cycle. Lobe B is still discharging.

Diagram D — Lobe A is still discharging on one side and filling its other chamber with intake gas. Lobe B has completed intake for its second chamber and is about to pass the discharge port.

Through this cycle, the rotors have turned through approximately 90 degrees. The next 90 degrees completes a similar cycle, Lobe B interchanging with Lobe A. There are four deliveries per revolution. The theoretical indicator card is a rectangle.

Some designs can handle a considerable amount of liquid carryover with the intake gas, others should be protected. These units generally are air cooled. Two-staging is available in some cases using two properly sized machines arranged in series.

The Helical- or Spiral-Lobe Compressor

This machine is a two-rotor positive-displacement rotary unit compressing gas between the intermeshing helical lobes and the rotor chambers of the housing. The basic element is the housing with its enclosed rotor assemblies. The lobes on the two rotors are not identical. The male, or driven, rotor (main rotor) has a form that fits into the pocket of the female, or gate, rotor. About 85 to 90 percent of the power is used by the main rotor, the gate requiring only 10 to 15 percent of the total power at the most.

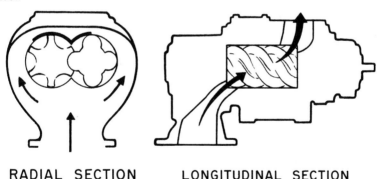

RADIAL SECTION   LONGITUDINAL SECTION

Fig. 1-H.   Illustrative sections of a typical helical-lobe rotary compressor.

There are two types, one using timing gears to properly phase the two rotors at all times. This kind requires no lubrication and sealing is by close clearances. The second type uses a flood of oil through the machine to lubricate and seal and to cool the compressed gas. In this style, the timing gears may, at times, be omitted.

These units have internal compression. The built-in or design compression ratio is determined by the location of the opening edges of the discharge port and the wrap angle of the lobes. There are no valves.

The rotors may or may not have the same number of lobes. Usually the main rotor has fewer than the gate and therefore operates at a higher speed.

Designs vary in the helix angle and in the contour of the lobes. The operation of one design is shown in Fig. 1-H and 1-I. Fig. 1-H shows two cross sections, illustrating in the radial section the inlet area at one end. The longitudinal section shows the gas flow through the machine.

In the Fig. 1-I, the shaded portions show the gas being compressed step by step when considering a single gate pocket and the corresponding main pocket during one complete revolution of the main rotor.

1. The gate rotor pocket is fully open and filled with inlet gas. The main rotor pocket is open to inlet, but is not yet filled its full length.

2. The gate pocket has been closed off and the main rotor pocket is filled, but still open to inlet.

3. The lobes have meshed, the mating pockets join and begin to shorten.

4. The spiral pockets become smaller. The gas is compressed as it is moved axially toward the discharge end. Throughout this sequence from 1 through 4 the discharge end cover has sealed the end of the pocket.

5. The discharge has been uncovered and compressed gas discharged.

While this is happening with one pocket, the other pockets are following the same cycle.

The pV diagram is similar to that of a reciprocating compressor if the actual compression ratio is the same as the design ratio. If the actual compression ratio varies, the unit will over- or under-compress (Fig. 1-E). The effect on efficiency is small over a rather wide range of compression ratios.

Helical-lobe compressors will handle reasonable liquid carryover although the limits vary with design.

Two-staging is possible by arranging machines (basic elements) in series. Occasionally the two stages are in the same casing connected by internal passages.

See Chapter 8.

The Dynamic Compressor

Compression in any dynamic compressor depends on the transfer of energy from a rotating set of blades to a gas. The rotor accomplishes this energy transfer by changing the momentum and pressure of the gas. The momentum (related to kinetic energy) then is converted into useful pressure energy by slowing the gas down in a stationary diffuser or another set of blades.

The *centrifugal designation* is used when the gas flow is radial and the energy transfer is predominently due to a change in the centrifugal forces acting on the gas.

The *axial designation* is used when the gas flow is parallel to the compressor shaft. Energy transfer is caused by the action of a number of rows of blades on a rotor, each row followed by a fixed row fastened to the casing.

A *mixed-flow designation* is used when the gas flow is between radial and axial.

Although the compressors are constructed differently, the same basic aerodynamic design theory applies to all three.

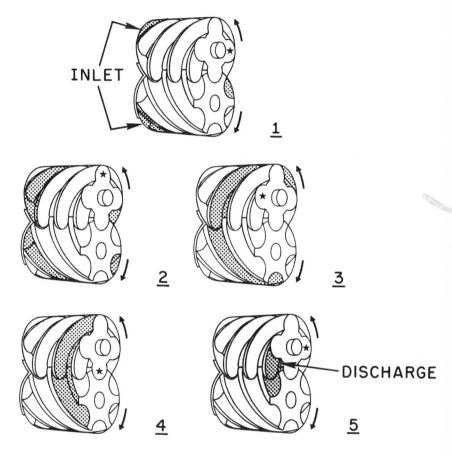

Fig. 1-I. Steps in compression by a typical helical-lobe rotary compressor.

Dynamic compressors require no internal lubrication and can provide oil-free gas, provided the inlet gas itself is oil-free. Shaft bearings are usually external to the casing, thus further limiting possibility of contamination.

The Centrifugal Type

The centrifugal compressor has an impeller with radial or backward leaning vanes usually between two shrouds. The gas is forced through the impeller by the mechanical action of the rapidly rotating impeller vanes, there being a component around the shaft forming a vortex and a component through the impeller. The velocity generated is converted into pressure, partially in the impeller (the amount depends upon design), partially in stationary diffusers following the impeller. Fig. 1-J illustrates in both radial and longitudinal section a single-stage centrifugal with radial vanes. This utilizes a radial diffuser and a volute gas collector ending in a volute diffuser.

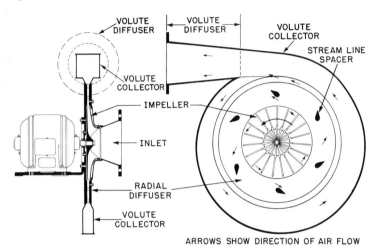

ARROWS SHOW DIRECTION OF AIR FLOW

Fig. 1-J. Typical overhung impeller single-stage centrifugal compressor.

Multistage centrifugal compressors utilize two or more impellers arranged for series flow each with a radial diffuser and return channel separating impellers. The number of impellers per casing is dependent upon many factors, but usually eight to ten is the limit. Fig. 1-K is a section of a typical uncooled multistage compressor.

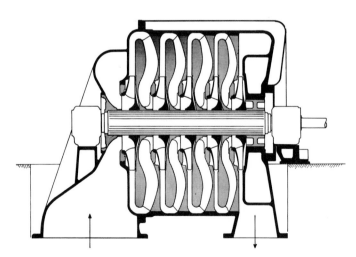

Fig. 1-K. Cross-section of a typical multistage uncooled centrifugal compressor.

Centrifugal compressors lend themselves to many arrangements, the principal ones being shown in Fig. 1-L. See also Chapter 9.

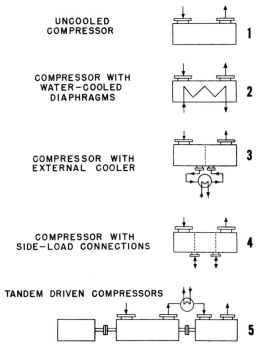

UNCOOLED
COMPRESSOR   **1**

COMPRESSOR WITH
WATER-COOLED
DIAPHRAGMS   **2**

COMPRESSOR WITH
EXTERNAL COOLER   **3**

COMPRESSOR WITH
SIDE-LOAD CONNECTIONS   **4**

TANDEM DRIVEN COMPRESSORS   **5**

Fig. 1-L.   Typical centrifugal compressor arrangements.

The Axial-Flow Type

The axial-flow dynamic compressor is shown in Fig. 1-M. It is essentially a large capacity high speed machine with characteristics quite different from the centrifugal. Each stage consists of two rows of blades — one row rotating and the next row stationary. The rotor blades impart

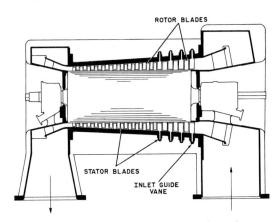

ROTOR BLADES

STATOR BLADES

INLET GUIDE
VANE

Fig. 1-M.   Cross-section of a typical axial-flow dynamic compressor.

velocity and pressure to the gas as the rotor turns, the velocity being converted to pressure in the stationary blades. Frequently about half the pressure rise is generated in the rotor blades and half in the stator. The figure shows a multistage unit. Gas flow is predominantly in an axial direction, there being no appreciable vortex action.

The Mixed-Flow Type

Intermediate between the above two designs lies a third, the mixed-flow dynamic compressor, which combines design features of each with characteristics also lying between the two. This type is not applied as frequently as the others. Because of the long length required for each stage, this type is generally not found in multistage designs.

The Ejector

An ejector consists of a relatively high-pressure motive steam or gas nozzle discharging a high-velocity jet across a suction chamber into a venturi shaped diffuser. The gas, whose pressure is to be increased, is entrained by the jet in the suction chamber. The mixture at this point has high velocity and is at the pressure of the induced gas. Compression takes place as velocity energy is transformed into pressure inside the diffuser.

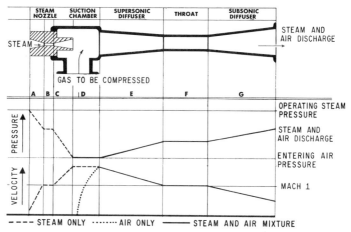

Fig. 1-N. A diagram of the pressure and velocity variations within a steam jet ejector handling air.

Ejectors are principally used to compress from pressures below atmosphere (vacuum) to a discharge close to atmospheric. They may, however, involve compression from a near atmospheric intake to some higher level in which case they are known as *thermal compressors*. See Chapter 10. Although the operating principles are identical for both types, the velocities reached and characteristics developed may be quite different.

A *vacuum* ejector, using steam as motive fluid and inducing air, is used in Fig. 1-N to show operating principles. Pressure and velocity changes are indicated for various sections of the device. Temperature changes follow the pressure curve closely. Mach 1, where referred to in

the notes, is the velocity of sound in the flowing medium. For this particular example it approximates 1000 ft/sec. The following notes refer to
Fig. 1-N.

A. Subsonic steam velocity generated to Mach 1 in a converging
nozzle as steam pressure drops.

B. Stabilization with pressure constant, velocity constant at
Mach 1.

C. Supersonic steam velocity raised in diverging nozzle as pressure drops.

D. Since suction chamber is at the lowest pressure in the system
the air flows into the chamber and is entrained in the steam jet.

E. Supersonic mixture pressure is increased in converging diffuser
until velocity drops to Mach. 1.

F. Stabilization with pressure constant, velocity constant at
Mach 1.

G. Subsonic mixture pressure is increased in diverging diffuser
as velocity drops.

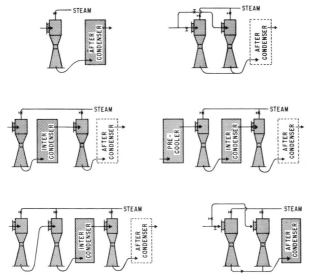

Fig. 1-O. Typical arrangements of ejectors with their coolers and condensers.

Ejectors may be arranged in either parallel or series. When two or
more steam ejectors are placed in series to form a multistage arrangement, it is usual, if water temperature is sufficiently low, to interpose a
condenser between successive elements to condense the steam used by the
prior jet plus any condensable vapor in the gas being compressed. This
materially reduces the steam required for the next stage since the weight
of mixture remaining to be handled is much less. Fig. 1-0 shows typical
arrangements. Both barometric and surface intercondensers may be used.

Ejectors have no moving parts. They can handle liquid carryover
without physical damage although they should not be exposed to a steady
flow of liquid.

Chapter 2

Standards - Symbols - Definitions - Units

Caption Index

Book Standards

Thermodynamics is the science that deals with energy and its transformations and with certain relationships of substances. It does not concern itself with what happens at the molecular level. The fundamental dimensions used can be limited to mass, force, length, time, and temperature.

Dimensions Used

Mass is a quantity of matter. The international basic unit of mass is a kilogram of metal located at Sevres, France. *Mass* and *Weight* are not identical scientific terms. Weight is the *force* exerted on a given mass by the attraction of gravity and will, therefore, vary with its distance from the center of the earth. Although one should understand the difference, this book, being concerned with practical engineering, will not differentiate. A negligible error will be introduced under certain conditions. For example, at 14,100-foot altitude and 39° Lat N, the weight (force of gravity) will be 17/100 of 1 percent less than the international standard at sea level and 45° Lat N.

The standard pound *force* is defined as that force which will accelerate one pound mass at the rate of 32.1739 ft/sec². The latter figure is the international standard of acceleration due to gravity and is again variable with the distance from the earth's center. Engineering practice notes that the variation is negligible on the earth and 32.2 ft/sec² is used at all times.

The standards of length, time, and temperature are well-known.

Units Used

The English system of units is used throughout. Tables to assist in converting to the Metric system are included in Chapter 34.

Standard Conditions

Standard conditions of pressure and temperature to which gas volumes are frequently referred will vary considerably between sections of the world and, to some degree, with the profession or industry involved. Within this book, unless specifically noted otherwise, *standard pressure and temperature conditions (SPT) are 14.696 psiA and 60°F.*

Accuracy of Calculations

Calculations within this book are generally of slide rule accuracy.

Symbols

(Based on pounds, feet, seconds and degrees Fahrenheit)

The following symbols are generally those recommended by ASA Y10.4 — 1957 — *Letter Symbols For Heat & Thermodynamics.* Some additions have been made as necessitated by the text. Subscripts and superscripts follow the recommendations of the Standard. A few additional symbols are assigned in other chapters as needed.

SYMBOL	Subject	Unit
a	Velocity of sound	ft/sec
A	Cross-sectional area	usually sq in
$Acfm$	Actual volume at specified conditions	cu ft/min
c	Cylinder clearance	% or decimal equivalent
cfm	Gas volume	cu ft/min
c_p	Specific heat at constant pressure	Btu/°F/lb
c_v	Specific heat at constant volume	Btu/°F/lb
C	Coefficient of flow	dimensionless
CE	Compression efficiency (see η)	%
d	Diameter	inches
D	Diameter	usually feet
D_n	Diameter of a flow nozzle	inches
e	Mouth of a flared nozzle (exit diameter)	inches
f	Friction factor	dimensionless
g	Gravitational acceleration (32.2 at sea level)	ft/sec²
G	Specific gravity referred to dry air at 14.696 psiA & 60°F	dimensionless

SYMBOL	Subject	Unit
h	Enthalpy	Btu/lb
H	Enthalpy	Btu
H_p	Polytropic head	ft lb/lb
$Icfm$	Volume at inlet conditions	cu ft/min
J	Mechanical equivalent of heat (778)	ft lb/Btu
k	Ratio of specific heats	dimensionless
L	Length	feet or inches
M	Molecular weight (MW)	dimensionless
M	Nozzle mouth or exit area	sq in
$MMCFD$	Million cubic feet per 24 hours at 14.4 psiA & intake temperature (perfect gas basis)	cu ft
Mc_p	Molar heat capacity — constant pressure	Btu/°F/mole
Mc_v	Molar heat capacity — constant volume	Btu/°F/mole
ME	Mechanical efficiency (see η_m)	%
N	Number of moles	dimensionless
$N_{a,b,c}$	Moles of constituents	dimensionless
n	Polytropic exponent	dimensionless
n	Speed	rpm
n_c	Specified speed (dynamic units)	dimensionless for practical purposes
p	Pressure	psiA
$p_{a,b,c}$	Partial pressure of constituents	psiA
p_a	Partial air pressure	psiA
p_c	Critical pressure	psiA
p_r	Reduced pressure	dimensionless
p_s	Saturated vapor pressure	psiA or inches Hg
p_v	Partial vapor pressure	psiA or inches Hg
$psiG$	Pounds per sq in gauge	psi
$psiA$	Pounds per sq in absolute	psi
P_T	Theoretical horsepower (work rate)	horsepower
P_G	Gas horsepower (work rate)	horsepower
q	Heat/lb	Btu/lb
Q	Heat	Btu
Q	Volume flow rate	usually cfm
rpm	Speed	rev/min
rps	Speed	rev/sec
r	Ratio of compression — total	dimensionless
r_c	Ratio of compression per stage	dimensionless
r_t	Critical ratio (orifice flow)	dimensionless
R_e	Reynolds number	dimensionless
R	Thermal resistance	$\dfrac{1}{\text{Btu/sq ft/°F/hr}}$
R_o	Universal or molar gas constant (1545 when p is in lb/sq ft)	$\dfrac{\text{ft lb}}{\text{Mole °R}}$
R'	Specific gas constant	$\dfrac{\text{ft lb}}{\text{lb °R}}$
RCE	Rankine cycle efficiency	%

SYMBOL	Subject	Unit
RH	Relative humidity	%
s	Number of stages of compression	dimensionless
S	Surface area	sq ft
S	Entropy	Btu/lb/°F
$Scfm$	Volume rate at 14.696 psiA, 60°F	cfm
SH	Specific humidity	lb moisture/lb dry gas
SPT	Standard pressure and temperature	14.696 psiA & 60°F
T	Absolute temperature	°R
T_c	Critical temperature	°R
T_r	Reduced temperature	dimensionless
u	Specific internal energy	Btu/lb
U	Internal energy	Btu
U	Over-all heat transfer rate	Btu/sq ft/°F/hr
v	Specific volume	cu ft/lb or cu ft/mole
$v_{a,b,c}$	Partial volume of constituents	cu ft/lb
v'_r	Pseudo specific reduced volume	cu ft/lb or cu ft/mole
V	Velocity	ft/sec
V	Volume flow rate	cfm
V	Total volume	cu ft
$V_{a,b,c}$	Partial volume of constituents	cu ft
V_p	Volume — perfect gas basis	cu ft
V_r	Volume — real gas basis	cu ft
VE	Volumetric efficiency (see η_v)	%
w	Work/lb	Btu/lb
W	Weight flow	lb/sec
W	Weight	lb
W_a	Weight of dry air in a mixture	lb
W_v	Weight of vapor in a mixture	lb
$W_{a,b,c}$	Weight of constituent in a mixture	lb
W	Work	ft lb
X	A factor $\left(r^{\frac{k-1}{k}} - 1 \right)$	dimensionless
Z	Compressibility factor	dimensionless
Δ	A difference between two values or the change during a process	
η_a	Adiabatic compression efficiency	%
η_i	Isothermal compression efficiency	%
η_m	Mechanical efficiency (ME)	%
η_p	Polytropic compression efficiency	%
η_v	Volumetric efficiency	%
ρ	Weight (density) at specified conditions	lb/cu ft
μ	Joule-Thomson coefficient	°F/psi drop
μ	Absolute viscosity	centipoise
μ_e	Absolute viscosity	lb mass/ft sec

Definitions

ADIABATIC PROCESS (see Process).

ABSOLUTE PRESSURE is the arithmetic sum of gauge and atmospheric pressures. It must be used in all calculations involving the basic gas laws.

ABSOLUTE TEMPERATURE is the temperature of a body referred to the absolute zero, at which point the volume of an ideal gas theoretically becomes zero. On the Fahrenheit scale this is minus 459.67°F; on the Centigrade scale it is minus 273.15°C. Engineering values of minus 460°F and minus 273°C are used herein.

AFTERCOOLING involves cooling of gas in a heat exchanger following the completion of compression to (1) reduce the temperature and (2) to liquify condensable vapors.

ALTITUDE is the elevation of a compressor above sea level.

BAROMETRIC PRESSURE is the absolute atmospheric pressure existing at the surface of the earth. It is the weight of a unit column of air above the point of measurement. It varies with altitude and, at any given location, with moisture content and weather.

BASIC SLIP (see Slip).

BRAKE HORSE POWER (see Horse Power).

BREAKING PRESSURE is that pressure of either the motive fluid or of the ejector gas discharge which causes an ejector to become unstable. Note that there are two different breaking pressures — one of motive fluid and one of ejector discharge.

CAPACITY of any compressor is the quantity of gas actually delivered when operating between specified inlet and discharge pressures. For ejectors, capacity is measured in lb/hr. For all other compressor types, capacity is a volume measured at the conditions of pressure, temperature, gas composition, and moisture content existing at the compressor inlet flange.

CLEARANCE in a reciprocating compressor cylinder is that volume contained in one end of the cylinder which is not swept by the movement of the piston. It includes space between piston and head at the end of the compression stroke, space under the valves, etc., and is expressed as a percentage of the piston displacement per stroke. Clearance may be different for the two ends of a double-acting cylinder. An average generally is used.

COMPRESSIBILITY is that property of a gas or a gas mixture that causes it to differ in volume from that of a perfect gas when each is under the same pressure and temperature conditions. Occasionally it is called *deviation*. It must be experimentally determined.

COMPRESSIBILITY FACTOR (Z) is the ratio of the actual volume of the gas to the volume determined according to the perfect gas law. As shown in the charts herein, it is a multiplier of perfect gas volume.

SUPER-COMPRESSIBILITY is a term used with various meanings, most frequently the same as compressibility, although this is not assured. A current ASME Power Test Code uses it as a ratio of gas densities rather than volumes. Therefore it is $1/Z$ in this case. Supercompressibility should never be used unless its meaning is clarified completely. *Compressibility* is much to be preferred and is used herein.

COMPRESSION EFFICIENCY is the ratio of the theoretical work requirement (using a stated process) to the actual work required to be done on the gas for compression and delivery. Expressed as a percentage, compression efficiency accounts for leakage and fluid friction losses, and thermodynamic variations from the theoretical process.

COMPRESSION RATIO is the ratio of the absolute discharge to the absolute intake pressure. It usually applies to a single stage of compression, but may be applied to a complete multistage compressor as well.

CORROSIVE GAS is one that attacks normal materials of construction. Water vapor when mixed with most gases does not make them corrosive within the sense of the above definition. In other gases, CO_2 for example, it makes them corrosive.

Note:—The words "corrosive" and "noncorrosive" are of the relative type. They do not define with exactness and there are differences of degree in the application of these terms. Specifications must make clear what is meant by these terms if they are used.

CRITICAL TEMPERATURE is the highest temperature at which a gas can be liquefied.

CRITICAL PRESSURE is the saturation pressure at the critical temperature. It is the highest vapor pressure that the liquid can exert.

Note:—Critical conditions must be experimentally determined for each pure gas. When calculated for a mixture, they are called pseudo (pretended) critical conditions.

DEAD-END PRESSURE is the suction pressure attained by an ejector or positive-displacement vacuum pump at zero capacity with the suction absolutely blanked off.

DEGREES KELVIN (°K) — an absolute temperature scale. See "Units of Measurement," page 2-16.

DEGREE RANKINE (°R) — an absolute temperature scale. See "Units of Measurement," page 2-16.

DEGREE OF SATURATION (See Saturation)

DENSITY is the weight of a given volume of gas, usually expressed in lb/cu ft at SPT conditions.

DESIGN (BUILT-IN) COMPRESSION RATIO in a rotary compressor refers to the compression ratio that has been attained when the fixed discharge port is uncovered. A helical-lobe compressor (and most other rotary units) can have an operating ratio somewhat higher or lower than the design ratio, with little change in efficiency.

DEW POINT of a gas is the temperature at which the vapor in a space (at a given pressure) will start to condense (form dew). Dew point of a gas mixture is the temperature at which the highest boiling point constituent will start to condense.

DISCHARGE PRESSURE is the total gas pressure (static plus velocity) at the discharge flange of the compressor. Velocity pressure usually is considered only with dynamic compressors.

Note:—Pressure may be expressed as gauge or absolute pressures. PsiG plus atmospheric pressure equals psiA. Note that psiG does not define a pressure unless the barometric pressure (atmospheric) is also stated.

DISCHARGE TEMPERATURE is the temperature existing at the discharge flange of the compressor.

Note:—In a multistage compressor, the various stages will have differing discharge pressures and temperatures.

DISPLACEMENT applies only to positive-displacement compressors. It is the net volume swept by the moving parts in a unit of time, usually one minute.

DRY BULB TEMPERATURE is the ambient gas temperature.

DRY GAS is any gas or gas mixture that contains no water vapor and/or in which all of the consituents are substantially above their respective saturated vapor pressures at the existing temperature. (See Wet Gas).

Note:—In commercial compressor work, a gas may be considered dry (even though it contains water vapor) if its dew point is low at the inlet condition (say minus 50° to minus 60°F).

DRY UNIT is one in which there is no liquid injection and/or liquid circulation for evaporative cooling or sealing. (See Evaporative cooling).

ENERGY of a substance is its capacity, either latent or apparent, to exert a force through a distance, that is, to do work.

EXTERNAL ENERGY is that energy represented by the product of pressure and volume. It may be regarded as the energy a substance possesses by virtue of the space it occupies.

INTERNAL ENERGY is that energy which a substance possesses because of the motion and configuration of its atoms, molecules, and subatomic particles.

KINETIC ENERGY is the energy a substance possesses by virtue of its motion or velocity. It enters into dynamic and ejector compressor calculations, but seldom into positive displacement problems.

POTENTIAL ENERGY is the energy a substance possesses because of its elevation above the earth (or above some other chosen datum plane).

ENTHALPY (Heat Content) is the sum of the internal and external energies.

ENTRAINMENT RATIOS are used with ejectors to convert weight of gas and/or water vapor handled to or from equivalent air. They are based on extensive tests.

ENTROPY is a measure of the unavailability of energy in a substance.

EQUIVALENT AIR is an ejector term—the calculated lb/hr of air at 70°F & 14.696 psiA and containing normal atmospheric moisture that is *equivalent to*, but not necessarily *equal to*, the weight rate of the gas handled by the ejector at suction conditions. Entrainment ratios are involved.

EQUIVALENT GAS is a mixture that is considered to have similar properties to a pure gas, although these properties must be calculated from the properties of the components.

EXTERNAL ENERGY (See Energy).

EVAPORATIVE COOLING takes place when a liquid (usually water) is injected into the gas stream before or during compression. As compression takes place, the gas temperature rises and some or all of the liquid is evaporated, the latent heat of liquid vaporization being removed from the gas, lowering its temperature.

FIXED COMPRESSION RATIO is the design (built-in) compression ratio for a rotary unit having this feature.

GAS HORSEPOWER (See Horsepower).

GAUGE PRESSURE is pressure as determined by most instruments and gauges. Barometric pressure must be allowed for to obtain the true or absolute pressure.

GRAVITY (See Specific Gravity).

HEAT is energy transferred because of a temperature difference. There is no transfer of mass.

HEAT CAPACITY (See Specific Heat).

HORSEPOWER is a unit of work equal to 33,000 foot-pounds per minute.

THEORETICAL HORSEPOWER is the work theoretically required to compress and deliver a given gas quantity in accordance with a specified process.

INDICATED HORSEPOWER is that obtained by indicator card analysis of compression or expansion in a cylinder of a reciprocating compressor. It is the same as gas horsepower.

GAS HORSEPOWER is the actual work required to compress and deliver a given gas quantity, including all thermodynamic, leakage, and fluid friction losses. It does not include mechanical losses.

BRAKE HORSEPOWER is the total power input required including gas horsepower plus all friction losses.

PEAK HORSEPOWER is the maximum power required by a given compressor when operating at a (1) constant discharge pressure with variable intake pressure or (2) constant intake pressure with variable discharge pressure.

HUMIDITY, in normal usage, has to do with moisture (water vapor) in the atmosphere. There are two engineering terms involved.

RELATIVE HUMIDITY is the ratio of the actual partial vapor pressure in an air-vapor mixture to the saturated vapor pressure at the existing dry-bulb mixture temperature, usually expressed in percent.

SPECIFIC HUMIDITY is the ratio of weight of water vapor in an air-vapor mixture to the weight of dry air. It is usually expressed as pounds of vapor per pound of dry air.

AN IDEAL GAS follows the perfect gas laws without deviation. Practically, there is no such thing, but it is the basis from which calculations are made and corrections applied.

INDICATED HORSEPOWER (See Horsepower).

INERT GAS, to a chemist, is one that does not enter into known chemical combination, either with itself or another element. There are four known gases of this type: helium; neon; argon; and krypton. To the engineer, however, the term usually means a gas that does not supply any of the needs of combustion.

INLET PRESSURE is the total pressure (static plus velocity) at the inlet flange of the compressor. Velocity pressure is usually considered only with dynamic compressors. (See note under Discharge Pressure).

INLET TEMPERATURE is the temperature at the inlet flange of the compressor.

Note:—In a multistage compressor, the various stages may have differing inlet temperatures.

INTERCOOLING involves the cooling of gas between stages of compression (1) to reduce the temperature, (2) to reduce to volume to be compressed in the succeeding stage, (3) to liquefy condensable vapors, and (4) to save power.

INTERNAL ENERGY (See Energy).

ISENTROPIC PROCESS (See Process).

ISOTHERMAL PROCESS (See Process).

KINETIC ENERGY (See Energy).

MACH NUMBER is the ratio of the actual gas velocity at a given point to the velocity of sound in the same gas at the conditions existing at this point. These are known as *local* conditions.

MAXIMUM DISCHARGE PRESSURE, as applied to ejectors, is the maximum absolute static recovery pressure against which the ejector will operate with stability.

MECHANICAL EFFICIENCY is the ratio, expressed in percent, of the Indicated Horsepower to the actual shaft horsepower (or Steam Indicated Horsepower in an integral steam driven unit).

A MOLE is a weight of gas in pounds numerically equal to the molecular weight of the gas or to the pseudo molecular weight of a gas mixture.

MOLAR HEAT CAPACITY or molar specific heat, is the heat in Btu's required to raise the temperature of one mole of gas 1°F.

NONCONDENSABLES are those constituents in the suction gas that cannot be condensed to a liquid with the cooling medium available.

NONCORROSIVE GAS is one that does not attack normal materials of constructions. See note under "Corrosive Gas."

NORMAL AIR is the term used for average atmospheric air at sea level in a temperate zone where it contains some moisture. It is defined in the ASME Test Code For Displacement Compressors as being at 14.696 psiA, 68°F, 36% RH and weighing 0.075 lb/cu ft. The k value is 1.395.

PARTIAL PRESSURE of a constituent in a mixture is the absolute pressure exerted by that portion of the mixture.

PEAK HORSEPOWER (See Horsepower).

PERFECT INTERCOOLING is obtained when the gas is cooled to first stage inlet temperature following each stage of compression.

PERFECT GAS (See Ideal Gas).

PISTON DISPLACEMENT of a reciprocating compressor cylinder is the net volume displaced by the piston at rated machine speed, generally expressed in cfm. For single-acting cylinders it is the displacement of the compressing end only. For double-acting cylinders it is the total of both ends. For multistage compressors, the displacement of the first stage only is commonly stated as that of the entire machine.

POLYTROPIC PROCESS (See Process).

POLYTROPIC HEAD is an expression used for dynamic compressors to denote the foot-pounds of work required per pound of gas.

POTENTIAL ENERGY (See Energy).

POWER (See Horsepower).

PRECOOLER is a heat exchanger located immediately preceding an ejector to condense and remove a portion of the vapor in the mixture and thus reduce the total lb/hr to be handled.

PRESSURE is force per unit area. (See Absolute, Breaking (ejectors), Critical, Dead End (ejectors), Discharge, Gauge, Inlet, Maximum Discharge (ejectors), Pseudo Critical, Recovery (ejectors), Reduced, Saturated Vapor, Saturation, Suction (ejectors), Vapor).

A PROCESS occurs whenever the system undergoes either a change in state or an energy transfer at a steady state (See State).

A REVERSIBLE PROCESS is an ideal process that may be stopped and made to retrace its steps and restore to the system or surroundings all work and heat previously removed. It is frictionless.

AN IRREVERSIBLE PROCESS is one in which a portion of the original system energy is dissipated and cannot be returned to the system through its own operation. The system and/or surroundings cannot be returned to their original state.

ADIABATIC PROCESS is one during which there is no heat added to or removed from the system.

ISENTROPIC PROCESS is one wherein the entropy remains constant.

ISOTHERMAL PROCESS is one in which there is no change in temperature.

POLYTROPIC PROCESS is one in which changes in gas characteristics during compression are considered.

PSEUDO CRITICAL PRESSURE (See Critical Pressure).

PSEUDO CRITICAL TEMPERATURE (See Critical Temperature).

PSYCHROMETRY has to do with the properties of air-water vapor mixtures in the atmosphere.

PUMPING is the reversal of flow within a dynamic compressor that takes place when the capacity being handled is reduced to a point where insufficient pressure is being generated to maintain flow.

RATIO OF SPECIFIC HEATS is the ratio of the specific heat at constant pressure to the specific heat constant volume. It may vary considerably with pressure and temperature.

RECOVERY PRESSURE is that pressure of either motive fluid or discharge at which an ejector returns to stable operation following a period of unstable operation due to having previously reached the breaking pressure. There are two recovery pressures, one for motive fluid and one for the discharge pressure.

REDUCED PRESSURE is the ratio of the actual absolute gas pressure to the absolute critical pressure.

REDUCED TEMPERATURE is the ratio in absolute units of the actual gas temperature to the critical temperature.

RELATIVE HUMIDITY (See Humidity).

SATURATION occurs when the vapor is at the dew point or saturation temperature corresponding to its partial pressure. A *gas* is *never* saturated with a vapor. The *space* occupied jointly by the gas and vapor may be saturated, however.

DEGREE OF SATURATION is the ratio of weight of vapor existing in a given space to the weight that would be present if the space were saturated at the space temperature.

SATURATED AIR-VAPOR MIXTURE is one in which the space occupied by the mixture is saturated with water vapor at the mixture temperature.

SATURATED VAPOR PRESSURE is the pressure existing at a given temperature in a closed vessel containing a liquid and the vapor from that liquid after equilibrium conditions have been reached. It is dependent only on temperature and must be determined experimentally.

SATURATION PRESSURE is another term for Saturated Vapor Pressure.

SATURATION TEMPERATURE is the temperature corresponding to a given saturated vapor pressure for a given vapor.

SLIP is the internal leakage within a rotary compressor. It represents gas at least partially compressed but not delivered. It is experimentally determined and expressed in CFM to be deducted from the displacement to obtain capacity.

SLIP RPM is the speed required of a rotary compressor to maintain a given discharge pressure, supplying leakage only (zero actual output). It is an experience factor.

SPECIFIC GRAVITY is the ratio of the density of a given gas to the density of dry air, both measured at the same specified conditions of temperature and pressure, usually 14.696 psiA and 60°F. It should also take into account any compressibility deviation from a perfect gas.

Note:—On pages 34-6 and 7, this compressibility deviation has been allowed for, or alternatively, a statement is made that the three properties above are based on perfect gas laws. Deviation is not accurately known for all gases, particularly certain hydrocarbons.

SPECIFIC HEAT (Heat Capacity) is the rate of change in Enthalpy with temperature. It is commonly measured at constant pressure or at constant volume. The values are different and are known as c_p and c_v respectively.

SPECIFIC HUMIDITY (See Humidity).

SPECIFIC VOLUME is the volume of a given weight of gas, usually expressed as cu ft/lb at SPT conditions.

STANDARD PRESSURE AND TEMPERATURE (SPT) in this book is 14.696 psiA and 60°F unless specifically stated otherwise.

STATE of a system (or part thereof) is its condition at an instant of time as described or measured by its properties.

SUCTION PRESSURE is the absolute static pressure prevailing at the suction of the ejector.

SUPER COMPRESSIBILITY (See Compressibility).

SUPERHEATED AIR-VAPOR MIXTURE is one in which the space occupied by the mixture is above the saturation temperature at the mixture temperature.

SURGE (See Pumping).

TEMPERATURE is the property of a substance that gauges the potential or driving force for the flow of heat. (See also Inlet, Discharge, Critical, Reduced, and Absolute Temperature, Degrees Kelvin, Degrees Rankine).

THEORETICAL HORSEPOWER (See Horsepower).

A THERMAL COMPRESSOR is an ejector used to compress waste or exhaust steam or any other gas through a moderate range of compression above atmospheric pressure.

VAPOR PRESSURE is the pressure exerted by a vapor confined within a given space. The vapor may be the sole occupant of the space, or may be associated with other gases.

VOLUME (See Specific Volume).

VOLUMETRIC EFFICIENCY is the ratio in percent of the actual delivered capacity (measured at inlet temperature, pressure and gas composition) to the piston displacement.

WET BULB TEMPERATURE is used in psychrometry and is the temperature recorded by a thermometer whose bulb has been covered with a wetted wick and whirled on a sling psychrometer. Taken with the dry bulb, it permits determination of the relative humidity of the atmosphere.

WET GAS is any gas or gas mixture in which one or more of the constituents is at its saturated vapor pressure. The constituent at saturation pressure may or may not be water vapor.

A WET HELICAL-LOBE UNIT is one which (1) handles a small constant flow of liquid with the gas; (2) utilizes evaporative (injection) cooling; or (3) circulates a liquid for sealing and/or cooling. The last may or may not be evaporative cooling.

WORK is energy in transition and is defined in units of Force times Distance. Work cannot be done unless there is movement.

The Units of Measurement

The user of compression equipment is interested primarily in the quantity of gas handled between the initial and final pressure and temperature conditions and in the power required. He may specify the conditions to be met in various terms and units. The designer must know positively what the buyer expects the compressor to do and what specific conditions are to be met. All too often he is not able, from the data given, to clarify the factors he must know.

It is the purpose of this section to outline and discuss the various units of measurement so there may be a more perfect meeting of minds and better communication between user and manufacturer.

Pressure

Pressure is expressed as a force per unit of the area exposed to the pressure. Since weight is really the force of gravity on a mass of material, the weight necessary to balance the pressure force is used as a measure. Hence as examples:

Pounds/sq in	(psi)
Pounds/sq ft	(lb/sq ft)
Grams/sq cm	(gr/sq cm)
Kilograms/sq cm	(kg/sq cm)

Pressure is usually measured by a gauge that registers the *difference* between the pressure in a vessel and the current atmospheric pressure. Therefore a *gauge* pressure (psiG) does not indicate the *true* total gas pressure. To obtain the true pressure, or pressure above zero, it is necessary to add the current atmospheric or barometric pressure, expressed in proper units. This sum is the *absolute* pressure (psiA). See Fig. 2-A.

For all compressor calculations the absolute pressure is required. If gauge pressures only are given, the inquiry is not complete. The atmospheric or barometric pressure must also be specified.

Note:—There is frequent confusion in transmission of pressure data. It is recommended that specific notation be made after each pressure as to whether it is gauge or absolute. Use the symbol *psiG* or *psiA*. If *psiG* is given, be sure the barometer is also specified.

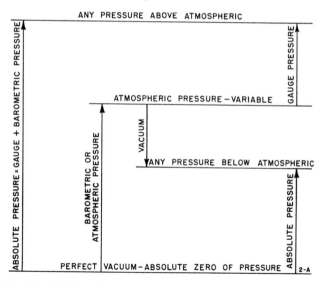

Fig. 2-A.   Relations between various methods of expressing pressure.

Since the earth's atmosphere has weight, a measure known as the International Atmosphere is sometimes used. It is the weight of the column of air existing above the earth's surface at 45° Lat and sea level. It is defined as being equivalent to 14.696 psiA or 1.0333 kg/sq cm and is usually expressed as ATA meaning atmospheres absolute. When specified as *ATM*, it is often uncertain whether atmospheres *absolute* or atmospheres *gauge* are meant and discretion must be used. Atmospheres absolute equals atmospheres gauge plus 1.

Occasionally an inquiry may specify a metric atmosphere which is 1 kg/sq cm or 14.233 psiA. However, the International Atmosphere normally is used throughout all engineering.

Also, since a column of a material of a specified height will have a weight proportional to its height, the height can be used as a force measure. It is reduced to a unit area basis automatically, since the total weight and the area are proportional. For example:

Feet of water	(ft H_2O)
Inches of water	(in H_2O)
Inches of mercury	(in Hg)
Millimeters of mercury	(mm Hg)

With the exception of barometric pressure, when pressures are expressed in the above terms, they are *gauge* pressures unless specifically noted as absolute values.

Atmospheric pressure is measured by a barometer. It is designed to read the height of a column of mercury. The upper end of the tube containing the mercury is closed and is at zero absolute pressure. The lower end of the tube is submerged in a pot of mercury, the surface of which is open to the atmosphere. The weight of this column of mercury exactly balances the weight of a similar column of atmospheric air. See page 20-4.

Although this gauge really measures a *differential* pressure, by design one of those pressures is zero and the actual reading is true *absolute* or total pressure of the atmosphere. 14.696 psiA sea level measure is equal to 29.92 in Hg.

Vacuum

Vacuum is a type of pressure. A gas is said to be under vacuum when its pressure is below atmospheric. There are two methods of stating this pressure, only one of which is accurate in itself.

Vacuum is usually measured by a differential gauge that shows the difference in pressure between that in the system and the atmosphere. This measurement is expressed, for example, as:

Millimeters of Hg vacuum	(mm Hg Vac)
Inches of Hg vacuum	(in Hg Vac)
Inches of water vacuum	(in H_2O Vac)
psi — vacuum	(psi Vac)

Unless the barometric or atmospheric pressure is also given, these expressions do not give an accurate specification of pressure. See Fig. 2-A.

Subtracting the *vacuum* reading from the atmospheric pressure will give an *absolute* pressure which is accurate. This may be expressed as:

Inches of Hg absolute	(in Hg abs)
Millimeters of Hg absolute	(mm Hg Abs)
Pounds/sq in absolute	(psiA)

The term *torr* means one mm absolute. It is infrequently used.

The word *absolute* should never be omitted, otherwise one is never sure whether a vacuum is expressed in differential or absolute terms.

See Chapter 20.

Volume

The compressor designer must determine the actual volume of gas to be handled at the inlet of most types of compressors. In the majority of inquiries, volumes are not so presented and translation is necessary. See page 4-2 for formulas.

Guarantees are based on the volume handled at the condition of pressure, temperature, moisture content, and gas composition existing at the first-stage inlet flange. Presumably, these are specified. Therefore, it is completely in order that the purchaser specify the *inlet volume,* even though it is also specified in other terms.

Quantities handled by compressors are really rates. For example:

Cu ft/min   (cfm)
Standard cu ft/min   (Scfm)
Millions of cu ft/24 hr   (MMCFD)
Cubic Meters/sec   (cu m/sec)
Pounds/hr   (lb/hr)
Kilograms/hr   (kg/hr)
Mole/hr (See page 3-10)

A weight rate can readily be changed to a volume rate at specified or known inlet conditions provided the properties of the gas or gas mixture are well-known or are specified by the customer. It is again best, however, to have *volume at intake conditions* definitely specified.

Volumes are frequently indefinite as to the temperature and pressure conditions at which they are measured. Conditions should be specific.

Scfm means cfm at standard conditions. However, *standards* vary and some care is necessary. In the United States, the *usual* standard is 14.696 psiA and 60°F. Some chemical engineers will use one ATA and 0°C, but usually will be specific about the reference point. Europeans normally use one ATA and 0°C. The buyer should leave no doubt.

MMCFD, called Million cu ft per day, is not the same to all people. It originated in the natural gas pipeline industry, where it usually refers to volume at 14.4 psiA and inlet temperature. It is best that the reference pressure and temperature be definitely specified.

Volume (Wet or Dry)

Whether a gas is wet or dry refers (as far as compressor volume terminology is concerned) to its water vapor content. The one exception is the term *wet* natural gas. This indicates a natural gas containing hydrocarbons that are easily condensed rather than a gas saturated with water vapor. As applied to natural gases, the term *wet* is entirely special.

Volume or weight rates are often given as dry (no water vapor). Specified conditions should include a flat statement that the relative humidity is zero (no vapor), 100% (saturated at inlet or some other specified temperature), or some *in between* figure (partially saturated). A dew point may be given, although this is infrequent.

Water vapor in a gas occupies space and the compressor must be sized to handle it. It is, therefore, a *must* that the amount of vapor be known.

This is especially important since many chemical process engineers make their calculations on dry gas, present the analysis of the dry gas, but neglect to pin down the water vapor content specifically. This can make a difference of several percent in capacity requirements.

A discussion of the methods of handling moisture starts on page 3-6.

Temperature

Temperatures can be expressed in several definitely interrelated terms:

Degrees Fahrenheit	(°F)
Degrees Rankine	(°R)
Degrees Centigrade	(°C)
Degrees Kelvin	(°K)

One degree Fahrenheit is equal to one degree Rankine, but the zero points are at different temperatures. The Rankine scale is zero at *absolute zero* which is 459.7° below zero in °F.

°F = °R −459.7

Degrees Rankine (°R) is sometimes expressed as degrees Fahrenheit Absolute.

°R = °F + 459.7 =°F ABS

The Centigrade and Kelvin scales are similarly related. The Kelvin thermometer is zero at *absolute zero* or 273.17° below zero in °C. The Centigrade scale is zero at the temperature of a mixture of ice and water.

°C = °K −273.17

also °K = °C + 273.17 = °C ABS

One degree Centigrade is 1/100 of the temperature difference between the freezing and boiling temperatures of water.

One degree Fahrenheit is 1/180 of the same temperature difference. Therefore:

One °F = 5/9 of one °C

One °C = 9/5 of one °F

Because of the different bases, it is convenient to use conversion tables. See page 34-167. Alternately, use these formulas:

°F = 9/5 °C + 32

= 9/5 (°C + 40) −40

°C = 5/9 (°F −32)

= 5/9 (°F + 40) −40

Power

The compressor engineer must determine the energy flow during compression, not only to properly size the driver needed, but to provide cooling media as required.

It is not always fully realized that the power or energy input to the compressor shaft is numerically equal to the heat energy removed from the system plus that discharged in the outgoing gas. This heat can all be accounted for in a complete heat balance. See page 5-2.

Units used are well-defined and as listed below are really rates:

Horsepower	(hp)
Kilowatt	(kw)
Btu/hr	(2545 Btu/hr = 1 hp-hr)
Ton of Refrigeration (this is the heat required to melt 1 ton (2000 lb) of ice at 32°F to water at 32°F during 24 hours).	

Chapter 3

Basic Theory

(Continued)

Introduction

It is the intent to provide in this chapter a summary of the basic thermodynamic gas laws and to review in the succeeding chapter their application to problems arising in the compression and use of gases. The practical engineering approach is used rather than that of the scientist and physicist. Where authorities differ on definition and approach in some areas, a certain amount of discretion has been used.

Symbols and definitions are given in Chapter 2.

The Basic Laws

The First Law of Thermodynamics

This states that energy cannot be created or destroyed during a process (such as compression and delivery of a gas), although it may change from one form of energy to another. In other words, whenever a quantity of one kind of energy disappears, an exactly equivalent total of other kinds of energy must be produced.

The Second Law of Thermodynamics

This is more abstract and can be stated several ways.

1. Heat cannot, of itself, pass from a colder to a hotter body.
2. Heat can be made to go from a body at lower temperature to one at higher temperature *only* if external work is done.
3. The available energy of the isolated system decreases in all real processes.
4. Heat or energy (like water), of itself, will flow only downhill.

Basically, these statements say that energy exists at various levels and is *available for use* only if it can move from a higher to a lower level.

In thermodynamics a measure of the *unavailability* of energy has been devised and is known as *entropy*. It is defined by the differential equation:

$$dS = \frac{dQ}{T} \tag{3.1}$$

Note that entropy (as measure of unavailibility) increases as a system loses heat, but remains constant when there is no gain or loss of heat (as in an adiabatic process).

Ideal or Perfect Gas Laws

An ideal or perfect gas is one to which the laws of Boyle, Charles, and Amonton apply. To the best of our knowledge there are no such gases, but these laws are used and corrected by compressibility factors based on experimental data.

Boyle's Law

At constant temperature, the volume of an ideal gas varies inversely with the absolute pressure.

$$\frac{V_2}{V_1} = \frac{p_1}{p_2} \tag{3.2}$$

$$p_2V_2 = p_1V_1 = Constant \tag{3.3}$$

This is the *isothermal law.*

Charles' Law

At constant pressure, the volume of an ideal gas varies directly as the absolute temperature.

$$\frac{V_2}{V_1} = \frac{T_2}{T_1} \tag{3.4}$$

$$\frac{V_2}{T_2} = \frac{V_1}{T_1} \tag{3.5}$$

Amonton's Law

At constant volume, the absolute pressure of an ideal gas will vary directly with the absolute temperature.

$$\frac{p_2}{p_1} = \frac{T_2}{T_1} \tag{3.6}$$

$$\frac{p_2}{T_2} = \frac{p_1}{T_1} \tag{3.7}$$

Dalton's Law

This states that the total pressure of a mixture of ideal gases is equal to the sum of the partial pressures of the constituent gases.

The partial pressure is defined as the pressure each gas would exert if it alone occupied the volume of the mixture at the mixture temperature.

Dalton's Law has been proved experimentally to be somewhat inaccurate, the total pressure often being higher than the sum of the partial pressures, particularly as pressures increase. However, for engineering purposes it is the best rule available and the error is minor.

This can be expressed as follows, all being at the same temperature and volume.

$$p = p_a + p_b + p_c + \ldots\ldots\ldots \tag{3.8}$$

Amagat's Law

This is similar to Dalton's Law, but states that the volume of a mixture of ideal gases is equal to the sum of the partial volumes that the constituent gases would occupy if each existed alone at the *total* pressure and temperature of the mixture. As a formula this becomes:—

$$V = V_a + V_b + V_c + \ldots\ldots\ldots \tag{3.9}$$

Note:—Dalton's and Amagat's laws are discussed further under "Partial Pressures," page 3-6.

Avogadro's Law

Avogadro states that equal volumes of all gases, under the same conditions of pressure and temperature, contain the same number of molecules.

This law is very important and is applied in many compressor calculations. Further discussion is given under "The Mole," page 3-10.

The Perfect Gas Formula

Starting with Charles' and Boyle's laws, it is possible to develop the formula for a given weight of gas.

$$pV = WR'T \tag{3.10}$$

where W is weight and R' is a specific constant for the gas involved. This is the perfect gas equation.

Going one step further, by making W in pounds equal to the molecular weight of the gas (one mole), the formula becomes

$$pV = R_oT \tag{3.11}$$

In this very useful form, R_o is known as the Universal Gas Constant, has a value of 1545 and is the same for all gases. The *specific* gas constant (R') for any gas can be obtained by dividing 1545 by the molecular weight.

Note that R_o is 1545 only when

p is lb/sq ft abs

V is cu ft/lb mole

T is °R (°F + 460)

When p is lb/sq in, R_o becomes 10.729.

Gas and Vapor

By definition, a *gas* is that fluid form of a substance in which it can expand indefinitely and completely fill its container. A *vapor* is a gasified liquid or solid — a substance in gaseous form. These definitions are in general use today.

All gases can be liquefied under suitable pressure and temperature conditions and therefore could also be called *vapors*. The term "gas" is most generally used when conditions are such that a return to the liquid state (condensation) would be difficult within the scope of the operations being considered. However, a gas under such conditions is actually a superheated vapor.

The terms *gas* and *vapor* will be used rather interchangeably, with the emphasis on proximity to the liquid phase when using the word vapor.

Changes of State

Any given pure substance may exist in three states; as a solid, as liquid, or as vapor. Under certain conditions it may exist as a combination of any two phases and changes in conditions may alter the proportions of the two phases. There is also a condition where all three phases may exist at the same time. This is known as the *triple point.*

Water has a triple point at near 32°F and 14.696 psiA. Carbon dioxide may exist as a vapor, a liquid, and solid simultaneously at about minus 69.6°F and 75 psiA.

Substances, under proper conditions, may pass directly from a solid to a vapor phase. This is known as *sublimation*.

Changes of state are involved in many processes requiring compressors. Typical are refrigeration, manufacture of dry-ice, separating a mixture of gases into its components, purifying gaseous mixtures, etc.

The only changes of state discussed in this book are those involving liquids and vapors, knowledge of which is essential to understanding compressor operation.

Changes of State and Vapor Pressure

As liquids physically change into a gas (as during a temperature rise), their molecules travel with greater velocity and some break out of the liquid to form a vapor above the liquid. These molecules create a "vapor pressure" which (at a specified temperature) is the only pressure at which a pure liquid and its vapor can exist in equilibrium.

If, in a closed liquid-vapor system, the volume is reduced at constant temperature, the pressure will increase imperceptibly until condensation of part of the vapor into liquid has lowered the pressure to the original vapor pressure corresponding to the temperature. Conversely, increasing the volume at constant temperature, will reduce the pressure imperceptibly and molecules will move from the liquid phase to the vapor phase until the original vapor pressure has been restored. For every substance, there is a definite vapor pressure corresponding to each temperature. In other words, the pressure will vary with temperature. Values are experimentally determined.

The temperature corresponding to any given vapor pressure is obviously the *boiling point* of the liquid and also the *dew point* of the vapor. Addition of heat will cause the liquid to boil and removal of heat will start condensation. The three terms, saturation temperature, boiling point, and dew point, all indicate the same physical temperature at a given vapor pressure. Their use depends on the context in which they appear.

Typical vapor pressure curves for common pure gases are shown on page 34-166. Tables starting on page 34-93 show the properties of *saturated* water vapor or steam, including its temperature—vapor pressure relationship. Pages 34-106 and 34-107 give in curve form the vapor pressure and specific volume for saturated water vapor temperature over the range usually needed in compressor work.

Critical Conditions

There is one temperature above which a gas will not liquefy due to pressure increase, no matter how great. This point is called the *critical temperature*. It is determined experimentally.

The pressure required to compress and condense a gas at this critical temperature is called the *critical pressure*.

The critical constants of many gases are given in tables starting on page 34-6.

Partial Pressures

Vapor pressure created by one pure liquid will not affect the vapor pressure of a second pure liquid, when the liquids are insoluble and nonreacting and the liquids and/or vapors are mixed within the same system. There is complete indifference on the part of each component to the existence of all others. The total vapor pressure for the mixture is the sum of the vapor pressures of the individual components. This is Dalton's law and each individual vapor has a *partial pressure* as differentiated from the total pressure of the mixture.

During compression of any gas other than a pure and dry gas, the priniciples of partial pressure are at work. This is true even in normal 100 psiG air compression, because there is always some water vapor mixed with the intake air and the compressor must handle both components. Actually, air is itself a mixture of a number of components, including oxygen, nitrogen, argon, etc. and its total pressure is the sum of the partial pressures of each component. However, because of the negligible variation in the composition of *dry air* throughout the world, it is considered and will hereafter be treated as a single gas with specific properties of its own.

After compression, partial pressures are used to determine moisture condensation and removal in inter- and after-coolers. Partial pressures are also involved in many vacuum applications and are encountered widely in the compression of many mixtures.

Dalton's and Amagat's Laws are utilized in working with partial pressures (and volumes). (See page 3-3).

Since water vapor is by far the most prevalent constituent involved in partial pressure problems in compressing gases, it is usually the only one considered in subsequent discussions.

In a mixture, when the dew point temperature of any component is reached, the space occupied is said to be saturated by the component. A volume is sometimes specified as being partially saturated with water vapor at a certain temperature. This means that the vapor is actually superheated and the dew point is lower than the actual temperature. If the moles (see page 3-10) of water vapor are known, the partial pressure of the saturated vapor can be determined. Otherwise, it is customary to multiply the saturated vapor pressure at the existing mixture temperature by the relative humidity to obtain the partial pressure.

The terms "saturated gas" or "partially saturated gas" are incorrect and give the wrong impression. It is *not* the gas which is saturated with vapor, it is the volume or space occupied. The vapor and gas exist independently throughout the volume or space. Understanding of this true concept is helpful when working with partial pressures and gas mixtures.

Relative Humidity

Relative humidity is a term frequently used to represent the quantity of moisture (water vapor) present in a mixture although it uses partial pressures in so doing. It is expressed as

$$RH\ (\%) = \frac{actual\ partial\ vapor\ pressure \times 100}{saturated\ vapor\ pressure\ at\ existing\ mixture\ temperature}$$

$$= \frac{p_v \times 100}{p_s} \tag{3.12}$$

Relative humidity is usually considered only in connection with atmospheric air, but, since it is unconcerned with the nature of any other components or the total mixture pressure, the term is applicable to vapor content in any problem, no matter what the condition.

The saturated water vapor pressure at a given temperature is always known from steam tables or charts. It is the existing partial vapor pressure which is desired and therefore calculable when the relative humidity is stated. (See "Psychrometry," page 3-8 for atmospheric air).

Specific Humidity

Specific humidity, used in calculations on certain types of compressors, is a totally different term. It is the ratio of the weight of water vapor to the weight of *dry* air and is usually expressed as pounds (or grains) of moisture per pound of dry air.

$$SH = \frac{W_v}{W_a} \qquad (3.13)$$

also

$$SH = \frac{0.622p_v}{p-p_v} = \frac{0.622p_v}{p_a} \qquad (3.14)$$

where p_a is partial air pressure.

A convenient chart for conversion from relative to specific humidity is given on page 34-118.

Degree of Saturation

The degree of saturation denotes the actual relation between the weight of moisture existing in a space and the weight that would exist if the space were saturated.

$$\text{Degree of Saturation (\%)} = \frac{SH \text{ actual} \times 100}{SH \text{ saturated}} \qquad (3.15)$$

$$= RH \times \frac{p-p_s}{p-p_v} \qquad (3.16)$$

Usually p_s and p_v are quite small as compared to p; therefore, the degree of saturation closely approximates the relative humidity. The latter term is commonly used in psychrometric work involving air-water vapor mixtures while degree of saturation is applied mainly to gas-vapor mixtures having other components than air and water-vapor.

A great many dynamic compressors handle air. Their performance is sensitive to density of the air which varies with moisture content. Page 34-116 shows the specific gravity of air-vapor mixtures versus temperatures and relative humidity. Page 34-117 gives information to determine most of the basic properties of the mixture working from a specific humidity basis.

The practical application of partial pressures in compression problems centers to a large degree on the determination of mixture volumes or weights to be handled at the intake of each stage of compression, the determination of mixture molecular weight, specific gravity, and the proportional or actual weight of components. The approach and method of application vary with the basic type of compressor involved and are discussed in Chapter 4.

Psychrometry

Psychrometry has to do with the properties of the air-water vapor mixtures found in the atmosphere. Psychrometric tables published by the U. S. Weather Bureau give detail data about vapor pressure, relative humidity and dew point at the sea-level barometer of 30 in Hg, and at certain other barometric pressures. These tables are based on relative readings of dry bulb and wet bulb atmospheric temperatures as determined simultaneously by a sling psychrometer. The dry bulb reads ambient temperature while the wet bulb reads a lower temperature influenced by evaporation from a wetted wick surrounding the bulb of a parallel thermometer. A much condensed table will be found on page 34-120. Complete tables are available in W. B. No. 235 from Superintendent of Documents, U. S. Government Printing Office, Washington, D. C. 20402.

Weather data, based on Weather Bureau records, are given in tables starting on page 34-130 for representative locations throughout the United States and Puerto Rico.

Although not classed as psychrometry, information about vapor content in gases at pressures above atmosphere is often useful. A chart arranged to give saturation moisture content per 1000 cu ft of *free* gas at 14.7 psiA between atmosphere and reasonable elevated pressures is presented on page 27-16. With this chart, one can estimate the moisture condensed in inter- and after-coolers as well as that remaining in the gas following these heat exchangers. The latter is the amount subject to condensation in distribution lines. See also page 27-15.

Compressibility

All gases deviate from the perfect or ideal gas laws to some degree. In some cases the deviation is rather extreme. It is necessary that these deviations be taken into account in many compressor calculations to prevent compressor and driver sizes being greatly in error.

Compressibility is experimentally derived from data about the actual behavior of a particular gas under pVT changes. The compressibility factor Z is a multiplier in the basic formula. It is the ratio of the actual volume at a given pT condition to the ideal volume at the same pT condition.

The ideal gas equation (3.11) is therefore modified to:—

$$pV = ZR_oT \qquad\qquad (3.17)$$

$$\text{or } Z = \frac{pV}{R_oT} \qquad\qquad (3.18)$$

In the above R_o is 1545 and p is lb/sq ft

A series of compressibility and temperature-entropy charts has been drafted to cover all gases about which reliable information could be found. These start on page 34-8. In some cases, they represent consolidation and correlation of data from several sources, usually with a variance of less than one percent from the basic data. These charts may be considered authoritative.

The temperature-entropy charts are useful in an isentropic or adiabatic process to determine the temperature change, not always consistent with ideal gas laws. Temperature at the end conditions in such a process is required to obtain the compressibility factor at discharge conditions before solving for volume and horsepower.

These specific Z and TS charts provide the necessary correction factors for most compression problems involving the gases covered.

Generalized Compressibility Charts

Because experimental data covering complete ranges of temperature and pressure are not available for all gases, scientists have developed Generalized Compressibility Charts. There are a number of these. One set, considered the best at present, starts on page 34-50.

These charts are based on reduced pressure and temperature conditions. Reduced pressure (p_r) is the ratio of the absolute pressure in psiA at a particular condition to the absolute critical pressure (psiA). Similarly, reduced temperature (T_r) is the ratio of the absolute temperature at the particular condition to the absolute critical temperature. The formulas are

$$p_r = \frac{p}{p_c} \tag{3.19}$$

$$T_r = \frac{T}{T_c} \tag{3.20}$$

It has been found that compressibility curves on the reduced basis for a large number of gases fall together with but small divergence. There are only a few gases that are too individualistic to be included. See the introduction to the charts on page 34-50.

Some charts show a reduced volume (v_r') also but this is really a pseudo (pretended) reduced condition obtained by use of the following formula. Reduced volumes are not shown on the charts included here.

$$v_r' = \frac{v p_c}{R_o T_c} \tag{3.21}$$

From this we can also write:

$$v = \frac{v_r' R_o T_c}{p_c} \tag{3.22}$$

In these formulas, v and v_r' are the specific volumes of one mole of gas.

Critical pressures and temperatures for many gases are given on pages 34-6 and 34-7.

For those who wonder why such a thing as a compressibility correction is needed, the following may bring a bit of sense to the phenomenon.

1. A perfect or ideal gas is one where there is no intermolecular reaction (attraction or repulsion) and where the molecules themselves occupy very little of the space involved. Distance between molecules is great. They may be considered as points.

2. When Z is greater than unity, it is the repulsion forces between the molecules and/or the greater percent volume of the molecules themselves that causes the gas volume to be greater than ideal.

3. When Z is less than unity, the attractive force between molecules causes lesser gas volume than ideal.

Mollier Diagrams

There are other diagrammatic methods of showing the variations in the properties of a gas. These give the absolute values of p-v-T-S-H at any point within the range of the charts. The best known is the Mollier diagram that plots enthalpy against entropy. Mollier also proposed other charts that are sometimes called by his name. The most common of these are:

> Temperature versus Entropy, and,
> Pressure versus Enthalpy

All have their uses and usually have other than the main properties plotted by diagonal lines or curves. Mollier diagrams, however, are frequently not on a sufficiently large scale to permit their use for accurate calculations. Mollier diagrams are not included in this book.

Gas Mixtures

Although not strictly true, gas mixtures can be considered as equivalent gases with computable properties for most compressor applications. Mixtures handled by compressors may contain from two to ten components. The chief properties required are:

> Specific volume
> Density
> Volume and mole percent
> Molecular weight
> Specific gravity
> Partial pressure
> Ratio of specific heats (k)
> Pseudo critical pressure
> Pseudo critical temperature
> Compressibility
> Gas constant
> Specific heats

The Mole

The *mole* is particularly useful when working with gas mixtures. It is based on Avogadro's Law that equal volumes of gases at given pT conditions contain equal number of molecules. Since this is so, then the *weight* of these equal volumes will be proportional to their molecular weights.

The volume of one mole at any desired condition can be found by the use of the perfect gas law

$$pV = R_oT \quad \text{or} \quad pV = 1545\,T \tag{3.23}$$

Choosing SPT conditions, solve for V in the above formula (p is lbs/sq ft and T is °R). This turns out to be 379.4 cu ft. For slide rule work use 379 cu ft/mole.

To repeat, this is the volume of a weight (expressed in pounds) of any gas at 14.696 psiA and 60°F — the weight being the same number as the molecular weight.

Thus, a mole of hydrogen occupies a volume of 379 cu ft standard conditions and weighs 2.016 pounds. A mole of air occupies 379 cu ft at the same conditions but weighs 28.97 pounds. A mole of isobutane, still

379 cu ft, weighs 58.12 pounds. This, of course, assumes that they act as perfect or ideal gases, which most of them do at or near standard conditions (SPT) or 14.696 psiA and 60°F. Most mole calculations involve these or similar conditions.

Note however, that a mole is a *weight* of gas. It is *not* a volume.

In spite of the deviation from a perfect gas being sometimes in question, the following methods of obtaining mixture properties are of great value, and in some cases are the only possible approaches.

Specific Volume and Density

Since the volume and the weight of a mole or any gas is known from the defined relations, it follows that the Specific Volume in cu ft/lb or Density in lb/cu ft is obtained by simple division.

Gas	Specific Vol. cu ft/mole	lb/mole and Molecular Weight	Specific Vol. cu ft/lb	Density lb/cu ft
Hydrogen	379	2.016	188.3	.00531
Air	379	28.97	13.1	.0763
Isobutane	379	58.12	6.51	.153

Note that these data are on the basis of perfect gas laws. Some gases — isobutane is one — deviate even at SPT conditions. The actual figures, for example, on isobutane are 6.339 cu ft/lb and 0.1578 lb/cu ft. See page 34-6.

Volume Percent of Constituents

Mole percent is the ratio of the number of moles of one constituent to the total number of moles of mixture. Mole percent also happens to be percent by volume. This statement should be questioned since a mole is defined as a weight. Look at the table below for proof. The gas analysis in these and following tables is that of a typical raw ammonia synthesis gas.

Gas	Mole %	Moles/Mole of mixture	Vol (SPT) of one mole	Vol/Mole of mixture	Vol %
H_2	61.4	.614	379	232.7	61.4
N_2	19.7	.197	379	74.7	19.7
CO_2	17.5	.175	379	66.3	17.5
CO	1.4	.014	379	5.3	1.4
	100.0	1.000		379.0	

Molecular Weight of Mixture

The average molecular weight of the mixture is often needed. It is obtained by multiplying the molecular weight of each component by its mole fraction (mole % ÷ 100) and then adding these values as shown below.

Gas	Mole % or Vol. %	Mol. Wgt.	Proportional MW
H_2	61.4	2	1.228
N_2	19.7	28	5.516
CO_2	17.5	44	7.700
CO	1.4	28	.392
	100.0		14.84

Therefore, the average or pseudo molecular weight of the mixture is 14.84.

Specific Gravity

Normally, specific gravity for gases is a ratio of the lb/cu ft of the gas involved to the lb/cu ft of air, both at SPT condition. Considering a mole of each gas, the volumes are the same and the weight of each volume is the same as the molecular weight. Therefore specific gravity is figured as the ratio of these molecular weights and becomes (for our example) 14.84 divided by 28.97 or 0.512.

Partial Pressure of Components

The fraction of the total pressure in a gas mixture due to a given component is equal to the fraction which that component represents in the total moles of gas present.

$$p_a = p \frac{N_a}{N} \qquad p_b = p \frac{N_b}{N} \text{ and } p_c = p \frac{N_c}{N} \qquad (3.24)$$

Thus, in a mixture of 15 moles at 15 psiA total pressure containing 2 moles of hydrogen, the partial pressure of the hydrogen would be 2/15 of 15 psiA or 2 psiA.

Volume fractions, if available, may be used in place of mole fractions.

Ratio of Specific Heats (k)

The value of k enters into many calculations. A definite relationship exists between specific heat at constant volume and specific heat at constant pressure. The heat capacity of a mole of gas may be determined by

$$Mc_p = Mc_v + 1.99 \qquad (3.25)$$

$$Mc_v = Mc_p - 1.99 \qquad (3.26)$$

In these formulas, M is the weight of a mole of gas — or the molecular weight. These are easily resolved into

$$k = \frac{Mc_p}{Mc_v} = \frac{Mc_p}{Mc_p - 1.99} \qquad (3.27)$$

Remembering the unit of specific heat as BTU/lb/°F temperature rise, we can calculate the heat required to increase the temperature of each component gas one °F and add them to get the total for the mixture. Mc_p is the heat requirement for one mole. For compressor work, it is quite usual to use this molar heat capacity at 150°F which is considered an average temperature. However, for certain applications, particularly refrigeration, 150°F is not sufficiently close and an average should be selected more nearly representative of the actual value during compression.

A calculation table follows:—

Gas	Mole %	Moles of Gas/ Mole of Mixture	Mc_p at 150°F of Component	Product
H_2	61.4	.614	6.94	4.26
N_2	19.7	.197	6.98	1.38
CO_2	17.5	.175	9.37	1.64
CO	1.4	.014	6.97	0.10
	100.0	1.000		7.38

The molar specific heat (Mc_p) of the mixture is therefore 7.38. Entering this in the formula:—

$$k = \frac{7.38}{7.38-1.99} = 1.369 \text{ (say 1.37)}$$

For convenience, the molar heat capacity at 150°F (Mc_p) is given on pages 34-6 and 34-7 for most gases.

Pseudo Critical Conditions and Compressibility

Mention has been made of reduced pressure and reduced temperature under the discussion of compressibility. Compressibility curves on this basis start on page 34-50. They are applicable to gas mixtures as well as pure gases.

It is necessary to figure mixture pseudo-critical pressure and temperature to be used in calculating the pseudo-reduced conditions to be used in entering the charts. Pressures and temperatures must be in absolute values.

Gas	Mole %	Individual Critical Temp. °R	Pseudo $Tc(°R)$	Individual Critical Press.-PSIA	Pseudo $Pc(PSIA)$
H_2*	61.4	83	51.0	327	201.0
N_2	19.7	227	44.7	492	96.9
CO_2	17.5	548	95.9	1073	187.8
CO	1.4	242	3.4	507	7.1
Mixture Pseudo-Criticals			195°R		493 PSIA

*Must use Effective Critical Conditions. See pages 34-50.

Using these values, the pseudo-reduced conditions can be calculated and probable Z factors obtained from generalized charts.

Weight Basis Items

To certain gas properties of a mixture, each component contributes a share of its own property in proportion to its fraction of the total *weight (W)*.

$$R' = \frac{W_a R'_a + W_b R'_b + W_c R'_c}{W} + \dots \dots \quad (3.28)$$

$$c_p = \frac{W_a\, c_{pa} + W_b\, c_{pb} + W_c\, c_{pc}}{W} + \ldots\ldots\ldots \tag{3.29}$$

$$c_v = \frac{W_a\, c_{va} + W_b c_{vb} + W_c\, c_{vc}}{W} + \ldots\ldots\ldots \tag{3.30}$$

Compression Cycles

Two basic compression cycles or processes are applicable to both positive displacement and dynamic compressors. A third process is widely used, but, since it is a modification involving an efficiency to more nearly represent actual conditions, it is not a true basic cycle. Although neither of the two basic processes are commercially attainable, they are useful as a basis for calculations and comparisons.

Isothermal compression occurs when the temperature is kept constant as the pressure increases. This requires continuous removal of the heat of compression. Compression follows the formula

$$p_1 V_1 = p_2 V_2 = \text{Constant} \tag{3.31}$$

Adiabatic compression is obtained when there is no heat added to or removed from the gas during compression. Compression follows the formula

$$p_1 V_1^k = p_2 V_2^k \tag{3.32}$$

where k is the ratio of the specific heats.

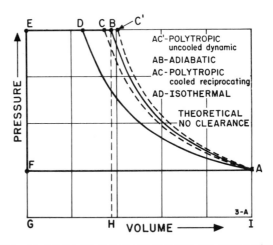

Fig. 3-A.   Theoretical indicator card showing various gas compression processes.

Fig. 3-A shows the theoretical zero clearance isothermal and adiabatic cycles on a pV basis for a compression ratio of 4. The area ADEF represents the work required when operating on the isothermal basis; and ABEF, the work required on the adiabatic basis. Obviously, the isothermal area is considerably less than the adiabatic and would be the cycle for greatest compression economy. However, it is never commercially possible to remove the heat of compression as rapidly as it is generated.

Therefore, this cycle is not as logical a working base as the adiabatic although it was so used for many years. Compressors are designed, however, for as much heat removal as possible.

Adiabatic compression is likewise never exactly obtained, since with some types of units there may be heat losses during part of the cycle and a gain in heat during another part. With other types of compressors there may be a definite heat gain. Nevertheless, the adiabatic cycle is rather closely approached *on an average* with most positive-displacement units and is generally the base to which they are referred.

Dynamic units, however, generally use the *polytropic cycle* where the pV relationship is

$$p_1 V_1^n = p_2 V_2^n \tag{3.33}$$

The exponent n is experimentally determined for a given type of machine and may be lower or higher than the adiabatic exponent k. In positive displacement and internally cooled dynamic compressors n is usually less than k. In uncooled dynamic units it is usually higher than k due to internal gas friction. Although n is actually a changing value during compression, an average or effective value, as calculated from experimental information, is used.

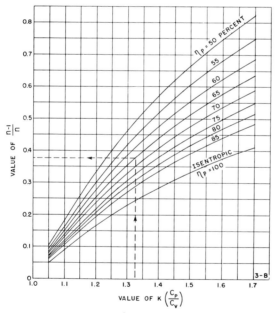

Fig. 3-B. Ratio $\dfrac{n-1}{n}$ versus adiabatic exponent k.

In addition to the isothermal and adiabatic compression curves shown in Fig. 3-A, the dotted lines show typical polytropic curves for a water-cooled reciprocating cylinder (AC) and for a noncooled dynamic unit (AC').

Thermodynamically, it should be noted that the isentropic or adiabatic process is reversible, while the polytropic process is irreversible. Also, all compressors operate on a theoretical *steady flow* process.

Although the exponent n is seldom required, the quantity $n\text{-}1/n$ is frequently needed. This can be obtained from the following equation, although it is necessary that the polytropic efficiency (η_p) be known (or approximated) from prior test. The k value of any gas or gas mixture is either calculable or known.

$$\frac{n-1}{n} = \frac{k-1}{k} \times \frac{1}{\eta_p} \qquad\qquad (3.34)$$

where (η_p) is the polytropic compression efficiency. Fig. 3-B solves this equation in curve form.

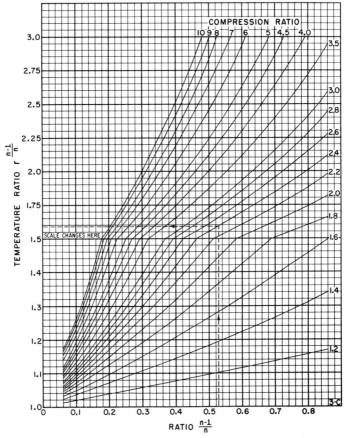

Fig. 3-C. **Polytropic temperature ratio versus ratio** $\dfrac{n-1}{n}$.

Either n or $n\text{-}1/n$ can also be experimentally calculated from test data if inlet and discharge pressures and temperatures are known. The following formula may be used

$$\frac{T_2}{T_1} = \left(\frac{p_2}{p_1}\right)^{\frac{n-1}{n}} = r^{\frac{n-1}{n}} \qquad (3.35)$$

This can also be used to estimate discharge temperatures when n or $n-1/n$ is known. For the latter, Fig. 3-C will be useful.

It is obvious that k and n can have quite different values. There has been a tendency in the past to use these symbols interchangeably to represent the ratio of specific heats. This is incorrect and the difference between them should be carefully observed.

Compressor Staging

All basic compressor elements (see page 1-4) regardless of type, have certain limiting operating conditions. When any limitation is involved it becomes necessary to *multistage* the compression process; that is, do it in two or more steps. Each step will utilize at least one *basic element* designed to operate in series with the other elements of the machine.

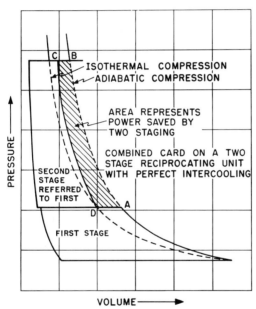

Fig. 3-D. Theoretical combined indicator card of a two stage positive-displacement compressor with perfect intercooling.

The limitations vary with the type of compressor, but the most important include

1. Discharge temperature — all types;
2. Pressure rise (or differential) — dynamic units and most positive-displacement types;
3. Compression ratio — dynamic units;
4. Effect of clearance — reciprocating units (this ties in also with compression ratio); and,
5. Desirability of saving power.

There are other reasons for multiple staging than the above, but they are largely for the designer of specific units to keep in mind.

A reciprocating compressor usually requires a separate cylinder for each stage with intercooling of the gas between stages. Fig. 3-D shows the pV combined diagram on a two-stage 100 psiG air compressor. Further stages are added in the same manner. In a reciprocating unit, all cylinders are commonly combined into one unit assembly and driven from a single crankshaft.

It was previously noted that the isothermal cycle (constant temperature) is the more economical of power. Cooling the gas after partial compression to a temperature equal to original intake temperature (back to the isothermal) obviously should reduce the power required in the second stage. Area ABCD represents the work saved over single stage adiabatic compression in this particular case. See also the definition of perfect intercooling — page 2-9.

Rotary positive-displacement compressors can, in some instances, combine two stages in one casing, but more often use two separate machines properly sized for their individual requirements, with cooling between stages. They will often have a common driver and a common baseplate. The pV diagram will be as in Fig. 3-D.

Dynamic compressors would, in most cases, have several staging elements in the same casing. There would normally be no intercooling between those stages contained in a given casing although the internal diffusors or diaphragms are sometimes water-cooled. The gas can be brought out to external exchangers for intercooling at the end of several stages of compression. Frequently, large units have two casings (separate machines) in series to cover the entire compression range, each machine equipped with several stages and with external intercooling between the machines. They are usually coupled in tandem to one driver. The extent to which intercooling is used depends largely on power cost.

Power Requirement

The power requirement of any compressor is the prime basis for sizing the driver and for selection and design of compressor components. The actual power requirement is related to a theoretical cycle through a *compression efficiency* which has been determined by test on prior machines. Compression efficiency is the ratio of the theoretical to the actual gas horsepower and, as used by the industry, does not include mechanical friction losses. These are added later either through the use of a mechanical efficiency or by adding actual mechanical losses previously determined. The mechanical efficiencies of positive-displacement compressors range from 88 to 95%, depending upon the size and type of unit. Dynamic compressors commonly add actual mechanical bearing and seal friction horsepower. See page 4-30. Dynamic units also have certain relatively small hydraulic losses that are often disregarded for estimating purposes.

Positive-displacement machines are compared to the adiabatic cycle while dynamic units generally use the polytropic.

In calculating horsepower, the compressibility factor Z must be considered since its influence is considerable with many gases, particularly at high pressure.

Positive-Displacement Compressors

An inlet volume basis is universal with this class of compressor. It is important to differentiate between an inlet volume on a perfect gas basis (V_{p1}) and one on a real gas basis (V_{r1}).

Volumes are at inlet pressure and temperature $(p_1$ & $T_1)$

$$V_{r1} = V_{p1} \, Z_1 \tag{3.36}$$

The basic theoretical single stage horsepower formula is developed from the pV indicator diagram, the net area of which represents the work required to compress and deliver the gas.

Adiabatic Basis

Referring to the adiabatic cycle curve of Fig. 3-A the net area is found to be

$$\text{Area ABHI} + \text{area BEGH} - \text{area AFGI} \tag{3.37}$$

Using calculus and algebra this becomes

$$P_{T(ad)} = \frac{p_1 V_{r1}}{229} \times \frac{k}{k-1} \times \left(r^{\frac{k-1}{k}} - 1 \right) \times \frac{Z_1 + Z_2}{2Z_1} \tag{3.38}$$

A frequently used basis for V_{r1} is 100 cfm at inlet conditions, in which case the formula becomes

$$P_{T(ad)}/100 = \frac{p_1}{2.29} \times \frac{k}{k-1} \times \left(r^{\frac{k-1}{k}} - 1 \right) \times \frac{Z_1 + Z_2}{2Z_1} \tag{3.39}$$

Another form current in the industry is the basis for frequently used charts. In this, a volume of 1 million cu ft per 24 hours or MMCFD is used. *In this book and in this case only,* V_1 is measured as *perfect gas* at *14.4 psiA* and intake temperature, and the actual compressor capacity must be referred to these conditions before computing the final horsepower. There are some variations in this base in certain industries so care must be used with this term. See page 34-146 for BHP/MM curves.

$$P_{T(ad)}/MMCFD = 43.67 \times \frac{k}{k-1} \times \left(r^{\frac{k-1}{k}} - 1 \right) \times \frac{Z_1 + Z_2}{2} \tag{3.40}$$

Isothermal Basis

Since the isothermal cycle is based on no temperature change during compression, heat is removed continuously as generated and there is theoretically no gain by multiple staging. Therefore, formula (3.41) below holds for any number of stages as long as r is the over-all or total compression ratio. It is derived in the same manner as the adiabatic formula above.

$$P_{T(iso)} = \frac{p_1 V_{r1} \, \log_e r}{229} \times \frac{Z_1 + Z_2}{2Z_1} \tag{3.41}$$

X Factor

For convenience, the factor $\left(r^{\frac{k-1}{k}} - 1 \right)$ found above, has been calculated for what is frequently called *normal air*. This has a density of 0.075 lb/

cu ft at 68°F and 14.7 psiA, a relative humidity of 36%, and a k value of 1.395. Values of this function of r (called the X Factor) are given starting on page 34-88. They may be used for air and most diatomic gases. Where k differs, a correction may be applied from the curve on page 34-92.

Compressibility Correction

In the foregoing formulas, a correction is indicated for deviation from the perfect gas laws — the compressibility. This involves the determination of compressibility at both intake and discharge conditions. Intake pressure and temperature are known and compressibility at these conditions can be obtained directly from specific gas charts or by the reduced condition method using generalized charts. To obtain Z at discharge conditions, it is necessary to determine the discharge temperature. Discharge pressure is known.

Discharge Temperature

In the adiabatic cycle, as applied to positive-displacement units, it is customary to use the *theoretical* discharge temperature in calculations. In an actual compressor, there are many factors acting to cause variation from the theoretical but, *on an average,* the theoretical temperature is closely approached and any error introduced is slight. Note:— These comments do not apply to the liquid piston compressor. See page 1-8.

Adiabatic compression is isentropic — that is, the entropy remains constant. If temperature—entropy diagrams are available for the gas involved (see pages starting at 34-8), the theoretical discharge temperature can be read directly. Otherwise it is necessary to calculate it by the following relationship

$$\frac{T_2}{T_1} = \left(\frac{p_2}{p_1}\right)^{\frac{k-1}{k}} = r^{\frac{k-1}{k}} \tag{3.42}$$

$$\frac{T_2}{T_1} = \left(r^{\frac{k-1}{k}} - 1\right) + 1$$

$$= X + 1$$

$$T_2 = T_1 (X + 1) \tag{3.43}$$

Note that all pressures and temperatures are absolute. For estimating purposes, page 34-155 may be used to obtain adiabatic discharge temperatures.

Influence of Other Factors

Formulas (3.38), (3.39), and (3.40) are theoretical and are not affected by gas characteristics such as molecular weight, specific gravity, and actual density at operating conditions, etc. These all have an effect on actual power requirements through their effect on efficiency. Proper allowances are made by designers.

Multistaging

It has been previously stated that there are practical limits to the amount of compression permissible within a single stage or element beyond which two or more steps or stages must be used with intercooling between stages in most cases.

Theoretically minimum power with perfect intercooling and no pressure loss between stages is obtained by making the ratio of compression the same in all stages. The following formula uses the *over-all* compression ratio, where

r_s is theoretically best compression ratio per stage

r_t is overall compression ratio $\left(\dfrac{P_{final}}{P_{initial}} \right)$

s is number of stages

$$r_s = \sqrt[s]{r_t} \qquad\qquad (3.44)$$

For example:—

Two stage; $r_s = \sqrt[2]{r_t}$

Three stage; $r_s = \sqrt[3]{r_t}$

Four stage; $r_s = \sqrt[4]{r_t}$

See also page 4-14.
Even though this method results in minimum power, the energy required will vary only a fraction of one percent for rather large variations in the actual compression ratios for individual stages. Designers take advantage of this fact for economic and other engineering reasons.

Each stage is best figured as a separate compressor, the capacity (V_1) of each stage being separately calculated from the first stage real intake volume, corrected to the actual pressure and temperature conditions existing at the higher stage cylinder inlet, allowing for pressure drop through cooler and piping and also allowing for any reduction in the moisture content if there is condensation between stages in an intercooler. The theoretical power per stage can then be calculated and the total horsepower obtained.

Note:—On the basis of perfect intercooling and equal compression ratios per stage, formulas (3.38), (3.39) and (3.40) can be altered to obtain *total* theoretical power by multiplying the first term by the number of stages *(s)* and dividing the exponent of r by s. Compression ratios, however, seldom are equal, there is always some pressure drop between stages, and perfect intercooling is seldom attained. It is therefore, felt that the best general method of figuring is to use one stage at a time.

Dynamic Compressors

The performance of dynamic compressors is usually based on the polytropic process. The basic theoretical power formulas are the same as (3.38), (3.39), or (3.40) except that the exponent n replaces k. Example:

$$P_{T(pol)} = \frac{p_1 V_1}{229} \times \frac{n}{n-1} \times \left(r^{\frac{n-1}{n}} - 1 \right) \times \frac{Z_1 + Z_2}{2 Z_1} \qquad (3.45)$$

Since the value of n depends on polytropic efficiency and is determined by use of Fig. 3-B, it is necessary to estimate the efficiency until the compressor design is well settled. Fig. 3-E gives a basis for such preliminary estimates. This efficiency will, of course, be influenced by many factors, including the degree of cooling within the stage during compression.

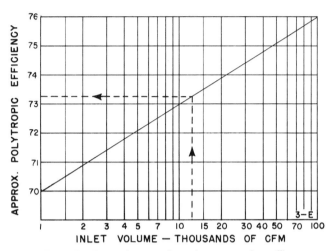

Fig. 3-E. Approximate polytropic compression efficiency of a dynamic compressor versus inlet capacity.

To obtain the discharge temperature for polytropic compression, n must be used in place of k in formula 3.42. Use Fig. 3-B, and an approximate efficiency from Fig. 3-E. This temperature will be needed if compressibility corrections are to be made.

When handling gas mixtures or a mixture of air and water vapor, the methods of prior discussions in this chapter are to be followed.

Polytropic Head

The concept of quantity and *head* in a power formula is well understood in centrifugal liquid pump practice. It also applies to dynamic compressors handling compressible fluids. In a *liquid* pump, discharge head is the height in feet of a column of the liquid which would produce at its base the same pressure per unit area that actually exists at the pump discharge. Intake head is on a similar basis. In practice, it is the difference between the two that is used and called *head*. It is the head *increase* produced by the pump.

Liquids are homogeneous and have the same density throughout. The pressure varies directly as the height of the column. This is not true when handling gases. The density is changing continuously throughout the column according to the formula

$$\frac{\rho_2}{\rho_1} = \frac{p_2}{p_1} \frac{T_1 Z_1}{T_2 Z_2} \qquad (3.46)$$

Polytropic head is the work in *foot pounds per pound* of gas and the formula (3.47) gives this result. In some dynamic compressors the work produced in a stage is stated in Btu/lb which is a simple conversion from or to polytropic head.

$$H_p = R'T_1 \times \frac{n}{n-1} \left(r^{\frac{n-1}{n}} - 1 \right) \times \frac{Z_1 + Z_2}{2} \qquad (3.47)$$

The fundamental theoretical property of polytropic head in ft lb/lb as applied to dynamic machines is that, for *a given machine at a given speed and inlet capacity*, the head (column height) produced is the same regardless of the nature of the fluid, its inlet temperature or whether it is cooled or not during compression. The polytropic head theoretically remains the same regardless of whether the gas is CO_2 (G is 1.528), air (G is 1.000), or helium (G is 0.138).

Since work is force times distance or in this case, weight times head, the theoretical gas power formula can also be expressed as:—

$$P_{T(p)} = \frac{WH_p}{33,000} \text{ where } W \text{ is lb/min} \qquad (3.48)$$

Polytropic Head versus Pressure

Although the polytropic head developed by a given dynamic compressor at a given speed and capacity remains constant regardless of the gas, the pressure rise generated definitely does not. This will vary with the density of the gas. Although influenced by other factors, the pressure rise will vary approximately as the density.

Bibliography

Many authoritative books have been consulted in the development of the theory presented here. Chief among these are the following:

Chemical Engineering Thermodynamics by Dodge — 1944

Textbook Of Physical Chemistry by Glasstone — 1946

Turboblowers by Stepanoff — 1955

Elements Of Physics by Smith and Cooper — 1957

Marks Handbook — 1958

Fundamentals Of Physical Science by Krauskopf — 1959

Principles Of Chemistry by Hiller and Herber — 1960

Concepts Of Thermodynamics by Obert — 1960

Compressed Air and Gas Handbook — 1961

Chapter 4

The Application of Theory

(Continued)

Introduction

This chapter considers, through theory, how certain gas and compressor element design characteristics influence capacity and performance. However, there are many factors that cannot be theoretically evaluated and the manufacturer's experience must be his guide. Typical is the effect of leakage on both capacity and power. The exact influence of these "experience factors" varies with the compressor type, design and operating conditions.

There is no difference between the application of theory to those compressors that operate at pressures above atmosphere and the application to those with intakes considerably below atmosphere (vacuum pumps). Differences exist only in the areas of efficiencies and leakage rates. Therefore, no differentiation is made here.

Volume Reference Summary

Since the most generally required quantities are the original inlet volume and the inlet volume to subsequent stages (both on a per minute basis), a summary of formulas is given below in which the word *dry* means there is no water vapor in the quantity of gas or gas mixture involved. Inlet volume to any stage may be calculated from these by using the proper inlet pressure and temperature and correcting for moisture content at those conditions.

From SCFM (cfm measured at 14.7 psiA, 60°F, dry)

$$V_1 = SCFM \times \frac{14.7}{520} \times \frac{T_1 Z_1}{p_1} \tag{4.1}$$

From weight flow (W lbs/min, dry)

$$V_1 = \frac{1545}{144} \times \frac{W\, T_1 Z_1}{M\, p_1} \tag{4.2}$$

From mole flow (N moles/min, dry)

$$V_1 = \frac{379 \times 14.7}{520} \times \frac{N\, T_1 Z_1}{p_1} \tag{4.3}$$

From cfm measured at conditions other than those at intake

(CFM$_g$ at p_g, T_g, Z_g, dry)

$$V_1 = CFM_g \times \frac{p_g T_1 Z_1}{p_1 T_g Z_g} \qquad (4.4)$$

In all the above, pressure is psiA. See page 2-2 for symbols.

If water vapor is a component in the gas analysis and the total analysis percentage amounts to 100, the above formulas may be applied to "wet" gas. Use the proper value for M in (4.2), however. Often water vapor is segregated and the space it occupies must be included separately. This is a partial pressure problem (see page 3-6). Multiplying any of the above formulas by the following will apply the correction.

$$\frac{p_1}{p_1 - p_v} \qquad (4.5)$$

where p_v is the actual vapor pressure of the contained moisture.

The Reciprocating Compressor
Cylinder Clearance and Volumetric Efficiency

Cylinder clearance cannot be completely eliminated. *Normal* clearance is the minimum obtainable in a given cylinder and will vary between 4 and 16% for most standard cylinders. Some special low ratio cylinders have normal clearance much greater than this. Normal clearance does not include volume that may have been added for other purposes, such as capacity control.

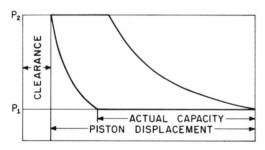

Fig. 4-A. Effect of clearance on the capacity of a reciprocating compressor.

Although clearance is of little importance to the average user (guarantees being made on actually delivered capacity), its effect on capacity should be understood because of the wide application of a variation in clearance for control and other purposes. There are many cases where extra clearance is added to a cylinder to

    1. Reduce capacity at fixed pressure conditions, and

    2. Prevent driver overload under variable operating pressure conditions by reducing capacity as compression ratio changes.

If a compressor is designed for a given capacity at a given condition, the amount of normal clearance in cylinder or cylinders has no effect on power.

When a piston has completed the compression and delivery stroke and is ready to reverse its movement, gas at discharge pressure is trapped in the clearance space. This gas expands on the return stroke until its pressure is sufficiently below intake pressure to cause the suction valves to open. On a pV diagram, Fig. 4-A shows the effect of this re-expansion on the quantity of fresh gas drawn in.

Note:—All illustrations unless otherwise noted are theoretical for k of 1.40 and are based on

$$p_1V_1{}^k = p_2V_2{}^k$$

The theoretical formula for volumetric efficiency expressed as a percentage is,

$$\eta_v = 100 - c \left(r^{\frac{1}{k}} - 1 \right) \tag{4.6}$$

As a practical matter, there are factors that modify this and an accepted formula becomes

$$\eta_v = 100 - c \left(r^{\frac{1}{k}} - 1 \right) - L \tag{4.7}$$

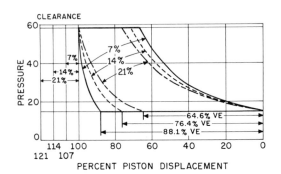

Fig. 4-B. Quantitative effect of various cylinder clearances on the volumetric efficiency at constant compression ratio.

Here, L is introduced to allow for the effect of such variables as internal leakage, gas friction, pressure drop through valves, inlet gas preheating, etc. This term is difficult to generalize. It may be 5% for a moderate pressure (45 psiG) oil lubricated air compressor. Due to increased leakage, a higher value of L will be necessary with a light gas than with a heavy one.

The above formula can be applied to vacuum pumps as well as to other types of compressors, although the value of L will be much higher, varying considerably with intake gas density.

Inspection of these formulas shows that the *VE decreases* (1) as the clearance *increases*, (2) as the compression ratio *increases*, and (3) as k *decreases*.

Fig. 4-B shows a series of theoretical pV diagrams based on an r of 4.0, k of 1.40, and clearances 7, 14, and 21%. The effect of clearance is clearly indicated.

Fig. 4-C illustrates the effect of clearance at moderate and high compression ratio conditions. A theoretical pV diagram for a ratio of 7 is superimposed on a diagram for a ratio of 4, all else being the same. A relatively high clearance (14%) has been used for illustrative purposes. The clearance for a commercial compressor designed for a ratio of 7 would be much less than 14%.

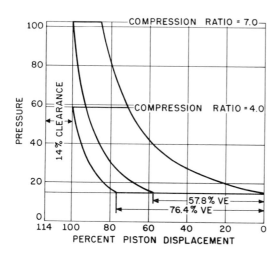

Fig. 4-C. Effect of different compression ratios on the volumetric efficiency of a given cylinder.

Effect of Specific Heat Ratio *(k)*

Fig. 4-D illustrates the effect of k on volumetric efficiency for a fixed clearance of 15% and a compression ratio of 4.0.

Clearance especially concerns the designer in high-compression ratios and when handling gases with low specific heat ratios, although he will always endeavor to maintain clearance at the lowest value consistent with adequate valving and running clearances.

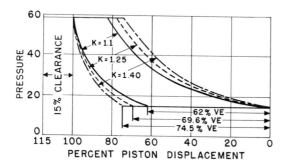

Fig. 4-D. Effect of various specific heat ratios on the volumetric efficiency of a given cylinder.

Clearance and Compression Efficiency

Just as clearance in a cylinder has predominant control over volumetric efficiency, the valve area has predominant control over compression efficiency. To obtain low clearance and a high *VE*, the designer finds it necessary to limit the size and number of valves. This may tend to lower the efficiency of compression and raise the horsepower. The designer must therefore evaluate both factors and arrive at a compromise, quite a common engineering procedure. The various types of compressor applications may be divided into four general classifications that the designer uses to determine which factor takes precedence or whether they are balanced. These classes are

	Compression Ratio	More Important Factor
Very High	10 to 30 (Vacuum Pumps)	Low clearance
High	8 to 10 maximum	Clearance principally, Valving secondary
Moderate	5 maximum	Balanced
Low	2 or less	Good valving

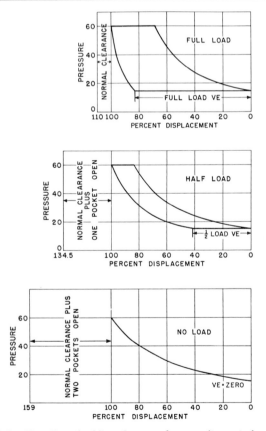

Fig. 4-E.   The effect of adding clearance for capacity control purposes.

Clearance Control

The effect of added clearance is often used as a means of capacity control. Fig. 4-E shows how this is accomplished. These are again theoretical diagrams at a compression ratio of about 4. They represent five-step control on a *double-acting cylinder*, although only one end is shown. Two clearance pockets are provided in each end of the cylinder in this case. These are sized so that the *VE* of either end with only one pocket open to the cylinder is about half the full load *VE*, while with two open the *VE* is reduced to zero. Pockets may be opened and closed manually or automatically. This gives full- half- and no load points on each end (only one end is shown). For the entire cylinder (two ends and twice the PD), full, 3/4, 1/2, 1/4 and no load are obtained. Note that at no load the compression and expansion lines are identical and theoretically all the compression power is recovered.

LOW-PRESSURE DIAGRAMS   HIGH-PRESSURE DIAGRAMS

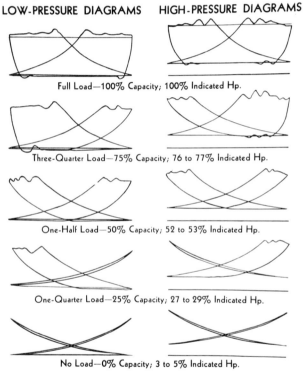

Full Load—100% Capacity; 100% Indicated Hp.

Three-Quarter Load—75% Capacity; 76 to 77% Indicated Hp.

One-Half Load—50% Capacity; 52 to 53% Indicated Hp.

One-Quarter Load—25% Capacity; 27 to 29% Indicated Hp.

No Load—0% Capacity; 3 to 5% Indicated Hp.

Fig. 4-F. Typical actual indicator cards from a two-stage 100 psiG air compressor with five-step clearance control.

On a *two-stage* air compressor, each *double-acting* cylinder is fitted with four pockets, two in each end. Corresponding pockets in low-and high-pressure cylinders are opened or closed at the same time by the regulator according to demand for compressed air. Discharge pressure is the item maintained. This maintains balance in capacity between the two cylinders at all loads. Actual indicator cards on this type of compressor are illustrated in Fig. 4-F.

When clearance control is used to prevent driver overload under variable pressure conditions, the pocket or pockets are often manually operated.

Clearance Control and Variable Compression Ratio

Fig. 4-E shows clearly that the *control* or capacity reduction is caused by the re-expansion of gas originally compressed into the clearance space. This space was sized for the capacity reduction desired at the *design* pressure conditions.

Most clearance control applications involve rather closely fixed intake and discharge pressures and therefore little variation in compression ratio. Other applications involve operation under varying conditions of either intake or discharge pressure, the ratio of compression changing from time to time.

Clearance control volume must be predesigned and built-in unless a seldom warranted variable volume pocket is used. See Fig. 6-AW, page 6-43. The ratio of compression is the controlling factor in the amount of unloading any given pocket will do. Actual operating pressure levels have no appreciable influence. The pV diagram in Fig. 4-G shows 1/2 load (one pocket open) condition of Fig. 4-E and percent of full load capacity attained when discharge pressure falls with a constant atmospheric intake. The left hand scale is in compression ratio, rather than pressure, to emphasize the basic variable. Thus, with a cylinder designed to give 50% of full load capacity at a ratio of 4, it is seen that the effectiveness of clearance control as a means of reducing capacity decreases as the ratio falls. Conversely, its effectiveness would increase if the ratio were greater than design. The table below gives the data of Fig. 4-G in another form. The last column relates it to full load *design* conditions with a ratio of 4.0.

Total Clearance	Ratio	VE	Percent Full Load Design Capacity (r = 4.0)
10% Normal-pockets closed	4.0	83.0	100% (Design)
34.5% For ½ load-one pocket open-Design condition	4.0	41.5	50% (Design)
34.5% One pocket open	3.0	58.7	71%
34.5% One pocket open	2.0	78.0	94%
34.5% One pocket open	1.5	88.5	107%
34.5% One pocket open	5.0	25.5	31%

Clearance control will provide design capacity reduction only when operating at design compression ratio.

Effect of Specific Heat Ratio (k) on Power

Referring to Fig. 4-D and remembering that indicator card area is proportional to the power required brings out the fact that theoretical horsepower varies with the k value of the gas. This is due to both the change in power per 100 cfm actual and the change in actual capacity. For the given example of Fig. 4-D, the power in percentage will tabulate as follows, the theoretical VE being calculated by formula (4.6).

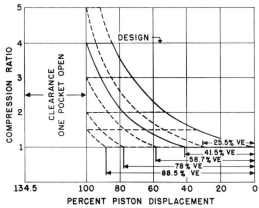

Fig. 4-G. Effect on volumetric efficiency of variations in compression ratio with one clearance pocket open.

k	Theor. Adiabatic HP/100 (3.39)	Theor. Total Adiabatic HP/cylinder (3.38)
1.1	100	100
1.25	108	121
1.40	115	138

Comparison of columns two and three emphasizes the effect on power of VE changes caused by changes in k. The lower k is, the less power required for a given cylinder or given capacity. These percentages will change with compression ratio and cylinder clearance.

Peak Horsepower

The theoretical total single stage adiabatic power formula, neglecting compressibility, follows for positive-displacement compressors.

$$P_{T(ad)} = \frac{p_1 V_1}{229} \times \frac{k}{k-1} \times \left[\left(\frac{p_2}{p_1} \right)^{\frac{k-1}{k}} - 1 \right] \qquad (4.8)$$

This gives the power required for given V_1, p_1, p_2 and k values.

With certain types of compressor applications, pressure conditions may vary considerably and it is necessary to provide for, or limit, the changes in power requirements as pressures change. The two general cases are

1. Where p_2 is constant, but p_1 varies widely. This is typical in vacuum pump and some types of gas booster applications; and,
2. Where p_1 is constant, but p_2 varies. This application may be found in many pipeline and gas storage applications.

Both of these cases may involve simultaneous changes in p_1 or p_2, r, and V_1 (since the VE changes with r). The effect of variations in r on VE (V_1 in this case) has been shown in Fig. 4-C.

The compressor cylinder must first be sized to meet certain specified conditions and must then be analyzed for power variations due to changing pressures. It will be found in both cases that, over a sufficiently wide change in pressures, there will be a peak or maximum horsepower with reduced power on either side of peak.

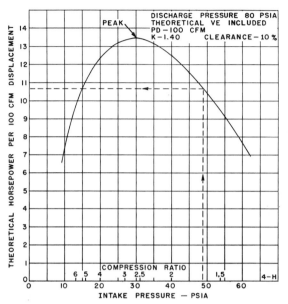

Fig. 4-H.   Example of peak horsepower with constant discharge and variable intake (theoretical adiabatic base).

Considering Case 1, Fig. 4-H has been developed for specific conditions of a reciprocating compressor cylinder displacement of 100 cfm, k of 1.40, clearance of 10%, and p_2 of 80 psiA. Peak power is required at an intake of about 29.5 psiA and an r of about 2.72. Case 1 cylinders normally have a relatively low clearance.

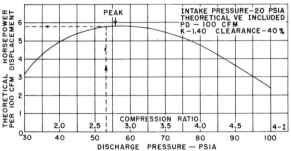

Fig. 4-I.   Example of peak horsepower with variable discharge and constant intake (theoretical adiabatic base).

Fig. 4-I shows an example of Case 2 based on k of 1.40, p_1 of 20 psiA, and clearance of 40%. Clearance is high compared to Fig. 4-H. This flattens the curve materially. Peak occurs at about 56 psiA discharge with an r of about 2.8.

Fig. 4-H and 4-I are theoretical examples only. *VE* changes are by formula (4-7). The results would be different for other values of k and clearance and would vary when compression efficiency is allowed for.

Still on a theoretical basis, the following formulas co-relate r, k, and clearance for peak conditions, clearance being a decimal.

Case 1, when p_2 is constant, p_1 varies

$$c = \frac{k - r^{\frac{k-1}{k}}}{(k-1)\, r^{\frac{1}{k}} - \left(k - r^{\frac{k-1}{k}}\right)} \qquad (4.9)$$

Case 2, when p_2 varies and p_1 is constant

$$c = \frac{k-1}{kr^{\frac{1}{k}} - r^{\frac{2-k}{k}} - (k-1)} \qquad (4.10)$$

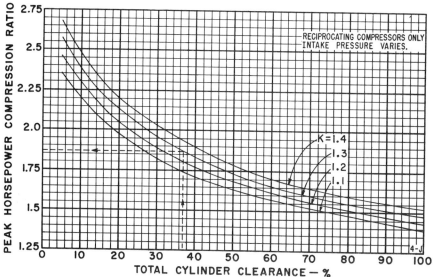

Fig. 4-J. Compression ratio versus clearance for peak horsepower with constant discharge pressure and varying intake pressure.

These are useful in certain applications and normally give a peak horsepower compression ratio slightly higher than would be obtained in an actual compressor. To eliminate much of the "cut and try" in an actual case, the curves of Fig. 4-J and 4-K have been prepared for reciprocating units, allowing for changes in both volumetric and compression efficiency as r varies. These are sufficiently accurate for most engineering computations.

Effect of Compressibility

The generally accepted method of correcting gas volumes and compressor horsepower is by the use of compressibility factors *(Z)*. See pages 3-8 and 3-13. Mollier charts may be used to calculate specific volumes, discharge temperatures, power required etc., but their scale is often such that the required accuracy cannot be obtained. Therefore, the methods outlined in Chapter 3 are the recommended standards. There are cases where comprehensive tables of gas properties are available (steam and ammonia are examples) and they may be used for accuracy.

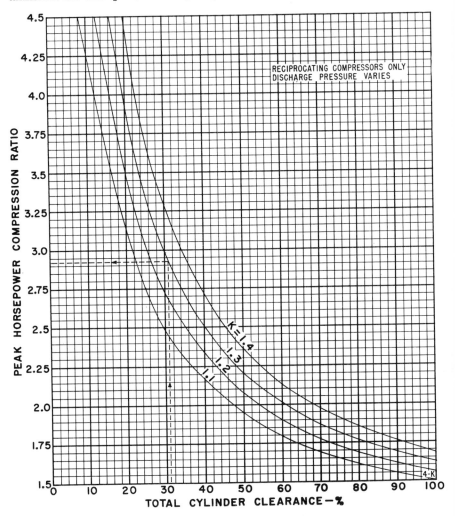

Fig. 4-K. Compression ratio versus clearance for peak horsepower with variable discharge pressure and constant intake pressure.

Deviation alters both capacity and horsepower as determined from the ideal gas laws, and the combination of effects is not always readily apparent. Considering *VE* first, note that there is a change in the re-expansion loss caused by the change in *Z*. Formula (4.7) can be rewritten into this form:

$$\eta_v = 100 + c\text{-}L\text{-}cr^{\frac{1}{k}}$$
(4.11)

Applying a Z correction brings:

$$\eta_v = 100 + c\text{-}L\text{-}\left(cr^{\frac{1}{k}}\right)\frac{Z_1}{Z_2}$$
(4.12)

The ratio Z_1/Z_2 changes the factor of clearance loss only. If compressibility is higher at discharge than it is at inlet, this ratio is less than unity and the VE will increase. If the compressibility at discharge is lower than at intake, the ratio will be above unity and the VE will decrease.

Considering power required per 100 cfm at intake and referring to formula (3.39), page 3-19 the correction for compressibility is $\dfrac{Z_1 + Z_2}{2Z_1}$ An increase in compressibility between inlet and discharge will then increase the factor (and the power per 100 cfm). A decrease in Z during compression will decrease the power per 100 cfm required.

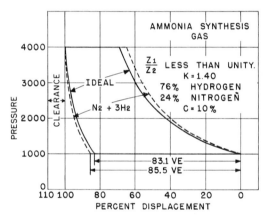

Fig. 4-L. Effect of compressibility on the volumetric efficiency and power of a cylinder handling pure ammonia synthesis gas.

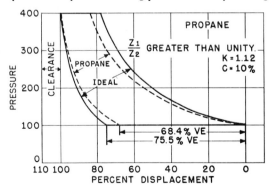

Fig. 4-M. Effect of compressibility on the volumetric efficiency and power of a cylinder handling pure propane.

Fig. 4-L and Fig. 4-M show the ideal and the corrected theoretical cards for two frequently handled gases. These show distinctly different compressibility effects. Fig. 4-L covers ammonia synthesis gas (H_2/N_2 in a 76%/24% mixture) before the reaction that forms ammonia. The VE is increased over the ideal and horsepower (indicator card area) is greater. Fig. 4-M is for pure propane. The VE is less than ideal and power is considerably reduced.

Fig. 4-N shows the above in tabular form for a compressor having a displacement of 100 cfm and 10% fixed clearance.

Gas Condition	Ammonia Synthesis		Pure Propane	
	Ideal Gas	Actual Gas*	Ideal Gas	Actual Gas*
k**	1.40	1.40	1.12	1.12
Clearance (%)	10	10	10	10
p_1 (psiA)	1000	1000	100	100
T_1 (°F)	70	70	70	70
p_2 (psiA)	4000	4000	400	400
r	4.00	4.00	4.00	4.00
T_2 (°F)	328	331	155	191
Z_1	1.000	1.037	1.000	0.880
Z_2	1.000	1.136	1.000	0.682
$\dfrac{Z_1}{Z_2}$	1.000	0.913	1.000	1.290
Theor. VE	83.1	85.5	75.5	68.4
Cfm at inlet Cond.	83.1	85.5	75.5	68.4
Cu ft/lb at inlet cond.	0.688	0.714	1.288	1.133
Lb/min	121.0	120.0	58.7	60.3
$\dfrac{Z_1 + Z_2}{2Z_1}$	1.000	1.048	1.000	0.888
Ad HP/100 cfm	744	780	65.2	57.9
Total Ad. HP	619	666	49.3	39.5

*Using Z corrections and T–S chart.
**At approximate average temperature.
Note:—The above are examples at arbitrarily selected conditions. The effects for other gases and conditions must be individually determined.

Fig. 4-N. Theoretical performance of 100 cfm PD compressor with and without compressibility.

Multistaging

For reciprocating compressors, multistaging is used

1. To save power;
2. To limit gas discharge temperature; and,
3. To limit pressure differential.

Power saving has been demonstrated by indicator card in Fig. 3-D, page 3-17. Since there is intercooling between stages there is a reduction in the maximum gas discharge temperature. Limitation of maximum discharge temperature is particularly important for safety when handling air or in large and high pressure compressors where distortion of cylinder parts may be a problem. This is true even though the gas may not become appreciably more hazardous when heated.

The limitations imposed by high pressure-differential involve avoidance of excessive strain in the frame, running gear, and other parts. This is a complex question to which designers must give thorough consideration. A problem of this nature occasionally is solved by increasing the number of compression stages.

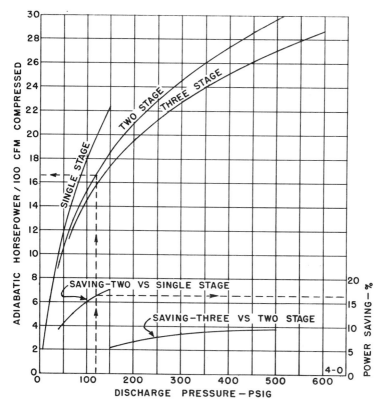

Fig. 4-O. Comparative theoretical adiabatic horsepower/100 cfm required for single-, two-, and three-stage compression. The percent saving through multistaging is shown by the two bottom curves.

Page 34-156 and Fig.4-0 show the theoretical effect of two- and three-staging on the discharge temperature per stage and the power required for compressors handling *normal air* at 14.7 psiA (sea level) intake pressure. These data are theoretical, with intercooling to intake temperature between stages (perfect intercooling), with equal ratios for all stages, and are based on 70°F intake temperature. Page 34-156 also gives corrections to be made in discharge temperature for higher or lower intake temperatures. These curves are based on formulas (3.39) and (3.43), pages 3-19 and 3-20.

Power savings are obvious. Percentages are also shown on Fig. 4-0. The weight to be given to power savings in unit selection will depend in large degree upon load factor (percent of total time the unit actually operates) and the size of the compressor. In actual practice, when compression stages exceed four, power savings are frequently slight through adding an extra stage, because of the greater gas friction losses through valves, piping, and coolers. There are often other practical advantages, however.

The desirability of maximum temperature limitation is not always fully appreciated. This applies particularly to air compressors where an oxidizing atmosphere exists and lubricating oil decomposition accelerates as temperatures rise. Actual discharge temperature will vary from the theoretical adiabatic to some degree depending upon compressor size and design, method of cooling, and compression ratio. No rules can be set, but the deviation is not apt to be serious and the theoretical is an excellent guide.

A compressor on continuous heavy-duty service should definitely be designed more conservatively regarding discharge temperature than one operating on a relatively light or intermittent cycle. One can look with certainty for an increase in relative maintenance costs and down time as discharge temperatures go up. As a guide, for medium- and large heavy-duty compressors (say 150 bhp and larger) handling air or any other oxidizing gas, the maximum discharge temperature should not exceed 350°F and for pressures over 300 psiG this should be scaled down. For gases containing no oxidizing components, a limit 25° to 50°F higher might be set. As cylinders get larger, the limits should come down.

Conservatism in connection with operating discharge temperatures will pay dividends even though the initial cost is a bit higher and power saving through the use of an extra stage is minimal. This is particularly true on large process units with high load factor and a heavy outage charge.

Probable Interstage Pressures

Actual interstage pressure readings are valuable indicators of the relative tightness of valves and piston rings and should be checked several times daily. Any variation from normal operating pressures is cause for immediate concern and investigation. See page 18-37.

Since cylinder sizes for any multistage compressor are proportioned for definite intake and discharge temperature and pressure conditions, variations from design first stage inlet pressure and temperature as well as changes in final discharge pressure and cooling water temperature will cause interstage pressures to vary slightly.

In some cases, theoretical approximations are helpful. The following may be used.

Two Stage

p_1 is first stage intake—psiA
p_2 is intercooler—psiA
p_3 is second stage discharge—psiA

$$p_2 = \sqrt{p_1 p_3} \qquad\qquad\qquad\qquad (4.13)$$

Three Stage

p_1 is first stage intake—psiA
p_2 is first intercooler—psiA
p_3 is second intercooler—psiA
p_4 is third stage discharge—psiA

$$p_2 = \sqrt[3]{p_1^2 p_4} \qquad\qquad (4.14)$$

$$p_3 = \sqrt[3]{p_1 p_4^2} \qquad\qquad (4.15)$$

Because of variations in cylinder proportioning and clearances in an actual compressor, the theoretical approach with equal compression ratios per stage cannot be considered as completely accurate. Actual readings from the specific machine, when in good condition and operating at design conditions, should be considered the standard for reference.

Effect of Altitude

The altitude at which a compressor is installed must always be given consideration. As altitude above sea level increases, the weight of the earth's atmosphere is less. This is reflected in the barometer and absolute intake pressure which decrease with altitude. This fact is well understood and allowed for with process compressors. It is not always considered with standard air compressors that are usually used for 100 psiG service to operate pneumatic tools and rock drills. These are, at times, moved from one site to another without thought as to original design conditions. A given compressor's ability to operate tools varies with the installation elevation.

The effect of moving a *two-stage* compressor designed for sea level operation to 10,000 ft altitude is shown in the table below.

Altitude Feet	Atmos. Pressure psiA	Over-all Compr. Ratio	Capacity Intake cfm	Capacity at 100 psiG cfm	Percent of Sea Level Compressed Air Volume	BHP
0	14.70	7.80	1000	128.0	100.0	187
2000	13.66	8.32	995	119.7	93.5	179
4000	12.68	8.89	990	111.5	87.1	171
6000	11.77	9.50	985	103.9	81.2	163
8000	10.91	10.15	980	96.5	75.4	156
10000	10.10	10.90	975	89.4	69.8	149

It will be noted that as the altitude increases

1. The actual capacity at intake (column 4) decreases only slightly;
2. The dense air delivered to the tools decreases materially (columns 5 and 6); and,
3. The bhp decreases materially. See comments below.

Column 6 is the measure of the number of tools operable *with this* compressor as compared to sea-level operation.

The example is somewhat extreme since commercial sea level rated two-stage reciprocating compressors are sold for operation only to 5000 ft altitude. At higher altitudes, the low-pressure cylinder size is increased to provide greater inlet capacity and to bring the BHP on the frame and running gear more nearly to normal values.

Single-stage reciprocating and other positive-displacement compressors are limited somewhat by the allowable compression ratio and discharge temperature. They frequently must be derated materially for altitude operation. The manufacturer should be consulted. See page 34-154.

Although the power required by a given compressor falls as the altitude increases, *the ability of engines and electric motors to safely develop this power usually falls even more rapidly.* Therefore, the question of the suitability of a compressor and its driver for other than design altitude should be discussed with the manufacturer.

Brake Horsepower — Reciprocating Compressors Only

Reciprocating units are calculated on the basis of theoretical adiabatic horsepower modified by compression and mechanical efficiencies which give bhp. Compression efficiency depends on many factors — effectiveness of valving, compression ratio, gas composition, compressor size, etc. Mechanical efficiency varies with machine type and size.

For preliminary estimation of *sea-level air* compressors for general power services, the data shown on page 34-122 are reasonable, but are subject to confirmation by the manufacturer. Information is based on 100 cfm actually delivered intake air and heavy-duty water cooled compressors. For altitude installation, the performance will differ. Page 34-122 also gives approximate altitude correction factors for bhp/100.

For gases other than air and conditions beyond the range of page 34-122, the BHP/million curves may be used. These start on page 34-146. These are for a single stage of a compressor and represent the bhp required to handle 1 million cu ft of gas per 24 hours measured at *14.4* psiA and inlet temperature. These are for units 200 bhp and above.

Multistage machines may be approximated by using equal compression ratios per stage and multiplying the single stage bhp/million by the number of stages. A compression ratio per stage of over 3.5 should not normally be used, although there will be exceptions. Compressibility, if involved, must be allowed for separately — stage by stage. So also must interstage pressure drop, imperfect intercooling, and vapor condensation between stages that reduces the volume handled.

If one prefers to work with bhp/100 at intake, it can be obtained from these curves by multiplying bhp/million by $p_1/100$.

The Rotary Sliding-Vane Compressor

This is a fixed port design (see page 1-6), but follows the basic theoretical power formulas. The normal rating is on actual cfm at intake conditions for a given discharge pressure. Clearance of a volumetric type does not exist in a well-designed sliding-vane compressor. Leakage or slip occurs, however, between adjacent cells across the vanes at their edges and ends. Leakage losses are based on manufacturer's tests, and cannot be theorized. Volumes to be handled at inlet are calculated using formulas on page 4-2.

The Helical-Lobe Compressor

This discussion applies in general to all helical-lobe rotary positive-displacement compressors, but more specifically to those manufactured by Ingersoll-Rand Company — known as the Axi units. A review of the appropriate description section, page 1-11 is recommended.

General

The basic theory of positive-displacement units applies for all types of helical-lobe rotaries. There are, however, more empirical corrections based on test data than would be the case with reciprocating machines. The corrections vary with the specific design. Volumes at inlet are developed in exactly the same manner as reciprocators and use the same formulas. See page 4-2 for a summary.

Helical-lobe compressors have a built-in, fixed compression ratio near which ratio the unit should be operated for greatest efficiency. Moderate variations from this compression ratio do not cause serious losses, but the unit should be initially selected for the built-in ratio best fitted to the actual operating range.

Clearance of the volumetric type does not exist in the helical-lobe rotary. Therefore, there are no clearance re-expansion losses as encountered in the reciprocator and capacity is affected principally by leakage.

Slip or Leakage

The capacity losses in a helical-lobe unit are the result of leakage between (a) the two rotors, (b) between the rotors and the housing, and (c) between rotor ends and the housing end walls. These losses are known as *slip*.

Slip will vary materially with the method of sealing. There are three methods:

1. Low clearance only (dry unit);
2. Addition of liquid injection; and
3. Addition of oil flooding.

Low-clearance sealing is the normal method, the others being applied to special applications. Water injection may also be used to obtain evaporative cooling, but additional liquid is required to attain sealing efficiency. Power may be increased materially with liquid injection or with any type of liquid containment in the gas, since the liquid introduces hydraulic losses and must be "pumped" as well as the gas.

With the simplest designs, slip does not materially vary with speed; with the more complex designs, it will vary. To illustrate the general effect of pressure rise and inlet gas density on slip, the following discussion uses a simple, relatively low compression ratio Axi compressor as a basis. The effects are in the same direction for more highly developed designs, but are modified by empirical factors. This unit is a dry design, sealed by low clearances, and a *basic slip* is set up by test for each size. Slip is actually the displacement the machine must provide to operate at rated pressure conditions with a closed discharge (zero delivery). Basic slip in this typical case, is expressed in cfm at inlet conditions on a dry unit when handling *normal air* at inlet (14.7 psiA, 68°F, 36% RH, and 0.075 lb/cu ft) with 1.00 psi differential pressure inlet and discharge. Slip is corrected for the actual pressure differential and for actual inlet density in accordance with the basic formula:

$$\text{Total Slip} = \text{Basic Slip} \times \sqrt{(p_2 - p_1)\ \frac{0.075}{\rho}} \qquad (4.16)$$

where ρ is density of the gas at inlet pressure and temperature. In practice, this simplified rule will contain added factors for different designs and sealing methods.

From the formula, pressure rise and density (molecular weight or specific gravity) are shown to be of major importance in determining the capacity delivered whereas they played minor roles in the capacity of reciprocators. To illustrate the effect of variations in density and pressure differential on the slip in a typical unit, refer to Fig. 4-P which shows the multiplier to be applied to basic slip for various values of gas density and/or pressure rise. The effect on slip of low MW gases or low inlet pressure is clearly shown.

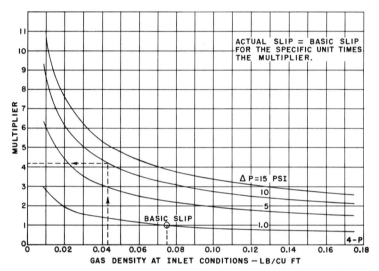

Fig. 4-P. Typical helical-lobe compressor basic slip multiplier.

Power Requirement

Power is based on the theoretical adiabatic method by compression and mechanical efficiencies determined by test. Because of the built-in compression ratio with this type of unit, over- or under-compression will occur if the operating ratio varies widely. Theoretically the power required will follow the laws laid down for the reciprocator, page 3-19.

Compressibility

Although this type of unit will usually be operated in a pressure range where compressibility is of no influence, there are certain applications where it must be considered. The correction is best left to the manufacturer as far as capacity is concerned but the power correction will be substantially as discussed on page 3-20.

Discharge Temperature

The discharge temperature from a helical-lobe rotary compressor will be substantially above that of an equivalent water cooled reciprocating compressors. The speed at which the rotary operates and its compactness provide very little time or surface for gas cooling to become effective. The discharge temperature limitations set by manufacturers are based upon the amount of housing and rotor distortion permissible. With the inlet end cool and the discharge end hot, clearances can be distorted if limits are exceeded. There is normally no lubricating oil present, so safety is not involved. Some designs are fitted with internally oil-cooled rotors and water-cooled housings, permitting higher discharge temperatures. Low-pressure units are air-cooled and have lower operating temperature limits.

Evaporative Cooling

Some applications lend themselves to carefully limited injection of water with the gas, to cool by the evaporation of the water. The slip can be reduced about 20%, but off-setting this to some degree is the necessity of compressing the vapor generated and added to the inlet gas. This involves an "experience" function utilizing partial pressures extensively, but there is definitely a net capacity gain when this cooling method is used, and because of the discharge temperature reduction, compression ratios might be attainable that would not otherwise be possible. In vacuum applications, the effect of water vapor pressure may effect capacity to a serious degree under certain conditions.

Some units have an oil-flooding system which is used to both seal and cool, but these are special applications.

Multistaging

Multistaging usually uses a separate machine for each stage, with an intercooler between stages. The reasons for multistaging are the same as for reciprocating (see page 4-14). The stages are sized as closely as possible to obtain the best interstage pressure (see page 3-21).

Altitude Operation

A given unit rated at sea level for a certain discharge pressure may be rerated for operation at any altitude. The discharge pressure may, however, be reduced to prevent exceeding the maximum compression ratio and/or discharge temperature permissible on this unit. Inlet capacity will fall off slightly due the reduced gas density at altitude.

The Dynamic Compressor

This discussion is concerned specifically with the radial flow centrifugal compressor and all examples are derived from that design. Comments, however, apply in general to all types of dynamic compressors.

The compression process in a centrifugal must be thoroughly understood when considering the effects of varying gas composition and properties. They are quite different from those experienced with positive-displacement machines.

General

A rapidly rotating bladed impeller is the motivating element. It is designed to produce two components of flow in the gas —a circular flow around the axis (a vortex motion) and a through flow along the streamline flow path. The vortex is the result of centrifugal force, hence the name.

When running at a given speed and handling a specific gas such as air, a single centrifugal compressor wheel will produce a polytropic head (see page 3-22) that varies with inlet capacity in accordance with a curve similar to Fig. 4-Q, typical of one design. This same impeller in actual use will produce very nearly the same curve when handling other gases, the degree of variation depending upon the relative mach number and the volume reduction through the impeller.

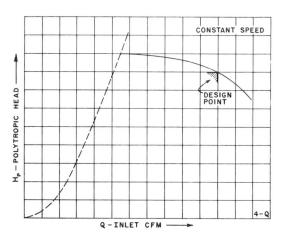

Fig. 4-Q. Typical head-capacity curve of a dynamic compressor.

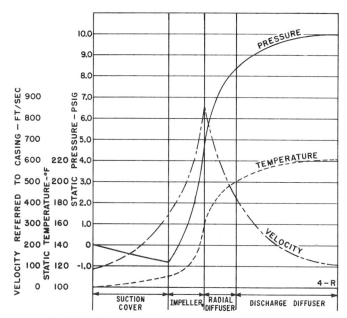

Fig. 4-R. Variations in gas conditions within a typical high-head single-stage centrifugal compressor.

Variations in impeller geometry will effect the stable operating range, the head rise from design to surge point, and the polytropic head at design capacity.

Fig 4-R, shows typical changes in pressure, temperature, and velocity (referred to the casing) as the gas passes from inlet to discharge through a typical high head, high capacity single wheel air compressor.

Effects of Various Factors

Variations in speed, operating conditions, and gas characteristics may alter certain of the relations shown in Fig. 4-R. Assuming *constant speed and inlet volume*, the following table shows the theoretical effect of a change in one item, the others remaining constant. The changes, in most cases, are the direct effect of a gas density change throughout the machine. The first table is quantitative on a specific 10,000 cfm compressor using a polytropic basis. The item changed from Column 1 (Design) is asterisked.

Column	1 (Design)	2	3	4	5
p_1 (psiA)	14.4	12.4*	14.4	14.4	14.4
T_1 (°F)	60	60	100*	60	60
MW	29	29	29	20*	29
k	1.40	1.40	1.40	1.40	1.20*
RH (%)	0	0	0	0	0
ρ (lb/cu ft)	0.0749	0.0645	0.0695	0.0516	0.0749
Total lb/min (W)	749	645	695	516	749
Δp (psi)	11.00	9.45	10.05	7.20	11.65
p_2 (psiA)	25.4	21.85	24.45	21.60	26.05
r	1.764	1.764	1.698	1.498	1.808
T_2 (°F)	180	180	220	142	130
$H_p \left(\dfrac{ft\ lb}{lb} \right)$	17,490	17,490	17,490	17,490	17,490
BHP	509	438	471	350	509

The following table puts the most important of this information on a qualitative basis and is based on an *increase* in the one respective item being considered as shown across the top. Inlet volume and speed are constant.

Item Increased	p_1	T_1	MW	k
Item Effected				
ρ_1	Increases	Decreases	Increases	Constant
Δp	Increases	Decreases	Increases	Decreases
p_2	Increases	Decreases	Increases	Decreases
r	Constant	Decreases	Increases	Decreases
T_2	Constant	Decreases	Increases	Increases
H_p	Constant	Decreases	Constant	Constant
Velocity	Constant	Constant	Constant	Constant
Power	Increases	Decreases	Increases	Constant

A study of the above tables will show that it is the *average* density (lb/cu ft) through the machine that has been changed. It is this that causes the variation in the compressor characteristics and performance and it makes no difference to the machine what causes the density change. In most cases, the inlet density will be changed, but in the case of an increase in k it is the average density throughout the unit that has been lowered, due (in this case) to the increase of temperature rise during compression. Gas density determines the pressure rise and compression ratio possible in a given impeller. The greater the density, the greater the pressure rise.

This is explained in simple terms by likening a single molecule of hydrogen (MW of 2) to a ping-pong ball and a single molecule of CO_2 (MW of 44) to a golf ball, both of the same diameter. If each ball is attached in turn to a string of a given length, and is twirled about a fixed axis at a given velocity, the tension in the string will be much greater when holding the golf ball than when holding the ping-pong ball. This tension corresponds to the pressure which is generated at the periphery of a single-stage wheel of a centrifugal compressor. For equal peripheral speeds, it will take many stages to compress hydrogen to the pressure created by a single stage when handling the denser CO_2.

Other things being equal, the lower the gas density the more complex and costly is the centrifugal. Consider the compression of 15,000 cfm of gas from 14.7 psiA to 19.7 psiA. If the gas is air it will be a simple single-wheel centrifugal. Should the gas be hydrogen, it will require a multistage centrifugal, probably in two casings. The hydrogen compressor, without the driver, would cost many times more than the air compressor.

If the percentage of constituents in a composite gas varies from time to time, so will the average molecular weight and density. A centrifugal compressor to generate the desired pressure when handling the rated flow of such a gas would have to be designed for the lowest expected density. Excess pressure rise resulting from *increased* density must also be considered because of resultant driver power requirements and casing pressure limitations. It is highly important that these effects be realized by the user and that the manufacturer be fully advised of variations in operating conditions to be expected before purchase. Even with a simple air compressor installation, seasonal variations in inlet temperature and relative humidity (and occasionally the barometric pressure) must be considered. Since these are "volume" machines, the dry air weight flow depends upon inlet conditions and if a constant *dry* weight is required by the application (this is frequent), the original compressor selection must provide this under the highest inlet temperature and moisture content conditions. It is simple to control the capacity sufficiently to maintain weight flow at lower temperatures and humidities (higher density).

The theoretical amount of pressure change for any given variation in density of a gas having a constant composition can be determined through formula (3.47) for polytropic head by substituting $p_1 v_1$ for $R'T_1$ and $1/\rho_1$ for v_1. The formula then becomes

$$H_p = \frac{Z_1 + Z_2}{2} \times \frac{p_1}{\rho_1} \times \frac{n}{n-1} \left[\left(\frac{p_2}{p_1} \right)^{\frac{n-1}{n}} - 1 \right] \tag{4.17}$$

Since polytropic head does not change, a variation in density must influence p_2.

Effect of Rotative Speed

One set of a group of "affinity laws" shows the effect of speed on any given impeller when handling a given gas at specified inlet conditions. These laws are essentially correct for small speed changes and technically apply, in a multistage unit, to one impeller at a time. Actually, they give close approximations when applied over a complete multistage compressor if the speed change does not exceed approximately 10 to 15%.

$$\frac{Q_2}{Q_1} = \frac{n_2}{n_1} \text{ (for Capacity–cfm)} \tag{4.18}$$

$$\frac{H_{p2}}{H_{p1}} = \left(\frac{n_2}{n_1}\right)^2 \text{ (for Polytropic Head)} \tag{4.19}$$

$$\frac{P_{T2}}{P_{T1}} = \left(\frac{n_2}{n_1}\right)^3 \text{ (for Theoretical Power)} \tag{4.20}$$

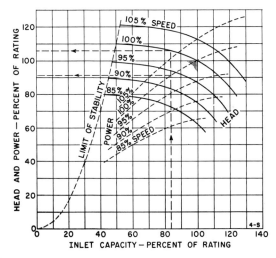

Fig. 4-S.   Performance of typical single-stage centrifugal compressor at varying speeds.

Since efficiency changes little with small speed variations, the bhp under such conditions would also vary as the cube of the speed.   Fig. 4-S shows the effect of speed through the change in the location of the characteristic curves of capacity versus pressure rise or head and bhp.   It is the head and pressure *rise* rather than total pressure that is effected by speed for any given intake condition.   These do not vary at the same rate, however.   Speed changes are used extensively for capacity control of dynamic units.

Surge Limit

The dotted line on Fig. 4-S is the limit of steady flow.   At lower capacities pumping or surge can be expected.   For any speed, this is the capacity at which compressor operation becomes unstable.   This point will vary from roughly 50 to 90% of the rated capacity, depending upon impeller design, number of stages, shape of the head-capacity curve, gas being compressed, etc.

The primary cause of pumping lies in the fact that the characteristic curve begins to droop toward the zero capacity region after reaching a peak of pressure. When the capacity is reduced below the peak, the pressure in the discharge line exceeds that produced by the machine and the flow tends to reverse momentarily. However, as soon at the flow reverses, the system discharge pressure drops and the compressor resumes normal flow. These pulsations in capacity and pressure are apt to be magnified by the characteristics of the discharge system and usually, but not always, result in noisy operation and evidence of distress. Pumping can cause an excessive temperature rise in the gas as well as vibration and stress in the machine and should not be permitted to occur.

Pumping points are not guaranteed, but are closely determined by specific test or prior knowledge. No dynamic unit should be operated at a capacity close to the surge limit line. The setting of surge prevention controls should be based on field determination of surge points on each individual machine as installed.

Effect of Moisture

Many gas mixtures, including air, contain moisture. This must be allowed for in calculating gas properties. It should be considered as another component in the mixture. Moisture in a gas effects MW, specific gravity, density, R, k and n. Polytropic head *for a given pressure rise* is altered and inlet volumes frequently must be corrected. Volume changes are calculated by formula (4.5).

Changes in MW, specific gravity, and k can be obtained by using the methods on pages 3-11 and 3-12. The value of n can be obtained from formula (3.34), page 3-16. R' (specific gas constant) can be obtained by dividing 1545 by MW or use the formula

$$R' = \frac{53.34}{G} \tag{4.21}$$

where G is specific gravity referred to dry air at 14.696 psiA and 60°F.

Many centrifugal units handle atmospheric air and moisture will be expressed as relative humidity. Special charts are available for these cases. Pages 34-116 thru 34-118 may be used to obtain specific gravity, specific humidity, k, R', MW, and c_p if desired for an air-water vapor mixture.

Although moisture in gas does not change the polytropic head developed, it does change the discharge pressure. The direction of change depends on whether the net MW or density is increased or decreased by moisture content. With air, increase in moisture will reduce compression ratio and final pressure for a given head.

Effect of Altitude

Since the barometric pressure varies with altitude and centrifugal compressor performance is closely allied to inlet gas density (which varies with pressure), it follows that knowledge of altitude of the installation is of vital importance in initial design and selection. See page 4-23 for the effect of intake pressure changes.

Compression Ratio Changes

The table on page 4-23 shows the changes in compression ratio that occur with a change in gas characteristics or inlet density. All such variations must be reconciled by both user and manufacturer before a specific unit is bought.

Other compression ratio variations are, however, possible and sometimes unavoidable even when the gas does not change. These are due to changes in the inlet and/or discharge pressure forced upon the compressor by external system resistance or other factors. Since centrifugals are essentially "constant-pressure variable-volume" units, any such anticipated demands must be made known before purchase. These can be met within limits by specifically designing for them. Variations in capacity and/or speed may be required and special controls may be involved.

Multistaging

Various reasons for multistaging of reciprocating compressors were given on page 4-14. Staging of dynamic units seldom involves the same reasons. The usual reason for multistaging is that impeller peripheral speeds must be limited for stress and mechanical reasons and the polytropic head per stage obtainable is thereby limited. However, the number of compression stages will always be kept to the minimum consistent with sound design.

Effect of Cooling

Gas cooling during compression reduces power by lowering the average gas temperature within the unit, increasing the average density, and decreasing the polytropic head required for a given discharge pressure. See formula (3.48) page 3-23. Power saving may or may not be the main objective in cooling. Process limitations on discharge temperature may be involved or the economies of machine cost may be a factor. Compared to uncooled compressors, cooling permits a reduction in speed and/or the number of stages. Cooling may, at times, make possible the use of less expensive materials.

The gas may be cooled within the casing or in external exchangers. Cooling within the casing has two forms — water cooled diaphragms between successive stages and direct liquid injection into the gas. For further discussion see page 9-27.

Specific Speed

The design and performance of centrifugal, mixed-flow, and axial-flow compressors is fundamentally affected by the variables of rotative speed, capacity and work input (head). Several methods of correlating these three variables are currently used by compressor designers. One is commonly called *specific speed* and may be expressed mathematically as

$$n_s = \frac{n \sqrt{Q}}{(gH_p)^{0.75}} \qquad (4.22)$$

where n = rotative speed (rps)
Q = inlet capacity (cfs)
H_p = polytropic head (ft lb/lb)
g = acceleration due to gravity (ft/sec²)

Note that n_s is not actually a rotative speed (rps) but is a dimensionless measure.

Although this form of the formula is technically correct, variations are frequently used. Any discussion of specific speed must first clarify the basic formula.

Note:—Specific speed also is used with centrifugal pumps. Since it is in this case figured in gallons rather than cu ft, direct comparisons cannot be made.

Impellers with the same work input, but with great difference in capacity can have the same specific speed provided the rotative speed is sufficiently different. For example, with the same work input an impeller for 2000 cfs at 50 rps would have the same specific speed as on impeller for 20 cfs at 500 rps.

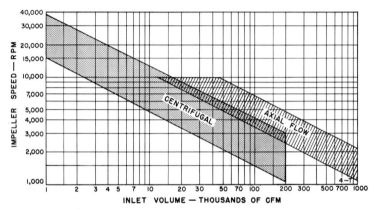

Fig. 4-T. Range of speed versus inlet capacity for near-optimum dynamic compressor efficiency.

The specific speed of a given impeller configuration is an indication of the design point with respect to optimum efficiencies. When the designer has a free hand, he will select the optimum speed that results in a good specific speed. Fig. 4-T can be used as a general guide for impellers with 10,000 ft head/stage for centrifugal units and 5000 ft/stage for axial-flow compressors. For any capacity, the bands show the speed range for maximum efficiency. Note that when rpm is a fixed specification, the performance of the compressor can be affected. For example, suppose 10,000 cfm is to be handled and a speed of 3600 rpm is specified. This is below the most efficient range of 4800 to 9000 rpm. Consideration should be given to increasing the speed.

Typical curves for specific speed versus efficiency are shown in Fig. 4-U. In general terms these show that there is an optimum efficiency range where there is slight variation. Smaller capacities (lower specific speed at same head and rpm) result in higher parasitic losses and therefore result in a fall-off in efficiency. As the specific speed increases beyond the optimum, there is a fall-off in efficiency to a lesser degree because of hydraulic loss increases.

It is not true that small and large impellers with the same specific speed will have the same performance. Manufacturing variations, including surface finish, result in lower optimum efficiencies for the smaller impellers. Fig. 3-F, page 3-22, can be used as a guide.

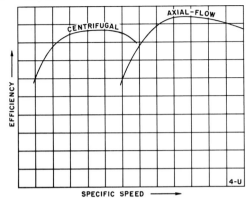

Fig. 4-U. Typical relation of specific speed and efficiency for dynamic compressors.

Stonewalling

Although it is infrequent, a phenomenon known as *stonewalling* can occur with dynamic machines. This occurs when the velocity of flow within a machine approaches the velocity of sound (sonic velocity or Mach 1) in the gas at the specific point under consideration within the unit. Velocities within these units are usually well below sonic, but in certain applications, particularly with heavy gases (such as some refrigerants), the designer must give this consideration.

$$a = \textit{sonic velocity} = \sqrt{kg\,R'T} \qquad\qquad (4.23)$$

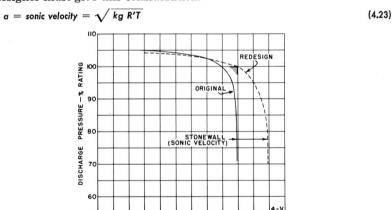

Fig. 4-V. Typical characteristic curves illustrating "stonewall" effect.

The term stonewalling has been applied because the characteristic pressure—volume curve becomes almost vertical as the capacity is increased and the velocity approaches the sonic value. In other words, there is a "stonewall" limit to capacity. See Fig. 4-V.

The solution is usually to use a different impeller or more stages, and a lower speed.

The Axial-Flow Compressor

Refer to Fig. 1-M, page 1-15, for a sectional of this type of unit. Note the alternating rows of fixed and rotating blades in the assembly. The progressive relations between velocity, temperature and pressure differ from the centrifugal and are shown in Fig. 4-W. There is no vortex in an axial-flow unit and the velocity throughout the main part of the machine is approximately constant.

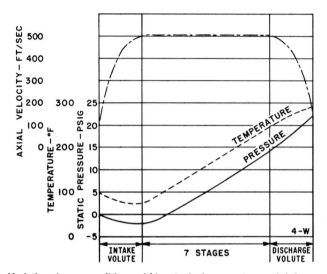

Fig. 4-W. Variations in gas conditions within a typical seven-stage axial-flow compressor.

Although the characteristic head-capacity curve is quite different from that of the centrifugal, the effects of speed, gas properties, and operating conditions are similar. Comparisons of characteristic curves are shown on page 9-34.

An axial-flow compressor is usually uncooled. In certain applications, spray injection cooling may be used, but this is quite special. It is possible to cool during compression by passing the gas through an external cooler after partial compression and then returning it to the machine. However, it is more common to do this only when there are two or more casings in series. Cooling between casings is less complicated than at some intermediate point within a single unit.

Brake Horsepower — Dynamic Units

To obtain gas horsepower, it is necessary to divide the theoretical horsepower by the polytropic efficiency (η_p). Adding mechanical losses plus certain hydraulic losses gives bhp. These losses are usually stated in bhp or percent. Mechanical losses vary between 7 and 50 HP depending upon speed and casing size. In exceptional cases these values may be exceeded. Casing and balance piston leakage losses will vary between 2.5 and 0.3% of gas hp depending largely on size. Mechanical losses (expressed in hp) increase as machines get larger and hydraulic losses (expressed in %) decrease.

A method of making quick, though approximate, estimates of bhp, number of stages, discharge temperature, and rpm is given starting on page 34-140. This is for a single casing "straight-through" uncooled centrifugal compressor. It is assumed that impellers are all running at optimum design speeds, and that each wheel develops a polytropic head of 9500 ft lb/lb. This is closely correct for most heavy-duty industrial units, but is by no means the upper limit of possible design. Any deviation from the limits set above nullifies calculation accuracy.

The Jet Ejector

Experience has shown that the ability of jet action to induce, entrain, and compress a gas does not necessarily follow theoretically predictable lines. Ejector design is largely empirically based, backed by extensive tests. This discussion includes only the application of theory as it is involved in the properties of the gas handled. For the most part the discussion is restricted to the compression of air-water vapor mixtures, the most prevalent use of ejectors. Steam, being the most widely used power medium is the only one considered here although other gases, particularly air, may be used in special cases. Discussion is limited to vacuum applications. See Chapter 10 for thermal compressors.

Ejector Ratings

Ejectors are rated on the weight flow of gas compressed, rather than on volume flow as is usual with other compressor types. Ratings are expressed in lb/hr of the gas or gas mixture handled. Steam (or other motive medium) is also stated in lb/hr.

Normally, manufacturers' basic ratings are on the weight rate of "equivalent air," which is air at 14.696 psiA and 70°F and containing normal atmospheric moisture. The user must specify the desired capacity in such terms that equivalent air can be calculated and the best ejector can be selected.

Capacities desired are perferably specified in one of three ways:

1. Lb/hr of a saturated air-water vapor mixture (AVM);
2. Lb/hr of a superheated air-water vapor mixture; and,
3. Lb/hr of a mixture of gases either including or excluding water vapor.

The proportion of air to vapor in (1) is known and no further information is needed for conversion to equivalent air.

In (2), it is mandatory that the relative weights of air and vapor be specified, otherwise it is impossible to determine the MW and equivalent air.

Method (3) requires that a complete analysis of the gas be given or that the user specify the average molecular weight. The analysis may be on a volumetric (molar) or a weight ratio basis.

One of the major problems in ejector selection is that information given is often insufficient to permit accurate evaluation of MW.

Transfer from specified lb/hr to equivalent air is based on two conversion curves involving *entrainment ratios*. These curves (Fig. 4-X and 4-Y) were established by tests run under the auspices of the Heat Exchange Institute and are accepted and used by all ejector manufacturers. Two conversion steps are involved, the first being based on molecular weight and the second on gas inlet temperature. These apply to each individual ejector as a single-stage basic element.

Molecular weight entrainment ratio is the ratio of the total weight of inlet gas that can be handled to the total weight of equivalent 70°F air that would be handled under the same conditions.

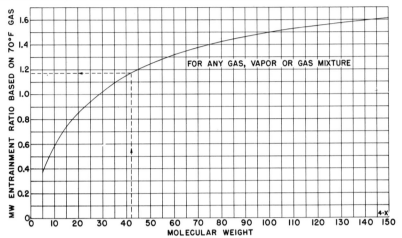

Fig. 4-X.   Molecular weight entrainment ratio for steam jet ejectors handling any gas.

Temperature entrainment ratio is the ratio of the total equivalent weight of air (or water vapor) at actual temperature that can be handled to the weight of equivalent air or water vapor at 70°F that would be handled. Dry gas and steam (water vapor) must be separately converted for temperature and totaled.

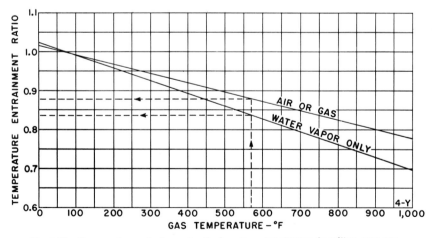

Fig. 4-Y.   Temperature entrainment ratio for steam jet ejectors handling any gas.

Note:—Fig. 4-X, Y,, and Z drafted from data in STANDARDS FOR STEAM JET EJECTORS, Third Edition. Copyright 1956 by the Heat Exchange Institute, 122 East 42 Street, New York, N. Y. 10017.

Entrainment ratios are divisors to obtain lb/hr equivalent air when lb/hr of the gas handled (and its vapor component) are known.

To Obtain Equivalent Air

The formula for obtaining equivalent air for any gas or gas mixture whether containing water vapor or dry is given below.

$$\text{Equivalent air} = \frac{\text{lb/hr Dry Gas}}{MWER \times TER_g} + \frac{\text{lb/hr Water Vapor}}{0.81 \times TER_v} \qquad (4.24)$$

MWER is molecular weight entrainment ratio (4–X).
TER_g is temperature entrainment ratio for dry gas (4–Y).
0.81 is molecular weight entrainment ratio for water vapor (MW = 18).
TER_v is temperature entrainment ratio for water vapor (4–Y).

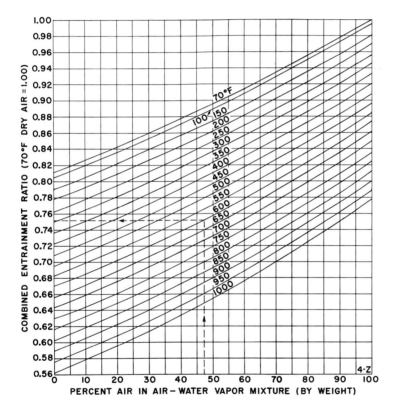

**Fig. 4-Z.   Combined molecular weight and temperature
entrainment ratios for air-water vapor mixtures only.**

In the case of a dry gas, only the left hand part of the equation applies. For an air-water vapor mixture use page 34-114 to obtain percent air in the mixture and obtain the overall entrainment ratio from Fig. 4-Z. This can be applied as a divisor directly to the total lb/hr of mixture to obtain the total equivalent air.

If an air water vapor mixture is given on a volume basis (as cfm), determine specific volume using page 34-115, convert total volume to weight (lb/hr) and then proceed as above.

In all cases, except air-water vapor mixture, the molecular weight must be known or calculated, the water vapor (steam) being separately calculated.

A dry gas analysis on a molar basis is the same as that on a volume basis. Proceed as on page 3-11 to find average MW.

If the dry gas analysis is on a weight basis, use the following method to obtain average MW.

Gas	Lb/hr	MW	Dividing gives Mole/hr
CO_2	6	44	0.136
N_2	24	28	0.857
Ar	62	40	1.550
He	108	4	27.000
	200		29.543

$$Average\ MW = \frac{200}{29.543} = 6.77 \tag{4.25}$$

If the example also contained 20 lb/hr of steam and the mixture temperature were 500°F, the following would be the step by step conversion to equivalent air.

	Portion Involved	Dry Gas	Steam
a.	lb/hr	200	20
b.	MW	6.77	18
c.	MW entrainment ratio	0.45	0.81
d.	Temperature entrainment ratio	0.897	0.859
	Equivalent Air (lb/hr) $= \dfrac{(a)}{(c) \times (d)}$	495	29
e.	Equivalent air (Total) lb/hr	524	524

Although the user has little need to utilize the equivalent air rating, it has been presented to assist in picturing the effects of gas composition, average molecular weight, and gas temperature on the capacity of a given ejector and to call attention to information the manufacturer must have to make a satisfactory selection.

Effect of MW and Temperature

Fig. 4-AA is a typical performance curve of a single stage ejector showing what happens to ejector performance with changes in the characteristics of the gas being handled. In this example, motive steam flow is held constant. Referring first to the equivalent air (MW 29) curve in the left hand group, it can be seen that for every ejector there is a definite relation between absolute suction pressure and capacity. The right hand curve shows the maximum stable operating discharge pressure obtainable with this particular ejector with a specified steam pressure and varying capacities.

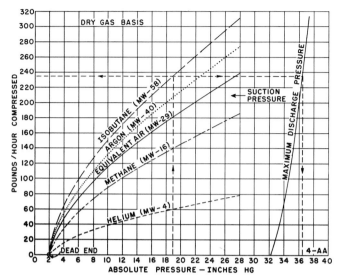

Fig. 4-AA. Typical ejector performance curve also showing the effect of changes in molecular weight (dry gas basis only).

Fig. 4-AA also shows the effect on the capacity (lb/hr) of changes in *MW* of the gas handled. It will be noted that the higher the *MW* the greater the total weight this ejector will handle. There will be no appreciable change in the maximum discharge pressure, however, when the gas composition varies.

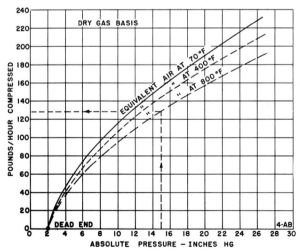

Fig. 4-AB. Typical ejector performance curve showing the effect of changes in inlet gas temperature (dry gas basis only).

Fig. 4-AB shows similarly the effect of suction gas temperatures above the 70°F reference value.

Fig. 4-AA and 4-AB are on a dry-gas basis. Inclusion of water vapor with the gas would lower the two top curves on Fig. 4-AA and raise the two bottom curves because of its effect on average *MW*. It would also lower the 400 and 800°F curves of Fig. 4-AB because of the reduced entrainment ratio for the steam component.

Conversely, what these curves indicate is that for a given total lb/hr of gas, (1) the lower the molecular weight, the greater the lb/hr of steam required and the larger the ejector; and, (2) the higher the gas temperature, the greater the steam quantity required and the larger the ejector.

Discharge Pressure

Any single stage ejector will operate stably at a given motive steam pressure and capacity against an increasing discharge pressure up to the *breaking pressure*. At this point the gas flow will stop or fluctuate. The ejector becomes unstable. If the discharge pressure is reduced slowly, the ejector will resume stable operation at a lower back pressure level. This is the *recovery pressure* and is known in the industry as *maximum discharge pressure*. The *maximum* pressure required *at the ejector discharge flange* must be known by the manufacturer from the specifications so that he can supply an ejector that will have a stable operating range equal to or exceeding this maximum.

Changes in Steam Flow

Changes in an ejector's motive steam flow may be made by altering the size of the motive steam nozzle, or by changing the steam pressure.

A change by the first method alters the ejector characteristic, especially as regards compression ratio. If a simultaneous change is made in the nozzle pressure so that the steam flow (lb/hr) through the nozzle remains unchanged, there is little or no change in the ejector characteristic curve.

Changes in steam pressure (and flow) with a fixed steam nozzle do not appreciably alter the suction pressure curve, but do produce a higher or lower discharge pressure, as the motive steam pressure increases or decreases. If steam pressure is increased too far above design, the excessive steam flow will choke the ejector throat and gas capacity will be materially reduced.

With superheated steam, any increase in superheat at constant pressure will have an effect opposite to a pressure increase. That is, an increase in temperature will lower the discharge pressure due to the reduced weight of steam flow.

The reduction of discharge pressure by changes in motive steam conditions can cause the ejector to break and become unstable.

Every ejector specification must show and the ejector must be designed for the *lowest* obtainable steam pressure and the *highest* obtainable superheat *at the steam nozzle*. This is important if the ejector is to stay on the line at all times and have the required capacity even with the most unfavorable steam conditions.

Minimum Pressures Obtainable

A great many ejectors are applied to remove noncondensables from a chamber of some sort. These may or may not be mixed with water vapor or the vapor of another liquid.

The ejector has a *dead-end* suction pressure obtained when the inlet is completely blanked off and the capacity is zero. This can never be attained except at shutoff. When handling a certain lb/hr of gas or mixture, there is another minimum attainable pressure that is dependent upon the properties and quantity of the gas coming to the ejector and whether moisture is contained therein. Water is the only vapor considered in the following cases. It is frequently necessary to handle other vapors; the same principles apply.

Cases 1, 2, and 3 have to do with the removal of the gaseous contents of a *closed* vessel assumed to be tight *with no inward leakage* during evacuation.

Case 1. The gas contained in the vessel is dry and no liquid is present. In this, the *pump-down* or pressure reduction proceeds along the capacity-suction pressure curve of the ejector and if operated over a sufficiently long period, the terminal pressure will reach the dead-end.

Case 2. The mixture in the vessel contains water vapor, but no water in the liquid phase. The results are as in Case 1 with capacities handled at any moment dependent on the original mixture composition, but dead-end can be obtained if operation continues long enough.

Case 3 is as Case 2, but with liquid phase water in the vessel. In this, the minimum pressure attainable is dependent upon the minimum temperature that can be reached by the vessel and contents. As the gaseous mixture is withdrawn, the pressure falls and some of the liquid evaporates, cooling both the liquid and the gas mixture. This continues until heat leakage inward is sufficient to evaporate liquid at the same rate it is being removed and equilibrium is reached. This point is close to the minimum pressure attainable (assuming the ejector has a dead-end substantially below this point) and its value will depend on the proportion of vapor in the mixture and the temperature reached.

For example, a mixture of 50% water vapor and 50% air (by weight) is contained in a vessel (with liquid water also present) and an equilibrium temperature of 40°F has been reached. The mixture has a specific humidity of 1.00 or would be said to be a 50% — 50% AVM. Reference to page 34-114 shows that a total pressure of 0.41 in Hg will have been reached.

Evacuation continues with no further reduction in temperature and will remove some of the air together with such water vapor as evaporates from the liquid. There will be a continuing decrease in the amount of air in the mixture (a lower percent noncondensables or a higher lbs of water vapor per lb of dry air) and the pressure will drop approaching, but never quite reaching the vapor pressure of water at 40°F which is 0.248 in Hg. See the table on page 34-96. If the equilibrium temperature is 32°F or lower, the liquid water will freeze.

Leakage into the vessel during evacuation in any of the above cases usually will be at a relatively constant rate and will influence results materially. *Leakage must* be estimated by the user *and made a part of the original specifications* to permit proper ejector selection.

It is impossible to rationalize the performance of ejectors on pump-down service sufficiently to permit the development of a reliable method for quickly estimating pump-down time under any of the above cases. The problem can best be referred to manufacturers, always advising the approximate time and minimum pressure desired. Be sure the minimum pressure specified is attainable using the applicable case above.

Cases 4, 5, and 6 involve the removal of noncondensables from a system into which there is a continuous flow, some of which usually is leakage.

Case 4, which may be somewhat hypothetical, requires the removal of a dry gas continuously and as fast as it may variably flow into the system. This is a problem of balance between inflow and removal, with the ejector holding a suction pressure depending upon the capacity which must be handled.

Case 5 involves the handling of a saturated mixture of air or gas and water vapor. An ejector serving a counter flow barometric steam condenser is typical of this application. There is a fairly constant quantity of atmospheric air leaking into the system which joins with the water vapor not liquefied by the condenser. A saturated mixture is formed at approximately 5°F above the condenser inlet water temperature. The vapor will be at the partial pressure corresponding to the mixture temperature regardless of the amount of air leakage with which it is joined. If the leakage were zero, the suction pressure of the ejector would be the saturated vapor pressure of the water at its existing temperature. The absolute minimum pressure an ejector (or any other type of evacuating machine) can maintain is therefore set by the saturated vapor pressure as determined by the mixture temperature plus the effect of noncondensables. With air in the mixture, reference to page 34-114 will show that there is an increase in total suction pressure as the air portion increases. Just follow a given temperature curve from right to left.

Case 6 in general, is the same as Case 5, but a modern surface type steam condenser is the example. Before entering the ejector, the mixture passes through a precooler to cool the air-vapor mixture that is saturated at the cooler outlet (ejector inlet) temperature. For a given continuous air leakage (lb/hr) inward, the minimum attainable pressure is again dependent only upon the temperature of the mixture leaving the precooler. The lower the temperature, the lower the pressure. The air leakage handled influences the pressure; the higher it becomes, the higher the pressure for a given temperature. Air leakage to a surface condenser is fairly constant.

The above limiting facts are not always understood and ejectors are sometimes requested for duty at pressures below that corresponding to the saturated vapor condition. Always check this point to be sure the request can be fulfilled.

When ejectors serve condensers or other apparatus involving fluids other than water, a vapor pressure curve of the liquid involved must be made available for the manufacturer's use.

Precoolers

Since the suction pressure of a given ejector on a given application is determined by both the noncondensable load and the saturated vapor temperature, it is sometimes possible to precool the suction stream before compression and reduce the vapor portion of the load. A part of the vapor is condensed and removed which reduces the total weight of mixture to be handled. The saturated vapor temperature is also reduced, resulting in a smaller ejector and less steam to maintain a given pressure, or, alternately, a lower pressure with the same steam quantity.

Multistage Ejectors

Any single stage ejector has compression ratio limitations for most efficient operation and its range may be insufficient for a given application. For compression ratios, usually exceeding 10, multiple staging is used with two to four, or even six, ejectors operating in series. The varieties of combinations are many, involving for a given primary (first-stage unit) the possible inclusion or exclusion of intercondensers between stages, various sizes of secondary ejectors, and variations in number of stages. The proper selection will depend upon the application, operating conditions, steam and water costs, load factor, etc.

Regardless of the final choice, each individual ejector is designed to and operates in accordance with the principles outlined. Each is an individual unit or element operating as part of a team and performs exactly the same function as do the stages of any other type compressor. However, the *maximum* water temperature used in intercondensers must be known and made a part of specifications. This is just as important in a multistage unit as is minimum steam pressure and maximum inlet temperature. The secondary stages must be designed to handle a certain vapor load and if designed for too low a temperature, they cannot do their job and the ejector will not function properly. See Fig. 1-0, page 1-17.

Chapter 10 discusses ejectors as thermal compressors for other than vacuum service.

Chapter 5

Miscellaneous Theory

Introduction

This chapter includes a group of items found to be of interest in connection with compression, the use of compressed gas, or in power recovery and gas cooling as used principally in process systems.

The Heat Balance in a Compressor

Occasionally a question arises concerning the distribution of the input energy when compression takes place. The first law of thermodynamics says that energy cannot be destroyed but takes other forms. The input energy to a compressor in the form of electric power, for example, is transformed into several other energy types and never again appears in the electrical form.

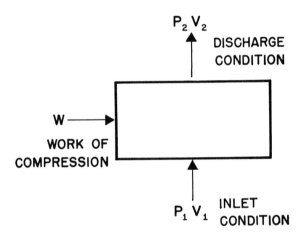

Fig. 5-A.   A diagram of a steady-flow compression system.

Consider the purely theoretical adiabatic (isentropic) approach. Compression and delivery of a gas is thermodynamically a *steady-flow* system. It is an open, not a closed, system. Such a system can be represented by Fig. 5-A. In any steady flow process the following holds *for one pound of gas*, where q is heat added, w_t is total work added, and Δh is enthalpy change.

$$q + w_t = \Delta h \tag{5.1}$$

In an isentropic process, q is zero and the above becomes

$$w_t = \Delta h = h_2 - h_1$$

Now: $c_p = \dfrac{dh}{dT}$ or: $dh = c_p dT$

Integrating: $h_2 - h_1 = c_p (T_2 - T_1)$

Substituting: $w_t = c_p (T_2 - T_1)$ $\qquad\qquad\qquad$ (5.2)

which means that all the theoretical isentropic work for a single process, if expressed in Btu, numerically equals the increase in sensible heat of the gas between inlet and discharge. This is work of both compression *and* delivery.

A study of compression *only* would show that

$$w_c = c_v \, (T_2 - T_1) \tag{5.3}$$

Do not confuse these two quantities, which differ only in the specific heat base used.

The only difference between theoretical and actual is in mechanical and gas friction and other compression losses. For a reciprocating compressor, the following items should be considered in calculating a heat balance.

1. Heat radiated from the frame, cylinders, coolers, and piping to the atmosphere;

2. Heat conducted from the frame to the foundation;

3. Heat carried from bearings by lubricating and cooling oil and radiated to the atmosphere or transferred to cooling water for disposal;

4. Heat carried away by the cooling medium in cylinder jackets;

5. Heat carried away by cooling medium in intercoolers; and

6. Heat carried out of compressor in the compressed gas as it leaves the system.

The total of these six items expressed in Btu must equal numerically the shaft horsepower (bhp) input, also expressed in Btu/hr. (One bhp hour equals 2545 Btu/hr).

Special Thermal Effects

Introduction

In the use of compressed gases (principally air), there are many cases where throttling is involved, or a vessel is blown down (emptied), or filled to store air. The following is based on air but is applicable to other gases.

When throttling is involved, the slight Joule-Thomson effect (see page 5-6) is disregarded. It also is assumed that moisture is not present. Moisture will influence results somewhat. Vessels are assumed to be perfectly insulated and to have zero heat capacity, hence there is no gain or loss of heat in the gas due to radiation or conduction.

This information is based on *AIMME Technical Paper 793* of March 1937.

All pressures and temperatures are absolute. Pressures are lb/sq ft.

Symbols

p_0 — initial air pressure in vessel

p_1 — air pressure in pipeline

p_2 — air pressure in vessel or atmosphere into which air is discharged

p_3 — final air pressure in vessel

T_0 — initial air temperature in vessel

T_1 — air temperature in pipeline

T_2 — final air temperature in vessel or in atmosphere into which air is discharged

T_3 — final air temperature in vessel

v_1 — specific volume at p_1 and T_1

v_2 — specific volume at p_2 and T_2
c_v — specific heat — constant volume
c_p — specific heat — constant pressure
J — mechanical equivalent of heat
R' — specific gas constant
k — ratio of specific heats

Throttling a Gas Stream

Consider the temperature effect, if any, on air flowing from a system through an open valve to atmosphere. The effect would be the same if the open valve discharged into a large chamber in which the pressure was constant. A compressor continuously supplies air and maintains upstream pressure.

One pound of air is moving out of the pipe. The air behind it does work on it to the extent of p_1v_1 ft lb. This work is really done by the thrust of the piston of the compressor and does not come from any energy that exists in the air in the pipe. The pound of air contains internal energy to the amount of c_vT_1. The total initial energy that must also appear in some form outside of the pipe, expressed in heat units, is

$$c_vT_1 + \frac{p_1\,v_1}{J} \tag{5.4}$$

The kinetic energy at this point is usually so small it can be neglected.

After the air gets outside, it has expanded and done work on the atmosphere to the extent of p_2v_2 ft lb. Its temperature is now T_2. The total energy accounted for ouside is

$$c_vT_2 + \frac{p_2v_2}{J} \tag{5.5}$$

This must be equal to the initial energy, so

$$c_vT_1 + \frac{p_1\,v_1}{J} = c_vT_2 + \frac{p_2\,v_2}{J}$$

Using for 1 lb: $pv = R'T$ and $R' = J\,(c_p-c_v)$ and applying algebra:

$$c_pT_1 = c_pT_2$$

$$T_1 = T_2$$

Therefore, when air flows through a valve at constant p_1 and p_2, there is no change in temperature when comparing conditions immediately above the valve and after the air has left the valve and lost its velocity. There *is* a temperature drop, however, during the passage of the air through the valve itself. At this point internal energy is transformed into kinetic energy with an accompanying temperature drop. The kinetic energy is transformed again into heat when the air comes to rest, and the air temperature returns to the value existing just ahead of the valve.

A valve operating in this manner (blowing down a receiver, for example) may frost externally if the atmosphere is sufficiently humid. The air a few feet away in the path of the jet is, however, theoretically unchanged in temperature. The flowing air has slowed down and warmed up.

Emptying a Vessel

In this case, the *closed* vessel is filled with air stored at an elevated pressure for some future use. Systems such as this are found in certain types of wind tunnels. At the proper moment a valve is opened and the air is rapidly released. The tank pressure falls and the vessel is "blown-down." As outlined above there is no drop in temperature *due to the valve itself*. However, the pressure of the air in the vessel is falling continually. The air is expanding adiabatically and is becoming progressively colder.

Each bit of air that leaves the tank, when brought to rest in the atmosphere, returns to the temperature it had *when about to leave*. Each bit of air that leaves is colder than the portion before, because adiabatic expansion is taking place in the tank. The net result is that the average temperature of all the air that flows out, when outside and at rest, is lower than its original temperature in the tank at the start of expansion. The final temperature of the air in the vessel is obtained from

$$T_3 = \frac{T_0}{\left(\dfrac{p_0}{p_3}\right)^{\frac{k-1}{k}}} \tag{5.6}$$

Thus, when k is 1.40 (for air), and solving for T_3

$p_3 = 14.7 \text{ psiA} \times 144$

$p_0 = 104.7 \text{ psiA} \times 144$

$T_0 = 70°F \text{ or } 530°R$

$T_3 = 302°R \text{ or minus } 158°F$

This is theoretical and the temperature would not fall this low in practice. However, the above is exactly what happens in many pneumatic tools and rock drills and explains why there are occasional freezing problems. These devices do not use air expansively to any extent, but do have a cylinder full of relatively high pressure air when the inlet shuts off and the exhaust opens. Thus, the conditions are as outlined above and the air flowing out the exhaust gets progressively colder and colder. If moisture is present in the air, it may freeze.

Filling a Vessel

The vessel is full of air at some pressure, usually atmospheric, when pump-up begins. It contains a certain weight of air at the beginning and more is added to increase the pressure.

There is a certain amount of internal energy in the contained air at the start of pump-up, and different value at the end. This value has been added from the enthalpy of the air entering from the line. Using basic formulas and considerable algebra, the final temperature is

$$T_3 = \frac{k\, p_3 T_1 T_0}{(p_3 - p_0)\, T_0 + k p_0 T_1} \tag{5.7}$$

Making the assumption that line air (T_1) is at the same temperature as the air in the vessel at the start (T_0) (often a good approximation) the formula becomes

$$T_3 = \frac{1.4\,p_3 T_1}{p_3 + 0.40\,p_0} \qquad (5.8)$$

thus with $p_0 = 14.7$ psiA $\times$ 144

$$p_3 = 114.7 \text{ psiA} \times 144$$

$$T_1 = 70°F \text{ or } 530°R$$

One finds that $T_3 = 705°R$ or $245°F$

It should be evident that the original air in the vessel has actually been compressed, compression converting energy to heat, the heat being distributed uniformly throughout the entire final mass of air in the vessel.

In a normal installation, however, the temperature would not reach this value because of the heat transferred to the walls of the vessel and then radiated from the vessel to the atmosphere. The degree of radiation would depend on many factors.

The Joule-Thomson Effect

The Joule-Thomson method of cooling through expansion without doing work is utilized in cryogenics (the science of low temperatures), principally for the liquefaction, separation, and purification of gases. See Chapter 23. The process is known as throttling. The gas pressure is reduced as it flows through a porous plug, a throttle valve, or other restriction. There is no change in enthalpy (total heat) and, for a perfect gas, there would be no change in fluid temperature after down-stream equilibrium has been reached. See page 5-4. Gases are not perfect, however, and there is usually a temperature change.

What happens depends upon the gas and the relative pressure and temperature conditions. Under different conditions the gas temperature may increase, remain constant, or decrease. No cooling is possible (by both experimental and theoretical analysis) if the temperature exceeds the *maximum inversion temperature* (μ equals zero) that approximates five times the critical temperature for the gas being throttled. For a few gases commonly involved in this process, approximate *maximum* inversion temperatures are given below.

Gas	Maximum Inversion Temperature	
	°F	°C
Air	625	329
Argon	842	450
Helium	−416	−249
Hydrogen	−109	−78
Nitrogen	658	348

The area where cooling can occur is best shown on a chart such as Fig. 5-B. This is typical only and represents no particular gas. Lines of constant enthalpy are plotted on a pressure temperature basis. The dotted line shows the locus of the inversion temperature as pressure changes. To the left of this curve, the temperature falls as pressure is reduced by throttling at constant enthalpy. To the right, temperature rises as throttling occurs. It is clear that the amount of cooling depends on the temperature and pressure conditions involved and that, for greatest effect, these conditions must be carefully selected.

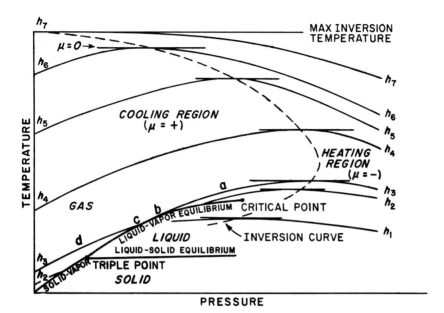

From *CONCEPTS OF THERMODYNAMICS by Edward F. Obert.* ©1960 *by the McGraw-Hill Book Company, Inc. Used by permission of McGraw-Hill Book Company.*

Fig. 5-B. Schematic pressure-temperature diagram to illustrate Joule-Thomson effects.

The Joule-Thomson coefficient μ is shown below. It is positive for a cooling process and is really the slope of the enthalpy curve at the conditions chosen. The higher the coefficient, the greater the cooling effect.

$$\mu = \frac{dT}{dp}$$

Over a specific pressure drop from given starting conditions it becomes

$$\mu = \frac{\Delta T}{\Delta p} \tag{5.9}$$

Condensation will occur when the final pressure and temperature correspond to the saturation curve of the gas. If the temperature is below the triple point, solids will appear.

Gas expansion in an engine or turbine *which is doing work* is a more efficient method of producing low temperatures although there are areas where the Joule-Thomson is the more practical method.

Rankine Cycle Efficiency

Any expansion type power generating device can be referred to a theoretically perfect basis for evaluating efficiency provided the characteristics of the gas or vapor being used are known. It is most commonly applied to steam-driven equipment such as engines and turbines and is called the Rankine cycle efficiency.

h_1 = enthalpy at initial condition – Btu/lb

h_2 = enthalpy at final condition after isentropic expansion – Btu/lb

RCE = Rankine cycle efficiency – a ratio

AWR = actual engine or turbine vapor or gas weight flow – lb/hp hr

TWR = theoretical isentropic vapor or gas weight flow – lb/hp hr

2545 = Btu/hp hr

$$TWR = \frac{2545}{h_1 - h_2} \tag{5.10}$$

$$RCE = \frac{TWR}{AWR} \tag{5.11}$$

$$AWR = \frac{TWR}{RCE} \tag{5.12}$$

The theoretical weight flow can frequently be determined from known properties. To estimate the actual steam or gas requirement, the RCE must be known from prior tests on a similar engine or turbine. Manufacturers have such information.

For weight flow on a kw hr basis, multiply the values for hp hr by 1.34.

Tables starting on page 34-108 provide theoretical steam consumption per hp hr in abridged form. Charts on pages 15-23 and 15-27 give approximate RCE for engines and turbines over a moderate range of sizes and conditions.

The Engineered Air Receiver

Air receivers, being simple volume tanks, are not often thought of as highly engineered items, but, on occasion, the use of simple engineering with receivers can reduce equipment costs. A pertinent example not infrequent in industry is the intermittent requirement for a fairly large volume of air at moderate pressure for a short period of time. Some boiler soot blowing systems are in this class. The analysis necessary to arrive at the most economical equipment often involves the storage of air at high pressure to supplement the compressor output when the demand requires. The following example is somewhat extreme for emphasis.

This application requires 1500 cfm free air at 90 psiG for 10 min per hour. This cycle of 10 min. at 1500 cfm demand and 50 min. with zero demand repeats hourly. Alternates obviously are possible; (A) install a 100 psiG compressor and standard accessories large enough for the maximum requirement; or, (2) install a smaller compressor but for a higher pressure and store the air in receivers during the "off" period. At least two storage pressures should be considered. In all cases commerical compressor sizes are to be used. For (B) assume 350 psiG, and for C, 500 psiG.

Selection of Compressors

For the 100 psiG machine for at least 1500 cfm output, unit A has 1660 actual capacity and requires 309 bhp at full load with a direct connected synchronous motor.

The minimum capacity for units B and C must be calculated, since these can be compressing the full 60 min.

$$Total\ cu\ ft/hr = 1500 \times 10 = 15,000$$

$$Minimum\ compressor\ capacity = \frac{15,000}{60} = 250\ cfm$$

Compressor B, for 350 psiG discharge, is found to have, in a standard size, a capacity of 271 cfm, requiring 85 bhp with a belted induction motor.

Compressor C, for 500 psiG, is found to be a standard size having 310 cfm capacity, requiring 112 bhp with a belted induction motor.

All selections provide some extra capacity for emergency and losses and are economical two stage machines.

How Much Must Be Stored

Air compressed to 100 psiG, to be used at 90 psiG, provides no possibility of storage. Storage is practical at the other pressures selected. Compressor units B and C will operate at full load at their rated or lower pressures. Since the receiver pressure will fall during the 10 min. period when air is used faster than the compressor can replenish it, the unit will be operating at full capacity and will supply some of the demand. The full demand need not be stored.

Cu ft to be stored = Total cu ft/hr required minus (compressor cfm x minutes of demand)

Unit	B	C
Capacity cfm	271	310
Demand period – min	10	10
Total cu ft required	15,000	15,000
Delivered during demand period	2,710	3,100
Cu ft to be stored	12,290	11,900

Receiver Volume Required

The cu ft to be stored represents the free air (at 14.7 psiA) that must be packed into the receiver *above* the minimum pressure required by the demand. In this case, the demand pressure is 90 psiG but an allowance for line losses and the necessary reducing valve pressure drop would prevent the use of any air stored below 110 psiG. The receiver has a volume of *(V)* cu ft.

$$Useful\ free\ air\ stored = \frac{V \times Pressure\ drop}{14.7}$$

$$V = \frac{Useful\ free\ air\ stored \times 14.7}{Pressure\ drop}$$

Unit	B	C
Storage pressure — psiG	350	500
Minimum pressure — psiG	110	110
Pressure drop — psi	240	390
Free air to be stored — cu ft	12,290	11,900
V — receiver volume — cu ft	752	448

This receiver volume may be in one or several tanks, the most economical number being chosen.

The Economic Comparison

The final selection can be made only after consideration of the first cost of the compressor, motor, starter, aftercooler, and receiver (unit A would also need a receiver as standard equipment); the cost of installation, including foundations, piping and wiring; and the power cost including demand charges.

In the example analyzed, the following percentage comparisons give the answer. Unit B with 350 psiG storage is the proper selection.

Unit	A	B	C
Pressure (psiG)	100	350	500
Installed Cost	100%	52%	63%
Fixed Charges	100%	52%	63%
Power Cost incl. Demand	100%	64%	93%
Oil, Water, Attendance	100%	100%	100%

Not all problems of this nature will result in the selection of the intermediate storage pressure. Although few will favor the 100 psiG level, many will be more economical at the 500 psiG level. Experience indicates that there is seldom any gain in using a higher storage pressure than 500 psiG since large receivers required become very expensive above this level and power cost increases.

Nozzle and Orifice Formulas

These data are intended to assist in the application of the jet action of nozzles and orifices as widely used in industry. (See Chapter 28 for metering and measurement of gas quantities).

The formulas presented are strictly theoretical, are often subject to empirical modification to suit the applications, and, as usually applied, must have suitable safety factors added. They will not give absolute answers, but do permit a logical approach to many problems of flow quantity through various types of holes, the velocity of the jet, and the energy available.

Subcritical and Critical Flow

There are two types of gas flow through any hole, the type depending upon the ratio of downstream to upstream absolute pressure. Consider an orifice discharging gas from a large vessel held at constant pressure into another large vessel where the pressure can be maintained at any desired level. Starting with the two pressures equal (no flow), slowly decrease the downstream pressure by bleeding gas out of the vessel. The flow rate will steadily increase until the ratio mentioned above reaches a value near 0.5, when a further decrease in downstream pressure will

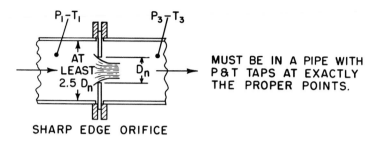

MUST BE IN A PIPE WITH
P & T TAPS AT EXACTLY
THE PROPER POINTS.

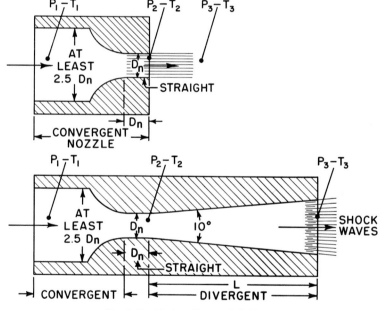

Fig. 5-C. Various Types of Orifices.

have no influence on flow rate. It remains as it was. This ratio, and there is one for every gas, is known as the *critical ratio*. Gas flow at ratios of downstream to upstream pressure greater than the critical is known as *subcritical* and follows specific laws. Those at ratios equal to or less than the critical are known as *critical* flows and follow other laws.

The critical ratio is found to be when the speed of sound (sonic velocity) is reached in the throat — smallest section of the gas stream. The velocity will depend upon the gas and the pressure and temperature conditions at the throat.

Types of Holes

An orifice is a round sharp-edged hole in a thin plate. A nozzle is a round hole having a rounded entrance and a short straight section at the smallest area or throat. For certain applications, a flaring section may be added to the discharge side of the nozzle to expand the gas further and obtain greater velocity. Fig. 5-C shows these three types and the flow pattern through each. In this discussion, the ratio of orifice or nozzle diameter to the upstream pipe diameter is considered to be low and the velocity of approach can be neglected.

Considering first the middle sketch, there is a smooth approach to the straight throat section and flow is streamlined with the throat full of gas. The same comment holds true of the bottom nozzle in which the gas is expanded beyond the throat with increasing velocity in a divergent (flaring) section.

The sharp edged orifice (top) is different. The orifice does not flow full, but forms a jet of decreasing cross section known as the vena contracta. The form is similar to the jet developed with the rounded entrance nozzle, but the actual ratio of the jet area to the orifice area varies with many factors. These are allowed for in the flow coefficients applied in all flow formulas.

Gases Covered

The formulas included are suitable for perfect gases with special adaptations for steam and air. Air is generally considered a perfect gas, although this is not strictly true. An excellent reference for properties of air and some other gases including the products of combustion is *Gas Tables* by Keenan & Kaye, published by John Wiley & Sons Inc. Where possible, suitable tables and charts should be used for steam, ammonia and other gases that deviate materially from perfect gas laws.

The Critical Ratio

Strictly speaking, critical ratios apply accurately only to rounded entrance nozzles. Their application to sharp edge orifices is rather approximate. In practice, they are applied generally to both. The *critical ratio* can be calculated for any gas if the ratio of specific heats is known.

$$r_c = \frac{p_2}{p_1} = \left(\frac{2}{k+1}\right)^{\frac{k}{k-1}} \tag{5.13}$$

For air and steam, accepted values follow.

Gas	Condition	k	r_c
Air	0° F (−17.8°C)	1.401	0.528
Air	250° F (121°C)	1.396	0.528
Air	500° F (260°C)	1.383	0.530
Steam	Saturated - 100 to 500 psiG (7 to 35 Kg/sq cm G)	1.295	0.547
Steam	Superheated - 100 to 500 psiG (7 to 35 Kg/sq cm G)	1.285	0.549

Symbols

A	Throat or orifice area	sq in
C	Coefficient of flow	dimensionless
c_p	Specific heat at constant pressure	Btu/lb/°F
D_n	Throat diameter	inches
e	Mouth of a flared nozzle (exit diameter)	inches
E_k	Kinetic energy	ft lb/sec
F	Coefficient of conversion of adiabatic heat drop to velocity (0.85 is conservative value).	dimensionless
g	Acceleration of gravity (32.2)	ft/sec.^{2}
h_1	Enthalpy at inlet conditions	Btu/lb
h_2	Enthalpy at throat conditions	Btu/lb
h_3	Enthalpy at exit conditions (no friction)	Btu/lb
h_{3F}	Enthalpy at exit conditions allowing for friction	Btu/lb
k	Ratio of specific heats	dimensionless
L	Length of divergent section	inches
M	Mouth or exit area	sq in
p_1	Upstream pressure	psiA
p_2	Throat pressure	psiA
p_3	Downstream or exit pressure	psiA
R'	Specific gas constant	$\dfrac{\text{ft lb}}{\text{lb °F}}$
r_c	Critical ratio	dimensionless
T_1	Upstream temperature	°R
T_2	Throat temperature	°R
T_3	Exit temperature	°R
v_1	Upstream specific volume	cu ft/lb
v_2	Throat specific volume	cu ft/lb
v_3	Exit specific volume	cu ft/lb
V_2	Throat velocity	ft/sec
V_3	Exit velocity	ft/sec
W	Weight flow	lb/sec

Coefficient of Flow

In metering, the coefficient of flow is highly important and has been extensively investigated. For the applications involved here, a high degree of accuracy is not so important and for a rounded entrance nozzle, a value of 0.97 may be used.

If an *orifice* is truly sharp edged, the coefficient will be close to 0.61. This only holds for a true, clean, sharp edge. A slight rounding of the corner or even a collection of dirt on the entering edge can increase the coefficient (and the flow) by 20% or more. An internal rough or burred edge on a hole in the wall of pipe can decrease the coefficient remarkably. Except under closely controlled conditions as in metering, the flow through any sharp edged orifice must be considered as an estimate.

Flow Quantity

This is expressed as weight in lb/sec. To obtain cfm, multiply by 60 times the specific volume at the desired reference conditions.

Subcritical Flow

$$p_3 \text{ Greater Than Critical, Equals } p_2$$

Air Below 500°F

$$W = \frac{2.05\ P_1 AC}{\sqrt{T_1}} \sqrt{\left(\frac{P_2}{P_1}\right)^{1.43} - \left(\frac{P_2}{P_1}\right)^{1.71}} \tag{5.14}$$

Saturated Steam Below 500 psiA

$$W = 1.97 AC \sqrt{\frac{P_1}{v_1}\left[\left(\frac{P_2}{P_1}\right)^{1.77} - \left(\frac{P_2}{P_1}\right)^{1.89}\right]} \tag{5.15}$$

Superheated Steam Below 500 psiA

$$W = 1.39 AC \sqrt{\frac{P_1}{v_1}\left[\left(\frac{P_2}{P_1}\right)^{1.54} - \left(\frac{P_2}{P_1}\right)^{1.77}\right]} \tag{5.16}$$

Critical Flow

$$p_3 \text{ Equal To or Less Than Critical } p_2$$

Air

$$W = \frac{0.53\ P_1 AC}{\sqrt{T_1}} \tag{5.17}$$

Saturated Steam Below 500 psiA

$$W = 0.3 AC \sqrt{\frac{P_1}{v_1}} \tag{5.18}$$

Superheated Steam Below 500 psiA

$$W = 0.316\ AC \sqrt{\frac{P_1}{v_1}} \tag{5.19}$$

Any Perfect Gas For Either Condition

$$W = 0.668 AC \sqrt{\frac{k}{k-1}\frac{P_1}{v_1}\left[\left(\frac{P_2}{P_1}\right)^{\frac{2}{k}} - \left(\frac{P_2}{P_1}\right)^{\frac{k+1}{k}}\right]} \tag{5.20}$$

$$W = \frac{8.02 P_1 AC}{\sqrt{R'T_1}} \sqrt{\frac{k}{k-1}\left[\left(\frac{P_2}{P_1}\right)^{\frac{2}{k}} - \left(\frac{P_2}{P_1}\right)^{\frac{k+1}{k}}\right]} \tag{5.21}$$

Velocity

Nozzle and jet calculations frequently require a knowledge of velocity at the throat and/or the velocity at the mouth (for divergent nozzles).

Note that a divergent nozzle is useful only when p_3 is less than the critical pressure. Its purpose is to further expand the gas to (or just above) p_3, thus increasing the velocity beyond the maximum throat value. This transforms additional heat into kinetic energy.

Subcritical Flow

$$p_3 \text{ Greater Than Critical, Equals } p_2$$

$$V_2 = \frac{144 W v_2}{A} \tag{5.22}$$

$$V_2 = \frac{R'T_2}{144 P_2} \tag{5.23}$$

$$V_2 = 223.7 \sqrt{F(h_1 - h_2)} \tag{5.24}$$

Critical Flow

$$p_3 \text{ Equal To or Less Than Critical } p_2$$

Under these conditions the flow reaches a maximum and the throat velocity reaches the velocity of sound in the fluid flowing at conditions p_2 and T_2.

For *Air*, use Keenan & Kaye tables if available.

Velocity of Sound (Theoretical)

Basic Formulas

$$V_2 = \sqrt{144 g k p_2 v_2} = \sqrt{k g R' T_2} \tag{5.25}$$

See Fig. 6-BC, page 6-49, for velocity of sound in atmospheric air.

$$V_2 = \sqrt{\frac{288 k g p_1 v_1}{k + 1}} \tag{5.26}$$

Velocity of Sound (Theoretical)

Specific Formula

$$\text{Air} \quad V_2 = 73.5 \sqrt{p_1 v_1} \tag{5.27}$$

$$= 44.6 \sqrt{T_1} \tag{5.28}$$

$$\text{Saturated Steam} \quad V_2 = 70 \sqrt{p_1 v_1} \tag{5.29}$$

$$\text{Superheated Steam} \quad V_2 = 72 \sqrt{p_1 v_1} \tag{5.30(}$$

Divergent Nozzle Sections
Air and Perfect Gases

Isentropic Heat Drop—Btu/lb $= h_1 - h_3$ (5.31)
(frictionless)

$$h_1 - h_3 \text{ (frictionless)} = c_p T_1 \left[1 - \left(\frac{P_3}{P_1} \right)^{\frac{k-1}{k}} \right] \tag{5.32}$$

Actual Total Heat at Exit—Btu/lb $\quad h_3F = {}^cpT_1 - F(h_1-h_3)$ $\qquad$ (5.33)
(with friction)

Actual Temperature at Exit $\quad T_3 = \dfrac{h_3F}{c_p}$ $\qquad$ (5.34)

Exit Velocity $\quad V_3 = 223.7\sqrt{F(h_1-h_3)}$ $\qquad$ (5.35)

$$V_3 = \frac{144\,Wv_3}{M}$$ $\qquad$ (5.36)

$$V_3 = 96.26\sqrt{\frac{k}{k-1}\,p_1v_1\left[1-\left(\frac{p_3}{p_1}\right)^{\frac{k-1}{k}}\right]}$$ $\qquad$ (5.37)

Specific Volume at Exit $\quad v_3 = \dfrac{R'T_3}{144p_3}$ $\qquad$ (5.38)

Exit Area $\quad M = \dfrac{144Wv_3}{V_3C}$ $\qquad$ (5.39)

Length beyond Throat $\quad L = \dfrac{e-Dn}{0.175}$ $\qquad$ (5.40)
(basis 10° Flare)

In the design of divergent nozzle sections, it is generally best to *under* expand rather than to *over* expand. Losses are much less with design p_3 slightly *above* actual exhaust pressure. Also, if initial pressure p_1 or downstream pressure p_3 varies, allowance should be made for such variation throughout the entire nozzle design.

Throat Temperature
For Air Or Any Perfect Gas

(Frictionless) $\quad T_2 = \dfrac{T_1}{\left(\dfrac{p_1}{p_2}\right)^{\frac{k-1}{k}}}$ $\qquad$ (5.41)

With friction the temperature will be higher dependent upon coefficient F. Use a chart for steam.

Kinetic Energy of Jet

(General) $\qquad E_k = \dfrac{WV^2}{64.4}$ $\qquad$ (5.42)

(Convergent nozzle) $\quad E_k\,(1000\text{ lb/hr}) = \dfrac{V_2{}^2}{232}$ $\qquad$ (5.43)

(Divergent nozzles) $\quad E_k\,(1000\text{ lb/hr}) = \dfrac{V_3{}^2}{232}$ $\qquad$ (5.44)

Applications of Orifices and Jets

Applications of the jet action obtained by nozzle flow with compressed air abound in industry. Typical are:

1. Ejection of parts from dies of stamping, punch, and forming presses in metal and plastics manufacture;

2. Blowing chips and cleaning machinery in all types of industry;

3. Blast cleaning of metal and other materials;

4. Atomization of liquids for spray painting, lubrication, etc.; and

5. Certain types of pulverizing machinery.

Typical uses of orifices drilled in the walls of pipe or in thin plates include:

1. Agitation of acids, milk, cement slurry, asphalt, and other liquids to either mix, prevent settlement of solids, or accelerate oxidation or fermentation;

2. Limitation of flow in a line to a certain maximum quantity; and,

3. Some types of transfer machinery for pulverized materials such as cement.

The above are typical only and in most cases the equipment has already been designed by an experienced supplier. Practical comments for those making their own applications follow.

1. The air consumption of an intermittently operating jet, frequent in automatic machinery, is practically impossible to calculate. The time during which the control valve is open is usually measured in seconds or less, the actual average pressure at the jet entrance is unknown and it is desirable that this type of application be designed by trial to do the desired work. Then consumption, if important, can be determined by test.

2. The same comment applies to the small open end tube, used sometimes to form a jet. The flow and exit velocity cannot be satisfactorily calculated.

3. There are many applications involving orifices made by drilling holes in pipe walls. These pipes may be mounted in front of a furnace opening, the jets to provide an air curtain to protect the operator, or the pipes may be laid on the bottom of a tank or vat, the air flow being used to cause agitation and mixing of the liquid. These applications can be reasonably estimated as to flow quantities or orifice size for given conditions using the formulas above. For further information about agitation, see page 32-6.

4. An orifice placed in a line to limit the maximum flow is usually (although not always) operating at the critical condition. In either case its size can be calculated by the formulas given.

Chapter 6

Reciprocating Compressors

(Continued)

Definitions

RECIPROCATING COMPRESSORS are positive-displacement machines in which the compressing and displacing element is a piston having a reciprocating motion within a cylinder.

SINGLE-ACTING cylinders are those where compression takes place on only one of the two piston strokes per revolution.

DOUBLE-ACTING cylinders are those where compression takes place on both of the piston strokes per revolution.

PISTON DISPLACEMENT (See page 2-10).

TRUNK PISTON machines are those where the piston is also the crosshead. There is no piston rod.

CROSSHEAD-TYPE machines have a separate crosshead with a piston rod connecting it to the piston.

AIR-COOLED cylinders are cooled solely by radiation from the usually finned heads and cylinder barrel.

WATER-COOLED cylinders are fitted with jacketed heads and/or cylinders through which water is constantly circulated.

CORROSIVE GAS (See page 2-6).

NONCORROSIVE GAS (See page 2-9).

DRY GAS (See page 2-7).

WET GAS (See page 2-12).

INLET PRESSURE (See page 2-9).

DISCHARGE PRESSURE (See page 2-6).

MAXIMUM ALLOWABLE WORKING PRESSURE is the maximum continuous operating pressure for which the manufacturer has designed the compressor, (or any part to which the term is referred, such as an individual cylinder) when handling the specified gas at the specified temperature. (See Rated Discharge Pressure, Safety Valve Setting, and Design Pressure).

DESIGN PRESSURE is a term also frequently used to denote Maximum Allowable Working Pressure.

RATED DISCHARGE PRESSURE of any compressor element is the highest continuous operating pressure to meet the conditions specified by the purchaser for the intended service. The Rated Discharge Pressure is always less than the Maximum Allowable Working Pressure by at least 10 percent or 15 psi, whichever is greater, for the operation of safety valves.

SAFETY VALVE SETTING is to be no higher than the Maximum Allowable Working Pressure.

Note:—Cylinders are not always installed to operate at their individual *rated discharge pressure*. This is due to specific conditions involved in a compressor design. Limitations other than maximum allowable cylinder working pressure are in control and the proper safety valve setting may be substantially below the maximum permissible for this particular cylinder.

MAXIMUM ALLOWABLE SPEED (rpm) is the highest speed at which manufacturer's design will permit continuous operation, assuming overspeed and governor mechanisms are installed and operated per manufacturer's recommendations.

DESIGN SPEED is the same as Maximum Allowable Speed.

RATED SPEED (rpm) is the highest speed necessary to meet the specified service conditions. Rated Speed and Maximum Allowable Speed may be the same, but Rated Speed can never exceed the Maximum Allowable Speed.

TRIPPING SPEED is that speed at which the overspeed device is set to function. It is normally 110 percent of the Rated Speed.

RATED HORSEPOWER is the continuous power input required to drive a compressor at rated speed and actual capacity under rated pressure and temperature conditions. For all machines *other than integral steam driven units*, it is the power required at the compressor shaft. It does not include losses in the driver or in the transmission equipment between compressor and driver, whatever these may be.

RATED STEAM INDICATED HORSEPOWER is the indicator card horsepower developed in the steam cylinders of an integral type steam driven unit operating under *rated* conditions.

General Comments

Reciprocating compressors are the most widely used of all compression equipment and also provide the widest range of sizes and types. Ratings vary from fractional to more than 12,000 hp per unit. Pressures range from low vacuums (at intake) to special process compressors for 60,000 psiG or higher.

Characteristics

In common with all positive-displacement compressors, the reciprocating is classed as a "constant-volume variable-pressure" machine.

Reciprocating compressors are the most efficient built today for most applications. They can be fitted with capacity control devices to closely maintain their efficiency at partial loads (reduced capacity output).

They can be built to handle almost any commercial gas provided corrosion problems in some extreme cases can be solved.

Gas cylinders are generally lubricated, although a nonlubricated design is available when warranted.

Because of the reciprocating pistons and other parts, as well as some unbalanced rotating parts, inertia forces are set up that tend to shake the unit. It is necessary to provide a mounting that will stabilize the installation. The extent of this requirement will depend on the type and size of compressor involved.

These machines are normally designed to be installed in a building, but can be fitted for outdoor installation.

Reciprocating compressors should be supplied with clean gas. Inlet filters are recommended. They cannot satisfactorily handle liquids that may be entrained in the gas, although vapors are no problem if condensation within the cylinder does not take place. Liquids tend to destroy lubrication and cause excessive wear.

Reciprocating compressors deliver a pulsating flow of gas. This is sometimes a disadvantage but pulsation dampeners can usually eliminate the problem.

Compressor Classification

Manufacturers design compressors to fill certain definite user needs. These fall into two general groups — moderate-duty machines and the heavy-duty units.

Moderate-duty compressors are designed for reliable operation over a reasonable service life, but should not be installed where continuous full-load long-time operation is required. This does not mean that these units will not operate for long full-load periods; it does mean that maintenance will be greater than normal. There are two classes within the moderate-duty group. One is the vertical or Y type trunk piston unit with cylinders lubricated from the crankcase. It is most often air-cooled and operates at higher speeds relative to size than do heavy-duty machines. These factors result in a higher cylinder operating temperature and thus a more rapid deposit formation on valves and other parts. The other class consists of larger machines of a heavy-duty crosshead design, but run at higher speeds levels than normal. They may be offered at lower speeds for true heavy-duty service. The reasons for this class are varied but were originally based on a need in the oil and gas fields for compact, semiportable, well balanced skid-mounted compressors that could be "packaged" and direct-connected to a gas engine driver. The package design with the usual radiator-type cooling and higher speed means generally higher operating temperatures and greater maintenance.

Heavy-duty machines are of the crosshead type with entirely separate and well controlled cylinder lubrication, water cooled cylinders, and a lower operating speed. They are permanently mounted on a good foundation and operate at full load for years with a minimum of attention.

Arrangements

There are many compressor arrangements.

The type illustrated by Fig. 6-A is a vertical single- or multiple- cylinder air-cooled unit. Machines are available for pressures to 5000 psig.

Fig. 6-A. Vertical, trunk-piston, two-stage, air-cooled compressor. Larger three-cylinder arrangement available. ¼ to 25 HP.

Fig. 6-B-1 and 6-B-2 illustrate a typical larger air-cooled design. The intercooler is a finned tube of the air-to-air design, frequently of a sectional nature.

Both these machines are best classed as moderate-duty units and are not intended to be run continuously at full load. Proper selection and application is important. Electric motors are predominant drivers but gasoline or diesel engines may be used.

Fig. 6-B-1. Vertical, trunk-piston, two-stage, air-cooled compressor. This general type available to 125 HP.

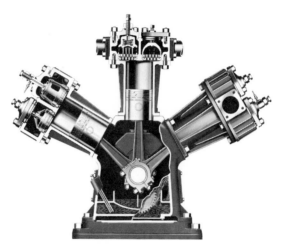

Fig. 6-B-2.   Transverse section of Fig. 6-B-1.

Fig. 6-C, 6-D, and 6-E show three typical *straight-line* continuous heavy-duty water-cooled compressors.   When multistaged, arrangements 6-C and 6-E have cylinders in tandem.   Intercoolers are mounted below or above the cylinders.   Arrangements 6-C and 6-D are usually driven by electric motor.   Fig. 6-E is an integral steam engine design.   The power cylinder is interposed between the frame and compression cylinder or cylinders.

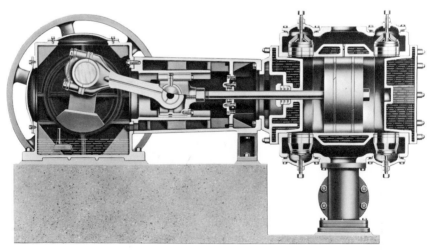

Fig. 6-C.   Horizontal, straight-line, single-stage, water-cooled, heavy-duty, crosshead-type compressor.   Also available with two and three stages to 2500 psiG.   20 to 150 HP.

Fig. 6-D. Vertical, straight-line, single-stage, water cooled, heavy-duty compressor. 20 to 125 HP.

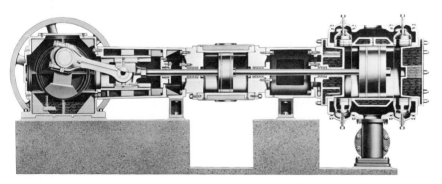

Fig. 6-E. Horizontal, straight-line, single-stage, water-cooled, steam driven compressor. Also available with two and three stages to 2500 psiG. 40 to 150 HP.

A typical *angle* cylinder arrangement is shown in Fig. 6-F. In some cases, this has the two cylinders arranged in a "V," each cylinder 45° from the vertical. Other arrangements include three and four cylinders arranged radially around the shaft, all operating from a common crank throw. Fig. 6-G is one such three cylinder unit.

Two-stage units are listed for pressures only to 125 psiG. The multi-stage machines in Fig. 6-G are designed for up to 500 psiG and special ones are available for as high as 6000 psiG.

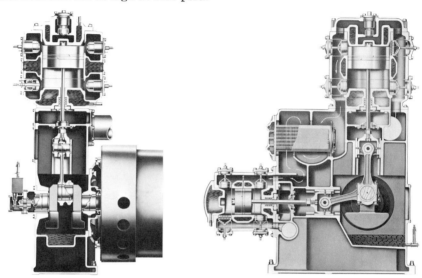

Fig. 6-F. One type of angle compressor. Two-stage, heavy-duty, water-cooled, built-in finned tube intercooler. 75 to 1250 HP.

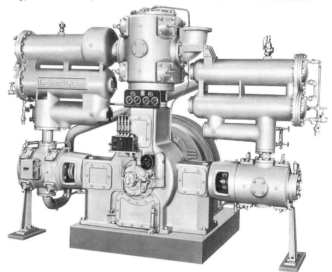

Fig. 6-G. Three-cylinder, three-stage angle arrangement for 500 psiG service.

A larger unit of the "L" type (as Fig. 6-F) is built to 1250 HP in a duplex arrangement and is also available in a horizontal opposed design, Fig. 6-H. These extremely compact designs are used primarily for 100 psiG plant air supply. The direct-connected synchronous motor is the normal driver.

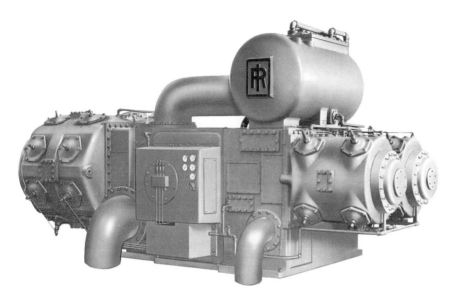

Fig. 6-H. Horizontal-opposed, two-stage, 100 psiG air compressor. 500 to 1250 HP. Also available in "L" arrangement.

Fig. 6-I. Typical horizontal duplex arrangement for engine-type synchronous motor drive. 400 to 1000 HP.

The *horizontal duplex* arrangement is typified by Fig. 6-I, 6-J. Additional designs possible include placing two cylinders in tandem on each of the frames of Fig 6-I, rather than using the four-corner design of Fig. 6-J. The cylinders in either case may all be for gas compression or there may be one steam power cylinder on each frame to drive the unit (Fig. 6-J).

Units are listed only to 125 psiG discharge, but can be built for very high pressures in special designs. Engine-type synchronous motors are the standard drive for electrically powered units.

Figure 6-K illustrates a horizontal-opposed design usually driven by a natural gas or diesel engine. Smaller horizontal-opposed units of this type find wide application in oil and gas fields.

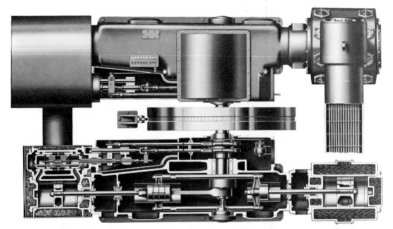

Fig. 6-J. Four-corner integral steam-driven compressor with compound steam cylinders at the left. 150 to 1500 HP.

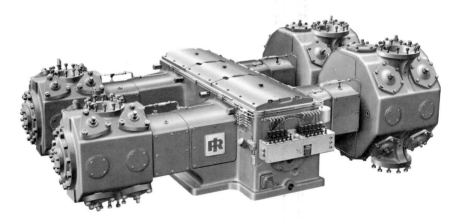

Fig. 6-K. Smaller size horizontal-opposed designs in the 500 to 2000 hp range operate at 1000 rpm.

Fig. 6-L and 6-M illustrate the L or V-angle type of integral gas engine-driven compressor. This arrangement is available in the smaller sizes as a diesel powered unit. Compressor cylinders are available for almost any desired pressure.

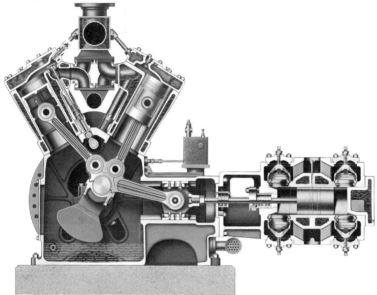

Fig. 6-L. A "V"-angle arrangement of an integral gas-engine driven compressor. Also built as an "L" design with engine cylinders vertical. 120 to 5500 HP.

Fig. 6-M. A typical 2000 HP integral gas engine and four-stage compressor.

The *horizontal-opposed* arrangement (Fig. 6-N and 6-O) is a heavy-duty and very flexible multicylinder type of compressor, all cylinders being driven from a common crankshaft. This design is most often used for special and process compressor applications. Synchronous motors are the prevalent driver although a geared motor or steam turbine may be used.

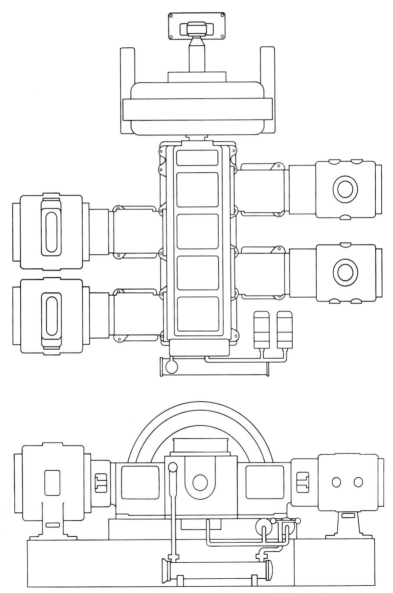

Fig. 6-N. Plan of a four-cylinder, horizontal-opposed, heavy-duty compressor, usually synchronous motor drive, but may be gear-driven from a steam turbine. Built with one to ten crank throws and cylinders. 200 to more than 12,000 HP.

Fig. 6-O. Two 3500 HP eight-cylinder, multistage, multiservice gas compressors in a synthetic ammonia plant.

Within the *packaged group* of compressors there are two categories;
one for compactness and convenience in making a permanent installation;
the other, for compactness and portability plus flexibility of adjustment to
changing operating conditions.

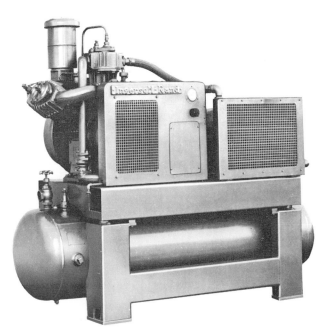

Fig. 6-P. Typical completely air-cooled packaged
compressor assembly, ready for installation.

Within the first category are the familiar small service station tank-mounted machines, plus larger air-cooled or heavy-duty water cooled units. The assemblies include the compressor and its capacity control, motor, starter, intake filter, intercooler (if needed), aftercooler, condensate separator, and receiver — all piped and built into a substantial readily maneuverable, compact assembly. They are ready to go when set on a substantial floor or simple foundation and connected to power and discharge air lines (and to water, if used). Such assemblies are shown in Fig. 6-P and Fig. 6-Q. These are available to approximately 150 HP.

6-Q. A compact, completely packaged, heavy-duty, water-cooled compressor.

Fig. 6-R. Straight-line oil-field package-type compressor belted to an industrial gas engine.

The second category is typified by the units shown in Fig. 6-R and 6-S. These include gas-engine drivers, belted or direct-connected to the compressor, and complete radiator cooling for both the engine and compressor water cooling systems.

Fig. 6-S. A completely packaged heavy-duty gas-engine driven gas compressor being set on its field foundation. The 660 hp assembly includes (at the left) an exchanger for engine cooling water and all necessary gas-to-air intercoolers and aftercoolers.

Design Fundamentals

It is not necessary to go deeply into the design of compressor components, but there are certain fundamentals that every user should understand.

Frame and Running Gear

Regardless of whether fractional horsepower or over 12,000 HP, two basic factors guide the designer of the frame and running gear. First is the maximum horsepower to be transmitted through the shaft and running gear to the cylinder pistons; second, the load imposed on the frame parts by the pressure differential between the two sides of each piston. The latter is often called *pin load* because this full force is exerted on crosshead and crankpin directly. It is the factor that largely determines the size of bearings, connecting rod, and frame, as well as the bolting between each cylinder and the frame.

There are other factors involved, but the above are fundamental. Each frame has a certain maximum design horsepower (at a given speed) that it can transmit and a maximum design pin load. Note that these are working limits for design purposes. They do not represent the physical limits of compressor strength, but are the maximum set by the designer to assure safe operation with a minimum of wear and a liberal safety factor. Each machine shown in Fig. 6-A through Fig. 6-S has such fixed limits.

Cylinders

Efficiency of compression is entirely dependent upon the design of the cylinder and particularly upon the valving. Unless the valve area is sufficient to allow the gas to enter and leave the cylinder without undue restriction, efficiency cannot be high. Valve placement for free flow of gas in and out of the cylinder is also important. Many of the figures so far shown illustrate valve arrangements.

The method of cylinder cooling must be consistent with the service intended, since both efficiency and maintenance are influenced by the degree of cooling during compression.

The cylinder and all its parts must be designed to withstand the maximum pressure to which it will be exposed, using those materials that will economically give the proper strength and the longest service under design conditions.

Design must provide for accessibility and ease of maintenance.

Valves

Compressor valves are devices placed in the cylinder to permit one-way flow of gas either into or out of the cylinder. There must be one or more for inlet and discharge in each compression chamber.

Early valves were usually mechanically and positively operated, but as speeds increased, these designs were unsuitable. About 1910, the first lightweight plate-type automatic valve was introduced into the United States by Ingersoll-Rand Company. It permitted higher rotative speeds and today all but a very few reciprocating compressors utilize some type of automatic valve. These are opened solely by the difference in pressure across the valve; no positive mechanical device is involved. Springs assist closing.

Each valve must open and close once for each revolution of the crankshaft. The valves in a compressor operating at 700 rpm for 8 hours per day and 250 days per year will have opened and closed 42,000 times per hour, 336,000 times per day, or 84,000,000 times in a year.

They have less than 1/10 of a second to open, let the gas pass through, and to close. They must do this with a minimum of resistance or power will be wasted. They must have small clearance space or there will be excessive re-expansion during the suction stroke and reduced volumetric efficiency. They must be tight under severe pressure and temperature conditions. Finally, they must be durable under many kinds of abuse.

The designer endeavors to build many characteristics into the valve.

Design

1. Good aerodynamics of flow;
2. Low clearance space;
3. Quietness;
4. Ease of servicing and maintenance; and,
5. Interchangeable parts, duplicating the originals.

Materials

    1. Corrosion resistance;

    2. High impact strength;

    3. Wear resistance; and,

    4. Fatigue resistance.

There are four basic valve designs used in various compressors. These are finger, channel, leaf, and annular ring. Within each class there may be variations in design details depending largely upon operating speed and size of valve required.

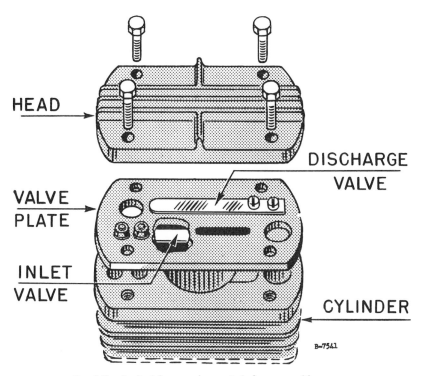

Fig. 6-T. Typical finger valve parts before assembly.

Fig. 6-T shows a typical finger valve before assembly. These valves are used for the smaller moderate-duty air-cooled machines. One end is fixed, the other end lifting when the valve opens. Lift is limited by means not shown.

Modern and widely used is the channel valve shown in Fig. 6-U. This uses a series of separate stainless steel channels as valves. This is a cushioned valve as explained in the figure, which adds greatly to life.

The leaf valve has a configuration somewhat like the channel. It is flat strip steel that opens against an arched stop plate so that the valve flexes with maximum lift only at the center. The valve is its own spring. See Fig. 6-V.

Valve closed — A tight seat is formed without slamming or friction, so seat wear is at a minimum. Both channel and spring are precision-made to assure a perfect fit. A gas space is formed between the bowed spring and the flat channel.

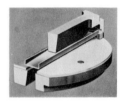

Valve opening — Channel lifts straight up in the guides without flexing. Opening is even over the full length of the port, giving uniform air velocity without turbulence. Cushioning is effected by the compression and escape of the gas between spring and channel.

Valve wide open — Gas trapped between spring and channel has been compressed, and in escaping has allowed channel to float to its stop; full opening has been attained without impact. The light pressure of the spring soon starts the closing action.

Fig. 6-U. Typical cushioned channel valve before assembly and sections showing operation.

Fig. 6-W illustrates both inlet and discharge disassemblies of a typical annular ring valve. The example has a single ring. Larger sizes may have two, in extreme cases, three. Some designs have the concentric rings tied into a single piece by bridges. The valve shown was the first *cushioned* valve built. Note the springs and valve move into a recess in the stop plate as the valve opens. Gas trapped acts as a cushion and prevents slamming, eliminating a major source of valve and spring breakage.

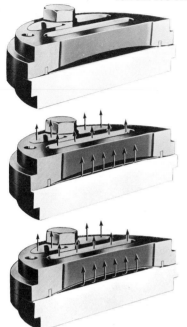

Fig. 6-V. Typical leaf valve showing method of operation.

Courtesy of Worthington Corporation.

INLET   DISCHARGE

Fig. 6-W. Inlet and discharge disassemblies of an annular ring valve.

The finger and leaf valves are not used for much higher than 500 psiG discharge pressures. Channel valves are available for pressures up to 1500 psiG. Annular ring valves are available for all pressures, with special designs to 60,000 psiG and higher.

A single valve design can not be the best for every compressor cylinder size, speed and pressure. The designer having a wide range of valve types and sizes can make the best application.

Valve Lift Area and Air Speed

Valve lift area is the minimum net gas flow area between the valve plate and its seat when the valve is fully open. This is usually also the least flow area existing in the machine.

Air speed is an industry term denoting the average velocity of the gas flowing through the valve lift area. It assumes that the valve is open for the *full* stroke and that the piston moves at a *constant* velocity. Actually, the piston has a velocity curve approaching that of a sine curve. The actual air speed will vary quite widely throughout a stroke. Air speed is only a "rating" velocity. Inlet valve area is used in calculations.

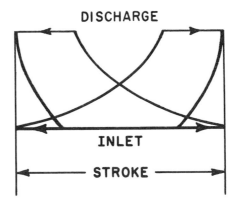

Fig. 6-X. Indicator cards of a double-acting cylinder. Arrows show direction of piston movement when gas is flowing through each set of inlet and discharge valves.

The left-hand indicator card of Fig. 6-X illustrates the action within a single-acting cylinder. Combined with the right-hand card, the pair shows the action within a double-acting cylinder. The direction of piston movement when air is flowing through the valves is shown. Gas actually flows through the inlet valves of one cylinder end only during one piston stroke. On the opposite stroke, the gas is flowing through the discharge valves and the inlet valves are closed. In a double-acting machine, each end is really a separate compressor with its own valving and pattern of flow.

To obtain air speed (a rate), the simplest method is to start with the average speed of the piston and modify this by the ratio of net piston area to total inlet valve lift area *per end*, the area actually in operation at a given time.

V is air speed (ft/min).

A is average net (sq in) of the piston faces which are used for compression during one revolution (two strokes). On a single-acting cylinder, only one face is used; on a double-acting cylinder, both faces compress.

a is the total *inlet* valve lift area for *one* cylinder end (sq in).

S is the average piston speed (ft/min) obtained by multiplying rpm by twice the stroke (ft).

$$V = \frac{A}{a} \times S \tag{6.1}$$

This formula gives values only nominally below actual average values. If the inlet valve opened exactly at the beginning of the stroke (100% *VE*), it would be exact.

Some purchasing standards and evaluation methods utilize the following formula.

$$V = \frac{144\ D}{a_1} \tag{6.2}$$

D is piston displacement of the *complete* cylinder (cfm).

a_1 is the *total* area of *all* the inlet valves in the cylinder.

This gives values just 50% of those of (6.1). For evaluation purpose it may serve to compare compressor makes or designs, but it is a less realistic value.

Cylinder Cooling

Heat in a cylinder comes from the work of compression plus friction of piston and piston rings on cylinder wall, and the rod packing on the rod. Heat can be considerable, particularly when moderate and high compression ratios are involved. Undesirably high operating temperatures can be developed.

Most compressors use some method of dissipating a portion of this heat, thus reducing both cylinder wall temperature and final gas temperature. There are several advantages in cylinder cooling, at least some of which apply to all but exceptional cases.

1. Lowering cylinder wall and cylinder head temperature reduces losses in capacity and horsepower per unit volume due to suction gas preheating during inlet stroke. There will be a greater weight of gas in the cylinder ready to be compressed.

2. Reducing cylinder wall and cylinder head temperature will remove more heat from the gas during compression, lowering its final temperature and reducing power required.

3. A reduction in gas temperature and in that of the metal surrounding the valves provides a better operating climate for these parts, giving longer valve service life and reducing the possibility of deposit formation.

4. Reduced cylinder wall temperature promotes better lubrication, resulting in longer life and reduced maintenance.

5. Cooling, particularly water cooling, maintains a more even temperature around the cylinder bore and reduces warpage or going out of round.

Cylinder designs may be classed very generally as noncooled, air-cooled, water-cooled, and still-cooled.

Noncooled Cylinders

Noncooled cylinders are used in two distinct applications. The first is in natural gas pipelines and similar service. Compression ratios are low (2.0 or less) and k values are also apt to be in the lower range. Discharge temperatures under these conditions will seldom exceed 200°F and cylinder cooling is unnecessary. Futhermore, obtaining clean cool water is at times a problem and it is advantageous to eliminate it. These cylinders are usually for pressures to 1000 psiG and have no water jacketing even though they are on heavy-duty service.

The second application is in cryogenics where intake temperatures may be as low as minus 250°F and the discharge not over minus 100°F. Conventional cylinder cooling would be in vain.

Air-Cooled Cylinders

Air-cooled cylinders are those used for moderate and high compression ratios in small machines such as are shown in Fig. 6-A and 6-B. The horsepower *per cylinder* will seldom exceed 20. Fins are added to the heads and cylinders of these small units to radiate a substantial portion of the heat generated. Compression temperatures will average 300°F and reach 400°F or more in extreme cases, therefore fins (extended surface) are a distinct help. These air-cooled units are not recommended for continuous- or heavy-duty service.

Water-Cooled Cylinders

Water-cooled cylinders constitute the work horses of industry and are used wherever water is available. They are almost invariably heavy-duty units as illustrated in Fig. 6-C through 6-O.

Determination of the amount of heat removed by cylinder jackets in specific cases is far from an exact science because of the number of variables involved. Such factors as cylinder size, rotative speed, gas characteristics, wall thickness, inclusion of dry cylinder liners, effective area of water jacketing, average temperature difference between gas and water, all influence the quantity of heat rejected to water. For example, cooling in small cylinders is more effective than in large cylinders; cooling is greater at low rpm than at high; cooling is greater at high compression ratios than at low; cylinder materials and designs vary and will influence the effectiveness of jackets; dry liner cylinders will have less effective cooling than nonlined cylinders. An excellent paper (Form 266) on this subject can be obtained from Ingersoll-Rand Co., Advertising Division, Phillipsburg, N. J.

Water Requirements

It is often necessary in designing an installation to have a reasonably accurate value of the water quantities required so that a proper supply can be provided. A convenient basis is the Btu rejected to the water per compressor bhp hour. A figure used widely in the industry for cast iron cylinders is 500 Btu/bhp hour, but tests run to study this subject in 1957 (see reference above) indicate that this is probably low and that for reasonable average conditions for air (k of 1.40) between a ratio of 2.5 and

4.0, a value of 700 Btu/bhp hour might be a more accurate average. This presupposes an open cooling circuit with water at an inlet temperature of about 70°F. This figure can be reduced if natural gas (k of 1.26) or an other low k value gas is being handled, since the gas discharge temperature is lower. See formula 3.43 on page 3-20. Fig. 6-Y shows the results of tests on a number of cylinders. Cylinders less than 12″ diameter are classed as small; those more than 22″ are classed as large. T_g is the average between initial and final *gas* temperature figured on the adiabatic basis. T_w is the average *water* temperature. Data from this curve can be used if closer results are desired.

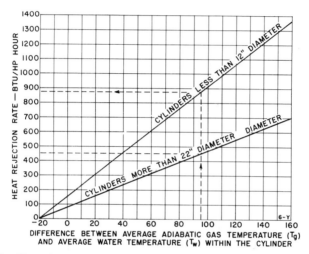

Fig. 6-Y. Chart of typical heat rejection rates to jacket and head cooling water.

For cylinders made of cast or forged steel, the heat rejection rate is lowered. This is because the walls are thicker, dry cast iron liners are used, and the jacketed areas are smaller.

For average estimating conditions, a table of heat rejection rates might be as follows, for *cylinders only*.

Cast iron cylinders	700 Btu/bhp hr.
Cast steel cylinders	250 Btu/bhp hr.
Forged steel cylinders	200 Btu/bhp hr.
Plunger type steel	125 Btu/bhp hr.

Whenever possible, inlet water temperature should be 15° to 20°F higher than the inlet gas temperature to prevent inlet condensation in the cylinder should the gas contain moisture or other condensables. This is particularly desirable for the second and higher stages of an air compressor.

Outlet water temperature should not exceed 120°F. There are cases, however, where this limit must be waived because of local conditions or the type of external water cooling system involved (such as an air-to-air exchanger), but these are the exception rather than the rule.

Multistage compressors preferably should pass the water first through the intercoolers and then the cylinder jackets. Intercoolers need the coolest possible water while jackets like warmer water; the combination provides ideal conditions.

Pages 5-2 and 5-3 give a logical approach to estimation of water quantities for a machine fitted with intercoolers and an aftercooler. One or two reasonable assumptions must be made, as shown in the following outline. Note that on multistage units with intercoolers, the cylinder material of only the last stage cylinder enters the picture, since on prior stages, if the heat is not removed by the cylinder jacket, it is removed by the subsequent intercooler.

1. One bhp hour equals 2545 Btu/hr.
2. Assume approximately 5% of the heat is radiated to atmosphere from frame, cylinders, coolers, and piping.
3. 2420 Btu/bhp hr. remains for possible rejection to the water.
4. When only intercoolers are used, all heat is removed except that in last stage cylinder discharge gas.
5. When an aftercooler is also used, all the above heat is rejected to the water.

Total Btu/bhp hr rejected to water

No. of Stages	Probable Cylinder material	Cylinders and Intercoolers only	Cylinders, Intercoolers, and Aftercoolers
1	CI	700 (Cylinder only)	2420
2	CI	1560	2420
3	CI	1850	2420
4	CS	1880	2420
5	F	1980	2420
6	F (Plunger)	2040	2420

Since one gpm is 500 lb/hr of water, the gpm requirement can be figured from the above table using the following.

$$gpm = \frac{Btu/bhp\ hr\ to\ Water \times Total\ bhp}{500 \times Water\ Temperature\ Rise\ (°F)} \tag{6.3}$$

Water Temperature Rise

The temperature rise of water has an appreciable effect on rejection rate, since an increase in average temperature reduces the amount of heat removed. See Fig. 6-Y. Manufacturers will usually recommend a rise of 15°F to 20°F under normal conditions. This keeps the cylinder bore at a relatively even temperature. It is also a good value when water is cooled in a cooling tower.

Where the water is cold, the flow should be restricted and temperature rise increased.

Clean, silt free, and nonscaling water should be used. When not available, keeping the temperature rise (and final temperature) down by circulating more water will reduce scaling and result in better cooling and less difficult jacket cleaning. Silting is also less apt to occur because of the higher water velocity.

In hot dry climates where water is scarce and the water is cooled by an air-cooled exchanger, the average water temperature will be high. The temperature rise through the compressor should be reduced, again by faster water circulation.

Water Circuits

There are two methods of circulating the water through the cylinder. In one, general on the 100 psiG compressors, water enters the bottom of one head, flows through ports between the head and the cylinder, circulates around the cylinder, through ports into the other head, and is discharged at the top. See Fig. 6-Z.

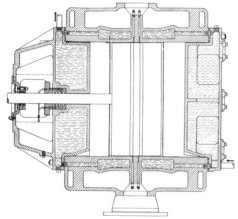

Fig. 6-Z. Cylinder jacket water circulating system using internal ports and passages.

In the second, there are no ports between heads and cylinder and the water flow is through external piping at these points. Use of these "blanked water ports" and external piping is most common in process type compressors handling gases other than air, often at high pressures. See Fig. 6-AA.

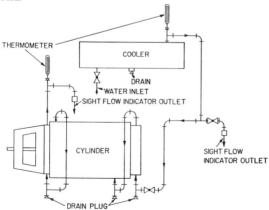

Fig. 6-AA. Typical water piping for a cylinder and its following intercooler or aftercooler. Water is externally piped between cylinder jacket and heads.

Multistage compressors with intercoolers usually tie the intercooler into the water circuit as mentioned on page 6-24. See Fig. 6-AA.

Closed Circuits

When the cooling water is to be recirculated (after passing over a cooling tower or through a heat exchanger to remove the rejected heat) or is to be used in some other service, a back pressure may be required at the cylinder water outlet. The discharge cannot be open to atmosphere. This should be discussed with the manufacturer before purchase, since the maximum water pressure permissible in jackets and heads (for intercoolers see Chapter 19) will vary with cylinder size and design. It is not always possible to meet excessive water pressure requirements without costly cylinder redesign. It is frequently less expensive to design the external system to permit use of a lower pressure.

Still-Cooled Cylinders

Still-cooled cylinders have jackets that are filled with a noncirculating liquid, the type depending upon the application. The primary purpose is temperature equalization around the cylinder bore rather than actual heat removal. This arrangement is never used where cooling is seriously needed.

The cylinder is frequently filled with oil, an expansion standpipe of modest proportions being connected to the cylinder jacket outlet. In the case of a cylinder handling a low temperature gas (as in a refrigeration application), the jacket may be filled with antifreeze.

When service conditions warrant, some circulation and cooling may be obtained by connecting the cylinder water connections to an elevated tank of considerable volume. The normal cylinder inlet is piped to the tank bottom; the normal outlet is piped to a point near the tank top, but below the level of the coolant. This sets up a thermosyphon.

Cooling may be materially improved if the water lines to the tank are of finned tubing. It may be found satisfactorily to use only a vertical loop of fin tubing, joined at the top, but vented. Making the vertical lines of two or more parallel lines will provide more surface for the same water flow area.

A modification to make flow more positive involves a small air lift in the cylinder outlet. See Fig. 6-AB.

This type of system must be placed so there is good air circulation and no chance of freezing.

Materials and Construction — Lubricated Cylinders *

Air-Cooled Units

The general construction of the air-cooled machines is illustrated in Fig. 6-A and 6-B. Cylinders are simple castings bolted between frame and head. Valves are mounted either between the head and cylinder or in the head itself. Pistons are of the trunk type and rings are of the automotive compression design with special oil wiper rings. Materials are almost exclusively cast iron, even for the high-pressure special designs. In this area, cylinder diameters on the upper stage become as small as ½" and the parts can be specially heat-treated for extra strength and better wearing qualities.

---

*For nonlubricated construction, see Chapter 14.

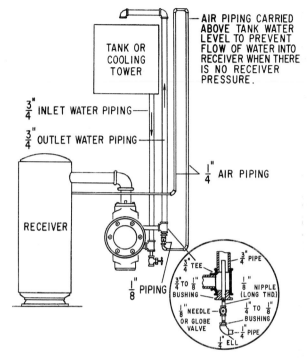

Fig. 6-AB. Schematic diagram of an air-lift for cooling water circulation for a small compressor.

Crosshead-Type Units

These units vary in size from 25 to more than 12,000 horsepower and will operate at pressures from 15 to 60,000 psiG or higher. Designs for pressures above 6000 psiG become quite special and will not be extensively discussed.

Cylinder Materials

Although materials are normally selected for strength, there are applications where thermal shock, mechanical shock or corrosion resistance may be the determining factor. These are usually covered by purchaser's specifications.

Cast iron is quite generally used for cylinders and heads up to 1200 psiG discharge. Size and complexity of design may require lower limits. Small cylinders may use specially formulated and heat-treated cast iron to 2500 psiG, but usually only for single acting relatively short stroke units of the straight line type. See Fig. 6-C and 6-E.

Nodular iron is used in cylinders for pressures to about 1500 psiG although in the small straight-line cylinders it may be used to 2000 psiG. Nodular iron is a high strength ductile cast iron specially processed to produce the graphite in spherical shapes rather than in flakes. The "as cast" condition is seldom used. Properties are improved by stress relieving for strength or by full annealing when maximum ductility is desired for shock resistance.

Cast steel cylinders are used for the 1200 to 2500 psiG discharge range, although on small cylinders and for pressures above 2000 psiG economic manufacturing considerations may dictate the use of forged carbon steel billets rather than cast steel.   Below 1200 psiG, cast steel would be supplied only to meet special cases, covered by purchaser's specifications.

Above 2500 psiG, on practically all units, either the *forged steel* billet or special forgings are used.   The type of steel depends upon the pressure, cylinder diameter, and service involved.

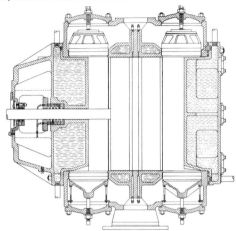

Fig. 6-AC.   Typical large low-pressure cylinder with aluminum piston.

Cylinder Designs

Typical designs of moderate-sized cast iron cylinders are shown in Fig. 6-C through 6-L.   Cast iron is the usual piston material although Fig. 6-AC shows a typical large diameter cylinder fitted with an aluminum piston to reduce inertia forces.   This cylinder is double-acting, 42″ diameter by 15″ stroke.   In special cases where aluminum cannot be used due to corrosive constituents in the gas and cast iron is undesirable due to weight and inertia force unbalance, lightweight welded steel pistons with special metal-sprayed antifriction wearing bands may be used.

Nodular iron cylinders will have the same design as cast iron.

Fig. 6-AD shows a typical large double-acting high-pressure cast steel process cylinder.   Water jackets are included around the cylinder barrel and packing, occasionally in the heads.

Forged steel cylinders will generally be simple blocks or slabs.   See Fig. 6-AE.   Water flows through holes around the cylinder and packing. Cast iron water boxes are bolted to each side of the slab.

Pistons in cast and forged steel cylinders are usually a cast iron or nodular iron sleeve fastened over the end of rod and fitted with snap piston rings.   See Fig. 6-AD.   When diameters become so small that the piston sleeve thickness becomes too thin for proper strength, it becomes necessary to make the piston and rod a single steel forging as shown in Fig. 6-AF. Two or more wearing bands of antifriction metal are usually inserted into the steel piston to improve wearing qualities.   Special antifriction wearing bands and surfaces such as metal spray are also used when border-line lubrication may be expected.

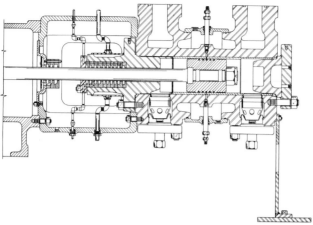

Fig. 6-AD. Typical cast steel cylinder with water-jacketed barrel, outer head, and stuffing box.

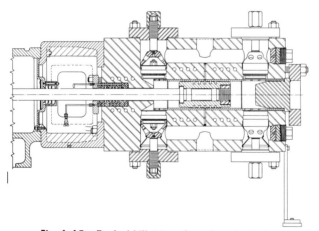

Fig. 6-AE. Typical billet-type forged steel cylinder

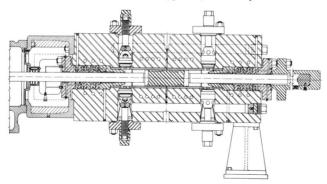

Fig. 6-AF. Small diameter high-pressure forged steel cylinder with one-piece piston, rod, and tail rod.

Some forged steel double-acting high-pressure cylinders operate under conditions where the pistons become relatively small and the stress loads caused by the differential pressure across the piston with normal designs are exerted in the same directions for both strokes. This nonreversing load on crank and crosshead bearings, particularly the latter, makes lubrication more difficult and one of two alternates may be used. A tail rod may be added to obtain equal and opposite loads on the two piston strokes, or special crosshead bearing construction may be installed. Fig. 6-AF and 6-AG show tail rods. However, the trend is toward the elimination of tail rods.

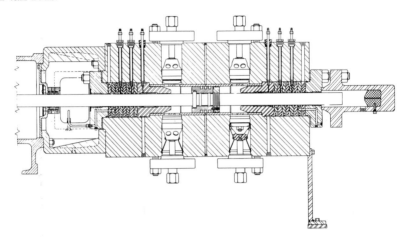

Fig. 6-AG. Typical forged-steel circulator cylinder equipped with a tail rod catcher.

Note that the packing stuffing boxes are a part of the cylinder and are bored on the same setup as the cylinder bore, ensuring proper alignment. There are no heads, as such.

A circulator is a cylinder with a high operating pressure but low differential across the piston. For example, the discharge may be 4500 psiG, intake 4000 psiG, and the differential 500 psi. The compression ratio is low. These cylinders always require a tail rod if reversing bearing loads are to be obtained. See Fig. 6-AG. Note the special tail rod catcher on the tail rod end to contain the rod if it should break and become a projectile due to the gas force acting on the broken end within the cylinder.

Multistage compressors occasionally make use of a two stage combination on a single crank throw in which the cylinders are in tandem, each being single acting. One cylinder compresses on the inward stroke; the other, on the outward. This opposed arrangement is most often utilized when the frame selected would not be fully loaded if each stage were put on a separate crank throw. The combining of two stages on one crank throw lowers cost and usually reduces floor space.

Fig. 6-AH shows a small straight-line compressor with single-acting opposed (SAO) cylinders, the second stage being located at the outer end and having a plunger form of piston. The space between the first and second stages is normally open to atmosphere or vented to first stage intake depending on the gas being handled. This design is *close-coupled*.

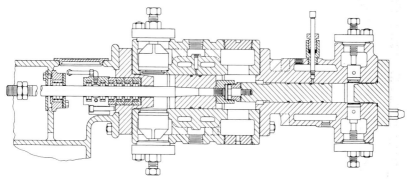

Fig. 6-AH.   Small single-acting opposed, two-stage, tandem, close-coupled cylinder assembly for mounting on one crank throw.

Another close-coupled arrangement on large process machines is the step-piston design of Fig. 6-AI. The cylinders may be truly single-acting opposed or the larger piston may be double-acting, while the smaller piston is single-acting.

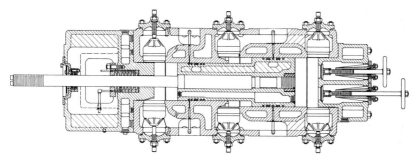

Fig. 6-AI.   Medium size step-piston, close-coupled, two-stage assembly. The first (right-hand) stage is double-acting. The second stage is single-acting.

The design shown in Fig. 6-AJ is to be preferred, particularly when the cylinders get large and it becomes more difficult (and more important) to establish and maintain alignment. Placing the larger cylinder outboard improves accessibility. The yoke or distance piece between the two cylinders is vented either to atmosphere or to the intake of the first stage. This particular design is fitted with an adjustable coupling between the second-stage piston and the first-stage rod so that the latter may be independently aligned. Such construction is more expensive than the close-coupled design, but for a large unit will pay off in longer life, reduced maintenance, and less down time.

There are several distinct disadvantages to the single-acting opposed design. (1) When the outboard cylinder is smaller than the inboard, it is more difficult to service the inboard cylinder, piston, piston rings, etc., since some piping and the outboard cylinder must usually be removed for access. (2) Lubrication is more difficult on a single-acting cylinder, especially at high pressures.   (3) There are, in most designs, two sets of piston rings leaking some gas to an intermediate space connected to atmosphere or a higher pressure. This is greater than the total of two double-acting cylinders and represents gas actually wasted to atmosphere or compressed twice. Economy suffers slightly.

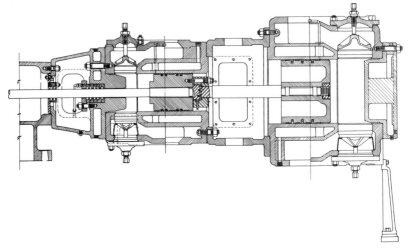

Fig. 6-AJ. Typical medium sized, single-acting opposed, tandem cylinder arrangement — not close-coupled.

A single cylinder of single-acting design is used with crosshead machines only under special circumstances. These are usually small high-pressure cylinders. Pin loads are apt to be heavy and will be in one direction. Fig. 6-AK shows such a cylinder for 15,000 psiG discharge pressure. Valves are mounted in series in the end of the cylinder. The design is such that, in areas of cyclic stress, there are no openings or ports to act as "stress-raisers." This tends to eliminate fatigue. These plungers are outside packed to atmosphere with full-floating mechanical packing.

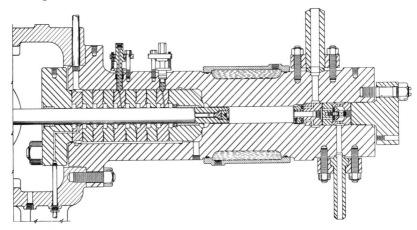

Fig. 6-AK. Typical single-acting plunger cylinder; this example designed for 15,000 psiG discharge. The plunger is packed for the full differential to atmosphere.

Such cylinders have been attached to single crossheads of special non-reversing load design. Another arrangement which amounts to a double-acting design has been developed for use at 10,000 psiG and higher. An auxiliary crosshead is driven by special drive rods from the main cross-head and mounts a cylinder (see Fig. 6-AK) on each end of the auxiliary crosshead support or yoke. A plunger is mounted on each side of the auxiliary crosshead by an adjustable arrangement permitting very close alignment. Fig. 6-AL shows three high-pressure compressors, each with three crank throws and six cylinders.

Fig. 6-AL. Three-crank throw high-pressure boosters using two single-acting plunger cylinders per crank throw. Pairs of plungers are mounted opposed in an auxiliary cross-head driven by tie rods from the main crosshead.

Cylinder Liners

Cylinder liners are inserted into the main cylinder body to either form or line the pressure wall. There are two types. The *wet* liner (Fig. 6-AM) forms the pressure wall as well as the inside wall of the water jacket. The joint between the cylinder and liner is usually at the ends. Liners are pressed or shrunk into place and then faced off at the ends. Liners must be sufficiently thick to withstand the pressure load.

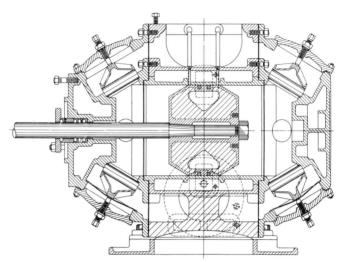

Fig. 6-AM.   Typical wet-liner cylinder. The liner is a part of the water jacket as well as the cylinder pressure wall.

The *dry* type lines the cylinder wall and are not required to add strength. They are the most prevalent type. Dry-liner cylinders are shown in Fig. 6-AD, 6-AE, 6-AF, and 6-AG. Fig. 6-AC, 6-AH, 6-AI, and 6-AJ show nonliner cylinders.

Standard cylinder liners are of cast iron. If specified to have special corrosion or wear resistance, special alloys may be needed.

Liners are frequently used in cast iron cylinders to make repair easier and facilitate changing cylinder diameter for changes in operating conditions.

Liners are required in cast and forged steel (and in certain nodular iron cylinders) to provide proper wearing qualities when piston rings are used. Packed plunger cylinders do not require liners.

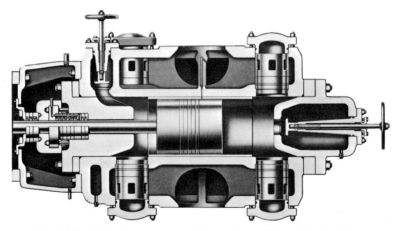

Fig. 6-AN.   Typical nonwater-cooled cast iron cylinder with short liner.

Liners should preferably extend the full length of the cylinder, head-to-head, and be pressed or shrunk into place. This is the sure way of holding liners in place. There are a few occasions where a *short* liner is used, (See Fig. 6-AN) principally in low compression ratio (and therefore low temperature) service. They are found predominantly in the gas pipeline field where the cylinder diameter may be altered by changing or reboring the liner. Movement is prevented by the press or shrink fit used.

Dry liners have certain disadvantages:

Increased clearance;

Decreased capacity from given diameter cylinder;

Less effective jacket cooling due to two walls in the bore; and,

Expensive and time consuming replacement.

Inlet and Discharge Connections

Screwed pipe connections are common for many of the smaller units. In some cases, a special companion flange is supplied even though the pipe may be relatively small.

Inlet and discharge pipe connections on the larger and higher-pressure machines are generally to the ASA-B-16.5 Standards if the maximum allowable working pressure of the cylinder is within the ASA rating and it is used in non-shock service. Types involved are shown in the first four sketches of Fig. 6-AO; the fifth is special and used at pressure levels beyond the ASA tabulation.

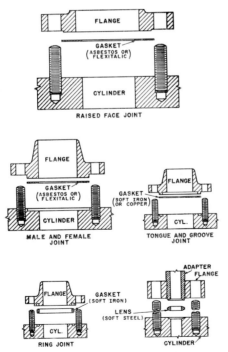

Fig. 6-AO. Various types of flanged joints and typical gasket materials used on medium- and high-pressure cylinders.

When the raised face joint is used, it is customary to face the cylinder flat. It is not necessary that both mating faces have the raised center and there is less possibility of damaging a cylinder during shipment and erection.

The ring joint is used mostly on nodular iron, cast steel, or forged steel cylinders. It is not practical on cast iron.

On large cylinders, the use of round gas connections makes the cylinder and piston longer and heavier than desirable. To shorten these, the connection is made oblong and fitted with an adapter to connect into a manifold. See Fig. 6-AP. Another adapter is available to convert from the oblong to round for a direct pipe connection.

Fig. 6-AP. Large cylinders use oblong adapters to connect cylinders to headers. This is a 51,000 cfm vacuum pump.

Flange Finish

Although the majority of flanges are finished with a flat finish, there are cases where a special "phonograph" or serrated finish may be used on the flange face. This is often specified for low density gases.

Gaskets

Gaskets are of various materials, depending largely on pressure. "Leakability" of the gas also has influence. Hydrogen and helium are among gases difficult to hold.

Referring to Fig. 6-AO, raised face and male-and-female joints will normally use asbestos ring gaskets. A semiflexible laminated gasket of metal with a filler material is available for the more difficult jobs.

The tongue-and-grove joint will generally utilize a flat soft iron ring gasket. Occasionally copper may be used.

The ring joint uses a solid iron gasket. See Fig. 6-AO.

The lens gasket in this type of joint is a soft steel ring. There are various designs of this high pressure joint.

Some joints for very high pressure use a totally confined copper gasket. This is special and not illustrated.

Rod Packing

Fibrous (soft) packing and the more permanent semimetallic preformed packing are seldom used on crosshead compressors. The standard, almost without exception, is the full floating mechanical packing that adjusts itself to wear. It is currently made for almost any gas, of many materials, and is in commercial service to more than 60,000 psiG. There are many designs but the principles are the same.

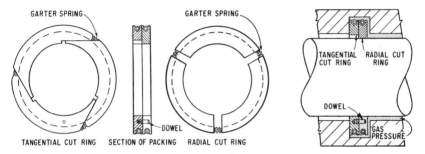

Fig. 6-AQ. Single pair of typical full-floating mechanical packing rings.

Fig. 6-AQ is typical and explains the operation. An actual packing would have from three to eight pairs of such rings in a single case or assembly, the number depending on pressure and service requirements. This packing must be lubricated unless special materials are used. See NL Compressors in Chapter 14. In small and the lower-pressure machines, enough oil comes from the cylinder to provide lubrication. Larger and higher-pressure machines require a separate oil feed or feeds from the lubricator.

The success of this packing stems from the extreme precision used in manufacture. It must be installed carefully and properly, and can quickly be damaged by dirt and liquid carry-over. Proper and carefully break-in is very important since it must wear-in to a satisfactory seal on the rod before being fully loaded.

Service life is long for the properly cared for packing. Replacement consists of new rings only. The case seldom wears out. Replacement rings must be broken in slowly. They are new parts.

Hydrostatic Tests

Hydrostatic testing of pressure parts may be made for a number of purposes, primarily to detect leaky and porous castings and to locate weak points that might fail. Some parts, such as the cylinders and heads of small vertical machines are so "over designed" for stiffness and other reasons that pressure stress is never a factor and few of these are tested.

Crosshead-type cylinders are almost universally tested by water pressure at 150% design pressure or higher, depending upon pressure, material, and service conditions.

Cylinder castings to handle toxic, suffocating, and very light gases may be given a further test using helium while the cylinders is immersed in a water bath. A halide, or tracer gas, test may also be made.

Capacity Control

Output of compressors must be controlled (regulated) to match the system demand. The controlled point may be discharge pressure (the most prevalent), temperature of a fluid being cooled (refrigeration), intake pressure of a system being evacuated (vacuum applications and some safety controls), a constant weight or constant volume output meter (certain process applications). The control point usually does not influence the type of capacity control used on a reciprocating compressor. This is determined more by the size, type of unit, type of driver, and the amount and range of control required. It is sometimes necessary to combine two types of control.

Chapter 25 (Control Systems) discusses a wider scope of controls, including, as one phase, the capacity regulation covered here.

Manual Controls

Nearly all types of capacity control may be arranged for manual operation. There are many examples, particularly in process industries, where changes in demand are infrequent and slow enough to permit manual operation. Some of these devices are illustrated later.

Essentials of Automatic Control

Every control includes four elements.

Sensing element measures any change in the control point condition.

Multiplying element amplifies any signal for change and provides power or motion for further action.

Actuating signal device is motivated by the multiplying element to send a signal and power to the receiving device.

Receiving device actually moves the control mechanism. The methods and combinations used are extremely varied and frequently complex.

Unloading for Starting

Practically all reciprocating compressors must be unloaded to some degree before starting so that the driver torque available during acceleration is not exceeded. This is often a manual operation, but on all automatic control systems and on many others, automatic starting unloading must be provided. There are many methods, the most frequently used being a vent to atmosphere, or some type of bypass. One type of bypass is the holding open of inlet valves. Unloading also may be by closing of the intake close to the compressor. This is infrequent and quite special.

Basic Types of Control

The basic capacity control methods are automatic start-and-stop, constant-speed, and variable-speed.

Automatic start-and-stop is almost entirely limited to use with electric-motor-driven units, although there are cases where turbine- or gas-engine drives can be so arranged. The compressor is run at full load for a period and is then stopped. These units usually maintain a relatively constant receiver pressure on an air system. The household refrigerator or room air conditioner compressor are examples of control from temperature. Almost any size compressor can be run automatic start-and-stop if starting unloaders are applied and it is not started too often.

Constant-speed control can be applied to all types of compressors, regardless of driver. With this, the compressor operates at full speed continuously, loaded part of the time and fully or partially unloaded at other times. There are a number of control methods.

Variable-speed control is used whenever the driver is capable of operating at a speed commensurate with demand. Integral-steam- and gas-engine drives are in this class. These units often have added constant speed control features.

Automatic Start-and-Stop Control

When automatic start-and-stop is used to control output, the discharge system must be large enough to prevent rapid cycling between start-and-stop conditions. Electric motors, the predominant driver, have a limited number of starts permissible per hour if damage from overheating is to be avoided. See Drivers, Chapter 15. With single-acting vertical compressors, it is desirable to run loaded at least 10 minutes per cycle. This will prevent excessive moisture condensation in the crankcase.

Automatic start-and-stop utilizes an electrical switch controlling motor operation plus starting unloaders that may be electrically operated or triggered by some other means, as a centrifugal device.

Dual Control

Automatic start-and-stop control is often combined with some type of constant-speed control and a manual selector switch so the unit can be operated automatically during light-load periods and constant-speed during more heavy and regular demand. Night and day operation is such a case.

Constant-Speed Control

This may be obtained by at least five methods, these having to do with the means provided to actually control the output. Sensing or other devices may not change.

Control may be in two steps, full and no load; three steps, full, 1/2, and no load; or five steps, full, 3/4, 1/2, 1/4, and no load. Two-step control is standard on small and single-cylinder machines. Three- or five-step is standard on many multistage and multicylinder units. The number of steps may depend on the method of control used.

Blocking the inlet is seldom used on new compressors. Many existing units are, however, operating with this type of two-step or "all-on all-off" control. This consists of closing a valve in the inlet line when capacity is to be reduced and opening it when full delivery is to be resumed. One of the problems is leakage that eventually develops in the valve. When it leaks, there is gas to be compressed to final discharge, over a much greater than normal compression ratio due to the decreased intake pressure. The resultant discharge temperature becomes very high. To partially solve this problem and decrease the unloaded power requirement, an automatic discharge line unloader to unload or vent the cylinder itself to atmosphere is added.

Intake throttling will provide an infinite number of steps between full load (wide open) and no load (closed). Capacity changes are caused by reduction in gas density as the intake is throttled (intake pressure is lowered) plus the reduced *VE* with increased compression ratio. Throttling control is used in a few special applications, usually vacuum services. It generally is not economical in power, the bhp per 100 cfm free gas compressed at part loads rising rapidly. For normal compression service, not vacuum, discharge temperatures may become excessive.

External bypassing of compressed gas back to intake gives an infinite number of steps, but requires the compressor to operate at full load and capacity at all times. It is uneconomical of power at part loads, and the gas returned to the intake must be cooled close to normal intake temperature else excessive discharge temperatures will result. This control is valuable in a few process applications, usually for fine adjustments unobtainable by other acceptable methods.

Inlet Valve Unloading is the most prevalent type of constant-speed control. This consists simply of holding inlet valves open during both suction and discharge strokes so that all air taken into the cylinder on the suction stroke is pushed back through the intake valves on the discharge stroke. Economy is good, the no-load indicator card having an area of 4 to 5% of the full-load card area. No-load bhp is usually about 15% of full-load bhp on heavy-duty units.

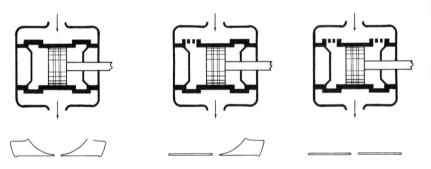

Fig. 6-AR. Diagrams illustrating the operation of three-step free-air unloading.

Inlet valve unloading, known as free-air unloading (FAU), will give a maximum of three steps per double-acting cylinder — full, 1/2, and no loads. See Fig. 6-AR. Although three steps are possible, on the straight-line single-cylinder units it is not considered good practice to operate with more than two steps — full and no load. When operated at half load, with full torque required on one stroke and low torque on the other, operation is apt to be rough. A larger two-cylinder compressor either single- or multistage, with a separate connecting rod per cylinder, can be operated at half load nicely since the torque unbalance effects can be offset sufficiently.

Typical mechanisms are shown in Fig. 6-AS. FAU may be combined with clearance control to obtain special control results.

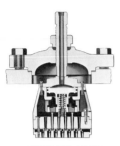

"INSIDE-OPERATED" UNLOADER

This inlet valve unloader is actuated by the same gas being handled by the compressor. The regulator admits gas from the receiver, depressing the piston and causing the fingers to hold the valve channels off their seats. Release of gas pressure by the regulator permits the valve to function normally.

"OUTSIDE-OPERATED" UNLOADER

When the gas being handled by the compressor is not suitable for use in the regulation system, the "outside-operated" unloader is available. Compressed air, admitted by the regulator to the top of an outside piston, actuates the unloader. No operating air mixes with the gas being compressed. The direct-acting type is shown above; a reverse-acting type is also available.

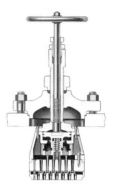

HAND-OPERATED UNLOADER

This type of inlet valve unloader is actuated manually by turning a wheel, depressing a piston which operates the fingers. There are positive stops at both ends of the movement, to prevent damage due to overtravel.

Fig. 6-AS. Typical free-air unloader mechanisms.

At times there is a need for an efficient control with an *infinite number of steps*. This is available in a modification of FAU which delivers a smooth variation in capacity from full to no load. It is available only as an automatic device. This uses a mechanism that

1. Allows inlet valves to open normally to fill the cylinder;
2. Holds them open for a timed interval of the compression stroke; and,
3. Releases them to close so that compression may begin.

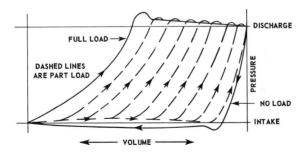

Fig. 6-AT. Progressive indicator card illustrating the operation of infinite-step control.

A progressive indicator card would look like Fig. 6-AT. This system has advantages when driver power loading is to be closely maintained over a wide range of intake and discharge pressure conditions. Infinite-step control permits close control of suction pressure, discharge pressure, flow, etc., without any sudden variations (large steps).

Clearance control, the second most widely used method of constant-speed control, has been theoretically discussed in Chapter 4. The action within a single cylinder is outlined in Fig. 6-AU. A typical cylinder cross-section through the valves is as shown in Fig. 6-AV. The control is entirely separated from the inlet and discharge valves that continue to function normally. In the picture, there are two clearance pockets in each end — four in all.

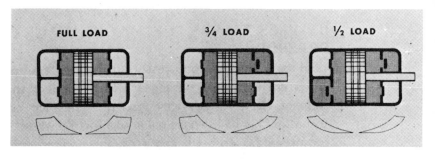

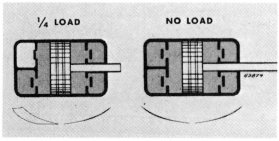

Fig. 6-AU.   Diagrams illustrating the operation of five-step clearance control.

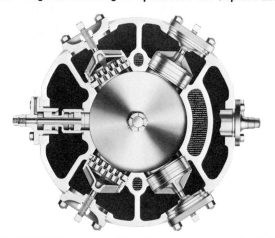

Fig. 6-AV.   Cross section through a clearance control cylinder.

There are a number of other clearance valves and pockets. See Fig. 6-AW.

Clearance control like FAU, is efficient. Power required (minus friction losses) is nearly proportional to capacity output with no-load bhp being 15% or less of full-load bhp.

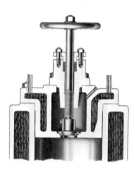  

MANUAL FIXED-VOLUME CLEARANCE POCKET VALVE This is generally located in the outer head of a cylinder as shown here. This type of control is used for many compressor applications which require limited and infrequent capacity changes.

MANUAL VARIABLE-VOLUME CLEARANCE POCKET VALVE This permits close capacity adjustment when required. The amount of clearance added and the capacity reduction is proportional to the movement of the clearance pocket piston.

OUTSIDE-OPERATED FIXED-VOLUME CLEARANCE POCKET VALVE For applications where gas being compressed is not suitable for control purposes. Compressed air pressure on an external piston operates the internal valve; air cannot mix with gas.

Fig. 6-AW. Typical clearance valve mechanisms.

Variable-Speed Control

Variable-speed control is the ideal if it can be supplied since it matches output to the demand directly. Steam-engine and gas-engine drives are best adapted to this control, although some steam turbine coupled-speed reducer drives can also use this control.

Integral steam engine compressors have a wide range of speed control and operate smoothly over a range of 100 to 20% speed and often lower.

Steam-driven machines may be controlled by a governor that throttles the steam pressure to vary speed and maintain the required output. The governor may alternatively vary the steam cylinder cutoff. Throttling governor are standard on straight-line machines and small duplex units. Automatic cutoff is usual on large units and particularly on those with compound (two-stage) steam cylinders.

Integral gas-engine-driven units can also operate with variable-speed control. Four-cycle naturally aspirated units are the best in this regard and operate well throughout a range of 100 to 50% speed with a smooth throttle control. Two-cycle and all supercharged units may have a narrower operating speed range due to their more complicated control systems. Critical shaft speeds, particularly in the larger sizes, may also reduce the speed range available for capacity control.

Control Point Pressure Variations

In many applications, particularly 100 psiG air service, the standard range of variation between pressures at full- and no-load points is 10%.

This range may be above or below the rated pressure, depending upon the type of unit.

One group of compressors, principally the vertical air-cooled and horizontal straight-line machines with all-on all-off control, has control range set below the compressor rated pressure; another, where the control range is set above the rated pressure, includes most of the larger units, usually with multistep control.

There is normally no need to give this thought when selecting a compressor, but occasionally applications arise where a certain pressure becomes the minimum allowable. It is then important that the compressor control setting be such that the minimum is always maintained.

Multistage Process Compressor Control

In the use of control on multistage service, it is sometimes possible that balance throughout the machine may be maintained at each load point. Each stage would be unloaded the same percentage, and interstage pressures would not change. Two-stage 100 psiG units are an example.

On many multistage process units, the upper stages are operating at high pressure, are frequently steel forgings, and the application of controls adds considerable complexity and expense. In some cases, it is impossible to include them. Control in such cases usually varies only the capacity of the lower-pressure cylinders using conventional methods. This reduces the number of control devices to be operated per step of control, and

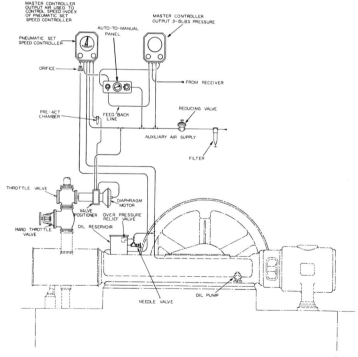

Fig. 6-AX. Typical instrument control for a variable-speed steam-driven compressor.

places all of them in the lower-pressure range. It does sometimes require care in the design of the compressor. In the operation of control, frame overload or excessive discharge temperature must not develop. Reducing the capacity of the first-stage cylinder acts on all the other stages exactly as though the intake pressure had been reduced (throttling intake control). Designs must take this into account.

Close Range Control

There are processes where the standard control elements and devices are not sufficiently sensitive to obtain the required limited variation in the controlled point value. For closer control, instruments are used for measurement (sensing), predicting, multiplying changes, and acting more rapidly and accurately to alter compressor output. These can be either simple or complex devices.

Fig. 6-AX shows a diagram of a control for a steam-driven variable-speed compressor, the control point being either intake or discharge pressure. It is the latter in this example. The governor is of the throttling type, the valve being fitted with a *diaphragm motor* having a *positioner*. This valve is accurately positioned by the air signal pressure delivered by the control instruments.

The master pressure controller is connected to the pressure to be controlled. Changes in this pressure are converted to a variable air signal pressure output of 3 to 15 psiG. This changes the index or speed setting of the pneumatic set-speed controller to a speed necessary to maintain desired operating pressure.

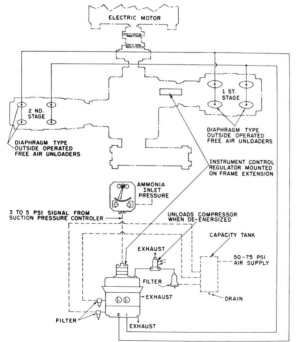

Fig. 6-AY. Close-range instrument operated three-step control on a two-stage ammonia compressor.

The speed of the compressor is controlled by the pneumatic set-speed controller. An oil pump driven by the compressor applies pressure to this instrument. Since pressure is a function of speed, variations in speed can be measured. When actual and desired speed are not the same, an output air signal from this controller is applied to the final control element until the correction is made.

An automatic-to-manual panel is provided between the master controller and the pneumatic set-speed controller. The operator may control the speed of the machine by manually setting the speed index of the set instrument.

With a variable-speed compressor, the output and demand can be matched.

Fig. 6-AY illustrates an instrument regulating the output of a typical constant-speed motor-driven ammonia compressor with three-step control. This is a two-stage machine and unloading is by holding inlet valves open on one end of each cylinder for 50% capacity and on both ends of each cylinder for zero output. Suction pressure is being controlled.

The pressure controller senses small changes in suction pressure and converts them to an air signal varying between 3 and 15 psiG. Signal pressure acts on a regulator that at appropriate signal values, operates the inlet valve unloaders through a diaphragm operator on each valve using an auxiliary air supply.

With close range step control it is important that the controlled system is of sufficient size to prevent too frequent loading and unloading.

Instrument control can be adjusted to hold pressures to 1% or less.

**Fig. 6-AZ. Two-stage straight line compressor
with intercooler mounted beneath cylinders.**

Gas Piping on Compressors

General

Larger crosshead compressors may be supplied with or without intercoolers and/or piping. Cooler designs (See Chapter 19) include those mounted on compressor cylinders. In many standard multistage compressors, particularly air compressors for 100 psiG and higher, the intercooler is either built in or mounted and connected directly to the cylinders. These are usually compact units and no piping is involved. See Fig. 6-AZ. When multiple cylinders must be piped, machines become more complex. The unit in Fig. 6-BA is a 3500 HP 11- cylinder, four-service multistage process gas compressor. Five coolers are mounted and all interconnecting piping supplied between inlet and discharge flanges of two services. There are two coolers for the third service mounted off the machine. The fourth service is single stage.

Fig. 6-BA. Complex 3500 HP multiservice compressors with mounted intercoolers, separators, and piping.

Pipe Sizing

Compressor piping *cannot* be sized by analyzing pressure drop under steady flow conditions since steady flow does not exist in either the intake or discharge of a reciprocating compressor cylinder. Flow is rapidly fluctuating and one of the main problems is to dampen these pulsations so that resonant peaks do not build up. Resonance in gas piping can cause undue pressure losses, increased power, reduced capacity, cooler tube leakage, and valve breakage. Resonance usually sets up severe piping vibrations, that can in time cause joint leakage, pipe breakage, and other problems.

Manufacturers provide generous (oversize by steady flow standards) inlet and discharge openings on cylinders and have insisted that piping connected to these openings be full size. When coolers are interposed between cylinders, they must contain sufficient volume to reduce pulsations below a damaging level. This is still to be done where mounted cooler designs permit, but there are cases where the pulsation limiting volume must be in separate chambers. See Fig. 6-BA.

Pulsation Chambers

There are several classes of pulsation chambers. A *volume bottle* is a pressure vessel, unbaffled internally, mounted on or very near a cylinder inlet or discharge. It is sized empirically and results are usually qualitatively guaranteed if the entire piping assembly is supplied by the manufacturer. A bottle, when placed at the inlet of an upper stage cylinder following an intercooler may be designed to act as a condensate separator.

**Fig. 6-BB. Suction and discharge manifolds on a
two-stage six-cylinder gas-engine driven compressor.**

A *manifold* is a volume bottle used to join the inlet or discharge connections of cylinders operating in parallel. It serves all cylinders to which it is connected. Fig. 6-BB illustrates this on a two-stage six-cylinder integral skid-mounted gas-engine driven compressor.

A *pulsation dampener* is a commercial, internally-baffled device as manufactured by specialists in pulsation reduction. A usual guarantee is that the residual pulse in the damped stream will not exceed plus or minus 1% of the absolute pressure in this stream. This holds for design condition and not necessarily for variable operating pressures and flows. Dampeners must be mounted as close as possible to the cylinder. The inlet dampener limits the pressure wave going from the cylinder *upstream* into the inlet pipe. The discharge dampener limits the wave going *downstream* into the discharge pipe. A 7% pressure fluctuation at the *cylinder* flange has been guaranteed by their manufacturers. These devices, which are not inexpensive, do prevent resonance in the piping they serve. They are offered in a combination dampener and condensate separator, which simplifies piping considerably.

Analog Analysis

Piping may be and often is analyzed before manufacture by an analog for possible resonance. Such analysis is unnecessary if commercial dampeners are used.

Materials

Piping will usually conform to ASA Standard B 165 for 350°F nonshock service within its range. Bottles and dampeners are usually built to the ASME Unfired Pressure Vessel Code (Section VIII).

Resonance in Air Piping

Most air compressors do not use pulsation dampeners on either intake or discharge. Although resonance (systematic vibration of the air column in the pipe as in an organ) is not frequent in these systems, every air compressor has inlet and discharge pipe lengths to be avoided.

Open End Intake Piping

A resonant condition in the open end inlet pipe normally causes supercharging and driver overload, valve breakage, and vibration, often with serious results. Supercharging is the overfilling of the cylinder at the end of the suction stroke, a building up of the pressure in the cylinder at that point to a value considerably higher than atmospheric. Compression starting at this higher value (greater p_1) results in greater horsepower. See formula (3.38), page 3-19.

The predominant resonant inlet pipe lengths can be predicted by the following. Piping should be selected to avoid these lengths.

Within the intake pipe, the air column pulses in accordance with the piston movement at a wave length dependent upon the speed of sound in air and the rpm of the compressor. Strong resonant waves are developed if the total equivalent pipe length is one-quarter or three-quarters of this wave length. These are the total pipe lengths to be avoided by a suitable margin.

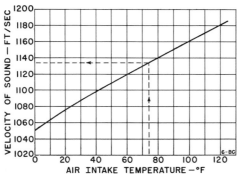

Fig. 6-BC.   Velocity of sound in atmospheric air at sea level.

The velocity of sound varies with temperature as in Fig. 6-BC. See formula (5.25) on page 5-15. The value of 1135 ft/sec (75°F) is frequently used as standard although it would be more accurate to figure the lower limits of lengths to be avoided at the lowest expected air temperature and upper limits at the highest temperature. A band either side of the theoretical bad spots is usually avoided.

Total Equivalent Lengths to be Avoided

Quarter Wave	Three-quarter Wave
Lower limit 0.17 Wave length Upper limit 0.33 Wave length	0.67 Wave length 0.83 Wave length

The full wave length for a *double-acting* cylinder can be obtained by the following:

$$\lambda = \frac{60a}{2n} \tag{6.4}$$

or when a is 1135

$$\lambda = \frac{34050}{n} \tag{6.5}$$

where λ is wave length-ft
a is speed of sound —ft/sec
n is rpm

For a single-acting cylinder (or a double-acting cylinder with one end unloaded), the wave length will be twice as long. It is wise to check resonance for this condition as well as at full load.

This formula is correct only when an intake pipe feeds air to a single cylinder and the pipe is of uniform size throughout.

Equivalent pipe length contained in the cylinder inlet passages and the cylinder end into which the air is flowing must be *subtracted* from the upper and lower limits of length to be avoided. This will give the actual pipe length from the cylinder inlet flange to the end of the inlet pipe. The air filter does not count. All bends must be measured on their centerline.

The equivalent pipe length *(L)* within the cylinder depends upon the cylinder and passage volume. Formula (6.6) has been empirically developed to estimate this.

$$V = \frac{2.58 \, \pi \, D^2S}{4} = 2.03 \, d^2S \tag{6.6}$$

where V is equivalent cylinder and passage volume — cu ft
D is cylinder diameter-ft
S is cylinder stroke-ft

$$L = \frac{\lambda}{360} \times tan^{-1}\left(\frac{2 \, \pi \, V}{A\lambda}\right) \tag{6.7}$$

where L is equivalent pipe length within cylinder-ft
A is inside area of inlet pipe-sq ft
tan^{-1} is the angle in degrees whose tangent is the second term.

Discharge Piping

Resonance in the discharge piping can cause driver overload, loss of capacity, objectionable receiver noise, and aftercooler tube damage. Annoying and possible destructive vibration can occur. It is not always simple to predict when this will happen, although a solution can usually be suggested. Supply the manufacturer with a sketch of the piping from compressor to receiver and a complete report.

Chapter 7

Vane-Type Rotary Compressors

Caption Index **Page**

General Comments

The operating principles of sliding-vane rotary compressors as discussed on page 1-6 should be reviewed. This compressor has a rather narrow range of capacity and pressure compared to reciprocating designs because of inherent limits imposed by vane length, rubbing speed on the cylinder wall, and the bending forces acting on the vane when in an extended position.

The machine is built in two types. One, used exclusively for stationary service, is fitted for standard lubrication from a force-feed lubricator, is water jacketed, and uses water-cooled intercoolers on multistage units.

The other has a combination lubrication and cooling system consisting of a flood of oil to the machine at all times. The heat of compression is picked up by the oil and dissipated through either a radiator-type oil cooler to the atmosphere or a water-cooled exchanger. Oil is separated from the air before being cooled.

The flood-lubricated machines are used in many portable compressors (see Chapter 11) and as a package stationary compressor to approximately 1000 **cfm**.

Most vane-type rotaries are direct coupled to the driver, although with proper engineering, may be V-belt driven. Drivers are predominantly induction motors in stationary service and either gasoline or diesel engines in portable **service.**

A number of small vane-type units, which may differ in design are not considered or illustrated here.

The characteristics of any vane-type rotary are similar to those of a reciprocator in many ways. They are classed as "constant-volume variable-pressure" units.

A unit designed for one condition cannot necessarily be used for another. Design compression ratios must not be exceeded without the manufacturer's approval. A machine rated at one altitude must be checked before being used at a higher altitude.

The Stationary Water-Cooled Unit

Fig. 7-A shows a typical single-stage unit with motor. Fig. 7-B presents a section of a two-stage unit with intercooler. Approximate maximum ratings for single units follow. The larger single-stage machines are offered only for the lower pressures. By using a double-ended motor or arranging two units in tandem, one driver can be used for twice the sizes shown **below.**

Stages	Maximum Pressure (psiG)	Maximum Capacity	Maximum bhp
1	50	3250	370
2	125	1850	430
3	275	Special	Special

Courtesy of Fuller Company.

7-A. A typical motor-driven single-stage sliding-vane rotary compressor.

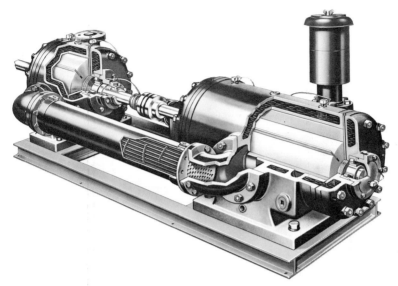

Courtesy of Allis-Chalmers Manufacturing Company.

7-B. A typical motor driven two-stage sliding-vane rotary compressor with intercooler.

Single-stage boosters can be supplied for working pressures up to 400 psiG depending on size and pressure differential.

When used as single-stage vacuum pumps, unit sizes go to approximately 6000 cfm (250 bhp) and 27″ Hg vacuum. Two-stage vacuum pumps can be supplied for 29.9″ Hg vacuum and three-stage for an even higher vacuum (lower absolute pressure).

Speeds range between 1750 and 575 rpm depending on size.

Two staging is accomplished by using entirely separate, properly sized units in tandem.

Characteristics

A series of cylinder diameters, each with its proper rotor diameter and vane dimensions, forms the basis of the line from which, by varying cylinder and rotor diameter and vane length, machines of varying capacities may be built. The maximum length is about 5 feet.

These units can be fitted for outdoor installation or for use in a dusty atmosphere.

The discharge and intake will have high frequency pulsations, usually not objectionable except as noise.

This unit has no inertia shaking forces or moments. The foundation need only be sufficient to spread the static load over sufficient soil and to maintain alignment.

Although used primarily for air it can handle other gases, provided lubrication can be maintained, corrosion problems can be solved, and it is fitted with proper shaft seals. Properly engineered, these units are often used as boosters.

Floor space requirement for stationary units will depend on the size and specific arrangement of the machines and driver and may or may not be favorable as compared with the corresponding reciprocating compressor.

Vane-type rotaries must have clean air or gas or wear will be unduly accelerated. Effective intake filters are mandatory. It is not recommended that gases containing liquid be handled, although the machine will handle limited occasional light carryover as long as lubrication is not destroyed. Vane breakage can occur when heavy slugs are permitted to enter.

This type, for ratings of 125 hp and higher, takes 6 to 20% more power than the equivalent reciprocator per cfm compressed. The lower percentages apply to the lower pressure ranges of a given unit.

The vane rotary has higher unloaded power than the corresponding reciprocator.

Water-cooled vane-type rotaries may generally be classed as heavy duty compressors suitable for long periods at full load.

Design Details

The following discussion is based on the *water-cooled designs,* but applies to flood-lubricated designs in many areas.

Cylinder

Cast iron is the standard material although other materials may be used if corrosive conditions exist. The heads contain the bearings and necessary shaft seal (or seals). On most standard air compressors, the latter is semi-metallic packing in a stuffing box. Commercial mechanical rotary seals can be supplied where necessary or desired, or oil sealed stuffers may be used.

Cylindrical roller bearings are standard.

The rotor is usually one piece with the steel shaft using either bar stock or a special forging. Occasionally, the rotor may be a separate iron casting, keyed to the shaft.

Vanes are usually asbestos or cotton cloth, impregnated with a phenolic resin, although bronze and aluminum have been used. Each vane fits into a milled slot extending the full length of the rotor and slides radially in and out of this slot once per revolution. Vanes are the most maintenance-prone part in the compressor. There are from 8 to 20 vanes in each rotor, depending upon diameter. The greater number of vanes increases compartmentalization and reduces the pressure differential across each vane.

Lubrication

A V-belt driven force feed lubricator is used on water-cooled units. Oil goes to both bearings and to several points in the cylinder. Ten times as much oil is recommended to lubricate the rotary cylinder as is required for the air cylinder of a corresponding reciprocator. The oil carried over with the gas to the line may be reduced 50% with a separator on the discharge. Use of an aftercooler ahead of the separator permits removal of 85 to 90% of the oil. An oil separator is a standard accessory.

Capacity Control

A review of Capacity Control, page 6-38, is recommended here. The control of a water-cooled vane-type rotary of the type illustrated, may be any of the basic types outlined. The discussion of *automatic start-and-stop* control on page 6-39 applies in general. Starting unloading is not always required.

Constant speed control methods include blocking the inlet; intake throttling; and, external bypass.

On stationary air compressors, *inlet blocking*, combined with a relief valve to reduce the pressure within the compressor while unloaded, is standard. A discharge check valve is necessary to prevent backflow from the line. The inlet shutoff valve and relief valve are usually combined in one assembly. This is a two-step control—full and no load only. It is used on both single- and two-stage compressors.

Intake throttling may be used within restricted limits if approved by the manufacturer for a specific unit. This is generally an uneconomical method and is justified only by operational or process advantages.

External bypass between inlet and discharge passages is rather widely used on gases other than air and on booster units. In this case, the hot gas must be cooled enroute to the inlet. There is no power saving since the unit always operates at full load. A modification is available on some machines to permit power recovery from the bypassed gas.

Variable speed control is possible with certain drivers. Standard stationary machines can operate down to about 50% full speed with sufficient centrifugal force generation to keep the blades extended. The exact limiting speed depends on the specific design.

Starting Unloading

Many rotary compressors and boosters may be started without the use of special unloading since the speed must reach 40 to 50% of full speed before the vanes are fully extended and compression begins. Boosters should usually start on a bypass. The size, service, type of capacity control and driver characteristics will determine requirements for starting unloading and the manufacturer's advice should be sought.

Intercoolers

Water-cooled stationary multistage units are always fitted with intercoolers for the same reasons as a reciprocator. See page 4-14. Intercoolers are sometimes built into the base of the unit, but more often are mounted alongside or overhead and piped to the respective compressor stages. Both water tube and air-through-the-tube designs are used.

Cooling Water

The temperature of the water at the compressor outlet should not be less than 70°F nor more than 110°F. A heat rejection rate of 750 btu/bhp hr may be used to estimate cylinder jacket requirements. The data for single- and two-stage units on page 6-24 gives close results and water quantity may be figured using formula 6.3.

Maximum Gas Discharge Temperature

A temperature of 350° to 375°F at discharge is a practical maximum for satisfactory lubrication, vane service life and maintenance.

Discharge Check Valve

Rotary compressors and vacuum pumps can run in reverse as engines if the discharge gas is permitted to flow back and the driver is not in operation (as in a sudden power cutoff). For this reason a discharge check valve is a required accessory.

Silencers

The noise from the intake of an air compressor or the discharge of a vacuum pump may be objectionable. A silencer at the proper point is a normal accessory on water-cooled stationary vane-type rotary machines. On air compressors, a combination inlet filter and silencer is often used.

When a unit is equipped with shutoff and relief valve unloading a silencer is needed for the relief line.

Installation, Operation and Maintenance

See Chapter 18.

The Oil-Flooded Compressor

The oil-flooded compressor is used widely in portable assemblies. The package design is generally identical, with adaptations for a stationary installation. There are no water jackets. Lubrication and cooling are both obtained by the continuous circulation of copious quantities of oil. The oil and air are separated following compression in a very efficient combination separator-receiver. The oil is recirculated through a cooler and filter back to the compressor. Some units use a metering pump in the circuit. The pump and differential pressure between receiver and compressor inlet maintain circulation.

This unit is illustrated in Fig. 11-I, page 11-7. Fig. 11-J shows the circulation system on a typical portable unit.

General construction of the compressor itself varies little from the water-cooled design described earlier.

The portable application is discussed in Chapter 11.

The Packaged Stationary Unit

These units are built in the general range of 5 to 1000 cfm actual delivery. Designs are available in both single-stage to 100 psiG and two-stage to 125 psiG. Two-stage units usually have the stages in-line as shown in Fig. 11-I.

All are electric-motor driven, commonly at 1750 rpm. Some are direct-coupled, others are belted, some are geared.

Capacity control methods are quite varied. Modulated intake throttling and inlet blockage are the more common. Combinations which include automatically timed start-and-stop if demand is light are also offered. Inlet blockage alone or in combination with a time-delay automatic start-and-stop would be the more economical.

Fig. 7-C.   Typical package rotary compressor ready for installation.

Packaged units usually include all or a majority of the following items.

> Compressor
> Motor
> Starter
> Capacity control
> Oil cooler
> Oil pump
> Oil filter
> Oil low temperature control
> Separator-receiver
> Intake silencer
> Intake filter
> Discharge check valve
> A control system of the protective type
> (see Chapter 25)
> Air-cooled oil cooler and fan
> Air-cooled aftercooler
> Enclosing covers.

These units are compact and simple to install, requiring only a solid floor for mounting. They are relatively vibrationless. Economy will not, however, be as good as the corresponding water-cooled reciprocator. A typical unit of this type is shown in Fig. 7-C and Fig. 7-D.

Fig. 7-D.   Typical package rotary compressor without covers.

Chapter 8

Helical-Lobe Rotary Compressors

Caption Index **Page**

References

See Chapter 1, page 1-11 and Chapter 4, page 4-18.

Introduction

The helical lobe or screw compressor is presently built in three general types, each with a rather specific maximum single-stage compression ratio which approximates 2.0, 3.0, and 4.5 respectively, when handling gases having a k of 1.4. These limit single-stage atmospheric-intake units to 15, 30, and about 50 psiG maximum discharge pressure. As boosters with elevated intake, each may be offered for higher discharge pressures. These units will hereafter be called low-, intermediate- and high-pressure units.

The screw compressor is built under several patents and by a number of manufacturers who incorporate their own modifications. The information given here is believed to apply generally, but cannot be considered absolute in all cases, particularly as to details of design and materials. Only the low-pressure and high-pressure types are discussed.

Arrangement

These units are designed to be driven by induction motors, steam turbines, gas turbines, and gas or diesel engines. Some drives will be direct; others will utilize gears to obtain the best speed characteristics for both compressor and driver. The application of gears may be different for the high- and low-pressure units, since their normal compressor speeds differ greatly. V-belt drive is available for the smaller sizes.

Two staging is normally accomplished by using two closely sized individual units coupled to a common driver. As with the sliding vane-type rotary, the best theoretical interstage pressure is not always obtained because standard units are used. Efficiency is not materially affected.

General Characteristics

These are positive-displacement "constant-volume variable-pressure" machines and are quite similar to the vane-type rotary in general characteristics since they have a fixed built-in compression ratio.

They require no lubrication within the compression chamber and deliver oil-free gas. Normally, only bearings and timing gears are lubricated.

These are heavy-duty compressors and, properly applied, can operate at full load for indefinite periods. They are useful primarily for process and vacuum services for the advantage of oil-free gas; for their ability to handle moderate amounts of liquid; or, for their adaptability to efficient steam turbine drive in cases where steam power is available and relatively inexpensive.

Helical-lobe machines are best applied as base-load units when constant speed drivers are used. With variable speed drivers, capacity variations can be obtained with a proportionate reduction in power. A 50% speed reduction is the average maximum permissible, but is normally adequate for large volume applications.

Helical-lobe units can handle all commercial gases when properly fitted and corrosion problems can be solved. They are well suited for handling a dirty gas since there is no metallic contact within the casing. An abrasive dirt will cause erosion of rotors and eventual loss of efficiency. Shaft seals and bearings must be designed to prevent dirt entry.

Most helical-lobe machines can handle limited amounts of liquid but are not designed to digest slugs. In some cases, liquid is deliberately injected into the inlet to both cool and seal.

Floor space comparisons with the reciprocator are generally good, but will depend greatly on the type of reciprocating machine being considered.

Foundations are simple blocks sufficiently large in area to support dead weight and strong enough to maintain alignment.

Their economy is not as good as the reciprocating unit of comparable size except in the lower pressure operating range.

They usually require inlet and discharge silencers to reduce the operating noise to acceptable limits.

Their ability to operate at other than original design conditions should be checked by the manufacturer if any change is contemplated.

A check valve in the discharge is usually required to prevent uncontrolled reverse operation.

Ratings

The low-pressure units are built for capacities to 12,000 cfm for a maximum of 15 psiG as air compressors (atmospheric intake). As vacuum pumps, they will operate at best efficiency to 22″ Hg vacuum single-stage and to 26″ Hg vacuum when two-staged. Speeds of the low-pressure machines will normally range from 3600 to 1200 rpm depending upon size. Horsepowers vary up to 800.

The high-pressure machines for atmospheric intake are built to 20,000 cfm delivery at approximately 50 psiG single-stage and 180 psiG two-stage. Speeds range from 12,000 to 2500 rpm depending upon size. Maximum horsepower is about 6000. These units are also used at vacuum pumps under certain conditions.

A unit located at an altitude may be rated at a lower *maximum* discharge pressure than at sea level. It is important that the altitude of the installation be given.

Booster limits depend on conditions. The high-pressure design covered above is available to 250 psiG in standard materials.

Operating Limitations

These units are primarily designed to operate dry, with *nonlubricated* compression chambers sealed at leakage points by close clearance. There is no metal-to-metal contact within the compression space. Since these clearances must be kept open at all times, any operational factor affecting them must be limited, else there might be sufficient expansion or distortion to cause rotor contact and consequent damage. These and other limiting factors include:

1. *Discharge temperature.* Limited to prevent excessive casing distortion and rotor growth with consequent clearance change from the "cold" condition when the unit was machined and assembled.

2. *Temperature rise* (or, alternatively the average between inlet and discharge.) A limit is sometimes set to prevent excessive relative distortion between the inlet and discharge ends of the casing and excessive rotor growth. The higher-pressure units are water-jacketed to even the casing temperature. Rotors may be also cooled to permit a higher limit.

3. *Compression ratio.* It is this, with the maximum inlet temperature, which determines maximum discharge temperature.

4. *Pressure rise* (or differential across the unit.) This acts to deflect the rotor and shaft. Any bending changes the original clearances.

5. *Bearing Loads.* Also caused by the differential pressures to which the rotors are exposed.

The actual limits set by manufacturers will vary with their specific compressor design. Typical maximum limits for the more important factors are:

Limiting Factor	Maximum Limits	
	Low-Pressure Unit	High-Pressure Unit
Compression ratio (k of 1.4)	2.0	4.5
Discharge temperature	*340°F	**450°F
Ave. of inlet and discharge temperature	*220°F	**275°F

*With oil cooler — lower when cooler is not furnished.
**With oil-cooled rotors — lower when rotors are uncooled.
Note: Temperatures are the actual expected, not theorectical.

Maximum allowable differential pressure (pressure rise), bearing loads and casing working pressure limitations vary with unit selection.

Normally, intake temperature may be as low as minus 65°F with standard materials, provided a Charpy impact test is not required. Lubricating oil heaters may be required.

Fig. 8-A.   A typical low-pressure helical-lobe compressor.

Design — Low-Pressure

A typical *low-pressure screw-type compressor* is shown in Fig. 8-A and sectionally in Fig. 8-B. This type has an air-cooled cast iron *housing*. The end housings are precision-fitted bearing carriers and also contain the shaft seals.

Rotors are normally precision-machined annealed cast iron, pressed and keyed to steel shafts. Ball or roller bearings support each shaft, one bearing on each end being designed to carry the thrust load and control the rotor end play.

The rotors are timed by helical gears. Only the gears and bearings are lubricated, the oil being effectively prevented from entering the compression chamber by an open space between it and each bearing chamber.

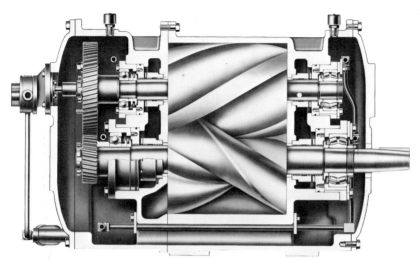

Fig. 8-B.   Vertical section of a low-pressure helical-lobe compressor.

Lubrication of small units is by oil slingers mounted on the main rotor shaft that dip into a reservoir in each end of the housing. Larger machines have an attached gear pump to force oil to all bearings and gears. An oil cooler is provided when machine size or operating temperatures necessitate. Force feed systems include an oil filter.

Standard shaft seals are of the labyrinth type as shown typically in Fig. 8-C. These can be arranged for purging or venting or both. Mechanical shaft seals are available, but force feed lubrication must be included.

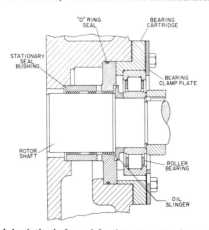

Fig. 8-C.   Typical labyrinth shaft seal for low-pressure helical-lobe compressor.

Design—High-pressure

A typical *high-pressure unit* is as shown in Fig. 8-D.   Fig. 8-E-1 and 8-E-2 show horizontal and vertical sections.

The water-jacketed *casing* is normally made of annealed cast iron and the *rotors* are precision-milled from bar stock or forgings.   Each rotor and shaft is one piece.   For operation at higher temperatures, the rotors are internally oil-cooled.   The seals and bearing assemblies are carried in the housing or in a closely-fitted end piece.

Fig. 8-D.   Typical high-pressure helical-lobe compressor.

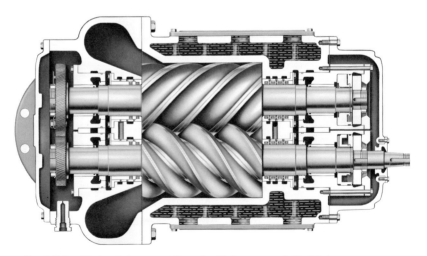

Fig. 8-E-1.   Horizontal cross section of a high-pressure helical-lobe compressor.

Bearings are normally of the sleeve type. The discharge end of each shaft carries a fully equalizing tilting-pad thrust bearing to take thrust and restrict end play.

Helical *timing gears* are normally used to prevent any contact between rotors.

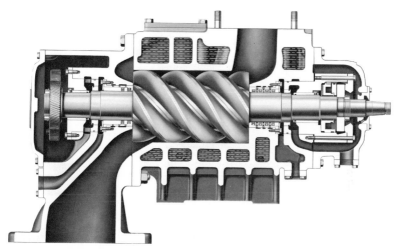

Fig. 8-E-2.   Vertical cross section of a high-pressure helical-lobe compressor.

The *lubricating oil system* (required for gears and bearings only) is normally a separately mounted package including a motor-driven pump, oil filter, oil cooler, low-oil-pressure and high-oil-temperature shutdown switches and a reservoir. This system also supplies oil for rotor cooling when used.

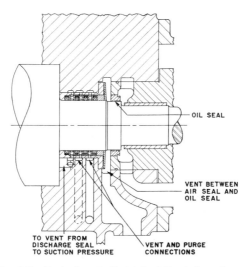

Fig. 8-F.   Typical controlled labyrinth shaft seal.

Standard *shaft seals*, Fig. 8-F, are of the floating ring controlled labyrinth design. Each ring is one piece of steel-backed carbon. Vent and purge connections are available as shown. The rings, although free to rotate, are actually stationary and are centered around the shaft during compressor operation. Other seal arrangements are available.

Cooling water is required for the casing jackets, the lubricating oil cooler, and the oil cooler on the speed up gear. The quantity will vary with size and cannot readily be prorated to bhp since its purpose is to even casing and rotor temperatures rather than to improve economy by actually cooling the gas. The cooling surface available within the compressor is not sufficient for appreciable gas cooling.

Couplings

Couplings are usually of the high-speed gear type with spacers to facilitate maintenance and repair without moving gear, driver, or compressor. They should be balanced dynamically.

Liquid Injection

While injection of liquid for reduction of compression temperature or more perfect sealing of clearances is possible, it is not recommended for normal compressor service. When the gas handled is such that normal discharge temperatures under dry compression will cause polymerization or a build-up of solids in the unit, liquid injection may be considered. Special fittings and accessories are required and care must be exercised in operation.

Vacuum pumps are normally dry, but may be specially fitted for liquid injection (usually water) where it is necessary or desirable. This permits higher vacuums, but has some possible limitations that should be understood. These involve drainage, corrosion, power consumption, etc. For example, the suction line should have a drain with an automatic check valve so that it will drain immediately when the unit is shut down. Special drying out and protection against corrosion may be necessary if shut down for a long time. Since power consumption increases with quantity of liquid handled, it is wise to limit liquid injection.

Economy

The screw type compressor is less efficient than a heavy duty *lubricated* reciprocating machine at the higher pressure levels in its range, but equals or exceeds in economy at low pressures. Based on air, at atmospheric intake, the bhp/100 of the helical lobe unit will compare roughly as follows:

Low- pressure unit — at 10 psiG or lower —equal to or better than reciprocator.
at 15 psiG — 22 to 15% higher.

High-pressure unit — at 20 psiG or lower — equal to or better than reciprocator.
at 30 to 50 psiG (single stage) — 24 to 7% higher.
at 100 psiG (two stage — 250 HP to 2000 HP) — 20 to 10% higher.

The larger the screw-type machine, the nearer the approach to reciprocator efficiency.

If the screw-type machine is being considered because of its oil-free discharge characteristic, the comparison should be with a nonlubricated reciprocating unit and the above percentages will be reduced slightly.

Capacity Control

These helical-lobe compressors may use automatic start-and-stop control, if applicable, provided proper automatic starting unloader systems are supplied.

Variable-speed control within limits is possible with steam turbine drivers, proper attention being paid to the minimum speeds applicable to the particular unit and to the conditions involved. These machines must not be run below a given speed dependent on the design and rating. The average minimum is near 50%, below which they will overheat.

Constant-speed control is most commonly obtained by either blow-off to atmosphere or bypassing to intake of unneeded compressed gas. By-passed gas must be cooled before return to intake. "Unloaded" horsepower will be the same as at full load. Modifications of the blow-off method permit some power saving in certain cases where demand is below 50% for extended periods and there is a large storage system.

Throttling of intake may be used for compressor capacity control purposes provided the intake is never throttled to the point where the discharge temperature becomes excessive. These machines must *never* be operated with a closed intake (dead-ended). Temperatures would then become so high that the machine would be damaged. Throttling will reduce the power input on units with high built-in compression ratio, but on those with low built-in ratio, power will increase. There is some saving in power when used with two-stage machines. Throttling control should be applied only under the guidance of the manufacturer.

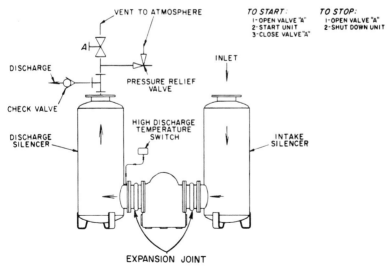

Fig. 8-G. Starting unloading and piping arrangement for a low-pressure helical-lobe compressor having atmospheric air intake.

Starting Unloading

Manufacturers generally recommend that all units be unloaded for starting if there is any pressure on the discharge. Unloading should be by blow-off vent, where possible, or otherwise a bypass from discharge to intake. A cooler must be included in the bypass if the starting cycle last any length of time or if the bypass is also used for capacity control. The bypass or vent can be sized for 12,000 ft/min velocity at inlet pressure or 5 psiG, whichever is lower. When the intake is more than 5 psiG, some manufacturers recommend that the compressor and system pressure between the check valve and the inlet stop valve be reduced to that value by venting the space before start-up. Fig. 8-G and Fig. 8-H show the piping for typical low-pressure units with atmospheric and elevated inlet pressures.

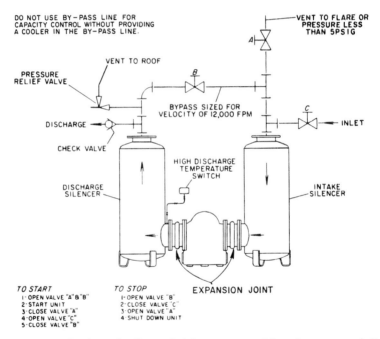

Fig. 8-H.   Starting unloading and piping arrangement for a low-pressure helical-lobe compressor having an elevated inlet pressure or handling a non-ventable gas.

Piping

Piping to and from these units should be sized no smaller than the machine connections. Reduction to steady-flow sizes is permissible beyond silencers or when a point is reached where flow is pulsationless.

It is important, as on all compressors, that the piping be well supported and accurately aligned with the machine inlet and discharge. The pipe must also be well anchored at the point of connection to any expansion joint used. See Piping in Chapter 18.

Expansion Joints

Low-pressure machines should be fitted with expansion joints unless excepted by the manufacturer. Housings on these units are more subject to distortion. Distortion from piping improperly aligned or improperly supported or anchored could change clearances seriously.

High-pressure units usually can be piped up without expansion joints, provided care is exercised in aligning, anchoring, and supporting the pipe, and the manufacturer's approval is obtained.

Design and materials of expansion joints must be based on actual temperatures and pressures to be encountered.

Check Valve

A check valve should be provided between the machines and the discharge system to prevent reverse operation (motoring) unless the system is such that the pressure immediately falls to zero when the compressor stops. Failure to do this could cause severe damage. Consult the manufacturer.

Safety Valve

A safety valve capable of passing full capacity must be placed in the discharge piping ahead of any shutoff valve to prevent excess pressure build-up if the unit should be started with the discharge and unloader valves closed. If above 15 psiG it should be sized and built to the ASME Code.

Safety Devices

Several safety devices are often used. Mandatory on all units is a high-gas-discharge-temperature switch and, when force-feed lubrication is used, a low-oil-pressure switch, each arranged for automatic shutdown. Also recommended on some units are a high-oil-temperature switch (force-feed lubricated machines), and occasionally low-oil-level and high-cooling water-temperature switches for either alarm or shutdown.

Silencers

Although these units are not quiet, the noise level can be kept within acceptable limits with silencers, usually required on both inlet and discharge. Silencers are pressure vessels and should be designed and built to the ASME Code when operating at pressures above 15 psiG.

Inlet Air Filter

An air inlet filter should be installed on all open intake installations. See Chapter 18.

Typical Piping Diagrams

To illustrate required equipment arrangement on a typical low-pressure unit, see Fig. 8-G and Fig. 8-H.

Similar diagrams for control and starting unloading on a typical high-pressure machine are shown in Fig. 8-I and Fig. 8-J. The upper layout is for motor drive at constant speed with bypass control. The lower layout includes steam turbine drive and variable-speed control to minimum speed, then bypass to zero capacity.

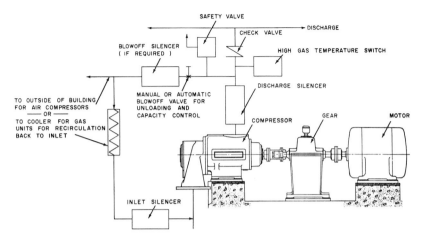

Fig. 8-I. Typical piping diagram for a motor-driven high-pressure helical-lobe compressor fitted with bypass capacity control.

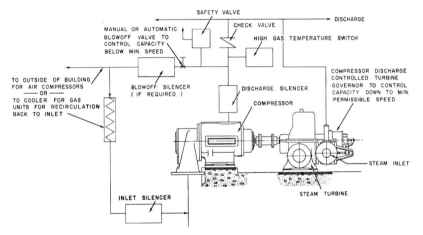

Fig. 8-J. Typical piping diagram for a turbine-driven high-pressure helical-lobe compressor, fitted with variable speed capacity control to minimum allowed, then bypass control to zero capacity.

The Helical-Lobe-Type Portable Air Compressor

This type, in high-pressure design, is used in several sizes of gasoline- and diesel-engine-driven portable compressors by a number of manufacturers. All are oil flooded for sealing and cooling. Some omit the timing gears and drive the gate rotor from the main rotor directly since lubrication is assured. The lubrication and cooling system is described in Chapter 11. Since the discharge temperature is reduced materially by the oil cooling, higher compression ratios are permissible and single-stage units may be offered for 100 psiG discharge.

Chapter 9

Dynamic Compressors

(Continued)

General Comments

The dynamic compressor is probably the most rapidly developing compressor type. As users demand larger single unit installations for reasons of cost, high availability, and operating economy, the field for the dynamic unit is becoming broader. The rapidly extending pressure range for which these units are available, together with the development of smaller sizes, is making this unit useful in areas that formerly were best served by other designs.

The centrifugal compressor is the most prevalent design in this growth, although the axial-flow unit has not been far behind in the large-capacity, moderate-pressure area.

References

　　1. Chapter 1, pages 1-12 through 1-16;

　　2. Chapter 3, pages 3-21 through 3-23; and,

　　3. Chapter 4, pages 4-21 through 4-31.

Definitions (Mechanical)

BASE PLATE is a metal structure on which the compressor and possibly the driver are mounted. (See Sole Plate).

BOOSTER is a compressor operating with an elevated intake pressure. The term frequently connotes single stage, but this is not a necessary requirement.

CASING is the pressure-containing stationary element that encloses the rotor and associated internal components. It usually includes integral inlet and discharge connections (nozzles). Casing supports and means for lifting are provided.

DIAPHRAGM is a stationary element between stages of a multistage centrifugal compressor. It may include guide vanes for directing gas to the impeller of the succeeding stage.

DIAPHRAGM COOLING is a method of removing heat from the flowing medium by circulation of a coolant in passages built into the diaphragm.

DIFFUSER is a stationary passageway following an impeller in which velocity energy imparted to the gas by the impeller is converted into static pressure.

DYNAMIC COMPRESSOR is any rotary continuous flow unit in which the mechanical action of rotating vanes or impellers imparts velocity and pressure to the flowing medium. The velocity energy is than converted to additional pressure. The term *blower* has been used for dynamic units in the lower pressure range, but today all dynamic units are known generally as compressors, whether centrifugal or axial.

EXHAUSTER is a term sometimes applied to a dynamic compressor in which the inlet pressure is less than atmospheric.

GUIDE VANES are nonrotating elements that may be fixed or adjustable and provide a desired flow direction to the inlet of an impeller.

IMPELLER is that part of the rotating element that imparts momentum to the gas by aerodynamic forces. The impeller may be open, semi-closed, or closed.

ROTOR is the rotating element composed of impeller(s) and shaft, and may include shaft sleeves, rotating seal parts, and thrust collar.

SEALS are devices used between rotating and stationary parts to minimize gas leakage between areas of unequal pressures.

SHAFT is that part of the rotating element on which the rotating parts are mounted and through which energy is transmitted from the prime mover.

SHAFT BEARINGS are lubricated stationary parts which support and radially locate the compressor shaft.

SHAFT SLEEVES are parts that may be used to position the impeller on the shaft and to protect the shaft.

SOLE PLATE is a mounted pad, usually embedded in concrete, on which the compressor is mounted. (See Base Plate).

THRUST BALANCING DEVICE (DRUM, PISTON, OR DISC) is that part(s) utilizing gas pressure to counteract the thrust developed by the impellers. Any residual thrust may be carried by the thrust bearing.

THRUST BEARING is a bearing that transmits the residual axial thrust of the rotor to the shaft bearing housing and maintains the axial position of the rotor.

VOLUTE is a stationary, spirally shaped passageway in the casing that collects the flow leaving an impeller or diffuser and converts velocity energy into static pressure.

Definitions (Conditions and Performance)

CORROSIVE GAS (See page 2-6)

DRY GAS (See page 2-7)

NONCORROSIVE GAS (See page 2-9)

COMPRESSOR RATED POINT shall be at the highest speed required to meet any specified operating condition, and shall be at the rated capacity required by compressor design to meet all operating points. This capacity point shall be selected by the manufacturer to best encompass the specified operating condition within the scope of the expected performance curve.

NORMAL OPERATING POINT is the point at which normal operation is expected and optimum efficiency is desired. This is generally the guarantee point.

POLYTROPIC HEAD (See page 2-10)

INLET PRESSURE (See page 2-9)

DISCHARGE PRESSURE (See page 2-6)

RATED DISCHARGE PRESSURE is that corresponding to conditions and gas characteristics that establish Compressor Rated Point and 100% Speed curve.

MAXIMUM OPERATING PRESSURE is the pressure at the worst simultaneous combination of gas properties and operating conditions resulting in the highest discharge pressure. In determining the maximum operating pressure, the speed shall be 100% Speed curve for constant speed motor drive or, Trip Speed curve for variable speed or turbine drive.

CASING DESIGN PRESSURE is the highest pressure that can safely be permitted to exist in the compressor. It shall never be less than Rated Discharge Pressure, but may be less than Maximum Operating Pressure by agreement with the user, provided the compressor is suitably protected.

CRITICAL SPEED is any speed equal to a natural frequency of a part of the compressor.

IMPELLER TIP SPEED is the velocity of a point on the outside diameter of the impeller.

MAXIMUM CONTINUOUS SPEED* is the upper limit of operating speed of the compressor. It may be higher than normal or 100% speed if the manufacturer and user have agreed to an additional speed margin.

NORMAL SPEED* corresponds to the requirements of the normal operating point, usually at maximum efficiency and a guarantee point.

100% SPEED* corresponds to the compressor rated point. It may be greater than or equal to normal speed. The 100% speed of motor-driven compressors shall be the full-load motor speed times the ratio of the gear (if any).

TRIP SPEED shall be approximately 110% of maximum continuous speed for *steam-turbine-driven* units, or 105% of maximum continuous speed for *gas-turbine-driven* units.

Note:—Under some circumstances, Normal Speed, 100% Speed, and Maximum Continuous Speed may be identical.

STABLE RANGE is the flow range, at constant head (pressure), between maximum capacity and surge limit.

SURGE LIMIT is any capacity below which, at a given head (pressure), compressor operation becomes unstable.

INLET TEMPERATURE is total gas temperature at the inlet flange of the compressor.

DISCHARGE TEMPERATURE is the total gas temperature at the discharge flange of the compressor.

TOTAL TEMPERATURE is the temperature that would be measured if a flowing gas stream were adiabatically brought to rest.

WET GAS (See page 2-12)

Fig. 9-A illustrates schematically certain of these definitions.

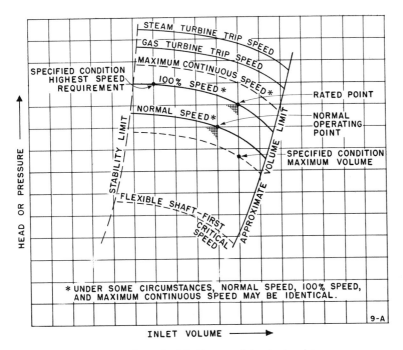

Fig. 9-A.   Illustration of certain definitions applying to dynamic compressors.

General Types of Centrifugal Compressors

A common method of classifying centrifugal compressors is by number of impellers and casing design. The table on the next page shows three general types. Approximate maximum ratings shown are intended to project in some degree the range of discharge pressure, capacity, and bhp available in each type, but the figures in one column do not necessarily go with the figures in the other columns. Each stands by itself.

	Approximate Maximum Ratings		
Casing Type	Pressure psiG	Capacity Inlet CFM	BHP
A. Sectionalized Usually multistage	10*	20,000*	600*
B. Horizontally split Single stage (double suction) Multistage	15* 1,000	650,000* 200,000*	10,000* 35,000
C. Vertically split Single stage (single suction) Overhung Pipeline Multistage	30* 1,200 over 5,500	250,000* 25,000 20,000	10,000* 20,000 15,000

*Based on air at atmospheric intake conditions

Sectionalized Casing

These small units are shown in Fig. 9-B and 9-C. Except in the larger sizes or with greater number of stages, impellers are usually mounted on the extended motor shaft. The machine is a bolted assembly of similar sections to obtain the desired number of stages. Casings are of fabricated steel or cast iron.

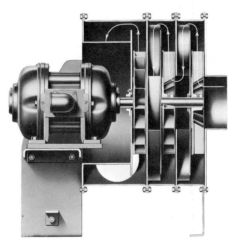

Fig. 9-B. Simple three-stage sectionalized compressor with rotor overhung on the motor shaft.

Such machines are simple and require limited supervision and maintenance. Within their operating range, economy is quite good. Capacity control is normally by blast gate. See page 9-31 for control types and operation.

This design is used extensively in supplying air for combustion in furnaces, ovens, and similar applications, as well as in pneumatic conveying of materials, agitation and aeration, and many miscellaneous applications requiring relatively low pressure and small volumes.

Sectionalized units are normally built to standard sizes and ratings.

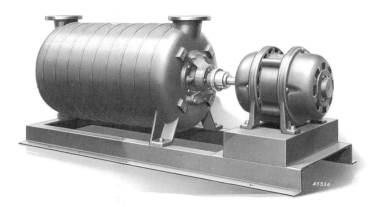

Fig. 9-C. Multistage sectionalized compressor with coupled motor.

Horizontally Split Casing

This is the preferred construction for the larger multistage units and for some single stage machines, both within certain pressure limitations. The casing is split on the horizontal center line, the top and bottom halves being bolted and doweled together. The interior, including shaft, impellers,

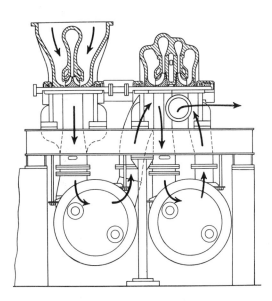

Fig. 9-D. Series-tandem arrangement of horizontally-split, two-casing air compressor with double suction first stage unit and intercoolers mounted beneath the compressor.

bearings, and seals is readily accessible for inspection and repair by removal of the top half. The casing is usually of cast construction (iron or steel). Other materials may be used where necessary.

Fig. 9-D shows a machine consisting of a single-stage double-suction casing in series with a two-stage casing, both being horizontally split. Asssembly shown is an air compressor with intercooling between stages.

Fig. 9-E illustrates accessibility of the horizontally split machine when the top is removed. The unit shown is similar in design to that in Fig. 9-D. Note the double suction first-stage at the left.

Fig. 9-E.   View of a similar compressor to Fig. 9-D, with the casing open.

Fig.   9-F.   Horizontally-split   compressors   totalling 16,000 hp on catalytic cracking service in an oil refinery.

Fig. 9-F shows more conventional horizontally split multistage compressors. The large unit delivers 123,000 inlet cfm of air at 19.5 psiG, requiring 10,000 bhp. The gas compressor is a tandem arrangement of two multistage units compressing 20,800 cfm from 4 to 205 psiG and requiring 6400 hp. The interior of a typical machine is shown in Fig. 9-G. These are used for a wide range of air and gas applications and are well-suited to process service.

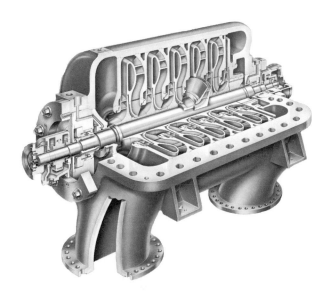

Fig. 9-G.   Internal arrangement of a horizontally-split, air-cooled, multistage compressor.

Vertically Split Casing

This is available in three distinct single-stage and two multistage designs. The former include

1. Low pressure with impeller overhung on motor shaft. Conditions are limited by motor speed. See Fig. 9-H. Fabricated steel casing construction is shown, but cast iron is also used.

2. Impeller overhung on a shaft carried by compressor bearings. The casing may be of fabricated steel or cast iron. See Fig. 9-I and Fig. 9-J.

3. High-pressure booster compressors (pipeline-type). See Fig. 9-K.

The multistage designs include

1. Specialized machines for pipeline service.

2. The more conventional type adapted from the horizontally split compressors.

The overhung impeller units are built in large capacities and horsepowers. See table, page 9-6. Steam-turbine drivers are often used. These units are installed in combustion processes, ventilation, conveying, and miscellaneous low- and intermediate-pressure applications for both air and

Fig. 9-H. Typical single-stage, low-pressure, compressor with overhung rotor and vertically-split casing.

Fig. 9-I. A large low-pressure single-stage compressor with coupled driver and cast iron casing.

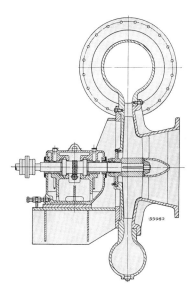

Fig. 9-J. Sectional view of a unit similar to Fig. 9-I.

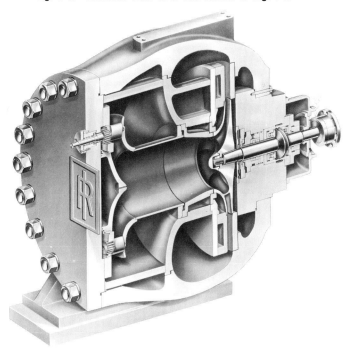

Fig. 9-K. Sectional view of a vertically-split single-stage natural gas pipe line booster.

The photograph above is an installation view of a 100 PSIG plant-air centrifugal compressor. This particular unit is rated at 2100 CFM free air compressed
to 100 PSIG. It has four stages of compression with integral intercoolers and
aftercooler. The opposite page shows the internal design. Units are usually
motor driven, but turbine drive can be supplied.

There are a variety of designs available for this service using either three or
four stages of compression. The nominal rating is at 100-110 PSIG for air-power
service, but 125 PSIG can be provided. Capacities range from approximately
1200 CFM to 25,000 CFM, with larger sizes in view if needed.

Capacity control for constant speed machines may be a full load - no load
type with an inlet shut-off valve and a discharge blow-off valve to atmosphere.
This may be supplemented with an intake throttling modulator which maintains
constant discharge pressure by reducing the capacity gradually down to a point
close to surge before the blow-off valve modulates open.

These units are of the package type. The unit is shipped with all components
including control and protective devices assembled and mounted on a common
base plate that may also be the oil reservoir for the lubrication system.

Methods of driving the impellers vary somewhat. The unit shown has a
single bull gear driven by the motor. Each impeller shaft is geared to operate at
its optimum performance speed.

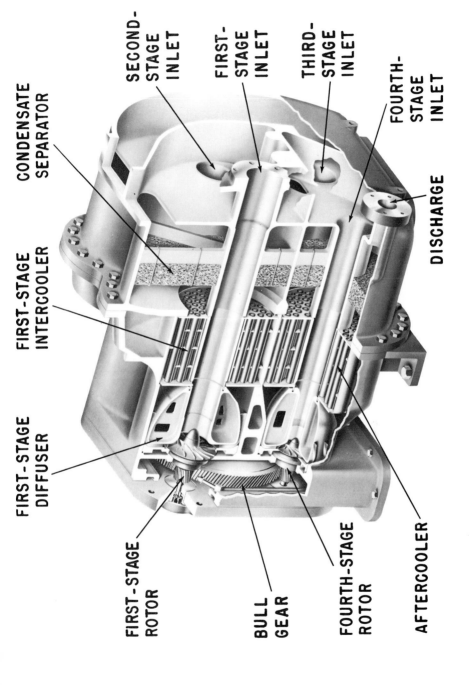

SECOND-STAGE INLET

FIRST-STAGE INLET

THIRD-STAGE INLET

FOURTH-STAGE INLET

CONDENSATE SEPARATOR

DISCHARGE

FIRST-STAGE INTERCOOLER

FIRST-STAGE DIFFUSER

FIRST-STAGE ROTOR

BULL GEAR

FOURTH-STAGE ROTOR

AFTERCOOLER

gas. When fitted with constant air weight control they are particularly adapted to furnishing combustion air to cupolas melting iron for castings. See page 9-33.

The pipeline unit shown in Fig. 9-K has a cast steel casing. It may also be built with two or more stages.

Fig. 9-L. A series-tandem arrangement of vertically-split compressors on refinery service handling hydrogen.

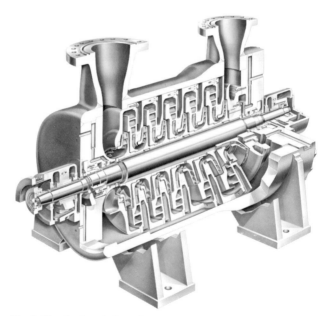

Fig. 9-M.   Sectional view of a vertically-split multistage compressor.

Multistage vertically split casings are used for pressures where the horizontally split joint becomes inadequate. The limiting pressure will depend upon many factors including the gravity of the gas and the size of the casing. Hydrogen-rich gases, for example, are difficult to contain at elevated pressures unless the gasket is confined as with this design. Casing materials vary from cast iron or steel to steel forgings.

Fig. 9-L shows two such units handling hydrogen rich gas and Fig. 9-M a section through a six-stage unit. For dismantling, the inner assembly slides out on a special cradle.

This has made possible use of centrifugal compressors in many services where a reciprocator would previously have been mandatory. An example is the repressuring of certain oil sands for greater oil recovery. Fig. 9-N shows such a plant with gas entering the compression system at 10 psiG and leaving at 1950 psiG. Both horizontally and vertically split units are used in this train of ten compressors operating in seven stages.

Application of Centrifugal Compressors

Centrifugal compressors are applied in a great many areas of industry, although the majority fall in a category that might be classed as processing. The following tabulation shows many of the principal fields and general applications involved. Gases handled vary widely, even including hydrogen rich (low specific gravity) mixtures in certain low ratio applications.

Industry or Application	Service or Process	Typical Gas Handled
Chemical and Petrochemical		
Acetylene	Oxidation	Oxygen
	Gas recovery	Acetylene
Butadiene	Catalytic regeneration	Air
	Gas compression	Hydrocarbons
	Refrigeration	Propane
Chlorine	Liquifaction	Chlorine
Ethylene	Feed gas	Hydrocarbons
	Refrigeration	Various HC
Ethylene oxide	Feed gas	HC mixture
Nitric acid	Oxidation	Air
Refining	Catalytic reforming	Various HC mixtures
	Alkylation	Hydrocarbons
	Gas recovery	Various HC mixtures
	Catalytic cracking	Air and HC mixture
	Fluid coking	Air
	Refrigeration	Propane and other vapors
Sulphuric acid	Contact process	Air
Synthetic ammonia	Raw gas supply	HC mixtures
	Air supply	Air
	Synthesis gas	Syn-gas
	Recirculation	Syn-gas with ammonia
Fractionation		
Air separation	Main supply	Air
	Oxygen distribution	Oxygen
	Nitrogen distribution	Nitrogen
	Refrigeration	Nitrogen

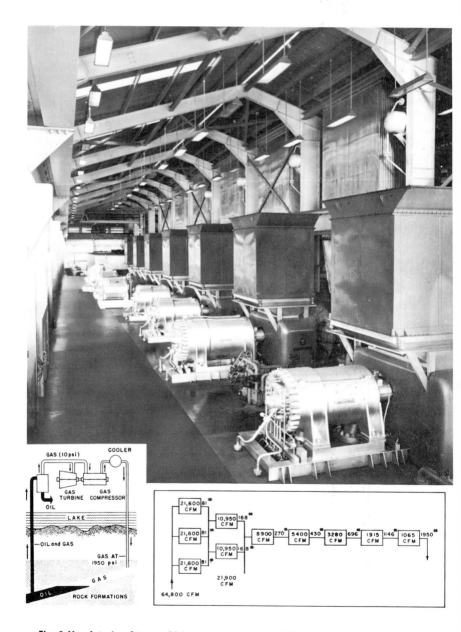

Fig. 9-N.　A train of ten multistage compressors handling natural gas on repressuring service in crude oil production. The ten units are arranged for seven steps of compression. All are gas-turbine driven. Final pressure on this group is 1950 psiG.

Industry or Application	Service or Process	Typical Gas Handled
Iron and steel		
Blast furnace	Combustion	Air
	Off gas	Blast furnace gas
Bessemer convertor	Oxidation	Air
Cupola	Combustion	Air
Coke oven	Compressing	Coke oven gas
	Exhausting	Coke oven gas
Mining and Metallurgy		
Power	For tools and machinery	Air
Furnaces	Copper and nickel purification	Air
	Pelletizing (Iron Ore concentration)	Air
Natural Gas		
Production	Repressuring oil wells	Natural gas
Distribution	Transmission	Natural gas
Processing	Natural gasoline separation	Natural gas
	Refrigeration	Propane and methane
Refrigeration		
Chemical	Various processes	Butane, propane, ethylene, ammonia, special refrigerants
Industrial and commercial	Air conditioning	Special refrigerants
Utilities		
Steam generators	Soot blowing	Air
	Combustion	Air
	Cyclone furnaces	Air
City gas	Manufacturing	Fuel gas
	Distribution	Fuel gas
Miscellaneous		
Sewage treatment	Agitation	Air
Industrial power	Power for tools and machines	Air
Paper making	Fourdrinier vacuum	Air and water vapor
Research	Wind tunnels	Air
	Engine research	Air
Contracting	Tunnel ventilation	Air
Material handling	Conveying	Air
Gas engines	Supercharging	Air
	Scavenging (2 cycle)	Air
Food	Agitation and bacterial growth	Air
Pharamaceutical	Agitation and bacterial growth	Air
Glass	Bottle molding	Air
Plant power	Instruments	Air
	Operate tools	Air

Characteristics of the Centrifugal

The centrifugal has a limited stable operating range. This may affect the economics of operation at part load. The minimum capacity may vary from 45 to 90% of rated capacity.

The centrifugal must be selected for the worst combination of conditions that exist at a given time and must be controlled to meet other requirements.

These are basically large capacity machines with compression ratio per stage dependent on gas density.

For commercial machines, an *exit* volume of approximately 300 to 400 cfm from the last impeller is generally considered the lower limit. Small specialty high-speed units have lower exit volume limits.

Operating speeds are high compared with other compressors. 50,000 to 100,000 rpm is considered in the aircraft and space industries where weight is a major factor. Most commercial centrifugal units operate at 20,000 rpm or lower, with the trend upward. The problems of bearings and their lubrication, as well as vibration and balancing, become more significant at higher speeds.

Centrifugal compressors are well suited for direct connection to steam- or gas-turbine drivers which permit variable-speed control.

These machines have a high *availability* factor (ratio of hours they are available for operation to the 8760 total hours/year). Under good conditions, they frequently operate without shutdown for 2 or 3 years.

Total maintenance and attendance costs on centrifugals are usually less than on an equivalent reciprocator.

These units provide smooth nonpulsating flow within the stable operating range.

Uncooled centrifugal compressors generally have a lower efficiency than reciprocating compressors. At very low compression ratios, the centrifugal may be more efficient.

Centrifugals require small and relatively inexpensive foundations as compared with a reciprocator for the same capacity. There are no inertia forces.

They generally have greater volume capacity per unit of building space than corresponding reciprocators.

Bearings and seals can be designed so that no oil can enter the gas stream. If intake gas is oil-free, discharge will be.

Operating life of centrifugal compressors can be affected by entrained liquid and solids. Controlled liquid injection for cooling and cleaning may be considered in design. When dirty gas must be handled, open-type impellers have been successful.

Centrifugals can be operated at 600 to 1000°F if proper materials are selected and provision made to maintain running clearances.

Fig. 9-O. Open, semiclosed, and closed impeller designs.

Major Centrifugal Design Details
Impellers

Impellers may be classed as open, semiclosed and closed. See Fig. 9-O. The open and semiclosed impellers may be cast, milled from a forging, or built up by welding.

Closed impellers are built using one of the following methods.

1. Three-piece welded, consisting of alloy steel vanes welded between a forged steel disc and forged steel cover;
2. Three-piece riveted, consisting of preformed alloy steel vanes riveted between a forged steel disc and forged steel cover;
3. Two-piece milled and riveted, consisting of blades milled integrally with a forged steel disc that is assembled with a forged steel cover by riveting;
4. Two-piece cast, having a riveted forged steel cover on a steel casting forming the disc and blades; and,
5. Single-piece cast, having a single aluminum, carbon, or alloy steel casting for the entire impeller.

Effect of Impeller Vane Exit Angle

Impellers can be classified by the direction of vane curvature, this being allied with the vane exit angle. Vanes are either forward curved, radial, or backward curved. Only the last two are normally used in centrifugal compressors.

Proper selection of vane exit angle determines to a considerable degree the shape of the characteristic curve as well as the head rise and efficiency. The vane exit angle may vary from 15 to 90 degrees from the tangent in normal commercial designs. A greater than 90 degree angle gives forward curved vanes. These are not used commercially on dynamic compressors, although they are used on some types of fans.

Fig. 9-P shows the comparison between a radial 90 degree exit angle and one of 45 degrees. On these charts, lines AB are theoretical head

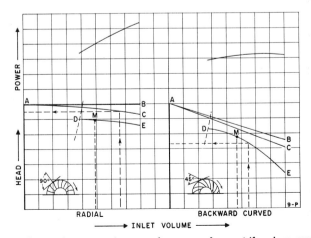

Fig. 9-P.   Effect of vane angle on performance of a centrifugal compressor.

versus capacity curves (no losses). Friction losses are represented by the difference between AB and AC, while circulatory and shock losses form the area between AC and the resultant head capacity curve DE. Point D is the maximum head or surge limit, the stable operating range lying to the right. Point M is maximum efficiency.

Speaking generally, the backward curved vane impeller will be more efficient than an impeller with radial vanes. The former also will have wider stable operating range at the same impeller diameter and speed, but will produce less pressure rise.

Impeller Testing and Balancing

Throughout manufacture, each impeller is subjected to extensive material tests and inspections. After the finish machining it is statically and dynamically balanced and given a centrifugal test at a speed above normal. Fabricated impellers are usually tested at 115 percent of maximum allowable speed when a steam turbine is the driver and 110 percent of maximum allowable speed when a gas turbine or electric motor is the driver. This test speed should be as agreed upon before purchase.

Diaphragms

Diaphragms are the dividing walls between individual stages in a multistage compressor. Fig. 9-G shows how each diaphragm (one per stage) forms one side of the discharge diffuser for one impeller and the intake passage to the next impeller. The contour and finish of the passages are important in compressor performance.

Individual diaphragms on both horizontal and vertically split casings are usually horizontally split. They are uncooled on vertically split machines, but may be internally water cooled on some horizontally split units. This is often done when the gas might reach a temperature that would be critical in an uncooled compressor. It is also done where it is possible, through cooling, to reduce the number of stages and in some cases to use one cooled casing instead of two uncooled casings.

In water-cooled diaphragms, the water circuits are normally separate for the top and bottom casing halves. Rapid flow is obtained by suitable manifolding. The water must be clean, pure and nonscaling, and should be delivered at not more than 85°F and 100 psiG. About 75 psiG is required for full flow through the circuit. When bad water conditions exist, a separate closed circuit cooling system should be used.

Cast iron or aluminum is normally used, although cast steel, special alloys, or cast bronze may be furnished because of high temperature, high pressure differential, or corrosive elements in the gas.

Interstage Packings

Areas in which leakage may flow from one stage downstream to the next are where the shaft passes through diaphragms and also around the impeller eye. Labyrinth packing rings, normally of a special aluminum alloy, are mounted in the diaphragms at these points. This material will yield without damaging rotating parts or rendering the packing ineffective. See Fig. 9-R.

Rotor Assembly

The assembly is relatively simple for the overhung single-stage design as illustrated in Fig. 9-J and 9-K. A multistage unit is somewhat more complex. The rotor or complete rotating element is composed of a steel shaft, shaft sleeves or spacers, impellers, impeller mounting rings (if used), balancing drum, thrust collar, and coupling. Fig. 9-Q pictures a seven-stage rotor assembly.

Fig. 9-Q. Typical seven-stage rotor assembly showing the balancing drum at the left.

The impellers are either shrunk on the shaft (smaller impellers only) or pressed over support rings of special metal that permit disassembly without danger of shaft damage. Methods vary with the manufacturer. The impellers are spaced by shaft sleeves that also protect the shaft from corrosion, erosion, or mechanical wear.

Balancing Drum

A single flow impeller is unbalanced; it has inlet pressure on one side and discharge pressure on the other. Means must be provided to balance the force exerted toward the inlet side. The usual method is to install a balancing drum at the discharge end of the assembly as shown in Fig. 9-R.

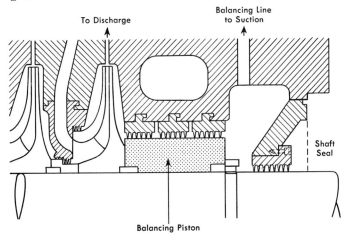

Fig. 9-R. Detail of various labyrinth seals and balancing drum arrangement with respect to impellers.

Discharge pressure is applied to the inboard end of this piston and the outlet end is piped to inlet. The differential force thus acts in an opposite direction to the forces acting on the impellers. The piston is sized to nearly balance at normal conditions, but is supplemented by an axial thrust bearing that maintains proper rotor position and takes the unbalanced load.

Double suction and "back-to-back" impellers (those mounted so that their thrusts oppose each other) normally do not require a balancing drum. A double suction impeller is shown at the left of Fig. 9-E.

Leakage across the balancing piston is controlled by a labyrinth packing. Both shaft seals are limited by this arrangement to sealing against inlet pressure.

After assembly the entire rotor is dynamically balanced.

Couplings are usually all-steel, flexible, sealed or continuously lubricated, gear type, dynamically balanced prior to assembly.

Vibration and Balance

The assembled rotor must be balanced dynamically before being installed in the casing. This is done to limit vibration at operating speeds and to prevent undue vibration at any critical speeds through which the machine may have to pass in starting and stopping.

Critical Speeds

Shafts (with the assembled parts) are known as *stiff* shafts if they always operate below the lowest critical speed. Most centrifugal compressors cannot do this and have *flexible* shafts. They are designed to keep the normal operating speeds away from any predictable critical speed. Flexible shaft compressors may operate through one or more of the lower criticals when starting up or shutting down. Care must be exercised that these periods are as short as possible.

Drivers have critical speeds also. The combination of driver and compressor must be designed to operate smoothly within the operating speed range.

Casings

The wide variety of casing designs is dependent on many factors such as size, pressure, temperature, gas composition, and presence of corrosive elements.

Piping Connections

In most cases, alternate arrangements of inlet and discharge connections are available to permit the best installation. Connections are to ASA-B-16.5 Standards, if applicable. See Fig. 6-AO, page 6-35 and accompanying discussion.

Additional connections may be provided for withdrawal or addition of gas between stages or for withdrawal and re-entry of gas for cooling or processing when partially compressed.

Hydrostatic Tests

Any required hydrostatic tests on centrifugal compressor casings should be jointly agreed upon between purchaser and manufacturer. In many cases, on air compressors especially, hydrostatic test are waived by mutual consent. A test, if required, is at 150 percent of the design pressure.

In a large multistage unit, the intake end of the casing may not be designed for the pressure existing at the discharge end. In such case, each end (or section) may be tested separately, a bulkhead being set up within the casing at the proper point.

Journal and Thrust Bearings

The main bearings are self-aligning sleeve, ball, or roller bearings. Means for centering the rotor are provided where desirable. Bearings on most compressors are external of the casing to provide greater accesibility and to prevent lubricating oil leakage into the gas stream or contamination of the oil by the gas.

Many overhung units have the rotor mounted on the motor or turbine shaft extension. Only the driver bearings are used. These must be designed to take whatever end thrust is developed.

Coupled overhung impeller units with pedestal bearings will normally have antifriction or ring-oiled sleeve bearings. On large units, force-feed lubrication may be used.

The Kingsbury axial thrust bearing is for larger machines where thrust may become a major force. On units where the thrust forces are low, a tapered land thrust bearing may be used. At times a combination is used.

Typical journal and Kingsbury thrust bearings are shown in Fig. 9-S-1 and 9-S-2. These are generally used in horizontally and vertically split casings.

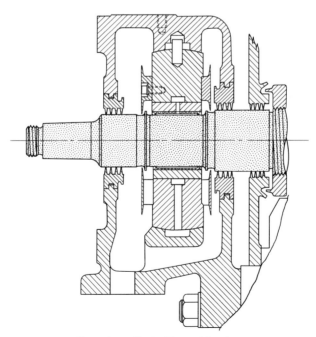

Fig. 9-S-1. Typical journal bearing.

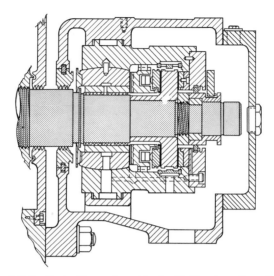

Fig. 9-S-2. Typical journal combined with Kingsbury thrust bearing.

Shaft Seals

Every centrifugal compressor must have some means of limiting or eliminating gas leakage along the shaft where it comes through the casing. Leakage will tend to be outward or inward depending on the relative atmospheric and intake pressures. Seals usually are arranged so that only intake pressure must be resisted. Even this may be substantially above atmosphere. There are many designs, those used on high-speed, high-pressure machines becoming quite sophisticated.

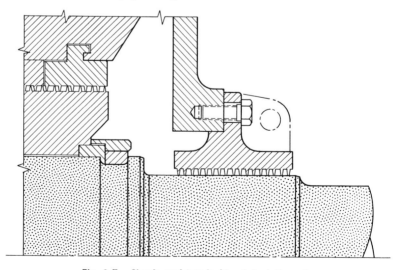

Fig. 9-T. Simple and interlocking labyrinth seals.

Labyrinth Seals

The labyrinth seal is the simplest and most prevalent on air compressors and some gas applications. See Fig. 9-T. The right-hand section shows a standard single labyrinth. The sealing action is the result of flow resistance by repeated throttling across the labyrinth teeth. On the higher pressures, an interlocking labyrinth may be used as shown in the left section of Fig. 9-T. This is a balancing drum seal that has teeth alternately on the drum itself and the packing ring.

The leakage across a labyrinth seal depends upon the number of teeth, diameter of the packing ring, clearance, and pressure to be sealed. There is always leakage and care must be taken that this leakage creates no hazard. This seal can be used on a dirty gas.

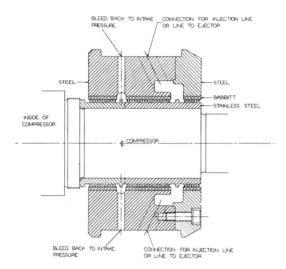

Fig. 9-U. Gas injection or ejection labyrinth seal.

It is possible to alter the labyrinth seal for many gas applications. See Fig. 9-U. The packing is exposed to full discharge pressure and a port or lantern to bleed off leakage through the first section is connected to intake. Another sectionalizing port is included that may be used to inject another gas at slightly higher than intake pressure. This prevents main gas leakage out, but permits injection gas leakage both to atmosphere and to intake. The operation may be reversed and the port connected to an ejector, maintaining a pressure below atmosphere. In this case, the main gas and atmospheric air would leak to the port and be removed.

Labyrinth seals are made so one of the two adjacent parts is relatively soft. It will yield on metal contact without damage.

Restrictive Ring Seals

This seal uses flat rings in a case mounted in a stuffing box. See Fig. 9-V. It is used only when the gas is relatively free from dirt and debris. The individual rings may be segmental and held together by a garter spring, or solid with a circumferential metallic reinforcing band.

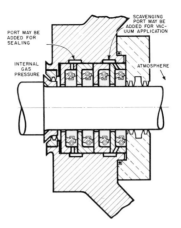

Fig. 9-V.   Restrictive ring shaft seal.

Since these rings fit more closely to the shaft than does a labyrinth tooth, leakage is well controlled.   Carbon is the usual ring material since it does not readily wear the shaft if there should be contact.   Design must be such that sides of the ring grooves are sealed.   This seal can be purged or vented like the labyrinth seal.

Mechanical Seals

To limit leakage this seal relies on continuous contact between rotating and fixed collars.   There are many designs of mechanical or contact seals, one being shown in Fig. 9-W.   This has a floating wearing or contact ring between the rotating and stationary seats that reduces the relative rubbing speed on wear areas.   These seals usually require a supply of some sealing medium.

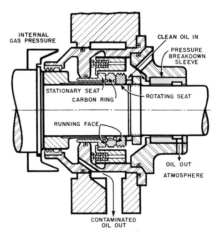

Fig. 9-W.   Mechanical (contact) shaft seal

Liquid Film Seals

The detail designs of this seal vary. Two types are shown in Fig. 9-X and 9-Y. The former is typical of an older design where sealing is by a liquid film maintained between cylindrical surfaces having close clearances. The sealing medium is circulated continuously, entering at a pressure above that of the gas being sealed. Means are provided to collect and recover the sealant that flows through the sealing rings, but that coming in contact with the gas being compressed may be contaminated and not reusable.

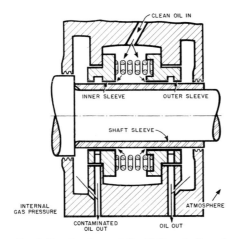

Fig. 9-X. One type of liquid-film shaft seal.

A newer design of seal uses the same principle but uses a cone shaped surface on the rotating shaft sleeve. This acts to generate a head on the sealing medium to minimize leakage into the compressor. See Fig. 9-Y. This seal not only prevents gas leakage out of the unit, but practically eliminates liquid carryover into the gas.

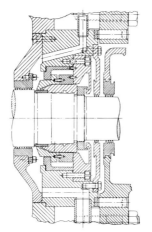

Fig. 9-Y. Typical cone type liquid-film shaft seal.

Automatic Shutdown Seals

Some applications require that when a unit is shut down there be no leakage of air into the casing or of gas from the casing. A device to accomplish this is an auxiliary to the regular seal. The latter often does not function if the unit is stopped.

Lubrication and Sealant Systems

Most of the larger horizontally and vertically split machines will require special systems for supplying and conditioning lubricating and sealing fluids. The smaller units, particularly those with overhung impellers, will not require this feature.

A lubrication system must be designed to positively supply oil to all bearing points before the machine is started and until after it has come to rest when stopping. It must do this without the slightest interruption. Oil must be clean, cool, under proper pressure, and in proper amount. Items lubricated by the system include compressor journals and thrust bearing(s), gear and coupling (as necessary), and, in many cases, the journals and thrust bearing on the driver. Oil also might be used to provide power for various driver and compressor controls. A common system may supply several compressors.

The usual system (see Fig. 13-F, page 13-26) will consist of a main oil pump, auxiliary oil pump, twin oil filters, oil coolers(s), an oil reservoir, and necessary controls. The main and auxiliary pumps may be either motor- or turbine-driven, often one of each. The auxiliary pump takes over when the oil pressure falls to a predetermined value. A reservoir oil heater is supplied when ambient temperatures are low.

When a sealant fluid is required, it may be supplied by an amplified lubricating oil system, but can be separate, It is also a service that must not be interrupted while the compressor is running. Flow must be maintained for a period long enough to shut the compressor down.

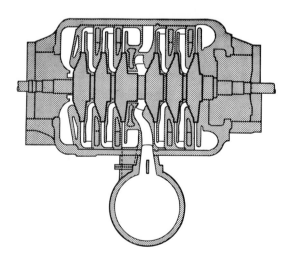

Fig. 9-Z. Six-stage compressor with an external intercooler connected after the third stage.

Gas Cooling

Page 4-27 discusses the possible value of cooling the gas during compression.

External heat exchanges (intercoolers) usually are mounted separately. The gas is brought out of the machine after one or more stages of compression and, after being cooled, is returned to the next stage or series of stages for further compression. When there are two or more machines in series, individual units may or may not be cooled or have intercoolers. An intercooler between casing would normally be used. Fig. 9-Z illustrates a six-stage compressor with gas being cooled externally between third and fourth stages. An external cooler may precool gas ahead of the first stage to advantage in some cases.

Water-cooled diaphragms in a multistage centrifugal compressor act as internal "intercoolers," reducing the inlet temperature to the following stage. See Fig. 9-AA. Use of water cooled diaphragms is limited because of the relatively poor heat-transfer rate obtained through diaphragm walls and problems associated with scaling and cleaning. To limit the latter, closed-circuit cooling systems are often required. Two separate pressurized water circuits, with two water boxes, are used — one for the top and one for the bottom half.

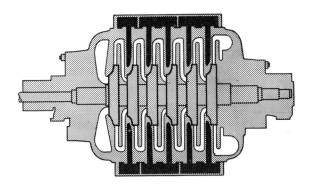

Fig. 9-AA. Six-stage compressor with water-cooled diaphragms.

Liquid injection cooling (See Fig. 9-AB) involves spraying controlled quantities of a suitable liquid into the return channel of the diaphragm where the liquid is evaporated, reducing the gas temperature to the next stage. Liquid used depends upon the gas being handled — in the case of refrigerants, the refrigerant itself would be used. Water is often used where an increase in vapor content can be tolerated and does not create a corrosive condition.

Control of injection requirements is a problem. Over-injection must be guarded against and casing must be provided with drainage. Too little will not provide the necessary cooling; too much will permit liquid carry-over into the next impeller with possible erosion problems. Materials used must be compatible with both the gas and the liquid injected. Before liquid injection is used, there should be a full and complete understanding of the subject between the user and the supplier.

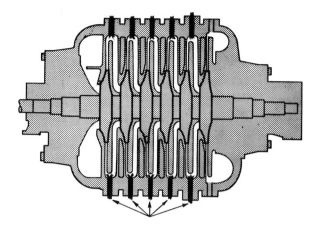

Fig. 9-AB.   Six-stage compressor with spray injection cooling on all except the last stage.

Pressure Ratio and the Centrifugal Characteristic Curve

Centrifugal compressors are frequently classed as constant-pressure variable-volume machines.   This is approximated only when the unit is single-stage, low pressure-ratio, and operating between the point of maximum efficiency and surge limit.   Even then, degree of pressure change with capacity is influenced by impeller design and other factors.   A surge or stability limit of 50 percent is frequently possible, giving a *stable operating range* of 50 percent below the rated capacity.

Whenever gas characteristics and/or the pressure conditions force the use of a high pressure-ratio machine (usually multistage), the stable operating range usually decreases and the characteristic curve becomes steeper.   See Fig. 9-AC.   The degree of change will depend on individual impeller characteristics, number of stages, etc.   Centrifugal compressors are built to ten stages.

The following table presents approximate estimates of the stable operating range variation in with number of stages on an *air* compressor. The range tends to increase with gases lighter than air, to decrease with those heavier.

Stages	Approximate Stable Operating Range Percent of Rated Inlet Capacity (Air)
1	55
2	53.5
3	51
4	48
5	43.5
6	38.5
7	33.5
8	29.5
9	26.5
10	24

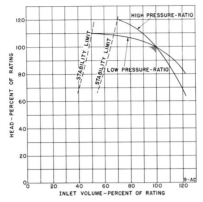

Fig. 9-AC. Comparative characteristic curves of single- and multistage centrifugal compressors.

Capacity Regulation and Control of the Centrifugal

Refer to the discussion of reciprocating compressor regulation on page 6-38. Centrifugal compressors utilize the same elements and do so to accomplish the same results. Methods are different in some cases because of the different characteristics of centrifugal machines.

Demand Curve

To carry the study a bit further, the different types of demand load should be considered. Refer to Fig. 9-AD which shows a characteristic head-capacity curve AE and the normal operating point A. This is a variable speed unit and there are other head-capacity curves for lower speeds.

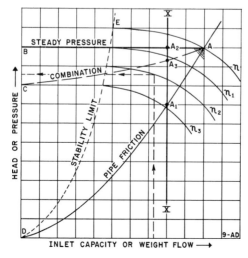

Fig. 9-AD. Types of load encountered by a centrifugal compressor.

If system resistance (or demand curve) is entirely pipe friction, head against which the compressor must deliver will be as curve AD. This is typical of pipeline service. If resistance is entirely a back pressure and there is very little piping, head will be a constant (AB). More often a combination of the two is encountered and the demand curve would be as AC.

The given compressor will meet normal demand (A) for any of these curves as drawn when running at speed n. Suppose the capacity or weight required falls to a certain lower value represented by vertical line XX. With variable-speed control, if the demand curve were AD, the speed would drop almost to n_3 at point A_1. If demand were AB, the speed would decrease only slightly, to a value between n and n_1 at point A_2. For the more usual case, demand curve AC, the required speed would be between n_1 and n_2, at point A_3. This shows that the type of load will influence the machine's reaction to a load change. It is important that the demand curve type be known when designing any control.

A change in capacity has been studied above, but if the base system pressure on demand curves AB or AC should be the variable, the results would be similar. Other methods of control, found on a constant-speed machine, will react in the same general manner, although the characteristic curves will be different.

Methods of Control

Three general methods are used to control centrifugal compressors with variations and refinements within each method. Control may be designed to maintain constant inlet or discharge pressure, inlet volume or inlet gas weight. The outline shows the methods.

1. Variable speed
     Steam turbine
     Variable speed motor
     Hydraulic or magnetic coupling

2. Blowoff of unwanted output
     To atmosphere
     Recirculated

3. Throttle intake
     Blast gate
     Inlet guide vanes

Variable-speed control is the simplest and most economical from the compressor standpoint. With steam turbine drive, it is ideal. This prime mover has excellent variable-speed characteristics.

Single-shaft gas turbines have low permissible speed change; two-shaft turbines are more flexible. Either, driving a centrifugal unit, can provide satisfactory variable-speed control on most applications because of compressor speed-capacity-head characteristics.

Variable-speed motors are available, but are expensive and not very efficient. Hydraulic or magnetic couplings (page 15-6) may be used on occasion but they have a low efficiency that falls even lower as output speed is reduced. Generally, steam turbine drive is predominant for variable-speed control. A typical performance curve is shown in Fig. 4-S (page 4-25). Power is reduced approximately in proportion to speed reduction.

Blowoff and recirculation control is used occasionally. Blowoff would normally relieve any excess gas to atmosphere. Recirculation would throttle excess gas to intake pressure and put it through the compressor again. Bypassed gas must be cooled to prevent an excessive rise in intake and discharge temperatures. There is no power saved with these regulation methods since the compressor always is operating at full load pressure and inlet volume at all times.

Intake throttling will reduce dicharge pressure for a given intake volume or reduce volume for a given discharge pressure. This method is widely used for control of constant-speed machines. In machines of low horsepower, the throttling is done with a "blast gate" or butterfly valve in the intake.

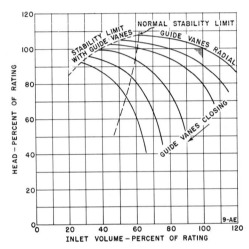

Fig. 9-AE. Effect of inlet guide vane rotation on the characteristic of a constant-speed compressor.

When larger units are involved, movable guide vanes are installed ahead of the first impeller. These not only throttle somewhat, but give prerotation to the gas entering this impeller. This has the additional effect of altering the characteristic of the first impeller and lowering the surge limit, frequently desirable. Fig. 9-AE is typical of the effect of such a regulation method. Power saving is less than with variable speed, but still is significant. The effect of guide vanes depends on the number of stages, decreasing as stages increase.

Either inlet butterfly valves or inlet guide vanes may be automatically or manually controlled. Fig. 9-AF shows a relatively small single-stage unit fitted with manually controlled inlet guide vanes that are partially closed.

Constant Air-Weight Control

A variation generally used with single-stage compressors serving iron-melting cupolas is the constant air-weight control. This is a blast gate throttling device applied to either the intake or discharge to so control air flow through the compressor that its weight is constant. Therefore the

Fig. 9-AF.   Single-stage centrifugal compressor with inlet guide-vane control.

amount of oxygen supplied to the cupola does not vary; melting is uniform. Once set, this device adjusts for changes in both inlet pressure (barometer), inlet temperature, and discharge pressure (cupola resistance). This can be adapted for use on other services.

Surge Control

Surge must be prevented during operation at reduced capacities. Control for this is essentially a minimum flow regulator. Throughput of the machine must be continuously measured. The control is arranged on *compressors* to open a valve in the discharge line when flow reaches a safe predetermined minimum within the stable range. On a centrifugal *vacuum pump*, the valve bleeds atmospheric air into the intake line. Such a device should be installed if there is any danger of the surge limit being reached.

A throttling valve or inlet guide vanes will extend the stable operating range of a machine, but they do not prevent surge.

Parallel Operation

There are times when it is necessary or desirable to compress a given load in two or more compressors. If the characteristic head capacity curves of the individual machines were identical and the piping resistance were equal, then as many machines as were needed could be paralleled without trouble. However, this is never the case and it is necessary to install a special control over each machine that will assure its taking only its proportion of the total capacity. As a rule, when paralleling centrifugal compressors, it is advisable to have their characteristics as similar as possible. Although dissimilar machines can be paralleled, control requirements are extensive.

Starting Unloading

Unloading of dynamic compressors for starting is primarily related to the torque-producing capabilities of the driver, as discussed on page 15-34. The problem with dynamic units is largely that of acceleration of the rotor.

Steam turbines have excellent starting torque characteristics and offer no problems. On electric motor and combustion gas turbine drives, some type of unloading may be required.

On small units, this can frequently be done with a blast gate in the suction line. On many of the more complicated process units, it can be done by utilizing adjustable inlet guide vanes, blast gates or, in some cases, by reducing pressure levels in the process.

In all cases, this subject should be discussed with the compressor manufacturer.

Axial-Flow Compressors

References

See pages 1-15 and 4-31.

Applications

Axial compressors within the industrial field fit principally into the low- and moderate-pressure, large-capacity range. Compression ratios on air vary between 2 and 5, with a maximum of about 7 for a large unit in one casing. Special designs for higher ratios are available, but are not generally applied industrially.

Some of the more important applications include supplying *air* for:
    Gas turbine combustion
    Wind tunnels
    Blast furnaces
    Air separation plants
    Steam boiler pressurized forced draft
    Agitation of sewage
    Ventilation
They are used to handle other gases in the following applications:
    Catalytic cracking
    Atomic reactor gas cooling
    Petrochemical manufacture
    Natural gas boosting
The capacities now being handled in axial compressors of the industrial type vary from 25,000 to above 1,000,000 inlet cfm. Smaller units may be built for special purposes. Pressures are generally well below 100 psiG, but may be as high as 500 psiG. Horsepowers may exceed 100,000.

Characteristics

Compared to the centrifugal compressor, the axial-flow compressor has the following characteristics.

The head-capacity curve is much steeper than that of a centrifugal, hence the operating range between normal and surge is much less. It can be extended by the use of adjustable stator blades. Fig. 9-AG shows a typical comparison including the effect of changing the axial stator blade angles.

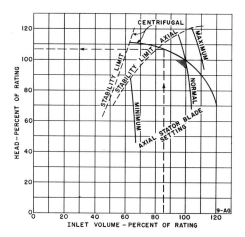

Fig. 9-AG. Comparison of axial and centrifugal characteristic curves. The effect of blade adjustment on axial performance is shown. The surge limit for each type and axial blade setting is dotted.

Efficiency generally will be better than the corresponding centrifugal, depending upon size and conditions. The variation of power with inlet volume is opposite to the centrifugal. See Fig. 9-AH.

Operating speeds for axials will be considerably higher than for equivalent centrifugal units.

Axials will have less rise per stage than a centrifugal, hence will require more stages for a given total pressure rise.

For the same conditions, the axial will generally be smaller and lighter weight than the centrifugal, requiring smaller foundation with easier erection.

The on-line availability of the axial will be about the same as the centrifugal, but it is more sensitive to erosion and corrosion.

These units are pulsation free (except when in surge) and will add no oil to the gas if seals and bearings are designed with this in view.

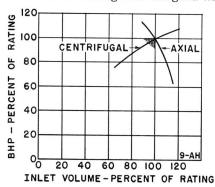

Fig. 9-AH. Comparison of horsepower characteristics of centrifugal and axial with variable inlet volume.

Major Design Details

Hydrostatic tests, journal and thrust bearings, supports, shaft seals, lubrication and seal systems, regulation and surge control will be generally as described for the multistage horizontally split centrifugal in earlier pages. However, the axial design lends itself to the use of regulatory items on any or all stages if required.

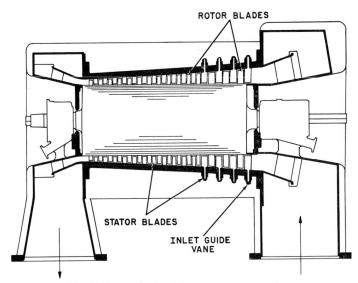

ROTOR BLADES

STATOR BLADES

INLET GUIDE VANE

Fig. 9-AI. Typical axial compressor assembly.

Stator Blading

The stator blades are mounted in the central section of the casing, as shown in the typical assembly, Fig. 9-AI. The blades are forged, cast, or machined from alloy steel to aerodynamic shapes and are spaced in rows between which the rotor blades move. The stator blades serve to convert a portion of the velocity head generated by the rotor blades into pressure head and to deliver the gas to the next set of rotor blades at the proper angle.

There are many axial applications where the gas composition or conditions may someday be changed. Since the range of peak efficiency is narrow in the axial compressor, this gas change may require a different stator blade angle for best efficiency. The adjustable type may be supplied. See Fig. 9-AJ. Necessary changes may readily be made and machine efficiency retained at the new conditions.

Adjustable stator blading has an appreciable effect on the stable operating range and is frequently used for range extension. The adjustment may be manual or automatic. Effect of these adjustments is shown in Fig. 9-AG. Any stator blade adjustment may be applied to one or more rows of stator blades as may be necessary.

Fig 9-AJ.   Fixed, individually adjustable, and continuously adjustable axial stator blades.

Rotor Assembly

The rotor assembly consists of a drum upon which the rotor blades are mounted, a stub shaft at either end, a balancing piston (usually a part of the main drum), a thrust bearing collar, and journals.

The drum is made in different designs. Some use hollow ring forgings or disks either bolted, welded together or shrunk on a shaft. Others are hollow cylinders with the stub shaft pressed or bolted into place. Alloy steel blades may be mounted with bolting from the inside, as the individually adjustable stator blades are fastened to the casing, or they may be fastened into a dovetail notch on the outside of the drum.

Fig. 9-AK. Individually replaceable rotor blades on a disk type axial rotor.

Fig. 9-AK illustrates a typical assembly in which each row of forged stainless steel rotor blades is mounted on a forged steel disk, the entire assembly including the stub shafts being tied together as one piece with fitted prestressed thrubolts. Blades in this case are dovetailed and locked in place. Some designs permit blade replacement at any time without disassembling or removing the rotor.

The entire assembly is dynamically balanced. Most rotor designs operate at speeds below the first critical stage so there is no resonance problem during start up.

Casing

Casings are split along the horizontal centerline and are often built in three sections; inlet, center section around the blades, and discharge. A wide range of materials is used, depending upon size, pressure, temperature, and manufacturer's preference. Cast iron and fabricated or cast steel are the more common materials, at times being used for different casing parts. When necessary, nodular iron and cast alloy steel may be used.

Inlet and discharge connections are usually in the form of a volute, although extremely large units may have special axial connection arrangements.

Chapter 10

Thermal Compressors

Introduction

An ejector is normally thought of as a compression device operating with an inlet pressure considerably below atmosphere and discharging at a level which, as a maximum, would slightly exceed atmospheric pressure. Under these conditions, while actually a compressor, an injector is classed as a vacuum producer or "pump." Its primary purpose is to pump unwanted gases and vapors out of a system into which their flow, or leakage, may be either continuous (as from a steam condenser) or practically zero (as from a very tight system being evacuated or pumped down). See Chapter 4 (pages 4-31 through 4-39) and Chapter 20. The present Chapter is concerned with the use of ejectors as *thermal compressors,* to handle gases and vapors at pressures above atmosphere.

Application

Thermal compressors are usually allied with use or reuse of available gas or steam, or of available energy in the gas or steam, which might otherwise be wasted. Energy conserved may exist in the low-pressure induced steam or may exist in the higher-pressure motive gas.

An example involving steam is recompression and recirculation of uncondensed steam from drying drums on a Fourdrinier paper machine. The high-pressure motive steam acts as makeup for the lower-pressure steam previously condensed in the drums. A constant supply of heat from the motive steam is always available for drying.

There are many chemical processes where low pressure exhaust steam can be compressed economically by an ejector. Substantial savings are possible with a relatively small outlay.

Another application involves the use of high-pressure natural gas as motive power, the ejector acting as a reducing valve on the high-pressure line. At the same time, it compresses gas from some lower-pressure source into a mixture storage or distribution system. An adaptation is found where high-pressure gas compresses atmospheric air into a distribution line, the gas-air mixture ratio being preset and automatically controlled by the respective initial air and gas pressures.

Characteristics

Compression ratios may be greater or less than 2 to 1, but for most applications will be less than this critical ratio. This changes the velocity pattern in the diagram of Fig. 1-N (page 1-16) in that throat velocity in area F will be below sonic. Ejector characteristics will not be the same as for an ejector with sonic diffuser throat velocity, the type discussed in Chapter 4 (page 4-31 through 4-39).

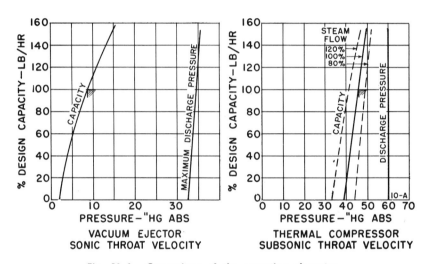

Fig. 10-A. Comparison of the operating characteristics of a vacuum ejector and a thermal compressor.

Fig. 10-A shows typical performance curves on both types of ejectors. In each, the left hand curve, or group of curves, shows variation of intake pressure with capacity. The right hand represents discharge pressure. In the vacuum ejector, it is the *maximum* discharge pressure obtainable. The *actual* discharge pressure may be lower with no change in the suction pressure-capacity curve. See page 4-36. This is not so with thermal compressors. Any change in actual discharge pressure is reflected in a similar change in suction pressure for the same capacity in lb/hr.

In each, there are four possible variables; steam weight flow, or steam pressure on a fixed nozzle; intake pressure; discharge pressure; and, capacity in lb/hr. The following chart is based on changing one of these at a time. Influence on the others is noted. (*Ratio* means compression ratio.)

Vacuum Ejector	Thermal Compressor
Increased Steam Flow	
Increases *maximum* discharge pressure; practically no other change.	Reduces intake pressure. Increased ratio. Alternately, can operate at constant ratio and increased capacity.
Increased Intake Pressure	
Reduces ratio; increases capacity.	Reduces ratio; increases capacity.
Increased Discharge Pressure	
No change (until reaches breaking pressure).	Entire family of curves moves with the discharge. Ratio remains practically constant.
Increased Capacity	
Reduces ratio; increases intake pressure.	Reduces ratio; increases intake pressure.

Two characteristics stand out in the functioning of a thermal compressor. One is the effect of varying steam weight flow for capacity control. The other characteristic is the way a change in discharge pressure causes the intake pressure-capacity curve to move, or *float*. This is at an almost constant compression ratio.

These characteristics are only within reasonable areas. For example, increasing steam weight flow on a thermal compressor too far could possibly increase throat velocity to the sonic range; the ejector would act like the normal vacuum ejector.

Chapter 11

Portable Compressors

Introduction

A portable compressor is a self-contained movable compressed air power-er plant consisting of an air compressor, prime mover, air receiver, and complete systems for capacity control, cooling, lubricating, and starting. It is mounted on a substantial frame and is usually enclosed by a canopy and side doors. When desired, a two- or four-wheel running gear may be attached to the frame.

In designing these compressors, the goals kept in mind include compactness, lightweight, no foundation requirement, ability to operate somewhat out of level, ability to operate under varying ambient conditions, etc.

The trend is toward higher-speed equipment, automotive-type accessories and designs. Reliability in a small package becomes more important than compression efficiency.

Applications

Portables service a wide variety of industries. Their service may be divided roughly into two areas; general utility work by electric, gas and water companies, municipalities, and small contractors; and, heavy work as in mining, quarrying, and contracting.

The load factor of a portable unit is generally much lower than that of a corresponding stationary compressor. It has been estimated that the average general utility compressor operates only about 700 hours per year. On heavy duty work, the average approximates 2000 hours/year. Although portables occasionally run at an 8000 hour/year rate, this is abnormal.

Fig. 11-A.   Medium size four-wheel mounted portable compressor.

Ratings

Portables are rated on actual free air delivery at full speed and 100 psig discharge pressure. Assemblies mounted on wheels range in size from 20 to 1200 cfm. One manufacturer builds such units for 36, 85, 125, 160, 175, 250, 365, 600, 750, 900, and 1200 cfm capacity. Smaller specialty units are available for manual or light truck transport.

Altitude Operation

Most portable compressors operate satisfactorily at rated discharge pressure up to 10,000 ft altitude. The power developed by the engine falls more rapidly at increased altitude than the power required by the compressor. On certain units it is necessary to throttle the compressor intake to reduce its capacity and power requirement. Use of a portable at 8000 ft altitude or above should be checked with the manufacturer.

Although actual compressor capacity at intake conditions may fall but little with an increase in altitude, it must be remembered that the number of tools the unit will run at a given gauge pressure is reduced. See page 4-17.

Fig. 11-B. Small two-wheel mounted portable compressor.

Mountings

Standard portables are available in a variety of arrangements:

1. With frame only, no wheels. Used for mounting on a flat truck or railcar, or setting on timbers at job site;
2. Frame with four pneumatic-tired wheels attached, equipped with tow bar and, usually, with springs and automotive-type steering;
3. Frame with two pneumatic-tired wheels attached and with springs and tow bar. Available only on the smaller portables because of weight limitations; and,
4. Such miscellaneous mountings of basic frame as on a self-propelled vehicle, or combined with a crawler drill to make a self contained combination.

See Fig. 11-A through 11-E.

Fig. 11-C. Small portable mounted crosswise on a utility service truck.

Fig. 11-D.   Basic portable assembly mounted on a railcar, driving
a tie tamper outfit.   The car is self-propelled through air motors

Fig. 11-E.   Two mobile self-contained deep-hole
drills powered by mounted portable compressors.

Special Designs

Among other portable compressors are the mine car, a machine designed specifically to provide air power underground in mines where head room is low. There are many small lightweight manually portable units available for labor saving in light work. Typical of this type is Fig. 11-F.

Fig. 11-F. Small one-man reciprocating portable — a complete power plant.

This can be carried by two men or fitted with a wheelbarrow mounting. It is a radial six-cylinder combination, three cylinders compressing air, and three providing the gasoline engine power.

Fig. 11-G shows a whisperized portable.

Fig. 11-G. A whisperized portable on a construction project.

Smaller sizes of standard stationary and portable units can often be designed for mounting on a truck, driven by the truck engine through a power take-off arrangement, with either direct or V-belt drives. Compressor size for this must be within the power limits of both truck engine and power transmission device. See Fig. 11-H.

Compressors

Three types of compressors are used in current portables — reciprocating, sliding-vane rotary, and helical-lobe rotary.

Most reciprocating units are of the two-stage air-cooled type as illustrated in Fig. 6-B-1 and 6-B-2. A few are built from water- or air-cooled engine enblock cylinder assemblies fitted for use as air compressors. These are single-stage. The principal U. S. manufacturers have turned to the two other types, however, because of their lighter and more compact construction.

Fig. 11-H. Small truck-mounted reciprocating portable, driven from the truck engine.

Sliding-Vane Portable

This compressor is used to a maximum of about 600 cfm capacity. The unit may be either single- or two-stage, the latter being more general. Most operate at modern engine speeds of 1800 rpm or higher. The second stage is usually an in-line compressor of the same diameter as the first stage, but shorter. It is a complete assembly with the first stage. See Fig. 11-I. A few use two stages, side-by-side, one being gear- or chain-driven from the other. See page 1-6, and Chapter 7 for more on this type of compressor.

Helical-Lobe Portable

This compressor operates as an oil-flooded lubricated single-stage unit, rather than as a dry-type. There are two designs, one requiring timing gears. The other has no sliding motion, and timing gears are not necessary. The gate is driven direct from the main rotor. See page 1-11, and Chapter 8.

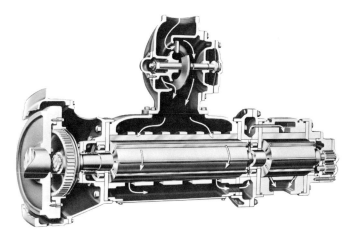

Fig. 11-I. Typical two-stage vane-type portable showing the volumetric regulator.

Cooling and Lubrication

Both *portable* rotary compressors have no water jacket for cooling but use a copious quantity of oil constantly cooled and recirculated to lubricate and seal the vanes and rotors, and to remove a substantial portion of the heat of compression as it develops.

A typical portable flood-lubrication system contains a positively driven oil pump, primarily to meter oil going into the compressor. It is then discharged with the air into a combination receiver-separator where most of

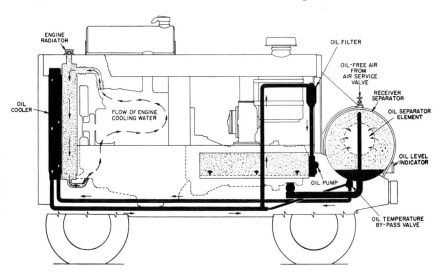

Fig. 11-J. Typical cooling system circuits of an oil cooled compressor and its engine driver.

the oil is dropped. Oil collected in the receiver bottom is piped through a radiator-type oil cooler and an oil filter, back to the pump inlet to be recirculated. See Fig. 11-J.

One advantage of the oil-cooling system used on the rotary units is that cooling is continuous during compression and air temperatures at discharge is 100° to 150°F cooler than air from a reciprocating unit. This means lower temperatures in all lines leading from the machine and longer hose service life.

Oil carry-over into hose is kept to a minimum through the use of a special secondary separator element, either following or built into the receiver. This removes substantially all remaining oil, the carry-over usually being less than with the equivalent air cooled reciprocating unit.

Engine Drivers

Drivers generally are commercial industrial gasoline or diesel engines, usually directly connected to the compressor through a flexible coupling or clutch. The diesel-engine driver is growing in popularity and is the principal driver on the larger units. Most engines are water-cooled, the heat being discharged to atmosphere through a fan-cooled radiator.

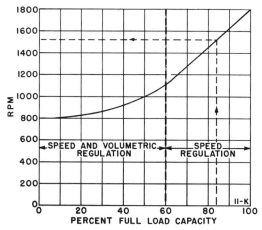

Fig. 11-K. Typical speed-capacity curve of a vane-type rotary portable compressor.

Capacity Control — Engine Drive

Portable compressors generally utilize a combination of control methods. One manufacturer's control design is to 60% capacity by speed, at which point a combination of further speed reduction, plus gradual throttling of the intake, takes place. The minimum speed is 45% of full speed and capacity is reduced to zero. This is a gradual, smooth, stepless control throughout the entire range from 100% to no load. Lest this seem to contradict the statement in Chapter 8 that the helical-lobe compressor should never be dead-ended, it should be said that if there is sufficient cooling, any machine of this type may be throttled to dead-end. Chapter 8 refers to a dry unit.

Fig. 11-K is a typical speed-capacity curve of a two-stage vane-type portable unit.

Electric Drivers

Fig. 11-L. Typical electric motor driven portable.

A special electric design is available in sizes from below 300 cfm up to 1200 cfm. It is driven by an induction motor usually mounted between the compressor and the radiator fan. The complete self-contained unit requires no enclosure or foundation and may be moved readily from place to place. It has found its principal application on long range construction projects where electric power is available. Capacity control is constant speed-throttling intake.

Equipment similar to engine driven models is available, including mountings.

Standard Auxiliary Equipment

Standard equipment on portable compressors will usually include a housing that can be locked, a fuel tank, air receiver, storage battery, electric starter, generator, intake air filter for both compressor and engine (this may be a common filter), an engine muffler, heat exchanger(s) for handling both engine and compressor heat dissipation, and an instrument panel. Wheel mountings may be added to the standard frame.

Towing Speeds

Maximum safe towing speeds are given in most instruction books and should never be exceeded. Towing speeds should always be consistent with the character of the road or terrain. It should be noted that wheel attachments are intended to provide easy movement around the job. Trucking should be used for long transport. Generally accepted maximum safe towing speeds, according to one authority, are

4 wheel-pneumatic tires with springs, 20 mph; and,

2 wheel-pneumatic tires with springs, 35 mph.

The heavier the vehicle, the slower the speed.

Light trucks should not be used to tow heavy portables unless the latter have brakes. Brakes may be supplied as an accessory item and are mandatory in a few areas.

Automatic Check Valve Sometimes Required

No *rotary* portable compressor should be connected to a common header with any other portable or other type of compressor, or to any other source of compressed air without placing an automatic check valve between the header and each rotary compressor. Back flow from the line can cause reverse operation and possible damage to the unit.

Highlights of Operation and Maintenance

It has been said that dirt is the greatest enemy to long-service life and satisfactory operation of portable compressors. It might also be added, careful lubrication is the greatest friend. To assure that dirt is kept out and that proper lubrication is maintained, it is essential to schedule maintenance procedures. This means keeping a log. Cleaning filters, changing oil, etc. are operations to be routinely done. A log will assist in routine maintenance.

Inlet Air Cleaners

Air entering both compressor and engine is always filtered. There may be a single filter, or two. They require frequent servicing, in dusty locations as often as once every 8 hours or more often. Dirt entering either compressor or engine will greatly accelerate wear, internal deposits, down time, and maintenance costs. The inlet air filter is the guardian against these occurrences. Keep it functioning.

Compressor Lubricating Oil

There are three types of oil that will give good service and performance, under certain operating conditions, in all rotary portable air compressors.

Motor Oils

Heavy duty, detergent-type crankcase oils, commonly called "motor oils," are Grade SAE-10W.

These oils must comply with the requirements of Specification MIL-L-2104B, Grade SAE-10W. They may, and will frequently, be qualified against the A. P. I. classifications for services ML-MM-MS-DG-DM. Such qualification is an added assurance of oil quality, though not a requirement for compressor service. Another statement may say "Exceeds car manufacturers new car warranty requirements" or "Exceeds carmakers MS Sequence Test Requirement." These qualifications are not necessary for compressor service but are also an added assurance of quality.

Oils of this type generally are made from good quality paraffinic base stock with naturally high viscosity index, and are compounded with additive packages containing detergent, dispersant, oxidation, and corrosion inhibitors; rust preventatives; antidepressants; and viscosity index improvers.

Such oils will give good service and result in a clean, varnish free, well-cooled, well lubricated compressor under most service conditions, *provided inlet air cleaners, air inlet piping and joints, oil filters, and oil changes are properly maintained.*

Oils of this type MAY NOT BE THE FIRST CHOICE under the following service conditions:

a Vane-type and screw compressors operating on light duty under conditions of high relative humidity. Under these conditions, condensed water would not boil off due to the cool running of the compressor on a light duty cycle. Condensation would tend to become emulsified by the detergent agents in the oil. This retained condensate could cause excessive vane slot wear in vane-type compressors and bearing corrosion in both vane and screw compressors. Under these circumstances use a "TURBINE TYPE OIL."

b Vane- *and* screw-type compressors operating under consistently low ambient conditions or *occasionally* below minus 20° to minus 40°F. Under these circumstances, use an Automatic Transmission Fluid. *NOTE:* Consult the manufacturer for operation below minus 40°F.

c Vane- *and* screw-type compressors operating under extreme heavy duty, high temperature conditions where oil oxidation with the resultant lacquers, varnishes, etc., could become a problem. Under these circumstances, use an Automatic Transmission Fluid.

Turbine-Type Oils

High quality, nondetergent, turbine and/or circulating oils containing rust and oxidation inhibitors and having a viscosity at 100°F of 150-200 S. U. S. These oils should have a pour point low enough to flow at the lowest starting temperatures that will be encountered. These oils are commonly called "Turbine Oils."

Oils of this type will comply with the principal requirements of Specification MIL-L-17672B, Grade 2110TH but need not necessarily have qualified against that specification. In addition to the rust and oxidation inhibitors mentioned, these oils may contain antiwear additives and antifoam agents. The base stock generally will be a high quality paraffinic oil of naturally high index.

Such oils are to be preferred for use in compressors operating on light duty under conditions of high relative humidity where condensation is likely to be a problem. Under these conditions, it is *very important that the receiver-separator tank be drained of accumulated condensate every day before starting the compressor.*

Automatic Transmission Fluids (Dexron*)

Dexron Automatic Transmission Fluids having a *maximum* pour point of minus 45°F, a *minimum* flash point of 390°F and complying with all the requirements of the Dexron specification. The oil must have been assigned a General Motors Corporation Dexron Approval or Qualification Number. These oils are commonly called "ATF's."

Oils of this type are to be preferred for use in vane- and screw-type compressors operating in cold, to very cold, ambient conditions (down to minus 40°F) and operating on very heavy duty under very high ambient temperatures.

*Dexron is a registered trade mark of General Motors Corporation.

DO NOT SUBSTITUTE torque converter fluids of any other type. *The fluid must be Dexron approved.*

Long life and good lubricant performance also will depend on:

a. Use of only clean, new oil from a reputable supplier;

b. Air cleaners serviced frequently and regularly;

c. Air inlet piping and joints maintained in good condition;

d. Oil filters serviced regularly as specified in the compressor operating instructions; and,

e. Oil changed regularly and as dictated by operating conditions and results of oil analysis.

DO NOT attempt to save money by using inferior lubricants. DO NOT attempt to wash or re-use replaceable cartridge-type oil filter elements. These are false economies that will lead to greater expense in the long run.

DO NOT MIX oils of different types. To change from one type of lubricating oil to another, the unit should be completely drained of all oil (including oil cooler, oil filter, and oil piping) and refilled with the new type. The new oil then should be drained and replaced after 50 hours of operation.

Where possible, mixing oils of different brands of the same type should be avoided, particularly turbine-type oils. If it is wished to change brands of oil, it is best to do so at the time of an oil change.

Compressor Oil Filter

The oil filter will usually be of the edge or replaceable-element type.

The edge type is cleanable by rotating a handle. This should be done every 8 hours. The filter shell should be removed after every 100 operating hours and the accumulated sludge removed. While disassembled, the filter should be examined for lacquer or varnish deposits. If deposits are found, the oil should be changed immediately. This is a sign of improper oil, a mixture of noncompatible oils, or some form of oil deterioration. It must not be allowed to continue. The deposits can cause clogging of the oil filter and oil cooler, sticking vanes, and possible vane breakage.

Replaceable-element filters should be serviced and the element replaced at each oil change. The filter shell should be cleaned each time a new element is installed. If there is any evidence of formation of varnishes, shellacs, or lacquers on the oil filter element or cartridge or in the filter shell or sump, it is a warning that the compressor lubricating and cooling oil has improper characteristics. The oil should be changed immediately.

Engine Lubricating Oil and Oil Filter

The engine lubricating oil will be different from that used in the compressor. The service to which it is exposed is more severe; more frequent oil changes will undoubtedly be required. Reference to engine instruction book and the guidance of a qualified lubricant supplier in setting up a schedule will bring the best results. Oil changes every 50 to 100 operating hours will probably be the rule.

Clean the oil filter on the engine regularly as directed in the instruction book.

Miscellaneous Lubrication

Follow the instruction book charts and lists for the proper schedule of lubrication of the many other points of wear, from running gear to control linkage. Attention will pay dividends.

Condensate Drainage

Moisture in the compressor intake air will condense in the system during compression and cooling. Condensate will collect in the bottom of the receiver beneath the oil and should be drained daily, after there has been time for settling out, preferably just before starting. At least one manufacturer provides automatic temperature control that largely eliminates the moisture problem.

Fuel Handling

Clean fuel, whether gasoline or fuel oil, is vitally important and the methods of handling fuel to the machine should be well organized.

Storage should be in clean, nongalvanized vessels. Transfer vessels, funnels and similar equipment must be kept clean. A fuel tank (Fig. 11-M is suggested. The sediment should always be drained before any fuel is drawn from the upper valve.

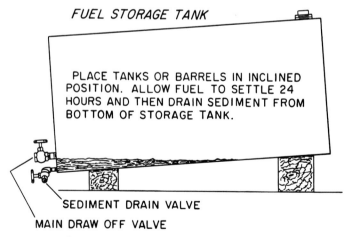

FUEL STORAGE TANK

PLACE TANKS OR BARRELS IN INCLINED POSITION. ALLOW FUEL TO SETTLE 24 HOURS AND THEN DRAIN SEDIMENT FROM BOTTOM OF STORAGE TANK.

SEDIMENT DRAIN VALVE

MAIN DRAW OFF VALVE

Fig. 11-M. Fuel storage tank arrangement.

A space is provided in the fuel tank on each portable for the collection of sediment and water. This should be drained regularly, preferably just before refilling.

Important Maintenance Items

Engines will require much more maintenance and more frequent inspection and tune up than will the compressors. Maintenance of the latter can therefore usually be done while the engine is being serviced.

Rotary compressor parts require infrequent checks if proper *operating* procedures have been followed. On helical-lobe rotaries, shaft oil seal, gears, and bearings are wearing parts and have long service life. They need not normally be replaced for many years.

The same is true with gears, shaft seal and bearings on vane-type machines, but the vanes need occasional replacement, and the rotor slots may, in time, wear sufficiently to require a new rotor.

Condition of vanes should be checked at least every 2000 operating hours (one manufacturer recommends 1000-hour periods). Any indication of sticking, chipping, or deterioration should be cause for complete replacement. Replace vanes every 4000 hours on a single-stage unit or the high-pressure side of a two-stage unit. Recommended replacement is not longer than 6000 hours on the low-pressure side.

Vane life on a portable is much shorter than on a stationary unit because of the higher average operating speed on the former, its more intermittent operation, and the less favorable conditions for operation and maintenance. Vanes tend to deteriorate when the interior of the machine is not kept dry by regular daily operation. Replacement of vanes before breakage occurs is important. Vane breakage frequently causes damage requiring extensive repair.

The secondary oil filter or separator on the oil flooded rotary units consists of a cartridge of specially packed material that removes all but a small fraction of the oil not previously deposited in the receiver. Need for replacement is indicated when the oil consumption of the machine increases, which is usually not oftener than every two or three years of normal operation. Inspection, however, should be made at least once every 4000 hours.

Chapter 12

Booster Compressors

Introduction

Compressors having an intake considerably above atmospheric have been known as *boosters*. It is probable that this class now comprises more than 50% of the compressor horsepower put into service yearly. Although the term is becoming obsolete, it still has a meaning to some when applied to *single-stage* compressors and will be so used here.

Boosters pose problems to some people, although it is simply the basic compressor element as described on page 1-4. Operation does not differ from any other compressor element of its type. The second stage of any 100 psiG air compressor is a booster by the above definition, as is each of the upper stages of any multistage unit, and often the first stage also.

Another term used for a certain type of booster is *circulator*. This is a low-compression-ratio compressor used to circulate gas through chemical process equipment. The gas has usually been through the equipment once, but must be recirculated.

References

The theory of compression as presented in Chapters 3 and 4 applies to boosters, particularly the section on peak horsepower starting on page 4-9. Also see comments covering specific compressor types in earlier chapters.

Compressor Types

All compressor types are used as boosters, the reciprocating and dynamic types having a broader range of application than the vane- and helical-lobe rotaries or the ejector. The role and action of the latter has been discussed in Chapter 10. Both types of rotary compressors are somewhat limited in application due to the lower pressures for which they are available.

Scope of Service

Pressure levels vary widely, from less than 100 psiG to many thousand. Of the more common applications, reciprocators have been used on all those listed, centrifugals on 1, 3, 4, and 5, and vane rotaries on 6.

1. Synthetic ammonia plant circulator operating at a pressure of several thousand pounds with approximately 10% pressure rise.
2. Ethylene booster in polyethylene manufacture. Compresses from a few thousand psi to 60,000 psi or higher. In this case, the high compression ratio is possible only because of the peculiar gas characteristics. Volume reduction is relatively slight.
3. Some hydrocarbon reforming processes operate from approximately 600 psiG to the 2500 psiG area.
4. Natural gas pipeline transmission compressors are low-compression-ratio boosters with about 1000 psiG current maximum discharge pressure.
5. Steam is occasionally compressed from an existing level to a higher pressure for a special purpose.
6. Ammonia is compressed from a low-temperature refrigeration system into a higher-pressure main system from which compression is completed in other compressors.

Frequent Problems

Two possible problems must be considered in the application and design of single-stage boosters or circulators. First is the problem of setting the expected operating conditions. A typical case is a basically low-ratio process where intake and discharge pressures are subject to serious error if pipeline friction losses are inadequately allowed for. This can, and has, resulted in a compressor and driver sized smaller than actually required. The differential pressure between intake and discharge must never be cut too close. Make a generous allowance. Both intake and discharge on reciprocators are subject to pulsating flow and pipeline pressure losses are much higher than with frequently used steady flow calculations. On machine types other than reciprocators, pulsation effect on friction is not so severe, but ample allowance must be made.

The second problem develops principally with reciprocating compressors, but may be involved in other positive displacement units. It has to do with the effect on horsepower when pressure conditions, either intake or discharge, vary materially from design.

This is frequently encountered when regulation of capacity is by intake-throttling controller. Centrifugals utilize this type of regulation at

times, but are so influenced in performance by intake gravity that their
operation should be carefully analyzed against the projected demand curve
by the manufacturer. See page 9-29.

Reciprocating Boosters

Peak horsepower for reciprocators is discussed extensively starting
on page 4-9. This applies theoretically to any positive-displacement unit.
Fig. 4-J and Fig. 4-K are practical curves for determination of the actual
peak compression ratio with good accuracy for reciprocators. The effect
of volumetric and compression efficiency changes with compression ratio
are included.

The estimating bhp per million curves starting on page 34-146 are
applicable to booster calculation for ratios of 1.4 and above. These are
actual bhp data for cylinders 200 HP and above. They must be considered
on the low side for smaller units. To place these data on the basis
of bhp/100 cfm at intake pressure and temperature, multiply bhp/million
by $p_1/100$.

Volumetric efficiency may be approximated by the use of Formula 4.7
on page 4-4.

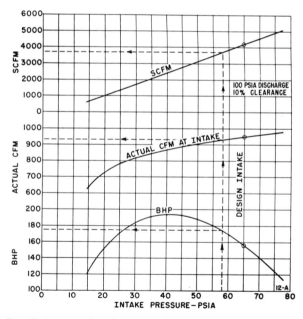

**Fig. 12-A. Actual performance of a 1000 cfm PD single-stage
reciprocating booster handling air with varying intake pressure.**

Fig. 12-A illustrates what happens on a reciprocator designed to operate on air with 1000 cfm displacement, an intake of 65 psiA and discharge
of 100 psiA. Intake varies from design due to either normal variations
or operation of capacity regulation. Design bhp is 155 which would per-

mit the use of a 150 hp 40°C motor as a driver if intake did not vary, but a 200 hp motor must be supplied if operation is ever to be at peak conditions. The effect of varying intake pressure on real capacity (SCFM) is clearly indicated.

Vane-Type Rotary Boosters

Single-stage vane-type rotary boosters are currently available to 400 psiG, depending upon the size and differential pressure involved. For both starting control and capacity regulation the bypass system is recommended. A cooler in the the bypass line will usually be necessary if it is used for regulation.

Helical-Lobe Rotary Boosters

Single-stage helical-lobe (screw-type) rotary boosters are currently available to a maximum of 250 psiG. Starting almost always requires a bypass. Inlet throttling may be used for regulation to a limited degree (see page 8-9), but it is normal to use a bypass with a cooler in the line.

Steam Boosters

The specification of steam booster operating conditions must be thoughtfully done *by the user*. It must be based on the final use to be made of the steam and the conditions desired at that point. Both capacity and temperature are involved.

The desired condition at the point of use may be either a relatively constant temperature or a constant pressure. If constant temperature is desired, as in an autoclave, the easiest way to maintain it is to condense saturated or slightly superheated steam at a constant pressure. This is often done.

The discharge temperature from a booster will be in the superheat range, but this heat will be of little value in most applications. It will generally be lost through discharge pipe radiation. It is usual to estimate compressor discharge temperature isentropically and to then reduce the discharge *superheat* about 25% due to losses within the compressor itself.

The amount of steam required at the point of use is a basic specification item. It must not be forgotten that there may be line condensation between compressor and point of use. This must be included in the quantity handled by the compressor or the usable amount of steam delivered will be insufficient. The smaller the desired output, the greater will be the relative condensation loss and the greater the required increase. The *purchaser* must estimate and include this allowance when stating the desired compressor output.

Steam at inlet is usually either saturated or at low superheat. It is important that adequate separation of condensate be provided before the steam enters the compressor. The existence of superheat at this point cannot be considered proof that the inlet steam is dry. Moderate superheat and condensate can exist together in a steam line.

Chapter 13

Stationary Compressor Lubrication

Introduction

Perhaps the most important operational item in compressing gases is proper lubrication. It is easy to provide *proper* lubrication; it does not require excessive training. It *does* involve a certain amount of intelligent care and attention.

Proper lubrication includes selection of high-quality lubricants suited to the particular service conditions, cleanliness in storage and dispensing, and application in correct quantities in a way that permits effective performance. Closely allied are factors of maintenance of clean gas into and throughout the compressor and the use of regular procedures for inspecting, cleaning, and maintaining mechanical perfection, both in the machine and its accessories.

Proper lubrication has five benefits:

1. Reliable operation;
2. Low maintenance cost;
3. Minimum power consumption;
4. Minimum lubrication cost; and,
5. Maximum safety.

The wide range of compressor types and applications precludes specific recommendations. Typical simple lubricant specifications are given for some types of machines.

No attempt is made to discuss the lubrication of specialized compressors for refrigeration and air conditioning, gears, drivers, or those gases that may require special attention because of adverse reaction with the lubricant.

Functions of a Lubricant

Functions of a lubricant are not simple. These are what a lubricant must do in most applications:

1. Separate rubbing parts;
2. Dissipate frictional heat through cooling and heat transfer;
3. Flush away entering dirt as well as wear debris;
4. Minimize wear;
5. Reduce friction loss and power required;
6. Reduce gas leakage;
7. Protect parts from corrosion; and,
8. Minimize deposits.

When the importance of each of these functions is fully appreciated, the value of intelligent and careful compressor lubrication cannot be questioned.

Lubricants

Refined petroleum lubricants are the most prevalent for compressors. Although requirements are complex, lubricants meeting them can be obtained. Additives to provide antioxidation, antirust, and/or anticorrosive properties have been highly developed. Other oil properties can be improved by additives and/or refining and purifying in special ways. Soaps, molydenum disulphide, and other materials may be added to obtain qualities needed for special applications. Involved in the upgrading of lubricants is the greater knowledge now available regarding the mechanism and requirements of lubrication in various applications. Today's lubricants are often *designed* for a specific application.

Oil Types

Petroleum lubricants are refined from crude petroleum. There are many sources of crude, each with its own particular properties. Among them are two basic types — the paraffin and the naphthene base. Naphthene-base oils are generally preferred for compressor lubrication, although paraffinic lubricants perform satisfactorily in most applications. When adverse temperature conditions cause deposits, as in compression chambers, those from naphthenic oils are much easier to remove. This does not exclude properly designed paraffinic-base materials. However, internal cleaning is a major maintenance item and anything reducing it is desirable.

Lubricant Tests

Laboratory tests made under controlled conditions at atmospheric pressure are often used as a guide to arrive at a specific lubricant selection for a specific compressor. They are basically screening devices.

Viscosity is indicative of a fluid's internal friction and ability to flow. It is a measure of resistance to deformation, or squeezing out of a bearing. Viscosity in normal lubricants is reduced as temperature increases.

Viscosity index (VI) is a measure of the rate of change of viscosity with temperature. Oils with high *VI* have low viscosity changes, whereas oils with low (or negative) *VI* have wide viscosity changes. When there are wide ambient or operating temperature ranges, high *VI* lubricants are desirable and frequently necessary. This index is usually important only in isolated cases or with certain special lubricants.

Flash point is the lowest temperature to which oil must be heated under standardized test conditions to drive off sufficient flammable vapor to flash when brought into contact with a flame. A high flash point is no longer considered a necessary requirement for reduction of fire hazard in air compressors. Naphthenic oil tend to have lower flash points than paraffinic oils of equal viscosity. Flash points of all petroleum-based lubricants increase with increasing pressure.

Auto-ignition temperature is that temperature at which the oil will ignite spontaneously in air. Generally speaking, the naphthenic oils, although having lower flash point, will have higher auto-ignition temperatures than the paraffinic. Auto-ignition temperatures decrease with increasing pressure.

Pour point is the temperature at which oil begins to flow under prescribed conditions. It is important because oil must flow quickly in crankcases when a machine starts cold and cylinder lubricants must be pumpable at the lowest ambient temperature encountered. There are isolated cases where the range of ambient versus operating temperatures is too great to permit handling the lubricant without heating.

Carbon residue is that carbon left after evaporating an oil under controlled conditions. It is not considered a firm indication of just how much deposit might build up in a compressor, since operating care and the rate of oil feed have a much greater influence. However, a low carbon residue rating is recommended.

Acid number is sometimes used as a determination of the acidic constituents. It does not necessarily indicate the possible corrosive effect of the oil.

Test Summary

Laboratory tests cannot be used as reliable guarantees of oil operation in a compressor; no two compressor plants are exactly alike. Although tests may be used as a guide, *final selection is a matter of experience.* Oil selection should be based on its effect upon production and maintenance, not on laboratory testing or any detailed specification. Cost of lubrication *and* maintenance problems associated with it, rather than the cost of lubrication only should determine the proper oil.

SAE Viscosity Classifications

Automotive *crankcase* lubricating oils have for many years been classified by the Society Of Automotive Engineers (SAE) by numbers representing a Saybolt viscosity range at a particular temperature or temperatures. SAE numbers refer *only* to viscosity and have no bearing whatsoever on oil quality or its other characteristics and properties.

Although some types of automotive crankcase oils are at times recommended for lubrication of certain compressors, lubricants are best selected on the basis of individual compressor requirements. Many oils of automotive crankcase quality definitely should *not* be used in compressors.

Normal compressor oils do not normally carry an SAE rating. When SAE numbers are referred to in compressor practice, it is solely to define viscosity range and is not to be taken as a general recommendation for automotive grade oils. SAE classifications are given on page 13-16.

Selection of a Lubricant

Manufacturers often list general specifications for lubricants in instruction books. They may not recommend brand names because of the wide difference between installations and operating conditions. Further, there is continual improvement and change in lubricants. Only the oil supplier can recommend the best oil for the job at any given time.

Many suppliers have developed a list of their provisionally acceptable lubricants in collaboration with each compressor manufacturer. These are available from the lubricant supplier. The user should in all cases purchase his lubricants from an oil company or dealer willing to *guarantee* the oil as satisfactory for the intended service. The cost of the best lubricant is a small percentage of the total cost of compressor operation. Buy quality.

Regarding Synthetic Lubricants

Synthetic lubricants are used mainly within *air* compression chambers, such as the cylinders of reciprocating and vane-type rotary units. In these special areas, two complaints against petroleum oils are frequent: carbonaceous deposits which necessitate frequent cleaning; and danger of fire. Largely because of these, certain synthetics having lubricating properties have been adapted for this service.

There are a number of commercial products available for this air compressor application and the field has been growing. Currently, most of them are phosphate esters or have a phosphate ester base. In general, these materials do a commendable lubrication job *when the machine is properly broken in, the lubricant is properly selected, and an adequate amount is supplied.* Furthermore, when synthetics are to be used in a new compressor, the manufacturer must be advised before purchase. Special fittings may be required.

The phosphate ester synthetic lubricants, being quite stable, have characteristics that minimize the petroleum lubricant problems. Under conditions found in air compressors, they are not nearly as prone to create deposits. They have an autogenous ignition point of about 1100°F, as opposed to about 600° to 750°F for most petroleum oils. Synthetics have distinct fire-resistant qualities in that they will not propagate a flame, but they will burn if heated sufficiently. They have excellent film strength.

Mixtures of petroleum oil and a synthetic are also used. The net result is somewhat an average of the properties of each, many advantages or disadvantages being modified in the mixture. It is claimed that there is a net gain in cleanliness and safety, the principal objectives, without the drawbacks of the pure synthetic.

There are certain disadvantages to synthetics.

Synthetics are five to seven times as expensive as petroleum based oils.

More lubricant may be required.

Viscosity index *(VI)* is low for synthetics. The grade must be such that it can be pumped by the lubricator at ambient temperatures, but have sufficient body at cylinder surface temperatures to lubricate properly. There can be low-temperature handling problems. Some synthetics are not available with as high a viscosity as petroleum lubricants.

There is evidence to indicate that break-in using a phosphate ester synthetic must be done with much greater care than when a petroleum lubricant is used. Break-in with petroleum oil and then switching to the synthetic is definitely recommended.

All conventional paint must be removed from the lubricator reservoir and from any other part contacted by the synthetic. In a single-acting vertical-type reciprocating machine, this means the crankcase. Failure to do this thoroughly may result in clogged oil lines or ducts, faulty lubrication, and possible damage. Special paints are available that are said to be resistant to attack and my be used where necessary.

Since synthetics are powerful solvents and looseners, particularly of hydrocarbons, applying a synthetic to a machine that has been operating for years on petroleum lubricants demands expensive cleaning of compressor and intercooler. Failure to do a complete job can mean later loosening of dirt and scale that will be carried through the machine, causing severe damage.

If phosphate esters are to be used, a survey of all gasket, seal, packing, and lubricator materials is mandatory. Many commonly used materials are attacked by the synthetic and changes may be necessary. The lubricant supplier, as well as the compresor manufacturer, should be consulted. Special lubricator sight glasses and fluids may be needed.

Separation and removal of moisture and condensate ahead of each compressor stage must be done carefully. Synthetics are more vulnerable to water-washing and afford poor internal thin-film rust protection. Moisture carryover will cause trouble under conditions a compounded petroleum oil might have handled satisfactorily. Under some conditions, rusting and corrosion may result in a wear problem. This is an especially bad characteristic when air compressors are run intermittently. Severe rusting may occur during shutdown.

Toxicity does not seem to be a problem unless the fluid in liquid or mist form is taken into the respiratory system. Prolonged skin contact should be avoided; normal sanitary practices are satisfactory. Eye contact can be painful.

Rubber soled footwear cannot be worn where there may be any spillage of phosphate esters. Shoes, rubbers, or boots become plasticized and slippery, making walking hazardous.

Sometimes the synthetic cylinder oil will carry over on the rod of a reciprocating compressor. Since synthetics and petroleum oils are compatible, the result is a build-up of the synthetic in the crankcase that eventually will attack the crankcase paint. It may also reduce the viscosity of the crankcase mixture below that needed for proper lubrication. Particular attention must be paid to the condition of the rod oil wipers. These usually act only to prevent carryover of crankcase oil into the cylinder. Most manufacturers can provide double-acting wipers; they are recommended. It is suggested that the synthetic lubricant supplier test the crankcase oil occasionally for possible contamination.

As with petroleum oils, feed the minimum quantity to properly lubricate the parts.

Safety Precautions

The danger of fire is inherent in almost any air compressor system. Although there are few such occurrences for the number of air compressors in operation, there are enough to cause concern. The reasons should be appreciated.

What is known as the "fire triangle" exists in any fire or potential fire. The triangle consists of oxygen, fuel, and an ignition source. In the air compressor system, oxygen is always present. Petroleum oils are used as a lubricant. These have fuel value; they and their vapors will burn if ignited. Two sides of the triangle are always present. The third side, an ignition source, is most apt to be brought into action when *too much* or an *improper oil* is used, or when *maintenance* is neglected.

Maintenance is most important because dirty water-cooled intercoolers, dirty fins on air cooled units, broken or leaky discharge valves, broken piston rings, and the like always tend to increase normal discharge air temperature, sometimes rapidly. These excessive temperatures cause more rapid oil deterioration and formation of deposits, both of which are further accelerated if too much oil or an improper oil is being used. See Chapter 18 for maintenance procedures.

Based on experience, fires and explosions are seldom if ever caused by reaching the autogeneous ignition temperature of the oil. This averages between 600° and 750°F. There appears little opportunity for the existence of such a temperature.

Petroleum oils do decompose and form carbonaceous deposits. They collect on valves, heads, and discharge ports, and in piping. Experiments have shown that, in time, they may absorb some oxygen from the air and, under favorable conditions, will themselves start to decompose, generating heat. This heat might reach a point where the mass glows and becomes a trigger for more violent burning. This action is speeded by high temperatures. It is believed this reaction applies to a majority of reported incidents.

Fires have been known to occur and to burn out, causing no damage. Others cause a high pressure rise due to the increase in temperature and attempted expansion of the compressed air. Since expansion is impossible, the pressure increases until relieved. This is an ordinary pressure rise followed by mechanical failure. Maximum pressure may be 6 to 10 times initial pressure.

A special and destructive type of explosion may occur, although its frequency seems to be very low in air compressor systems. This is the rather unpredictable *detonation*, caused by development and propagation of a very high-speed pressure wave. As the originally ignited fuel burns, it gets hot, expands, and sends pressure waves ahead that push into the unburned gas. These waves compress the unburned gas ahead of the flame and materially heat this gas. As the flame follows through this hot, but unburned, gas, a normal explosion takes place. This builds a pressure front just ahead of the flame and sends ahead additional, faster moving, pressure waves that catch up to the slower waves and build up a *shock wave*. This travels at many times the speed of sound. It may reach extreme pressures of 60 to 100 times the initial pressure and ruptures vessels, pipe, and fittings with great violence. Although simplified, this illustrates the mechanism of detonation. The shock wave may move against the actual flow of the air.

As mentioned, these do not seem to be frequent in air compressors. One exception is found in air systems used to furnish starting air at about 250 psiG to gas and diesel engines. There is strong evidence that leakage from the engine through a faulty starting air valve provides both fuel and ignition in many explosions. Detonations often occur.

There is an obvious approach to the prevention of fires and explosions.

1. Keep the compressor in good repair;
2. Replace broken and leaking valves and parts immediately;
3. Check and record discharge temperatures frequently;
4. Keep the compressor clean internally and externally;
5. See that the coolant is actually flowing and in proper quantity;
6. Drain separators and receiver frequently;
7. Use the proper lubricant; and,
8. Use only enough lubricant.

An *aftercooler* should be used with every air compressor. If a fire starts between the compressor and aftercooler, it will go no further than the cooler, as a rule, and usually there is no explosion. A safety valve upstream of the aftercooler is recommended.

Storage and Handling of Lubricants

The lubricant manufacturer packages and ships his lubricant in containers specifically designed to prevent contamination. After the lubricant reaches the user, guarding against contamination and deterioration is his responsibility. The extent of this responsibility is not always appreciated. Areas in which damage to lubricants can occur are:

1. Dust and dirt entry;
2. Moisture entry, especially absorption from the atmosphere;
3. Extremes of temperature; and,
4. Mixing of different oils.

Involved also are safety and the prevention of leakage.

Effects of contaminating oil with dust, dirt, or moisture are so obvious that it is hardly conceivable that is should be a problem, but it is. Mixing of oil (designed to ease friction) with dirt and dust will result in a marked reduction in effectiveness and increased wear and maintenance. Permitting mixing of oil with water or moisture often destroys or nullifies the effect of certain additives, at times present in only minute quantities. In some oils, moisture may make the material useless.

Drums of oil should always be stored on their sides to prevent water accumulating on the tops. Since many drums breathe with temperature changes, storage at constant temperature will avoid the possibility of a drum sucking in moist air.

Extremes of temperature can cause temporary or permanent damage to quality. Low temperatures are the more prevalent due to storage in unheated buliding or outdoors in areas where the weather is seasonally cold. At the least, this makes oils difficult to handle, often necessitating heating. Use of direct heat should not be permitted. If heating is necessary indirect very low-pressure steam is advocated.

Mixing of different grades, qualities, or brands of oil is to be avoided. Oil is not "the same oil" just because it "looks right". There may be considerable difference between two similar types.

Oil leakage and safety are closely allied. Leakage and spillage are, first of all, pure waste. Invariably they cause serious safety and fire hazards. Oil on a floor is not conductive to surefootedness; an oil-soaked floor is always ready to be ignited.

Recommendations for storage and handling are best obtained from the lubricant supplier.

Methods of Lubricant Distribution

Regardless of lubricant or compressor, the lubricant does no good unless it is delivered to all the points to be lubricated and delivered in proper amounts. It must be distributed from a point or points of storage on the machine by some mechanism both automatically and reliably.

Circulation Systems

In circulation systems the oil is used over and over; recirculated. It may or may not be cooled or filtered in its travels.

Gravity or flood distribution is used for the frame and running gear of a few moderate sized horizontal reciprocators. The oil is carried by the crank disk from the sump in the crankcase to a trough in the top from which it flows by gravity to the various points to be lubricated. Closely allied to this method is the familiar ring oiled shaft bearing, in which rings ride and rotate on the journal. As they turn, they dip into oil in the base and carry it to the top of the journal.

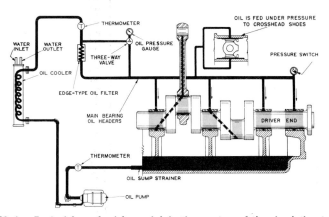

Fig. 13-A.   Typical force-feed frame lubrication system of the circulation type.

The *splash* system involves distribution of oil throughout a compressor by splash from a sump. Most small single-acting reciprocators use this. Some have the connecting rod dipper splash oil from a trough in which a constant level is maintained by a gear or disk. This accurately controls the amount of lubricant distributed because the oil level from which the dippers splash remains constant at all times. A machine with this type of lubrication is shown in Fig. 6-B-1, page 6-5.

Neither of these systems permits oil filtering. In a few cases, the sump may contain a watercooler to remove some of the heat developed.

Forced or *pressure* circulation is the most prevalent method for bearing lubrication in all but the smaller compressors. The oil pumps vary in type, with the gear and centrifugal predominating. Filtering of the oil as it circulates is usual and it is cooled in the larger sizes. A typical reciprocator frame system is diagrammatically shown in Fig. 13-A.

Once-Through Systems

Once-through systems are used principally for gas compression chambers of reciprocating and stationary water-cooled vane-type rotary compressors. A few bearings also use this system. As implied, the oil fed to lubrication points is used only once, usually leaving the machine with the gas. These all use some type of mechanical pump or *lubricator*.

The simple and widely used *force feed* lubricator is usually driven by the compressor through a belt or a mechanical linkage. It can also be motor driven. Its shaft operates the required number of oil pumps by means of cams, each pump feeding oil to a single lubrication point. The pumps are of the plunger type, usually with ball valves. The oil sump or reservoir in which the pumps are mounted may be compartmented to permit use of different types of oils for different applications. In all cases, means are provided for varying the amount of oil being fed by each pump.

There are many designs. One may have a single plunger pump in which the drop is visually shown in a liquid filled sight glass as it leaves the lubricator on its way to the compressor at the oil discharge pressure. Another type utilizes two pumps — one to measure the oil, the other to actually deliver it. The sight glass is on the discharge of the metering pump at atmospheric pressure. A third type keeps a dry sight glass under vacuum in the flow line to the suction of a single pump.

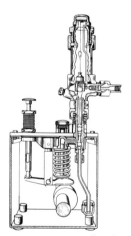

Courtesy of McCord Corporation.

Fig. 13-B.　Single-plunger liquid-filled-sight-glass lubricator mechanism.

The first type has been extensively used. It does a good job but is subject to gradual carry-over of the sight glass liquid (frequently a glycerine and water mixture), which will eventually destroy the usefulness of the sight glass. It will become cloudy or full of oil and drops cannot be seen. Occasional cleaning and replacement of the fluid is required. Carry-over is more prevalent with certain additive oils. If extreme, the oil supplier should be consulted to obtain a sight glass fluid more likely to stay put.

The disadvantage of the second and third types is that there is no positive evidence that the oil is actually being discharged into the line. It could be leaking by a worn plunger and returning to the reservoir. This is infrequent in today's designs, which are standard equipment for many heavy-duty and high-pressure compressors.

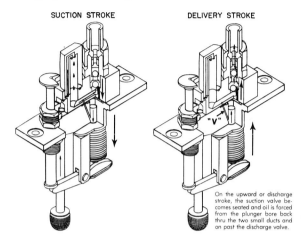

SUCTION STROKE DELIVERY STROKE

On the upward or discharge stroke, the suction valve becomes seated and oil is forced from the plunger bore back thru the two small ducts and on past the discharge valve.

Courtesy of McCord Corporation.

Fig. 13-C. Vacuum suction type of single-plunger lubricator.

Fig. 13-B and Fig. 13-C show, respectively, typical inner workings of the first and third types. Fig. 13-D shows a large motor-driven lubricator mounted on a compressor to provide cylinder and packing lubrication.

Devices that can sound an alarm or shut a machine down are available to protect against any stoppage of the oil flow from any individual lubricator, stoppage of the entire lubricator, or low oil level in the reservoir.

The principal difficulty with these lubricators is that they measure the oil in *drops* and this is, on the basis of extensive field tests, not entirely reliable *as a measure* under variable conditions of temperature, pressure, oil type, lubricator design, lubricator mechanical condition, and the like. As an example, a drop of oil from a normal liquid filled sight glass lubricator will be about three times as large as that shown in the sight glass of a vacuum feed lubricator. Additionally, oil viscosity variation and other factors will influence the size of a drop from time to time on a given pump.

To illustrate the effect of variable drop size, note the following on spheroid drops:

Diameter		Volume		Approximate Total Drops		Drops per min for One Unit Volume/24 hr	
inches	mm	cu in	cu cm	per quart	per liter	quart	liter
1/16	1.588	.000128	.00297	452,000	478,000	314	332
3/32	2.381	.000431	.00706	134,000	141,500	93.0	98.2
1/8	3.175	.001023	.01678	56,500	59,700	39.2	41.4
5/32	3.969	.001996	.03265	29,000	30,600	20.2	21.4
3/16	4.763	.00345	.0565	16,700	17,650	11.6	12.3

When a given lubricator on a specific compressor has once been adjusted to feed the *proper* amount of oil by actual internal inspection (see page 13-20), then the drop measure may be accepted as denoting approximate continuity of feed, provided the oil characteristics are not changed and the lubricator is in good condition. A visual internal inspection of the compressor should be made not less than once in six months to confirm the effectiveness of lubrication.

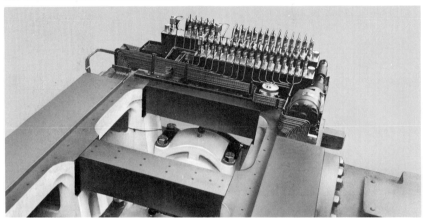

Fig. 13-D.   Multiple-feed motor-driven lubricator for a large process compressor.

A relatively new addition to lubricating systems utilizes an oil pump of adjustable capacity as a primary device to deliver the *total* oil quantity required by all feeds. This may be one of various types, but frequently is a force feed lubricator (or a portion of it) operating at its most accurate, long stroke setting.

Following the pump, a special meter panel indicates the oil pressure and the amount of oil flowing. Additional devices feed positively proportioned amounts to each lubricating point. The *total* amount fed is varied by adjusting the primary pump. The proportion going to each feed is predetermined by the size of the distributors, one for each feed. Regardless of the total amount of oil used, each feed gets its proportional amount.

Originally developed for lubrication of gas engine power cylinders, this system, although more expensive, is being applied to some large compressors.

Lubrication of Reciprocating Compressors

Three general divisions must be made in discussing lubrication of reciprocators.

    1. Single-acting machines, where the cylinders are lubricated from a splash crankcase system;

    2. Crankcase lubrication only in crosshead machines; and,

    3. The crosshead cylinders themselves, lubricated independently of the crankcase. Within this division there are two categories: normal lubrication and partial lubrication.

Single-Acting Splash-Lubricated Units

Oil used in the crankcase of single-acting splash-lubricated units also lubricates the air cylinders. Some manufacturers permit the use of automotive oils in certain smaller units. However, a quality air cylinder oil, specifically designed for compressor service, although it may be more expensive per gallon, will be less expensive per 100 hours of operation and will be satisfactory for the crankcase bearings. Preferably it should be a naphthenic base oil without detergent additives. The grade or viscosity of the oil used will depend on the ambient temperature in which the unit operates. The instruction book should be closely followed.

Complete oil changes will be necessary every 60 to 90 days or every 300 to 500 hours operation. whichever comes first. The importance of this cannot be overstated. Manufacturers may vary in the time period to be followed. Refer to the instruction book.

If the oil is very dirty when drained or contains an appreciable amount of water, the crankcase should be flushed using regular flushing oil. DO NOT use kerosene, gasoline, or any inflammable solvent.

Under certain conditions, moisture may form in the crankcase. The oil should then contain rust and oxidation inhibitors. These are most apt to be required when units operate very intermittently and ambient conditions provide high humidity and/or low temperatures. Condensation leads to oil breakdown and the formation of sludge. In such cases, discuss the problem with the oil supplier. If operating periods are at least 10 minutes long, the machine and the oil will become well heated and condensation is less likely.

The single-acting compressors being discussed are equipped with special rings on the piston to prevent excessive oil carry-over into the top of the cylinder. Only enough should get by these rings to lubricate the valves and compression rings. More will cause heavier and more rapid deposit build-up on the valves, compression rings and head. Furthermore, oil that gets by cannot return to the crankcase for reuse and is wasted. Oil must then be added to maintain the proper level.

Manufacturers work to solve this problem with special designs of piston rings accurately fitted. There are three or four rings on a piston. These will do a satisfactory job for a long time, but both rings and cylinder will wear eventually and rings will need replacement. One manufacturer has developed a method of determining when rings should be replaced. This requires keeping a record of both operating time and oil added to the crankcase. Although this is "rule of thumb", it is a good one. Periodically (say once a month) go through the following calculation.

$$\frac{\text{Motor hp} \times \text{Operating hours}}{\text{Oil used (oz)}}$$

(Ounces are weight). If the ratio falls below 25, it is time for a repair job. Ring replacement can be expected about every 5000 hours of running time, although the exact service life is greatly dependent upon care taken to maintain a clean air filter and to supply proper lubrication.

It is important to follow the manufacturer's instructions closely in making ring replacement, particularly as to fitting rings and reconditioning the cylinder bore.

Crankcases of Crosshead Machines

Crankcase bearings, by themselves, present only moderate problems. The following factors influence selection of their lubricants:

1. Oil is exposed to some oxidation as it is circulated; the deterioration is cumulative since the oil is used over and over; and,

2. Operating temperatures may be high, depending on how the oil is cooled. If this is done only by crankcase radiation, temperatures may reach 150° to 200°F on some machines operating in a high ambient temperature.

Viscosity must be such that, under the load, speed, and operating temperature, a proper oil film will be maintained between moving parts. During a long shutdown, the film must be maintained so that metal-to-metal contact cannot occur during start-up. The oil film must not squeeze out. Film strength must be high.

These oils should be free from fats or fixed oil compounding. Oils containing rust and oxidation inhibitors are preferred and the presence of a defoaming agent is sometimes desirable. However, the use of additives for this (or any other) purpose must not increase the surface activity of the oil sufficiently to cause inordinate carry-over of oil on the piston rod. These oils must be noncorrosive to the common bearing metals. The pour point should be at least 10°F below ambient temperature at starting time, or oil heating should be used.

Moisture or water is not normally a problem in crankcase oil on electrically powered compressors. Integral steam engine-driven units should have special attention. Special crankcase oils will be necessary on integral gas-engine-powered compressors.

Oil Changes

Manufacturers can recommend crankcase oil change periods only in general terms. A great deal depends on the actual lubrication system and whether oil filters and oil coolers are used.

In all cases, an initial oil change should be made within a period of 24 hours (minimum) to 72 hours (maximum) after start-up. The crankcase should be drained, together with any oil filter, cooler, pumps, and, insofar as possible, piping. Flush the crankcase and all accessible parts with "VARSOL" or similar safety solvent, using an air jet spray. Then drain.

Refill the crankcase to the high level mark with new or properly reconditioned oil. Be sure the cooler, filter, and other components are filled also. Thereafter, since most crankcases are dust tight and the majority have continuous oil filtration, it should not be necessary to change the oil more often than every 4000 to 8000 hours.

Where the compressor is operated in extremely dirty atmosphere, is installed outdoors, is operated intermittently, is handling foul gas in the compressor cylinder, or where the oil reaches high temperatures, or there is no oil filter, it may be necessary to change the oil more often.

Most reputable oil companies will make a laboratory analysis of oil samples if requested to do so. Use of this service is highly recommended and will usually result in safely extending what might be called normal oil change periods.

Normal Lubrication of Crosshead Cylinders

Its Importance

Cylinder lubrication is the most important feature of reciprocating compressor operation. It reduces wear and maintenance, assures continuous reliable operation, and provides the maximum in safety. Too many compressors are fed too much oil or an improper oil. Too much oil results in excessive oil cost, increased cleaning cost, greater fire hazards in some cases, and abnormal contamination of gas with the lubricant. Use of an improper oil carries with it probabilities of the above problems plus abnormal wear and maintenance. To properly lubricate a cylinder requires:

1. Proper break-in;
2. Use of the proper oil;
3. Careful determination of the proper amount for each lubrication point; and,
4. Continuing checks to assure that the proper oil in sufficient amount is actually being delivered to each point.

Parts to be Lubricated

There are three places within a cylinder that require lubrication; (1) between the piston, compression rings, and cylinder; (2) between the packing and the piston rod; and (3), between the moving parts of valves on most designs.

The oil is always positively pumped to one or more points in the cylinder bore and sometimes to the metallic packing. There is enough carryover from the cylinder on the piston rod in many units to lubricate the packing and a separate feed is not required. Each lubrication point has a separate adjustable pump.

Valves require very little lubrication and usually obtain it from the oil carried in the gas. Some large cylinders, particularly when the inlet gas may contain condensate, are provided with a separate feed to the inlet pipe near the cylinder to assure sufficient inlet valve lubrication. This also aids cylinder lubrication.

Break-in Procedure

All newly machined surfaces have hills and valleys. The height and depth of these are dependent upon such variables as material, metal structure, and type of finish machining operation. During break-in it is necessary that these roughnesses on the piston, compression rings, cylinder bore, piston rod, and packing be worn, rounded off, or bent to form good mating bearings. This is probably the most critical period in the life of these parts and the demands on the lubricant are extreme. During break-in, the cylinder parts are also apt to be exposed to dirt, welding beads, sand, and pipe scale from poorly cleaned intake piping. Although this is true for all types and sizes of machines, it is especially so for large, high-pressure, and other heavy-duty compressors. See page 18-11 for pipe cleaning methods and page 18-12 on the use of temporary line filters.

To rush a machine into production before properly breaking it in is false economy. Take time for a thorough break-in and it will extend the life of the wearing parts and reduce the number of emergency shutdowns.

To best lubricate cylinder parts during break-in, *it is highly desirable* to use both a heavier oil in the cylinder and more than a normal amount. General rules call for an oil two SAE grades heavier (more viscous) than the regular oil to be used. For heavy-duty and large high-pressure units, use an SAE 60 grade. Since cylinder oils are not rated in SAE grades the following table will approximately correlate this with viscosity at 210°F, a value which guides oil suppliers. See also page 13-4.

SAE Grade	SSU Viscosity at 210°F (99°C)	
	Minimum	Maximum
20	45	58
30	58	70
40	70	85
50	85	110
60*	105*	125*
70*	125*	150*

*Obsolete rating not presently list by SAE

Oil should be fed to each point at a rate several times the anticipated normal, preferably with each feed pumping its maximum. The excess is necessary to flush out wear particles and trash materials.

With the heavy oil recommended, it is essential that checks be made to assure oil is actually flowing to the cylinder. This is particularly necessary when breaking-in under low ambient temperatures. It may be necessary to heat the oil in the lubricator and piping.

When Is a Compressor Broken-in?

Break-in cannot wisely be hurried. The larger the cylinder, the higher the ultimate pressure, and the greater the complexity of the unit, the longer the break-in time. As a rough guide, the following is a probable minimum for *complete* break-in.

HP Rating	Operating Hours	
	No Load	Gradually Increasing Load
UP to 150	2	20 to 50
150 to 500	5	30 to 70
500 to 1500	10	110

Heavy-duty and high-pressure units, or those using special materials, should be on break-in for a total of 300 hours minimum, the division of this period depending upon size, pressure, and complexity.

Break-in is complete only when each cylinder has a high polish with no dull spots, and the oil from the stuffing box is clean and clear, indicating no further packing wear.

It is necessary during break-in to shut the unit down frequently to remove one or more valves from each end and observe the condition of the cylinder bore. Each inspection should include a check for dirt, sand, scale, liquid, etc., in the cylinder counterbore or on the head, piston, or valves. If present, clean before restarting. For safety, block the piston or crosshead before working within the cylinder. Take steps to *prevent* liquid carry-over.

Initial break-in should preferably be done under the guidance of the manufacturer's supervisor of erection, especially when large or complex units are involved.

A similar procedure should be used after replacing worn parts, such as cylinder, cylinder liner, piston, piston rings, piston rod, or packing, although it may often be done more quickly since at least one of the mating surfaces will have already been broken-in.

The above minimums can be safely reduced only under certain conditions, such as where the unit has been run in the shop before shipment or where field conditions are unusually favorable. The most important steps toward obtaining reduced break-in time are the complete elimination of dirt and liquid carryover into the cylinders. Shop run machines are often broken-in within 50 percent of the above times under favorable circumstances. Only careful inspection can determine when the process is actually completed. Longer parts life and less maintenance is assured with a properly broken-in compressor. *Do not rush to put a compressor on the line.*

The Proper Oil

Once the cylinders on a compressor are broken-in, the oil should be gradually changed to the proper viscosity for regular use. The exact oil should be selected after full discussion with a reputable oil supplier familiar with compressor requirements. It should be one the supplier will guarantee for the particular service involved. It should also meet the following general recommendations and any instructions book specifications. Bear in mind that oils on the more viscous side are preferred.

Pending determination of the final requirements for each lubrication point, the drops per minute may be reduced to about half that of the wide-open setting.

Recommendation for Cylinder Lubricating Oil

The following recommendations deal with five types of petroleum lubricating oil suitable for the cylinders of vacuum pumps or single- and multistage compressors handling air, hydrocarbon gases, nitrogen, hydrogen, carbon dioxide, and all of the inert rare gases. Lubricating oil recommendations for refrigerating compressors or for units where the cylinders are splash-lubricated from the crankcase are not included.

These oils are to be well-refined petroleum products. They should be prepared from selected naphthenic or paraffinic stocks (naphthenic is preferred), processed to minimize deposit formation. Superior rust-preventive properties are desired. Pour point must be consistent with the lowest ambient, gas intake, and cylinder jacket temperatures to be encountered. The pour point must always be sufficiently lower than ambient temperature to permit proper rate of feed by the lubricator. In handling low-temperature gases, an oil of suitably low pour point must be selected, on the basis of intake and jacket temperatures, to maintain a fluid film of lubricant in the cylinder.

Type 1 — Rust- and/or oxidation-inhibited oil or straight mineral oil is acceptable.

Type 2 — Internal-combustion engine lubricating oil of one of the following classes: (A) straight mineral oil; (B) rust and oxidation inhibited oil; and, (C) detergent engine oil of low detergency level.

Type 2X — Compounded compressor cylinder oil or detergent engine oil is recommended. This oil must be capable of providing an improved state of boundary lubrication and must resist the washing effect of the particular condensate involved.

Type 3 — Rust- and/or oxidation-inhibited oil or straight mineral oil is acceptable.

Type 3X — Compounded compressor cylinder oil or detergent engine oil is recommended. It must be capable of providing an improved state of boundary lubrication and must resist the washing effect of the particular condensate involved.

Notes

For *Type 1, 2 and 3 oils,* gases handled must be dry; they may not carry suspended liquid but may contain water vapor or other condensables that remain in the super-heated vapor state throughout the compression cycle.

For *Type 2X and 3X oils,* gases handled may occassionally carry *small* quantities of suspended liquid into the cylinder or may deposit some condensation in the cylinder.

Type 2 oils are for applications identical to those where Type 1 oil is normally recommended and where for commercial reasons, the operator wishes to use internal-combustion engine lubricating oil.

All Tests shall be conducted in accordance with the Standard Methods (latest edition) of the American Society For Testing Materials.

Service Considerations

(a) When Type 1 oil is recommended, oils on the high side of the viscosity range are favored for single-stage compressors.

(b) In the food, beverage, pharmaceutical, and chemical industries, even traces of conventional lubricating oil are sometimes objectionable. The user should obtain special recommendations from the oil supplier and the compressor manufacturer.

(c) Certain chemical process catalysts are "poisoned" by lubricating oil additives. Straight mineral oil of the viscosity recommended for the operating conditions should be used.

(d) Certain lubricating oil additives will cloud the glycerine-water mixture ordinarily used in the lubricator sight feed, necessitating frequent changes of the mixture.

(e) The continuous carry-over of liquid to compressor cylinders requires the installation of efficient separators.

Summary of Lubricating Oil Recommendations

OIL TYPE	Type 1	Type 2	Type 2X	Type 3	Type 3X
Cylinder Diameter (in.)............	26 Max	26 Max	26 Max	*** Over 26	*** Over 26
Discharge Temperature (°F)..........	350 Max	350 Max	350 Max	Over 350	Over 350
Is Condensed Water Vapor Present.....	No	No	Yes or possible	No	Yes or possible
Is Suspended Liquid Present..........	No	No	Yes or possible	No	Yes or possible
Are There Special Requirements: All multistage or circulator cylinders with discharge pressure of 2000-7000 psiG........	No	No	No	Required	Required
Physical and Chemical Requirements..					
Flash Point (Open Cup) °F..........	350 Min	380 Min	380 Min	410 Min	410 Min
Viscosity at 100°F (SSU)............	420 Max	....	780 Max	....	....
Viscosity at 210°F (SSU)............	50 Min	54–65	60 Min	105 Min.	105 Min.
Carbon Residue (Conradson).......	0.25 Max	*0.45 Max	*0.45 Max	0.65 Max	0.65 Max
Sulfated Ash.......	....	0.40 Max	....	....	....
Approximate SAE Number..........	20	20–30	30	60	60
Neutralization Value (color): Total Acid Number..........	....	**0.15 Max	....	....	....
Strong Acid No. ASTM D-974-58T..	0.00 Max	0.00 Max	0.00 Max	0.00 Max	0.00 Max

*Ash-free basis. **On straight mineral or additive-treated, non-detergent oils. ***See (f) below.

(f) On multistage and circulator compressors, use a higher-viscosity oil than is indicated by cylinder size. Cylinders that operate at discharge pressures in the range of 2000 to 7000 psiG should use a Type 3 or Type 3X oil to obtain an adequate seal of piston and/or packing rings. The oil selected for the high-pressure cylinders can also be used in cylinders operating at pressures below 2000 psiG in order to reduce the number of oils to be handled. Consult the manufacturer for recommended oil specifications at pressures above 7000 psiG.

For oils for refrigerating cylinders and other low-temperature services, obtain recommendations from both the manufacturer and a reputable oil supplier.

What is the Proper Quantity?

A compressor cylinder is properly lubricated when all parts requiring lubrication are covered with a thin film of oil — no dry spots — and there are no puddles, which would indicate an excess. Valves should be oily and the oil coming from the packing box should be clean, with the rod just oily when wiped on the top with tissue. Cylinders, too should be tested with tissue.

If there are any dry spots, the appropriate oil feed should receive more oil. If there are puddles in the counterbore or valve pockets, or other evidences of excess oil, the feed should be reduced, but very *gradually*. The compressor cylinder bore, valves, and gas passages should be carefully examined shortly before and after any reduction in oil feed. Each reduction must be a small step.

It is impossible to say ahead of time what quantity (volume) of oil will be proper for a given cylinder. There are many variables: the gas; whether it contains condensables or not; diameter and stroke of the cylinder; its operating pressure and temperature; weight of parts; rpm; method and location of oil feed openings; and, materials of mating parts. Proper oil quantities must be set by inspection and feed adjustment. There is no other sound method.

Once proper lubrication is attained, the drops per minute may be used as an approximate measure. See page 13-11. This is never absolute; every time the cylinder is opened for valve replacement (and at least once every six months) the cylinder should be inspected, its condition through-out well noted, and any necessary oil feed adjustments made.

Once the minimum oil feed for proper lubrication is set, the actual amount being used can be determined by (1) filling the lubricator reservoir, (2) operating until a substantial amount is used, then refilling from a graduated container so that the amount added is known. This, referred to the operating time, will give a pints per 24 hour rate. On most compressors this will be an over-all figure rather than a value for individual feeds, since all feeds may use the same oil from a common tank.

A record or log of oil used in a given period and of the corresponding compressor running time should be kept. If analyzed weekly or even monthly, it will point up any divergence from the established correct usage. Appropriate action can then be taken.

One of the decided advantages of a properly lubricated compressor is its relative freedom from valve and cylinder deposits caused by excessive amount of oil or the wrong kind. Over lubrication particularly will multiply rapidity of build-up and need for maintenance.

Partial Lubrication of Crosshead Type Cylinders

Most lubricated compressor cylinders are over-lubricated, a fact realized by some who use intelligent procedures to keep lubrication to a minimum. These are usually operators troubled more or less severely by the effect of the lubricant in a process or subsequent gas use. An excellent example is air compressed for an air separation plant where lubricant carry-over congeals on cooling coils and forces undesired shutdowns for cleaning. It also may pose serious hazards due to oil breakdown in minute quantities. In this application, oil quantities have been controlled to a seemingly unbelievable minimum. Careful operation brings success.

It might be expected that in such cases one would turn to nonlubricated (NL) designs and eliminate the lubricant entirely. This might be done if NL units were available for the particular service conditions involved or if the reciprocator could be replaced by either the dynamic or helical-lobe units that deliver oil-free gas. However, the latter are often unsuitable and the higher maintenance and down time of the current NL reciprocator may preclude its use, even if available. The problem of gas contamination may not be sufficiently severe.

However, there is a desire by some to limit lubricant use to a still lower limit than is possible using normal methods. This has led to the advancement of cylinder designs that utilize what is known as *partial lubrication*, requiring special designs and materials to permit successful operation with a reduced lubricant quantity. These materials will "live" with very small oil quantities and still give reasonable service life. Actually, these modifications utilize a great deal of NL cylinder technology. See Chapter 14.

Partial lubrication is still somewhat of a joint experiment between the compressor builder and the operator. Experience is accumulating; a sound technology will eventually develop. Thus, only the generalities of the art as it exists in late 1966 is presented. Other materials will be developed and it is possible that the quality and reliability of materials for a true NL will extend its service life and reduce its maintenance to a point where it generally will be used instead of *partial lubrication*.

Construction

One must design for partial lubrication. It cannot be obtained by minimizing oil fed to a normally lubricated machine. Nor can it become NL, because *some* lubricant must always be used; the amount will vary with the design. The construction of the unit will vary between the fully lubricated and the strict NL machine, somewhat in proportion to the amount of lubricant admitted. TFE is the material presently used in piston rider and compression rings. TFE or carbon, usually the former, is the rod packing ring material most frequently used, although two classes of *partially* lubricated units retain metallic packing. Four typical arrangements will illustrate. *In each case no lubricant is fed to the cylinder*. TFE is a fluorocarbon resin or plastic.

Packings Rings	Valves	Rider Rings	Compression Rings	How Lubricated
Metallic	Std	None	TFE	Full feed to packing
Metallic	Spcl*	TFE	TFE	Reduced feed to packing
TFE	Spcl*	TFE	TFE	Minimal feed to packing
TFE or carbon	Spcl*	TFE	TFE	Carry-over from crankcase

*depending upon application

The first of these is rather dangerous unless carefully watched and is seldom recommended. It will require more lubricant than the others.

In considering this subject, each cylinder of a multistage unit must be considered separately in making final adjustments. There will, in some cases, be a bit of oil carry-over to the upper stages to assist lubrication.

To emphasize some of the potential problems of *partial* lubrication, it is suggested that the functions of a lubricant (page 13-2) be reviewed. It is more important than ever that no lubricant function be interferred with. For example, the gas must be clean and liquid entry prevented.

Also, in partial lubrication, there is a certain oil feed rate where the wear debris from TFE or carbon parts will form an abrasive paste with the very small amount of oil involved. Severe damage to compression and rider rings and packings may result. Rods and cylinder bores may be scored. This feed rate is not predictable and must be a concern for study and observation in any partial-lubricated operations.

Plunger Cylinders

Outside packed plunger-type cylinders (see Fig. 6-AK, page 6-32) are at times spoken of as nonlubricated. These are actually partially lubricated because some of the packing oil will always enter the cylinder and mix with the gas. The degree of contamination will depend upon the amount of the lubricant fed to the packing.

Lubrication of Water-Cooled Vane-Type Rotary Compressors

Chapter 7 describes the principal type of sliding-vane rotary compressor for heavy-duty industrial use. There are also a number of small rotaries (not discussed or illustrated). They differ in construction details, but all involve the same principles of operation. These small units are usually available for only low pressure air service.

Lubrication of these smaller units may be a once-through system (see page 13-10), utilizing drip feed cups or a gravity-feed recirculation system. In the latter, the oil fed into the cylinder in considerable quantities is discharged with the gas into a chamber where it is separated from any condensate by settling. The oil is then recirculated to the machine by gravity and the discharge pressure in the separator.

The following applies only to the larger water-cooled units of Chapter 7. Lubrication of the package-type oil-flooded design is discussed in Chapter 11 (Portable Compressors).

Parts to be Lubricated

The sliding vanes and cylinder walls, as well as shaft bearings and packing or shaft seals, must be well lubricated. A rather copious quantity is normally used. Oil also must seal the ends of the blades and rotor against leakage.

Methods of Lubrication

The once-through system uses a belt-driven force-feed lubricator (see page 13-10). There is a feed to each bearing, two or more to the top of the cylinder, and in many cases a feed to a quill located in the inlet passage. Each feed is independently adjustable.

Break-in

Break-in is discussed on pages 18-25 and 18-37.

The Proper Oil and Oil Quantity

Manufacturers usually present typical oil specifications in instruction books. An average might be:

	Up to 30 psiG	Over 30 psiG and Two Stages
Flash Point — °F	425	425
SSU at 210°F	55 to 70	70–95
Max. Pour Point — °F	25	25

Oil on the heavier side is recommended for the larger units.

One manufacturer definitely prefers paraffinic-base oils and specifies the inclusion of rust, anti-oxidant, and antiwear additives.

The amount of oil may or may not be specified in the instruction book. Quantities, if specified, will be based on the particular lubricator supplied.

Synthetic lubricants have been used in vane-type rotaries but should be applied only after consultation with the manufacturer.

Lubrication of Helical-Lobe Rotary Compressors

The helical-lobe rotary unit requires lubrication on only the bearings, timing gears, and at times the shaft seals. No lubrication is required within the compression chamber itself. See Chapter 8 for a description of this machine. The following is typical of one make only.

Distribution Methods

The low-pressure units in the smaller sizes generally utilize a form of splash distribution, the oil being picked up by disks on a rotor shaft and thrown around the end chambers from reservoirs in the housing. Those operating at discharge temperatures above 250°F are supplied with oil coolers. Larger units in the low-pressure design use a gear-type oil pump to positively circulate the oil. It is driven from one of the rotor shafts. Oil is filtered by an edge-type filter.

Fig. 13-E illustrates a typical edge-type oil filter used on many compressors having circulating oil systems. The oil flows between concentric metallic disks of two diameters. There is a very small difference between the outside diameter of the smaller and the inside diameter of the larger disk. This is the filtering gap through which the oil flows, the dirt particles being retained on the outside where they are periodically scraped off when the disk assembly is rotated. A handle on the outside is used for turning as often as necessary.

The high-pressure compressors use a forced circulation system from an off-unit or console assembly. This will usually consist of a reservoir, motor- or steam-turbine-driven oil pump, cooler, filter (a fiber replaceable cartridge-type is sometimes used), and high oil temperature and low oil pressure alarms or shut-down switches. This assembly must be piped to the compressor.

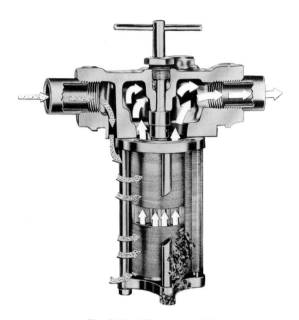

Fig. 13-E.   Edge-type oil filter.

The Proper Oil

As always, the lubricant supplier should be willing to guarantee his product for the service. For the lower-pressure units, one manufacturer provides the following guide:

The oil should be a well-refined petroleum product and should not contain fats or fixed compounding. Oil containing rust and oxidation inhibitors and a foam depressant are preferred. They must be substantially noncorrosive to the bearing metals. Detergent or low-grade oils are not recommended. Pour point should be at least 10°F below minimum ambient temperature. The viscosity at operating conditions should be at least 100 SSU.

Ambient Temperature	Below Freezing	Above Freezing	Extremely High
SAE Classification	20	30	40–50
Flash Point (Open Cup)	350°F min	380°F min	410°F min
Viscosity at 100°F (SSU)	420 max	780 max	. . . .
Viscosity at 210°F (SSU)	50 min	60 min	80–105
Carbon Residue (Conradson)	0.25 max	0.45 max	0.65 max
Strong Acid Number ASTM D 974–58T	0.00 max	0.00 max	0.00 max

The high-pressure units, operating at a much higher speed, require a somewhat different oil:

The lubricating oil should be a high quality, turbine-type oil. It is recommended that is contain an antifoam agent and rust inhibitors. The use of detergent or low-grade oils is not recommended.

Flash Point, °F (Open Cup)	370 Minimum
Viscosity at 100°F (SSU)	150 - 300
Viscosity Index	85 Minimum
Rusting Test ASTM D-665-60 Procedure A	Shall Pass
Turbine Oil Stability Test	1000 Hours Minimum
Emulsion Test ASTM D-1401-56T	3 ml Lacy Emulsion Maximum in 30 Minutes
Strong Acid Number	0.00 Maximum
Total Acid Number ASTM D-974-58T	0.15 Maximum

Oil Changes

With units having a built-in lubricating oil sump, on the initial start, change the oil after 100 to 200 hours of operation. Thereafter, a change every 1500 to 2000 hours should be sufficient. Alternatively, have the oil supplier test the oil to determine change periods.

On units having a separate console oil system, all piping should be thoroughly cleaned and flushed prior to the initial start. Oil change periods may extend to 5000 hours or more, depending upon operating contions.

Lubrication of Dynamic Compressors

Dynamic compressors normally require lubrication for shaft bearings, thrust bearings, and oil-type shaft seals (if used). The coupling is frequently lubricated, usually from the bearing system. With steam-turbine drive, either direct or geared, although the lubrication systems can be separate, the compressor, turbine, and gear systems are more often combined.

Methods of Application

The small machines may use antifriction bearings with either grease from a pressure system or grease cups. Others may deliver oil to the bearing from a sump in the housing by a disk or oil ring. Some of these units use sleeve bearings. The larger and often higher speed units utilize sleeve bearings and a pressure circulation system. The following is concerned only with this type.

A Typical System

Fig. 13-F illustrates a typical lubrication system for a direct-coupled turbine-driven centrifugal compressor. This system also may lubricate the coupling and supply hydraulic power to the turbine governor or regulator.

The auxiliary and separate-driven oil pump shown is necessary to maintain oil pressure at all times in case of failure of the main oil pump. The auxiliary unit may be electrically or steam driven (at times one of each is used) and is automatically started when the oil pressure falls to a preset minimum.

Most main oil pumps are separately driven, thus providing full oil pressure regardless of the compressor speed during both starting and stopping operations. In the case of the occasional main oil pump geared to the compressor, the auxiliary oil pump takes over starting and stopping duties. Regardless of speed, full oil pressure must be maintained.

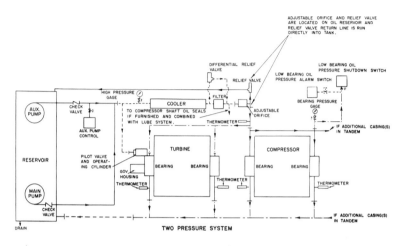

Fig. 13-F. Typical flow diagram for lubricating oil for a large turbine-driven dynamic compressor.

The Proper Oil

Responsibility for supplying the proper oil for the lubricating system rests with the oil vendor and the user. This responsibility includes specifications for inspection, flushing, purifying, and treatment of the oil during operation, and maintenance and replacement as necessary to insure satisfactory equipment performance.

A typical oil specification follows:

A premium-quality turbine oil prepared from selected petroleum stock, so refined and/or additive-treated to obtain unusual oxidation stability, preferential metal-wettability and rust-preventive properties. It must be substantially noncorrosive to the common bearing metals.

Flash Point (Open Cup)	370°F Minimum
Viscosity at 100°F (SSU)	140-170
Strong Acid Number	0.00 Maximum
Total Acid Number ASTM D-974-58T	0.15 Maximum
Emulsion Test ASTM D-1401-56T	3 ml Lacy Emulsion Maximum in 30 Minutes
Oxidation Stability Test ASTM D-943-54	1000 Minimum Hours to Acid Number of 2.0
Rusting Test ASTM D-665-60 Procedure A	Shall Pass
Viscosity Index	85 Minimum

When a combined lubrication system is furnished for all components — turbine, motor, gear, coupling, or compressor — care should be exercised to ascertain that the lubricant is compatible with all items.

Oil Treatment

Success in the use of oil is attained only by continual observation, care, and treatment. As oil passes repeatedly through bearings, it becomes contaminated with water, dust, metallic wear particles, loose paint, and other rubbish. If properly filtered and cared for, oil may be used for many months, depending on initial quality of the oil, effectiveness of the strainers, filters, and treating devices, and, the number of hours per day that the unit is in operation.

Since many dynamic units operate without shutdown for 1, 2 or even 3 years, effective lubrication is most important. Some form of continuous oil conditioner should be considered. The system should be such as to remove all water and other foreign matter. However, since some reclamation equipment will remove additives from the oil along with the foreign material, the oil supplier must be consulted.

Chapter 14

Nonlubricated Compressors

Caption Index **Page**

Introduction

The term, Nonlubricated Compressors, includes only those units that utilize *no* liquid lubricant of a petroleum, synthetic, or other type within the compression chamber. The dry helical-lobe rotary, dynamic, and ejector units may be said to be nonlubricated in *normal* designs. With the first two, precautions may be required to assure there is no possibility of lubricant leakage into the gas stream from bearings, gears, seals, etc. even though none is required within the compression space. Reciprocators are normally lubricated; by the use of special designs and materials, they may be run without lubricant of any sort in contact with the gas. This chapter discusses *only the reciprocating* nonlubricated (NL) unit.

> Note:—Any lubricant or lubricant vapor entrained with the inlet gas stream is the responsibility of the purchaser and is a possibility that should be guarded against in connection with any nonlubricated installation.

Reasons for NL Use

A number of reasons may be advanced for eliminating the normal lubricant. With some, NL design is mandatory; with others, there may be some question. Typical reasons include

1. Safety (oxygen compressors);
2. Lubricant contaminates gas stream (agitation and transfer of milk);
3. Gas attacks lubricant (chlorine and boron-trifluoride);
4. Lubricant carry-over fouls heat exchangers (many processes);
5. Lubricant carry-over "poisons" catalyst (catalytic reformers and ammonia oxidation);
6. No suitable lubricant available for very low temperatures (expander engine); and,
7. Lubricant fouls air powered instruments (control devices).

Gases Handled in NL Reciprocating Compressors

Many gases have been handled in NL compressors. Inclusion below does not mean that NL is always used. Special conditions requiring an oil-free product may have been present, although the compressor would normally be lubricated; for example, Freon* type refrigerants.

Air	Hydrogen
Ammonia	Hydrogen-HC mixture
Ammonia synthesis gas (H_2 plus N_2)	Hydrogen chloride
Argon and nitrogen mixtures	Hydrogen sulphide
Butadiene	HC mixtures
Chlorine	Methane
Carbon monoxide	Methyl chloride
Carbon dioxide	Nitrogen
Ethane	Orthodichlorobenzene
Ethyl chloride	Oxygen
Ethylene	Phosgene mixture
Ethylene oxide	Propylene
Freon* type refrigerants	Sulphur dioxide
Helium	Vinyl chloride

* *Registered Trademark of DuPont Company*

Typical Industries Utilizing NL Reciprocating Compressors

Air fractionation	Helium production
Brewing	Oxygen production and distribution
Chemical	Petrochemical
Cryogenics	Starting air units
Food and milk	Refinery
Gas transmission	Synthetic ammonia

Instrument air — in many industries

Economics of NL Units

Compared to lubricated machines, NL units will have a higher first cost, at times a higher power cost, usually more floor space, a higher maintenance cost, and more down time for maintenance. The latter frequently will be many times greater because of the more frequent need for routine checkups and renewal or adjustment of parts.

Also involved is the fact that the discharge gas contains no oil to coat piping, and possibly exchangers, and corrosion may occur. Rusting with NL units is possible.

Offsetting these added costs are such items as elimination of oil removal equipment on the discharge stream, no spoiled product, longer catalyst life, reduced maintenance of process equipment, etc. NL machines may even make a process or manufacturing method feasible; without NL designs, it could not be attempted.

Before buying an NL compressor, a complete economic study is recommended, balancing the NL operation against the overall cost of using a lubricated unit. The lesser down time of the latter and possible lower power cost may make the conventional unit the better. However, if oil *must* be completely eliminated and the reciprocator is best suited to the compression job, then an NL machine is the answer.

Historical Note

The first NL units (called the Class 1 or Class A design by manufacturers) had a form of partial lubrication (see page 13-20) since the rod packing used was expected to obtain some lubrication through oil carryover from the crankcase. The fact that this was still too much for some uses, particularly with food products and instrument air, did not really become evident for some years. Designs to prevent this carry-over, plus packing that would run with no lubrication, brought the true NL machine into being. This was known as the Class 2 or Class B design and is the type built today. It is available single stage to 100 psiG. Multistaging is usual for higher pressures.

Regarding the Future

New materials are continually being developed and evaluated. The art is in a progressing state (late 1966) and in time, many of the present NL problems and limitations may be reduced or even eliminated. However, it does not seem possible that NL compressors can ever match the on-line record of normally lubricated reciprocating units. Cleaner gas, more frequent inspections, and greater operating care will always be required.

NL Materials

Carbon was the original basic low-friction material used in piston and packing parts to supplant a lubricant. Many hundreds of machines are in operation using this material and giving satisfactory service. Carbon has certain disadvantages, however, and other materials are beginning to take its place.

The development in the late 1940's of TFE, a fluorocarbon resin or plastic, together with filler materials to permit its use as rider rings, compression rings, and rod packing rings has sped and expanded the technology of NL compressors. The range, scope and life of NL parts has been greatly broadened. Although, only TFE is mentioned here, comments should apply quite well to most future plastics, which is the area where improvements seem most likely. Currently, there is no universal material or compound that gives optimum service under any and all conditions.

When the NL idea was first introduced, tests on compressors equipped with carbon rings and packing showed an average loss in capacity of about 5 percent over the same size units with conventional lubrication. The use of TFE shows the potential of substantially decreasing this loss.

Neither carbon nor TFE are self-lubricated materials. The value of these materials rests solely in their low coefficient of friction.

TFE has been replacing carbon principally because of its superior wearing qualities, ability to withstand abuse (it is not fragile and parts do not chip or break if dropped or mishandled), its lower coefficient of friction, and the greater ease of manufacturing and assembling parts. It is elastic and may be stretched over a piston into a groove. Compression rings may be of the conventional snap ring type whereas carbon rings must usually be segmental. TFE will withstand occasional slugs of liquid carry-over that might break carbon parts. TFE compounds, however, must be more carefully engineered and selected in application than carbon.

Both carbon and TFE have excellent corrosion resistance. Carbon wears rapidly with a very dry gas (dew point below approximately 20°F). TFE, although having improved performance with moisture present, will give satisfaction on very low dew point gases if the unit rubbing pressure is kept low.

Both materials are machinable to close tolerances. There are occasional problems with TFE, due to its being somewhat less dimensionally stable in one direction than in the other. TFE is apt to extrude under high pressure and temperature conditions.

TFE performance improves as temperatures decreases, hence permits handling gases at low temperatures. Limits are not known, but minus 250°F should be within the operating range.

TFE is the generally accepted material for most applications today and is even being used to replace carbon in some existing machines. There are many commercial TFE compounds, the pure material having been blended with other materials to enhance certain properties. The most common "fillers" are carbon, graphite, fiber glass, and bronze. Others are used or several fillers may be in one final product.

To attain maximum success, any NL compressor must have a much finer cylinder bore finish than a lubricated machine. A honed finish is required but there seems to be an optimum to the degree of smoothness and a super finish may be undesirable. Piston rods are often harder and are given a finer finish than normal.

When an NL material is rubbed over a surface for a time, it tends to fill the minute pores in the contacted material, thus decreasing friction and wear. This is a break-in process. Vital as adequate break-in is to a lubricated machine, it is doubly so to one running without a normal lubricant.

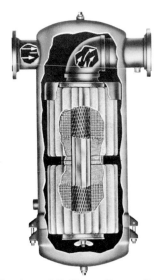

Courtesy of Dollinger Corporation.

Fig. 14-A.   Typical dry pipeline filter suitable for dirt removal to five microns.

The greater use of and need for fine finishes makes it even more necessary than usual that dirt be kept out of the compressor, not only during start-up, but during every day operation. An effective continuous-duty intake filter should be supplied (and maintained) for every compressor, regardless of the gas. In all NL cases, it must be of the dry type so there is no oil carry-over from this source. See Fig. 14-A.

Design of NL Compressors

Distance Pieces

The true NL cylinder must receive no liquid lubricant from any source, even from the piston rod that normally travels into both the crankcase and the cylinder packing. Fig. 14-B shows (top) the normal distance piece between frame and cylinder as used on lubricated units. Below, the modified design, usually longer, is shown with a baffle on the rod to prevent any oil creep. This is the simplest design. Other modifications are sometimes needed, particularly if the gas handled becomes corrosive when in contact with moisture, even that contained in the atmosphere. Chlorine is one example.

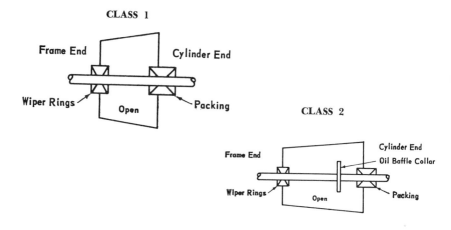

Fig. 14-B. Class 1 distance piece used with oil lubrication of cylinder. Class 2 distance piece used with NL cylinders.

Cylinder

The cylinder is of normal design, the only usual modification being the honed finish on the bore. A few cylinders may be lengthened, or otherwise modified, to accommodate the longer piston that may be needed to provide sufficient rider ring surface. When handling certain gases (chlorine, for example) any internal cooling water ports between the heads and cylinder must be blanked and the water circuit externally piped. Any chance of water leakage into the cylinder must be eliminated.

Large or high-pressure cylinders, or those operating under unusually severe conditions, may be fitted with liners. A high-grade cast iron seems to give the most satisfactory results in most applications. Other materials may be used as the gases handled and conditions warrant.

Valves

Valves must be designed to operate in an environment that has no lubricant in the gas or in the cylinder. Fig. 14-C shows a channel-type valve fitted with special NL inserts to prevent wear between valves and springs. Special inserts also guide the valves at the ends. Other valve types usually provide inserts at wearing points. In all cases, rustable parts should be treated to prevent corrosion.

Pistons

Piston designs vary widely, depending principally upon size, pressure, and NL material used. The principle is to provide a sufficient wearing surface of some NL materials plus compression rings of the same material.

When carbon is used, the piston support may be either a solid ring clamped into a built-up piston or blocks of carbon fastened into the bottom of the piston. TFE support parts are frequently solid rings stretched over the piston into grooves. In other cases, they are split and spring over the piston, fitting tightly into their grooves. The wearing surface must always

Fig. 14-C. Channel-type valve especially designed for NL compressors.

prevent the piston from contacting the bore. These NL piston-support parts are variously known as wearing rings, wearing bands, wear bands, and *rider rings*.

Fig. 14-D shows a typical single-stage straight-line NL compressor. This could use either carbon or plastic. Fig. 14-E is an exploded view of this assembly.

Piston assemblies using TFE are shown in Fig. 14-F, 14-G and 14-H. Fig. 14-F is a relatively small piston in a horizontal unit. Fig. 14-G and Fig. 14-H are the pistons for an L-arrangement machine with the larger low-pressure cylinder vertical. Since the rider ring in the latter only guides the piston and need provide no support, it is narrow and only one ring is used.

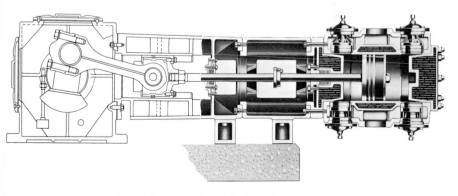

Fig. 14-D. Typical straight-line NL compressor.

Fig. 14-E. Disassembled view of the cylinder shown in Fig. 14-D. Either type of NL material may be used.

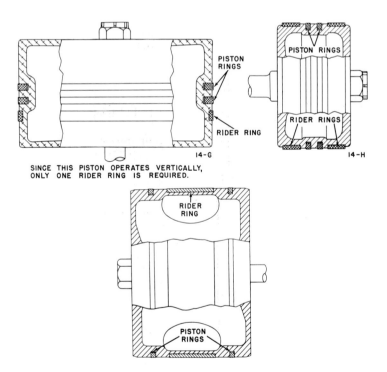

PISTON RINGS

RIDER RING

14-G

PISTON RINGS

RIDER RINGS

14-H

SINCE THIS PISTON OPERATES VERTICALLY, ONLY ONE RIDER RING IS REQUIRED.

RIDER RING

PISTON RINGS

Fig. 14-F.   Typical horizontal NL piston with TFE rider and compression rings.

Fig. 14-G.   Medium size vertical piston with TFE rider and compression rings.

Fig. 14-H.   Typical small horizontal TFE-fitted piston.

Carbon compression rings must be segmental. TFE rings can be of the conventional snap ring design easily expanded over the piston into the ring grooves. An internal expander ring must be used with carbon.

There is wear of rider and compression rings. They should be replaced when worn to about half their original radial thickness. Service life of fixed rider rings may be extended by rotating the piston approximately 120°F to present a new wearing surface. Carbon blocks on the piston bottom may be shim-adjusted to restore original clearances after wear takes place.

A few designs use tail-rod construction with an auxiliary outboard crosshead and usually a heavier-than-normal rod to limit deflection. This supports the piston free of the cylinder bore. The tail-rod crosshead may have an NL slipper or it may be conventionally lubricated with provision for preventing any lubricant entering the cylinder. When a tail-rod is used, NL pressure seal rings only are necessary. This construction is rather limited, usually to very large-diameter horizontal cylinders.

Packing

The packing almost universally used in NL compressors is of the full-floating mechanical type, consisting of a case containing pairs of either carbon or plastic rings of conventional design.

One of the more difficult problems in the operation of any packing is the dissipation of the frictional heat. Stuffing boxes in the cylinder head are usually water jacketed; this in a lubricated cylinder permits going to rather high pressures without auxiliary cooling.

Carbon has good heat conductivity. No unsolvable problems due to heat build-up have been experienced within the pressure ranges at which this packing is used. However, special cooling methods have been necessary in some cases. Pressure is somewhat limited by some of the physical characteristics of the carbon.

TFE, although having a much lower friction coefficient than carbon, also has a much lower heat-transfer coefficient. Heat generated tends to build up. TFE also has a tendency to soften and flow (extrude) at elevated temperatures. Temperature limits and scope of this problem will vary with the exact compound being used. TFE packings need auxiliary cooling at much lower pressures than do normal lubricated or carbon ring packings. In the lower-pressure range, cooling may be necessary only during break-in.

It should be realized that the requirement for cooling is not to make the packing cold, but to control or *limit* its temperature. Packing temperatures of several hundred degrees are not unusual on lubricated packing and even higher values may possibly be satisfactory on NL designs with suitable materials.

Methods of Cooling Available

Various methods of cooling packing might be:

1. Air cooling — obtained by not inserting the packing into a stuffing box, but letting it extend into the air; not very effective;
2. Water-jacketed stuffer — standard with most manufacturers, but its effectiveness is sometimes limited by the head design and distance the heat must travel;

3. A metallic back-up ring — a ring on the sealing side or on both sides of the plastic pair, used to improve heat transfer between packing rings and case, and to better prevent extrusion;

4. Liquid coolant circulated outside the packing cups — used in many high-pressure lubricated designs. Requires careful sealing of the coolant circuit and a special packing coolant system with coolers, pumps, etc.;

5. Liquid cooling the cups internally — more effective than (4). Quite often used with NL packing;

6. Liquid cooling a hollow piston rod — very effective, but expensive and of complex design. Has not been widely used.

7. Running coolant directly on the rod — very effective, but raises many problems. A modification using an air jet as the coolant is effective in some cases.

Degreasing

When handling oxygen, and occasionally other gases such a nitrogen and helium, it is absolutely necessary that all traces of hydrocarbons be removed. With oxygen, this is required for safety; with other gases, for cleanliness or to prevent system contamination.

Degreasing may be done in a number of different ways, using various procedures and cleaning agents. Those best suited to a given piece of equipment depend on size of equipment, number of parts, type of parts, and contaminants involved. Methods should be as mutually agreed between purchaser and manufacturer.

Basic steps include

1. Determine and list contaminants possibly present;

2. Select a cleaning method to remove all contaminants.

3. Clean parts and remove all contaminants and loose particles.

4. Remove all residual cleaning agent.

5. Dry parts with oil-free air or nitrogen.

5. Inspect for cleanliness. Methods vary from a visual check to the use of complex precedures.

7. Protect parts from recontamination and rusting. They must be carefully packed and sealed.

These are all shop procedures. Great care must be exercised in handling and assembling parts when they are being reassembled to prevent recontamination. A good cleaning can be destroyed by improper handling.

Conclusion

A review of the functions of a lubricant (page 13-2) will emphasize the problems faced by the designer *and the operator* of a machine that has *no* lubrication. There are many questions as yet not completely resolved. Manufacturers seldom are in a position to guarantee life of parts or maintenance costs. To complicate matters, different gases act differently in NL units and some even seem to provide a modicum of lubrication. As examples, gases saturated with water vapor give longer parts service life than dry gases; HC mixtures handled in certain catalytic reforming processes carry a constituent of lubricating value.

Compared to a lubricated compressor (and regardless of the NL materials used), wear will tend to increase; corrosion is more apt to occur; cooling of certain cylinder parts may become a problem; and wear from extraneous material entering the cylinder will be more damaging.

NL designs, materials and compounds are being developed and improved constantly. Machines have been built for 3000 to 4000 psiG. Larger cylinder sizes are being put into operation.

Installation, Operation, and Maintenance

Chapter 18 deals with this subject as it applies to compressors in general. Pages 18-26 through 18-37 cover special facts regarding reciprocators. NL units differ only in that they require more, *and more careful*, attention to some details.

Unpacking

Once an NL cylinder is machined, procedures must be undertaken to prevent rusting of any part. A coating of oil should not be used; this would tend to defeat the NL principle. This protection extends to preparation for shipment. One manufacturer uses the following procedure, although there may be variations depending on the size and type of cylinder

1. Pistons, rods, packing, oil wiper rings, and packing cups are removed;
2. For units run in the shops, the coolers are removed and dried before reassembly, cylinders and their passages are dried, rust spots are cleaned up;
3. Packing cups, pistons, ring grooves, cylinder bores, and piston rods are cleaned with a solvent, then with a fingerprint remover, and a second solvent wash;
4. Packing cups, rods, pistons, and packing are wrapped in VPI paper (vapor-phase inhibitor) that protects against rusting by inhibiting moisture. They are wrapped again with a heavier paper and sealed with tape;
5. Cylinders are lined with VPI paper and heads are replaced;
6. All cylinders and cooler openings are solidly closed, the edges of the closure sealed with special compound;
7. Packing stuffers are filled with VPI paper and are blocked shut and sealed; and,
8. Markings prominently proclaim to purchaser, "Material Not Slushed — Store in a Dry Place".

This seemingly extravagant procedure should not be lost on the purchaser. Do not disturb this protection until just before the cylinder is to be assembled. The unit should be started soon thereafter. Extreme care must be taken during this period to prevent rust and corrosion.

Piping

Much has been said about the need for clean piping when connected to the inlet or between stages of any compressor. This is doubly important with NL machines where dirt can quickly do much damage. The piping should be absolutely clean when installed and precautions taken to prevent the formation of rust before start-up. A temporary inlet screen (Figs. 18-D and 18-E is mandatory unless a permanent inlet filter is provided.

Where possible — as with an air compressor having atmospheric intake — plastic inlet piping should be considered. It is well to coat a steel inlet pipe internally, particularly an air inlet, with a good-grade aluminum or neoprene paint and install the pipe in sections so it can be inspected occasionally, recleaned, and recoated.

Inlet Filter

Most manufacturers recommend a dry type inlet filter to prevent entry of any particle five microns or larger. Suitable commercial filters for either atmospheric air or for pipe line use on gases are available. Filters limiting dirt passage to two-micron size can also be obtained. Fig. 14-A shows a filter of this type, available to 33,000 SCFM and for relatively high pressures. Complete protection from dirt is a must for the best NL machine life.

Care must be taken that the intake pulsation from the compressor will not damage the filter. A pulsation dampener may be required.

Interstage Piping and Coolers

There are many multistage NL machines in operation. These require special care and understanding. With oil lubrication, a coating is formed on all surfaces of the intercoolers and interconnecting passages and piping, which limits corrosion. This coating is not present with an NL unit and many parts must have special coatings. They are usually a neoprene or aluminum paint or a coating compatible with the gas. Specially corrosion-resistant materials are seldom used because of cost.

These coatings do not last forever and must be inspected yearly. Watch must be kept for evidence of rust or flaked coating. After two or three years, a recoating may be necessary.

Break-in

Break-in, a general term in industry, has the wrong connotation. It implies rough treatment. Actually, the term *wear-in* connoting gentle treatment, is more indicative of the operation. The idea is to gradually and gently wear parts to a seating surface that will have long service life. Wear-in on the NL unit is one of the most crucial steps and is not to be hurried. The idea is to *wear-in* not *wear-out*.

The instruction book should be followed explicitly. It will probably recommend a short run at no load (no pressure) and other periods at gradually higher pressure levels, watching always for excess heating and calling for immediate pressure reduction when found. Packing will be the principal item to be checked. Compression and rider rings tend to wear-in more easily and quickly in a properly prepared cylinder.

Keep screens and filters clean.

Replacement parts must be as thoroughly and carefully worn-in as the original unit before going on full load.

Life of Parts

The service life of NL parts is seldom guaranteed. It will be influenced materially by the following factors, many of which are the complete responsibility of the operating and maintenance crews:

1. Discharge pressure;
2. Discharge temperature;
3. Piston speed;
4. Rotation speed (rpm);
5. Piston diameter;
6. Piston weight;
7. Air dryness;
8. Air cleanliness;
9. Wear-in quality;
10. Quality of maintenance; and,
11. Continuity of operation.

The first seven are well set when the compressor is purchased. The last four are controlled by the purchaser.

It is hazardous to attempt an estimate of the life of NL parts, but after careful wear-in and with proper operation with a *clean* gas, NL parts should give 8000 hours service or better on low- or moderate-pressure applications.

Continuity of Operation

Continuity of operation, particularly when handling a moist gas such as air, can influence NL life considerably. Cylinders are apt to rust quickly when shut down if any moisture is present unless steps are taken to prevent condensation. Overnight shutdown is probably not dangerous. Circulation of water at 100°F, or higher, is recommended for weekend stoppages. Increasing use is being made of thermostatically controlled cylinder jacket water to preclude internal condensation during shutdown periods. Any long shutdown, however, warrants additional protection. See Extended Shutdown — page 14-14.

Maintenance Priority

Maintenance on the NL section of a compressor, disregarding the frame and driver, can be divided into:

1. Piston compression rings;
2. Rider rings or piston support;
3. Rod packing;
4. Rod oil wiper rings; and,
5. Valves.

Refer to instruction books for details of fitting parts, clearances, disassembly and reassembly, adjustments, and the like. Compression rings wear more rapidly than rider rings. Replace carbon compression rings shortly before they have worn to half their original radial thickness. TFE compression rings may be allowed to wear somewhat longer.

It will be necessary to remove the piston from the cylinder to inspect or replace these rings. Carbon rings, if used, must be very carefully handled so they will not be chipped or broken. *Never* pull the threaded portion of the piston rod through the packing or oil wiper rings. To do so will ruin the rings. Remove the rings first.

Each time a cylinder is opened, check the bore finish. After proper wear-in, it should have a high polish. If it doesn't, water or dirt are being carried over. Investigate and remedy.

There are many types and arrangements of rider rings. Watch bottom clearance between piston and cylinder bore. It is reduced as the support material wears. Since minimum recommended clearance varies, refer to the instruction book for details. There is no good substitute for actual bottom clearance measurements. For large cylinders, these may be obtained through a valve hole. On small cylinders it is best to pull the outer head.

Full-floating packing may wear sufficiently to cause ring segments to butt together. They will then leak and must be repaired or replaced. Consult instruction book. Wear-in replacements as for new machine.

Wear rates will be higher than normal during wear-in and for approximately 500 hours. Check piston clearance carefully and at frequent intervals. All parts and clearances must be measured before assembly and dimensions recorded to provide starting reference data. Wear-in wear rates will be less on replacement rings and packing.

Rod oil wiper rings should be checked for performance occasionally. Be sure they wipe excessive crankcase oil from the rod.

Keep Records

No NL compressor can be properly operated or maintained without a complete record of wear. A record should be kept for each cylinder. Inspections should be made of piston clearance several times during the first 500 hours of operation and of the compression and packing rings at the end of 500 hours. These, compared to the prestart-up measurements, will show the extent of wear. Parts should always be near the same temperature when measurements are being taken. A log of actual running time should also be kept. It is then possible to calculate, for each part, the hours of operation per 0.001 inch of wear. Plot these wear rates as inspections are made. The rate will be high at the start, but will become less and the curve will flatten out. Only when this happens, usually within 500 hours, can the next inspection be planned. These records will show when replacements must be made. See next page.

Keep replacements parts on hand. Before the chart shows replacements must be made, check the stock to be sure needed parts are actually there — *and in good condition.* Reorder immediately those used.

Extended Shutdown

The problem with extended shutdown is rust formation in the cylinder. Every precaution should be taken to prevent this. Even so, careful inspection should be made before restarting.

Remember, carbon has an affinity for moisture. Carbon packing rings will corrode the rod if allowed to contact in one place too long.

CHART OF WEAR ON NONLUBRICATED COMPRESSORS

All measurements should be taken at the same place every time and the piston should be at the same temperature.

| Cylinder or machine serial no._____Cylinder diameter_____Stroke_____ |
| Speed (rpm)_____ Piston displacement_____ Intake pressure_____ Discharge pressure_____ |

Date	Before Start-up					
Hours since last inspection	0	100	250	500	*	*
Piston ring end gap		**	**			
Piston ring thickness		**	**			
Diametral clearance of piston in cylinder						
Clearance of rider rings in cylnder						
Gap of packing rings (meas. from gap between ring segments when clamped around rod)		**	**			
Hours per 0.001'' wear on piston rings		**	**			
Hours per 0.001'' wear on rider rings						
Hours per 0.001'' wear on packing rings		**	**			
Comments and description of replacements						

*Succeeding time intervals between inspections must be determined from rate of wear, remaining thickness of compression rings, and clearance of rider rings in cylinder.

**Not normally necessary at this interval.

For even relatively short shutdowns, it is recommended that the machine be barred over twice a day, taking care that the rod is in a different position each time. Circulate warm water through cylinder jackets to prevent moisture condensation and rusting of interior, or purge with a dry gas.

If shutdown will be for a considerable period of time, special steps should be taken in accordance with manufacturer's recommendations, for example the following:

1. Drain intercooler and water jackets;
2. Remove cylinder heads and frame end valves;
3. With lint-free cloth or synthetic sponge, wipe off moisture from cylinders, and move piston so entire bore can be dried;
4. Pack cylinder loosely with a vapor-phase inhibitor paper;
5. Replace outer head and valves;
6. Blank off inlet and discharge passages to prevent circulation of moist air; and,
7. Inspect unit before restarting and remove any rust that may be found.

Chapter 15

Drivers For Stationary Compressors

Caption Index   **Page**

(Continued)

Functions of a Driver

A driver (together with any connecting medium between it and the compressor such as a gear and/or coupling) must do more than just drive the unit at a rated condition. It must first start the compressor from rest, accelerate it to full speed, and then keep the unit operating under any design condition of capacity and power. Following are areas where engineering thought regarding the assembly may be required;

1. Starting torque available and required;
2. Acceleration requirements;
3. Avoidance of excessive electrical current pulsation;
4. Avoidance of shaft torsional and lateral resonance and excessive speed variation during each revolution;
5. Power requirements during seasonal changes; and ,
6. Power requirements due to upsets from rated intake and discharge pressures.

Driver Selection

At times, the type of power most readily available determines the economic reasoning for the selection of a particular type of driver. At other times, relative cost provides the answer. Heat balance, power recovery, or some other special factor will often influence selection.

Buy a Co-Ordinated Assembly

Regardless of the type of driver, there is usually considerable engineering involved to assure proper co-ordination with the compressor. Some of these engineering requirements are discussed later. It is to the user's advantage to have the compressor manufacturer supply the driver and accessories required that there may be undivided responsibility for all engineering decisions.

Compressor Type	Reciprocating	Vane Rotary	Helical-Lobe Rotary	Dynamic
Driver Type				
Induction Motor	B–C–F–G	B–C	B–C–G	C–G
Synchronous Motor	C–E–F–G	Seldom	C–G	C–G
Steam Engine	I	. . . . . .	. . . . . .	. . . .
Steam Turbine	G	G	C–G	C–G
Gas Turbine	. . . . . .	. . . . . .	G	C–G
Hydraulic Turbine	G	. . . . . .	C–G	. . . .
Gas Engine (Heavy-Duty)	C–I	. . . . . .	G	G
Diesel Engine (Heavy-Duty)	C–I	. . . . . .	G	G
Industrial Engine	B–C	B–C	C–G	B–G
Expander	I–G	. . . . . .	C–G	C

Key—B—Belted   F—Flange-Mounted
      C—Coupled   G—Geared
      E—Engine-Type Direct-Connected   I—Integral

Fig. 15-A.   Common compressor drivers.

Summary of Driver Characteristics

Fig. 15-A shows drivers generally used with compressors. Wound rotor motors are not mentioned, since their possible advantage of variable speed is generally negated by other and more economic methods of capacity control, and there is little power saving at reduced speeds.

Not all possible combinations of compressors and drivers are shown.

Fig. 15-B tabulates the approximate size-range and characteristics of the principal drivers for compressors. Characteristics are typical and may not be exact for all sizes of a given driver. The maximum sizes shown are commercial; larger units are often available. Comments follow on some drivers not included therein.

Driver	Horsepower Range	Available Speed (rpm) (60-cycle power)	Possible Speed Variation	Efficiency	Starting Torque and Amperes % Full-Load	Stalling Torque % Full-Load
Induction Motor	1 to 5,000 (or larger)	3,600/N less 2% N = 1 thru 8 ***	Constant Speed	10 hp – 86% 100 hp – 91% 1000 hp – 94%	60 to 100% Torque 550 to 650% Amperes	150% min. (or more)
Synchronous Motor	100 to 20,000 (or larger)	3,600/N N = 2 thru 20 ***	Constant Speed	93 to 97%	40% Torque under 514 rpm. 40 to 100% Torque 514 rpm and over 300 to 500% Amperes	150%
Steam Engine	55 to 4,000	400 to 140	100% down to 20%	50% to 75% RCE	about 120%	About 115%
Steam Turbine	To 20,000 (or larger)	34,000 to 1,800	*100% down to 25%	35% to 82% RCE	175 to 300%	Up to 300%
Combustion Gas Turbine	3,000 hp at 10,000 rpm to 20,000 hp at 3,000 rpm (1,000 ft altitude and 80°F)	100% down to 55%	16 to 25% overall Thermal Efficiency for simple open cycle. 27 to 30% with regenerator.	Both single- and two-shaft designs require a sizable starting motor or turbine. The single-shaft design has poor part load torque characteristics and requires a larger starter. Two-shaft turbines have good torque characteristics.		
Integral Gas Engine	From 85 hp at 600 rpm to 5000 to 6000 at approx. 300 rpm.	*100%down to 60%	Up to 40% over-all Thermal Efficiency	Nil—started with compressed air.	About 120%	
Integral Diesel Engine	From 100 hp at 600 rpm to approx. 1300 at lower rpm.	*100% down to 60%	32% (HHV) **	Nil – started with compressed air.	About 120%	
Coupled Gas or Diesel Engine	From 100 hp at 600 rpm to 5000 hp or more at approx. 360 rpm.	*100% down to 60%	41% on gas (LHV) and 36.6% on oil (HHV) **	Nil – started with compressed air.	About 120%	

Tabulation is limited to the commercially applied ranges of hp and rpm.
***N is number of pairs of poles.
**High heat value or low heat value.   *Depends on design and existence of critical shaft speeds.

Fig. 15-B.   General characteristics of compressor drivers.

Hydraulic Turbines

The hydraulic turbine, as used for compressor drive, is a specially developed power recovery driver. Essentially it is a centrifugal pump operating in reverse. It may be an economical driver when a suitable liquid exists at a pressure level above that at which it is to be used. Power may be recovered and the pressure reduced at the same time. There are no standard designs.

Industrial Engines

Many natural gas, gasoline, and diesel engines of the *industrial* type (as compared to heavy-duty designs) are used to drive compressors by V-belt or direct connection. These industrial engines are medium speed (600 to 1700 rpm) and vary from 100 to 2000 hp. Although there are some variations between different manufacturers' models, they all have a basic maximum horsepower rating to which must be applied a service factor to obtain the allowable maximum *operating* horsepower. These factors vary with the service requirements of the driver. They may be roughly classified for naturally aspirated engines at sea level and 60°F ambient as:

1. *Maximum* (100%). This is the maximum horsepower available to which a production tolerance of plus or minus 5% is usually applied. This is the highest horsepower and speed at which the ingine may be run for very short periods (say 5 minutes maximum) followed by periods of reduced output.

2. *Intermittent* (90%). 8his rating is used when the maximum power and speed is required for one hour or less and is followed by one hour or more operating at or below the continuous rating (see Continuous).

3. *Continuous* (80%). Operation may be 24 hours per day with a reasonable amount of off time for adequate maintenance. This is the maximum power output for such applications as stand-by, peak shaving in gas distribution, and pump-up. It is the top limit for continuous noncycling applications and is frequently modified as in the Heavy-duty classification.

4. *Heavy-duty or extended continuous* (65%). Power output ratings of 65% should be used for 24 hour/day applications where minimum down time and maintenance are a consideration. This rating is assigned to many specific applications and particularly to oil and gas field pump or compressor drives.

Note:—Some industrial engine manufacturers rate their *natural gas* engines for continuous duty at 100% of maximum output. The basis for this is that both stress loading and power are less than for a diesel engine on the same frame. There should be some discretion exercised when applying these ratings. In most cases, these ratings should be reduced by 10 to 15% for heavy-duty gas field applications.

Supercharged engines may have further reduced *continuous and heavy-duty* ratings. Higher altitudes and ambient temperatures also alter the service factor in all cases. Basic ratings must make allowance for the influence of such accessories as water pump, fan, intake and exhaust manifolds, and inlet air cleaners.

Again, this type of driver cannot be selected by maximum horsepower rating only. The applications must be considered. Failure to properly derate will bring excessive maintenance and down time.

Expanders

Expanders are used for two purposes. One is pure power recovery, using gas that exists at an elevated pressure but is useable only at a lower pressure. The reduction must be by mechanical means if its energy is to be conserved. The second purpose is to obtain refrigeration or to lower gas temperature by the process of removing work energy mechanically. There are various expanders, the reciprocating and turbine types being most prominent. Helical-lobe rotary compressors are sometimes used in reverse as engines or expanders.

All expanders must be loaded. To produce the desired result, they must do work. Hence they often use some type of compressor, pump, or generator as a loading device.

Expanders are discussed in Chapter 21.

Hydraulic and Magnetic Couplings

Although hydraulic and magnetic couplings are not drivers, they are sometimes a part of the driving mechanism designed to provide variable-speed operation from a constant-speed driver. A hydraulic coupling is essentially an oil pump on the driver side and an oil turbine on the driven side. An electrical magnetic or eddy-current coupling utilizes a magnetic field, with a slip that may be varied, to tie together the driving and driven shafts.

Although these couplings have been used on a number of compressor drives including reciprocating, helical-lobe rotary, and centrifugal units, their acceptance has been prompted more by adaptability to a peculiar problem in setup or process than to the economics of cost or efficiency. Actually they are usually inefficient when compared to other available methods of obtaining the desired variation in capacity or other operating condition.

Electric Motors

The squirrel-cage induction motor is the most widely used compressor driver, particularly in the range to 200 hp. Above 1000 or 1250 hp it becomes less economic, although larger sizes are available and used when operational and process reasons dictate.

Squirrel-cage induction motors are simple, rugged, and reliable and have no rotating windings, slip rings, or commutators, generally associated with other motors. They are utilized with all compressors and may be belted, geared, direct coupled, or flange mounted. In the latter, the motor stator is fastened to the compressor frame and the rotor is mounted on the compressor shaft. The impeller of small dynamic compressors is often mounted directly on the motor shaft.

The induction motor has reasonable efficiency but its lagging power factor is often a disadvantage, particularly in large sizes. Its current inrush is apt to be quite high.

The synchronous motor is a fixed-speed machine. Some consider it less reliable than the squirrel-cage induction motor because it has a wound rotor to which direct-current excitation must be applied, usually through rotating slip rings. Consequently, a small direct-current supply (motor-generator set or rectifier) is required, together with more elaborate starting equipment. Synchronous motors may be flange-mounted, coupled, geared, or mounted (engine type) on the compressor shaft. The synchronous motor on compressor drive usually has a relatively low current inrush. It frequently is selected for its high or leading power factor. See page 15-14.

A Guide to Selection

Fig. 15-C is a rough guide to selection between induction and synchronous motors considering the motor only without too much attention to the compressor type or the type of connection to the compressor. It indicates approximate areas where one or the other motor type is generally preferred.

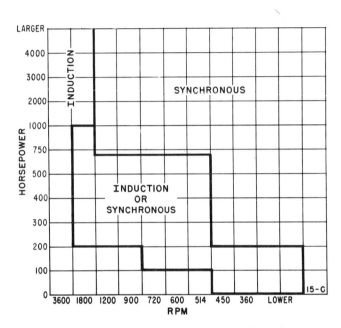

Fig. 15-C. General areas of application of induction and synchronous motors.

Speeds

Synchronous motors operate at a speed fixed by power cycles and the number of poles in the stator. Induction motors operate at speeds below synchronous by a value known as slip which varies with the load. Full-load (maximum) slip varies from 1% for very large motors to 5% for very small units. An average might be 3%. High-slip motors are available for special applications, but are seldom found driving compressors.

Synchronous speeds are tabulated on page 34-160.

Duty Cycle

Motors should never be selected for other than full-load continuous compressor operation. The fact that the compressor may be unloaded part of the time should not be considered.

Applying a motor for automatic start-up-and-stop control requires attention to the number of starts per hour. Motor manufacturers limit these to prevent overheating and undue deterioration of insulation. Limitations depend upon the compressor type, motor size, actual operating cycle, and other factors. Based on available recommendations, a motor of 1/2 to 20 hp should start no oftener than eight times per hour, with the rate reducing to four starts per hour for 100-hp units. Larger motors must be more severely limited and one manufacturer suggests for the 1000-hp rating, or larger, not over two starts per day. These figures are applicable only to standard simple drives with normal acceleration loads and open motors. The inclusion of a heavy flywheel or dynamic impeller, for example, requires special analysis.

For normal air compressor service where automatic start-and-stop is most common, the demand is usually such that a combination of the standard range between loading and unloading pressures and the standard receiver will keep the frequency of starts within these limits. If the load, or air demand, is unusual, a special analysis by the compressor manufacturer may indicate a need for larger receiver volume or a wider regulation range (or both) to keep within the motor-starting limits.

Altitude

Altitude must be considered in motor selection because the lower the air density the less the cooling. Standard motors are given their full rating to an altitude of 3300 feet. At greater elevations, the *temperature rise* allowable must be reduced 1% for each 330 ft above 3300 ft (3% per 1000 ft). To compensate, the service factor may be reduced, a higher class of insulation used, or a special design selected. It is best that the motor manufacturer assist in the decision.

Service Factor

Service factor is a multiplier, usually 1.0 or 1.15, which, when applied to the rated horsepower, indicates a continuous horsepower loading permissible without injurious heating. The maximum horsepower of most compressors is well established and many are designed to load motors so that much of the permissible loading is used.

It is particularly important that the application of *maximum rated* motors (1.0 service factor) be carefully made so that overload is not possible.

Insulation

Insulation systems are divided into classes according to their thermal endurance. Four classes are recognized: Classes A, B, F, and H. Class B and Class F are the two in most common use. For alternating current motors that have no continuous overload capability (service factor is 1.0) the allowable temperature rises based on an *ambient temperature not exceeding 40°C (104°F)* are shown in the table opposite.

Motors that have a service factor greater than 1.0 have their temperature rise specified at the service factor load (values higher than those tabulated) with no temperature rise specified at rated load.

Type of Enclosure	Method of Temperature Determination	Temperature Rise of Insulated Windings in Degrees Centigrade			
		Class A	Class B	Class F	Class H
Open, including all variations thereof such as drip-proof, splash-proof, pipe-ventilated, and weather-protected.	Resistance	60	80	105	125
Totally-enclosed fan-cooled and and water-air-cooled	Resistance or	60	80	105	125
Motors with Encapsulated Windings	Resistance	65	85	110	
Totally-enclosed nonventilated	Resistance	65	85	110	135

Typical ratings follow.

Class B Insulation

    1. 90°C at 1.15 service factor load

    2. 80°C at 1.0 service factor

    3. 85°C at 1.0 service factor

Class F Insulation

    4. 115°C at 1.15 service factor load

    5. 105°C at 1.0 service factor

    6. 110°C at 1.0 service factor

With some motor ratings, manufacturers reserve the right to supply either Class B or Class F at their option. Rating (1) and (2) are normally used with open motors; (3) with totally enclosed nonventilated or encapsulated winding designs. All temperatures are measured by resistance.

Atmospheric conditions materially influence insulation life. The motor manufacturer should be advised of any unusual contaminants in the cooling air. Tropical protection is a feature required in some localities and normally includes special insulation and designs to combat higher ambient temperatures, high humidity, and fungus growth. Additional modifications may be desirable.

Modifications

There are many modifications that may be made to a standard motor to better adapt it to the application and the surrounding conditions. More important among these are torque requirements and those special enclosures required by the presence of hazardous atmospheres, water, and dust.

Motor Torque

A driver must not only operate the compressor at rated speed and capacity, but must start the unit from rest and accelerate it to full speed.

These requirements force consideration of other than the 100% or full-load operating torque characteristic, the degree depending upon compressor type, method of unloading, value of WK^2 (inertia factor) to be accelerated, etc. There is also a time limit for the starting cycle, set by motor manufacturers and based on the allowable temperature rise. Full speed must be reached without exceeding this limit, otherwise motor modifications may be required.

Torque is a twisting force, in this case, that is developed by the motor to rotate the shaft. It is expressed in pounds at one foot radius or lb ft. Formulas for calculations are:

$$Torque = \frac{5250 \ BHP}{RPM}$$

$$BHP = \frac{Torque \times RPM}{5250}$$

These apply to any driving or driven shaft.

One of the critical values is the *starting torque,* sometimes called *locked rotor* torque. This is the torque at zero speed when normal voltage and frequency are applied. Another, is the *break-down* torque where induction motor speed drops abruptly. Break-down, in the case of the synchronous motor, is called *pull-out* torque. Break-down and pull-out are high enough to meet requirements with the motors generally used with compressors. With the synchronous motor, which starts and accelerates to approximately 97% speed as an induction motor, there is also a *pull-in* torque. This is the torque required to accelerate the machine to synchronous speed against the then existing load. This torque must be considered in all compressor applications.

NEMA Authorized Engineering Information

The National Electrical Manufacturers Association (NEMA) has issued data typical of many synchronous motor applications. It is to be understood that this information is typical of the requirements of the *driven machine* rather than the torque values for which the motor should be designed. The latter usually includes some allowance for voltage drop during the starting cycle.

These data are equally applicable to induction motor drives although there is no NEMA authorized information. Tables are based on normal acceleration loads for the particular compressor type involved and for direct connection of motor to compressor. Gear drive and high inertia WK^2 may require more torque than normal. The helical-lobe rotary requirements have not been standardized and should be settled by the manufacturer.

Although this table (opposite page) is a guide to the majority of applications, the compressor and motor manufacturer should be consulted in any torque problem.

Current Inrush

Closely allied to torque is current inrush. All motors draw much more than full-load current when starting. Since most motors are started at

	Torque in Percent of Full Load		
	Starting	Pull-In	Pull-Out
Reciprocating			
Air or Gas-starting unloaded........	30	25	150
Ammonia-starting unloaded			
(Discharge 100-250 psiG).........	30	25	150
Freon-starting unloaded............	30	40	150
Vacuum Pumps-starting unloaded.....	40	60	150
Vane Rotary			
Bypass open....................	60	60	150
Bypass closed..........	60	100	150
Centrifugal			
Inlet or discharge valve closed.......	30	40–60*	150
Inlet and discharge valve open......	30	100	150

*Varies with design and operating conditions. Consult the manufacturer.

full voltage (across-the-line) with a momentary inrush of several times full-load current, it is important that the power feed system and wiring carry the instantaneous demand without undue voltage drop. The alternate of reduced-voltage starting limits current inrush materially but also reduces available torque in accordance with the square of the applied voltage. In such cases, the torque requirement of the compressor should be checked to assure startability.

It must be remembered that high torque requirements increase the rated starting current inrush in proportion to the torque increase.

Induction Motors

The induction motor generally has good efficiency, excellent starting torque, but rather high inrush current. There are currently three designs available in sizes *through 200 hp*. Similar variations are available in larger ratings.

NEMA Design	Starting Torque	Starting Current
A	Normal	High
B	Normal	Normal
C	High	Normal

NEMA Design B motors are used with most reciprocators and with many other compressor types.

Generally speaking, 60-cycle induction motor torques and current inrush follow the pattern shown in table on page 15-12.

Full load efficiencies of induction motors in the 5 to 200 hp range vary from 83 to 91.5%, with a power factor variation from 83 to 91%. Larger motors will have higher efficiencies and power factor.

Induction Motors

NEMA Design	HP Range	Percent of Full-Load Values	
		Starting Torque	Current.Inrush
B	To 500 hp	70 or more	550 to 650
None	Over 500 hp	60 or more*	550 to 650
C	To 200 hp	200 or more	550 to 650

*Usually adequate

Synchronous Motors

Synchronous motors, because of their generally lower torques, must be more carefully engineered. Current inrush will vary from 300 to 500%. Normal torques are given below for unity power factor 60 cycle ratings.

Speeds	HP Range	Torque—Percent of Full Load	
		Starting	Pull-in
1800 to 514	to 200	100	100
1800 to 514	250 to 1000	60	60
1800 to 514	1250 and higher	40	60
450 and below	All ratings	40	30

Although usually sufficient, there are many applications where higher values of both starting and pull-in are required. Any increase in torque entails proportional increase in the current inrush.

Unity power factor synchronous motors will have a full load efficiency of 93 to over 97%, depending upon the rating. 80% power factor motors will be lower.

Enclosures

Environment often requires modifications in motor enclosures. These may be designed to prevent the entry of water, solid particles or dirt, or to permit operation in a hazardous location. In the latter category are several classes, divisions, and groups. Not all apply to compressor drive but some are quite frequently involved in refinery and chemical plant installations.

Hazardous Locations

Hazardous locations have been codified by the National Electric Code. *Class 1* is the section usually applicable. Within this class are two divisions. *Division 1* locations are those in which hazardous concentrations of flammable gases or vapors exist, either continuously or periodically during normal conditions. *Division 2* locations are those in which (for compressors) flammable gases are handled, processed, or used. The gas will normally be confined within closed systems from which they can escape only in the event of accidental break-down or abnormal operation.

In Division 1 areas, the equipment must be approved by Underwriters' Laboratory, Inc. as *explosion-proof* and carry such certification when shipped or be so approved after erection. The latter is seldom exercised.

In Division 2 locations, motors without sparkable contact, brushes, or relays need not be explosion-proof but are to be suitable otherwise for the atmosphere involved. This permits use of squirrel-cage motors without special protection. Open synchronous motors, when collector rings are housed in approved enclosures, are also acceptable.

Within Class 1 there are also four groups. Group D is the more general in compressor applications. Motors in this group are satisfactory for atmospheres containing natural gas or the vapors of gasoline, petroleum, naphtha, alcohols, acetone, or lacquer-solvent. A Class 1 Group D design is not explosion-proof unless specifically so designated and certified by Underwriters' Laboratory, Inc.

Firewalls

Many motors — and other driver types, as well — present hazards in atmospheres similar to those codified by the NEC but cannot be designed to NEC requirements for these conditions. An alternate sometimes possible is the segregation of the compressor and driver in separate rooms with a gas tight *firewall* between. The room containing the driver is extremely well ventilated, in some cases held under a positive clean air pressure.

Enclosure Selection

Selection and specification of the proper enclosure is a matter for decision between the purchaser, his insurance company, and the local enforcing authority in safety matters. It is not possible to obtain Underwriters' Laboratory certification on all ratings or designs. Other designs, sometimes a compromise, are available.

Induction Motor Enclosures

This motor design is currently offered in the following enclosures:

1. *Open.* A basic design.

2. *Drip-proof.* A basic design.

3. *Weather-protected.* Available for outdoor installation.

4. *Totally enclosed.* Small ratings are not ventilated (TENV), but most ratings include a fan for positive ventilation around the winding case, then called TEFC.

5. *Totally enclosed explosion-proof* (Class 1 Group D) and certified. Within this class, maximum ratings currently approximate the following (not all ratings are necessarily offered by every manufacturer):

RPM	Maximum HP
3600	3000
1800	1750
1200	1500
900	1250
720	1000
600	800
514	600
450	500

Synchronous Motor Enclosures

There is a greater variety of enclosures for synchronous motors, because of the generally larger sizes and the nonavailability of explosion proof designs. More compromise designs are required to meet varying needs.

1. *Open.* The basic design.

2. *Enclosed collector rings.* The enclosure may be unventilated but is usually ventilated from an air blower or inert gas source. The carbon brushes used on the collector rings require a slight amount of moisture for lubrication to prevent wear. Atmospheric air is satisfactory, but if a dry inert gas (as nitrogen) is to be used, it must first be bubbled through water.

3. *Explosion-proof collector-ring enclosure only.* This enclosure is built to NEC requirements, but must often be field mounted and must be certified by an inspector in the field if it is to have a Class 1 Group D label.

4. *Drip-proof.*

5. *Splash-proof.*

6. *Outdoor (weather-protected).*

7. *Self-ventilated (pipe type).* The enclosure has connections for purchaser's ventilating piping. The motor includes necessary fans to circulate fresh air in and out with limits on the total air pressure loss allowable.

8. *Forced-ventilated.* Circulation of air from outside by an external blower through purchaser's ductwork.

9. *Totally enclosed, water-air-cooled.* Integral fans circulate air in the enclosure over a water-cooled exchanger.

10. *Totally enclosed, inert-gas-filled.* Same as (9) except the enclosure is filled with an inert gas and fitted with seals to limit leakage outward.

Brushless Excitation System

There is now available a synchronous motor design that combines the exciter and necessary controls with the motor itself in such a way that no brushes are required. This design should be checked for suitability in Class 1 Division 2 locations without any enclosures.

Power Factor

Selection of the driving motor may be influenced by the effect it will have on the plant power factor. There are, however, other factors to be considered and the power company should always be consulted before any final decision is reached.

A-C Power Principles

Voltage (E) and current (I) each vary in a sine wave. The waves may reach their peaks at the same time (be in phase) or they may be displaced by a certain number of electrical degrees (θ). In the normal three-phase circuit, there are three sets of these E and I wave pairs, one in each of the three wires. The sets are 120 degrees apart.

Power factor is the cosine of θ. It may be negative or positive, known as lagging or leading, depending upon whether the current (I) wave lags behind or leads the voltage (E) wave.

Basic A-C Loads

A-C loads may be placed in three general classifications, each having its own effect on power factor.

Resistance load does not displace the E and I waves, θ is zero and cos θ is 1.0. This is unity *pf*.

Inductance load makes I lag behind E, developing a lagging *pf*. Pure inductance gives zero *lagging pf*.

Capacitance load makes I move ahead of E, developing leading *pf*. Pure capacitance gives zero *leading pf*.

The net, or combined, effect of all these loads is called *impedance*. It is usual for a system to have at least two classes of loads and, since predominant loads are apt to be induction motors, the plant system *pf* will almost universally be found to be lagging. Fig. 15-D (next page) shows the *pf* of typical loads.

Power

Power (P) expressed in kilowatts is shown in Fig. 15-E (page 15-17). The familiar product of E and I appears in *all* the formulas but for A-C is modified in the numerator by *pf* in all cases. This indicates that whenever *pf* is less than unity, there must be a portion of I that produces no useful power. This nonproductive power is known as *kvar* (kva reactive).

The Significance of Low, Lagging Power Factor

Low power factor detrimental for four important reasons:

1. It cuts down system loadability; that is, it reduces the capacity of the plant or supply power system to carry kilowatts. The capacity of all apparatus is determined by the KVA it can carry, hence larger generators, transmission lines, transformers, feeders, and switches must be provided for each kilowatt of load when power factor is low. Capital investment per kilowatt of load is higher.

2. Low power factor means more current per kilowatt, hence makes each kilowatt of power carry a higher burden of line losses . . . . . makes it cost more to transport each kilowatt of power.

3. Low power factor may depress the voltage, with a detrimental reduction in the output of practically all electrical apparatus and a reduction in its efficiency.

4. This all has an effect on the power bill. Many power companies have a penalty for low lagging *pf* and at times a credit for high *pf*. The cost of power may possibly be decreased by raising *pf*.

A resultant system *leading pf* is just as inefficient as a lagging *pf*. The goal is unity with none wasted in reactive power.

Plant power factor improvement should be considered when any of the following conditions exist.

1. When the power company charges extra for a *pf* below a certain figure, say 0.9. There also may be a cost *reduction* when *pf* is, say, 0.95 or higher. Not all power suppliers consider *pf* in rates, but many do.

2. When plant distribution lines, switch gear, and transformers are heavily loaded. Improvement in *pf* will possibly permit the addition of the new compressor load without major changes.

3. When *pf* is below 0.90.

4. When the new load is 10% or more of the existing load.

NEAR UNITY POWER FACTOR

LOAD	APPROXIMATE POWER FACTOR
Incandescent Lamps	1.0
Fluorescent Lamps (With built-in capacitor)	0.95 to 0.97
Resistor Heating Apparatus	1.0
Synchronous Motors (Also built for leading power factor operation)	1.0
Rotary Converters	1.0

LAGGING POWER FACTOR

LOAD	APPROXIMATE POWER FACTOR
Induction Motors (at rated load)	
Split-Phase, below 1 hp	0.55 to 0.75
Split-Phase, 1 to 10 hp	0.75 to 0.85
Polyphase, Squirrel-Cage	
High-Speed, 1 to 10 hp	0.75 to 0.90
High-Speed, 10 hp and larger	0.85 to 0.92
Low-Speed	0.70 to 0.85
Wound Rotor	0.80 to 0.90
Groups of Induction Motors	0.50 to 0.85
Welders—Motor-Generator Type	0.50 to 0.60
Transformer Type	0.50 to 0.70
Arc Furnaces	0.80 to 0.90
Induction Furnaces	0.60 to 0.70

LEADING POWER FACTOR

LOAD	APPROXIMATE POWER FACTOR
Synchronous Motors	0.9, 0.8, 0.7, 0.6, etc. leading power factor depending on the rated leading power factor for which they are built.
Synchronous Condensers	Nearly zero leading power factor. (Output practically all leading reactive kva.)
Capacitors	Zero leading power factor. (Output practically all leading reactive kva.)

Courtesy of Electric Machinery Mfg. Company.

Fig. 15-D. Power factor of typical A-C loads.

Power Factor Correction

The selection of the type of motor used to drive a compressor will depend upon the results of a study of the need for *pf* correction and the advantages to be gained by a given motor type and rating. The motor alternatives are:

Squirrel cage induction motor;

Unity power factor synchronous motor; and,

0.8 leading power factor synchronous motor.

Preliminary to this, however, should be a careful check of all present induction motors to be sure they are operating at or close to full load. An induction motor has a poor power factor at best, but it falls materially at partial load. This should be considered, too, if the compressor is to operate at part load much of the time. A 1.0 *pf* synchronous motor, on the other hand, will generate *leading kvar* at reduced loads.

Required	Direct Current	Alternating current		
		Single-phase	2-phase-4 wire*	3-phase
Amperes when hp is known	$\dfrac{746(\text{hp})}{(E)\,(\text{eff})}$	$\dfrac{746(\text{hp})}{(E)\,(\text{eff})\,(\text{pf})}$	$\dfrac{746(\text{hp})}{2(E)\,(\text{eff})\,(\text{pf})}$	$\dfrac{746(\text{hp})}{1.73(E)\,(\text{eff})\,(\text{pf})}$
Amperes when kilowatts are known	$\dfrac{1000(\text{kw})}{E}$	$\dfrac{1000(\text{kw})}{(E)\,(\text{pf})}$	$\dfrac{1000(\text{kw})}{2(E)\,(\text{pf})}$	$\dfrac{1000(\text{kw})}{1.73\,(E)\,(\text{pf})}$
Amperes when kva is known		$\dfrac{1000(\text{kva})}{E}$	$\dfrac{1000(\text{kva})}{2(E)}$	$\dfrac{1000(\text{kva})}{1.73(E)}$
Power Kilowatts	$\dfrac{(I)\,(E)}{1000}$	$\dfrac{(E)\,(I)\,(\text{pf})}{1000}$	$\dfrac{2(I)\,(E)\,(\text{pf})}{1000}$	$\dfrac{1.73(I)\,(E)\,(\text{pf})}{1000}$
Power kva		$\dfrac{(I)\,(E)}{1000}$	$\dfrac{2(I)\,(E)}{1000}$	$\dfrac{1.73\,(I)\,(E)}{1000}$
Power Output Horsepower	$\dfrac{(I)\,(E)\,(\text{eff})}{746}$	$\dfrac{(I)\,(E)\,(\text{pf})\,(\text{eff})}{746}$	$\dfrac{2(I)\,(E)\,(\text{pf})\,(\text{eff})}{746}$	$\dfrac{1.73\,(I)\,(E)\,(\text{pf})\,(\text{eff})}{746}$

I = amperes
E = volts
eff = efficiency (as a decimal)
hp = horsepower
pf = power factor

kw = kilowatts
kva = kilovolt amperes
*In 2-phase, 3-wire circuits the current in the common conductor is 1.41 times that in either of the other conductors.

If actual voltage is above or below rated value, the correct value should be used in the above formulas.

For Synchronous Speeds — see page 34-160.

Fig. 15-E. Summary of electrical formulas.

It must be pointed out that 0.8 leading *pf* synchronous motors are less widely used because they are more expensive than 1.0 *pf*, are less efficient, and require more expensive accessories. It can cost less to use other *pf* correction methods and these should be investigated.

Fig. 15-F illustrates a number of arrangements of equipment that may be used for correction. Note the use of the capacitor in various typical spots. These devices must be considered in any study. They may provide good correction at lower cost than the use of a synchronous motor on the compressor. They may at times be arranged to cut-in or cut-out as an induction motor is started or stopped, this providing correction close to the point where lagging *pf* is generated. Sizing should be determined in consultation with the power company and electrical equipment manufacturer.

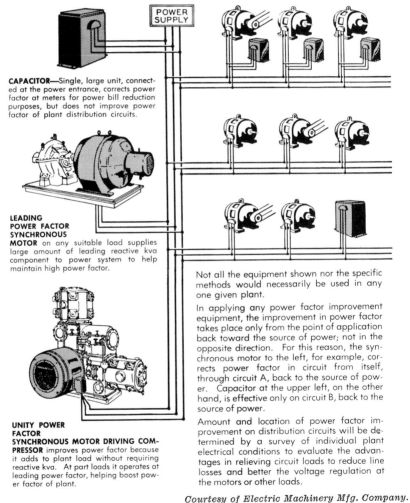

POWER SUPPLY

CAPACITOR—Single, large unit, connected at the power entrance, corrects power factor at meters for power bill reduction purposes, but does not improve power factor of plant distribution circuits.

LEADING POWER FACTOR SYNCHRONOUS MOTOR on any suitable load supplies large amount of leading reactive kva component to power system to help maintain high power factor.

UNITY POWER FACTOR SYNCHRONOUS MOTOR DRIVING COMPRESSOR improves power factor because it adds to plant load without requiring reactive kva. At part loads it operates at leading power factor, helping boost power factor of plant.

Not all the equipment shown nor the specific methods would necessarily be used in any one given plant.

In applying any power factor improvement equipment, the improvement in power factor takes place only from the point of application back toward the source of power; not in the opposite direction. For this reason, the synchronous motor to the left, for example, corrects power factor in circuit from itself, through circuit A, back to the source of power. Capacitor at the upper left, on the other hand, is effective only on circuit B, back to the source of power.

Amount and location of power factor improvement on distribution circuits will be determined by a survey of individual plant electrical conditions to evaluate the advantages in relieving circuit loads to reduce line losses and better the voltage regulation at the motors or other loads.

Courtesy of Electric Machinery Mfg. Company.

Fig. 15-F.   Typical methods of applying power-factor-improvement equipment.

Plant and compressor variations are far too wide in range to permit any economic comparison here. The following method of developing the degee of correction obtained by any of the above methods will, however, assist in studying the relative effect of each type. Costs and savings must be balanced against each other for evaluation of alternate methods.

The Tangent Table Solution

The basic diagram used in this method of analysis is the power triangle with assistance from the tangent table of Fig. 15-G. This method utilizes a tabulation of present kw and $kvar$ to which are added algebraically the additional kw loads proposed and the corresponding $kvar$. From totals of these two items is found the corrected pf.

Power Factor	Ratio KVAR/KW	Power Factor	Ratio KVAR/KW	Power Factor	Ratio KVAR/KW
1.00	.000	.80	.750	.60	1.333
.99	.143	.79	.776	.59	1.369
.98	.203	.78	.802	.58	1.405
.97	.251	.77	.829	.57	1.442
.96	.292	.76	.855	.56	1.480
.95	.329	.75	.882	.55	1.518
.94	.363	.74	.909	.54	1.559
.93	.395	.73	.936	.53	1.600
.92	.426	.72	.964	.52	1.643
.91	.456	.71	.992	.51	1.687
.90	.484	.70	1.020	.50	1.732
.89	.512	.69	1.049	.49	1.779
.88	.540	.68	1.078	.48	1.828
.87	.567	.67	1.108	.47	1.878
.86	.593	.66	1.138	.46	1.930
.85	.620	.65	1.169	.45	1.985
.84	.646	.64	1.201	.44	2.041
.83	.672	.63	1.233	.43	2.100
.82	.698	.62	1.266	.42	2.161
.81	.724	.61	1.299	.41	2.225

If power factor is lagging, KVAR will be lagging (negative).
If power factor is leading, KVAR will be leading (positive).

Courtesy of Electric Machinery Mfg. Company.

Fig. 15-G. The tangent table.

The power triangle is shown in Fig. 15-H. The left sketch illustrates a lagging pf and the right a leading pf. It will be seen that kw/kva is the cosine of θ, or the pf, and that $kvar/kw$ is the tangent of θ. Fig. 15-G is therefore a table of tangents as compared to cosines (pf) from which, knowing kw, a number of calculations may be made.

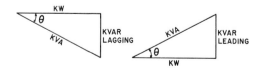

Fig. 15-H. The power triangle.

Example

Assume a 600 *kw* load at 0.7 lagging *pf*. From the table the ratio of *kvar/kw* is 1.020, so the *kvar* is 612. This will be lagging or below the *kw* line. See Fig. 15-I (A).

To this it is proposed to add a 250 hp compressor with 1.0 *pf* synchronous motor. With a motor efficiency of 92%, the *kw* required at full load will be 203. Since this is a 1.0 *pf* load, the *kvar* is zero. Tabulating:

	kw	kvar
Original load	600	−612 (lag)
Added load	203	0
Resultant	803	−612 (lag)

The *kvar/kw* ratio is 0.762. From the table, one reads 0.795 lagging *pf*. See Fig. 15-I (B).

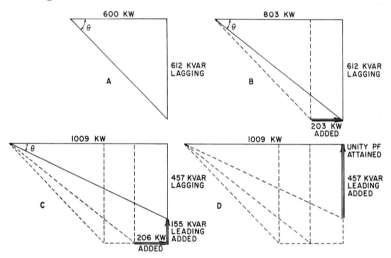

Fig. 15-I.   Use of the power triangle to develop the effect of added loads of different types.

Assume now that further addition is planned using another compressor with a 250 *hp* 0.8 *leading pf* motor. The *kw*, because of lower efficiency, is approximately 206. In this case the *kvar/kw* is 0.75 (from the table) and the *kvar* becomes 155, but this time it is *leading*.

The tabulation now becomes:

	kw	kvar
Original load	600	− 612 (lag)
Added load (1)	203	0
Added load (2)	206	+ 155 (lead)
	1009	− 457 (lag)

kvar/kw ratio becomes 0.453 and (from the table) *pf* is about 0.91 lagging. See Fig. 15-I (C).

If this is still not good enough, a 457 *kvar* capacitor could be added to bring the *pf* to unity, as follows:

	kw	kvar
Original load	600	−612 (lag)
Added load (1)	203	0
Added load (2)	206	+ 155 (lead)
Capacitor	0	+ 457 (lead)
	1009	0

See Fig. 15-I (D).

Steam Engines

The steam engine was probably the first prime mover to drive a compressor. It is still used to some extent, although electric motors, steam turbines, and internal combustion engines have superseded steam engine power to a large degree. Steam engines are used only for reciprocating compressors.

The steam engine is a very reliable driver. In most designs it is extremely flexible in operation. The economy holds up well at reduced load (speed).

This driver is best applied where (1) it satisfies a plant heat balance need, or (2) the flexibility of variable-speed control is a decided process advantage. For some processes utilizing exhaust steam, however, the steam engine is ruled out because it introduces cylinder lubricating oil into the exhaust steam. Where oil in steam cannot be tolerated, the less efficient, somewhat less flexible turbine driver must be used.

All steam-engine-driven units are of the continuous heavy duty type. Most are built integrally with the compressor, only a few being coupled.

Types and Arrangements

There are three basic frame arrangements.

1. The horizontal straight-line design, as shown in Fig. 6-E, page 6-7.

2. The horizontal four-corner design with two steam cylinders at one end of the frame and two compression cylinders at the other end, as shown in Fig. 6-K, page 6-10, and,

3. An "L" arrangement with steam cylinders vertical and compressor cylinders horizontal, as in Fig. 15-J.

The multiple steam cylinders for arrangements (2) and (3) may use either single- or two-stage steam expansion (simple or compound cylinders, respectively).

Sizes

The single steam cylinder units, arrangement (1), are available up to about 150 hp in a number of sizes and compression ends to suit require-

Fig. 15-J.   Typical "L" arrangement of steam power and compressor cylinders.

ments.   Arrangement (2) is built for 150 to 1500 hp in a wide range of sizes.   Arrangement (3) is available from 900 to 4000 hp depending upon the number of steam cylinders used in line.

Cylinder, Valve, and Control Types

The straight-line compressors utilize a *simple piston valve* with a fixed steam inlet cut-off point, the latter, however, being manually adjustable for cut-off position to obtain the best economy with each basic steam condition.   Control is normally by a throttling governor that limits maximum speed and adjusts actual operating speed to maintain a preset gas pressure.   This is known as *speed-and-pressure control*.   Control to about 25% of full speed is usually possible.

A double or *riding -cut-off piston valve* is used on all arrangement (2) units and on some arrangement (3) designs.   Control may be either *constant-speed or speed-and-pressure*, depending upon the application, and may be by throttling the intake or by altering the steam inlet cut-off point. They can operate over a speed range from 100% to about 20% with excellent control and economy.

These steam ends with their manually adjustable cut-off possibilities are well suited to operating efficiently under such varying conditions as condensing in the summer and against a back pressure (for space heating purposes) in winter.   Proper adjustments are readily made.

A third cylinder design occasionally used on "L" (arrangement 3) frames is the *uniflow* with poppet inlet valves.   The exhaust is solely through ports in the center of the cylinder which are uncovered by the piston toward the end of each stroke. This design is efficient when steam conditions are proper, but it is not as flexible as the double-piston-valve unit. Applications generally have been for relatively fixed steam and load applications. An automatic cut-off governor is used to maintain desired speed.

Steam Conditions

Standard units of the straight line and four corner horizontal designs are available to 250-psiG steam pressure and 550°F total steam temperature (about 150°F superheat). The four corner type can be built for higher pressures and temperatures, 700 psiG and 725°F total temperature being about the maximum. Proper lubrication and materials then become a severe problem.

Starting

Single steam cylinder straight-line compressors must be unloaded for starting, but most of those units having two or more steam cylinders may be arranged for starting against load if necessary.

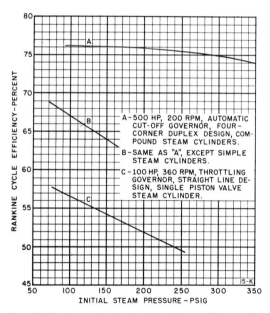

Fig. 15-K. Approximate Rankine Cycle efficiency for various types of reciprocating steam driven compressors.

Efficiency

The Rankine Cycle Efficiency *(RCE)*, as discussed on page 5-7, is the basis for rating the efficiency of steam-driven machines.

Typical full-load and full-speed *RCE* values for various types of units are shown in Fig. 15-K. These are for basic conditions of saturated inlet steam and atmospheric exhaust. The table below gives modifications to be applied for variations as listed. All data are of necessity somewhat generalized and approximate. The additions or subtractions are units by which the curve data are to be changed.

The straight uniflow engine with suitable pressure conditions will have an efficiency close to curve A, but the modifications do not necessarily apply.

Modification To Rankine Cycle Efficiency

Curve	A	B	C
For 1500 HP unit.....................	Add 3	Add 2	....
For each 50°F superheat to 150°F maximum.	Add 2	Add 3	Add 2
For each 5 psi increase in back pressure to 15 psiG maximum................	Subtract 3	Add 3	Add 4.5
For 26″ Hg Vacuum..................	Subtract 17	Subtract 23	Subtract 16

Steam Turbines

Certain applications, including those requiring oil-free exhaust steam, may be served to advantage by steam-turbine drivers. They are adaptable to all types of positive-displacement and dynamic units.

Direct-connected turbines are readily available to any desired horsepower. The speed of turbines can well match the speed of centrifugal and axial compressors, making direct-drive units common practice. Turbines with speeds to 35,000 rpm are available. The horsepower available decreases as the speed increases. Steam conditions play a very important role in horsepower versus speed. Condensing turbines with very low exhaust conditions are limited to moderate speeds in the range above 6000 hp. By decreasing the amount of vacuum, higher speeds and horsepowers become readily available.

Direct drive is possible with many helical-lobe rotaries, but reducing gear drive is required with all other rotaries and reciprocating machines. Some centrifugal compressors use speed-up rather than reducing gears to adapt commercially available lower speed turbines to higher speed compressors.

Good commercial gears are available with a single speed-change up to nine or ten to one. Double-gear trains are required for higher ratios.

Types and Arrangements

There are two general turbine classifications, based on methods of utilizing energy in the steam. In the *impulse* type, the steam is fully expanded in nozzles or stationary vanes. There is no further pressure drop in the rotating vanes. The alternate is the *reaction* design in which there is pressure drop throughout both fixed and rotating vanes. The energy transfer between steam and rotor in either case is caused by the reduction in velocity and transformation of steam kinetic energy into mechanical energy of rotation. Commercially there is little difference in efficiency.

Fig. 15-L shows a turbine-gear-driven reciprocator. A large direct-connected turbine-driven centrifugal is shown in Fig. 15-M. To illustrate one of the more special turbines available for compressor drive, Fig. 15-N

Fig. 15-L. Steam turbine driving a reciprocating compressor through a reduction gear.

shows a topping unit designed to run at relatively high initial pressures and a high back pressure. Tihs provides inexpensive compressor power by using only the "top" of the steam pressure.

Steam Conditions

Steam turbine drivers may be designed for a wide range of steam conditions and are therefore readily adaptable, within economic limits, to whatever steam may be available. Where exhaust steam from the turbine can be utilized in the plant system, a back pressure turbine may be used. Where steam consumption is of prime importance, a multistage con-

Fig. 15-M. Steam turbine driving a large centrifugal air compressor in blast furnace blowing service.

densing turbine may be selected. When low-pressure steam is available continuously or intermittently to supplement high-pressure steam, a mixed-pressure turbine may be selected. Also, an automatic-extraction turbine can be designed to bleed varying amounts of low-pressure steam to a process or other equipment.

Pressures to 1415 psiG initial and total temperatures to 1000°F may be handled. Back pressures run to 300 psiG or higher. Turbines operate with improved economy when condensing, utilizing high vacuums more effectively than the reciprocating engine.

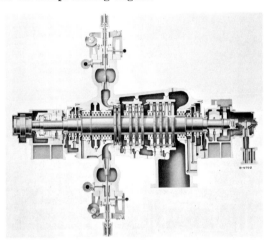

Fig. 15-N.   Section of a topping steam turbine designed to drive a centrifugal compressor.

In single-stage designs for 5000 hp or smaller, 600 psiG and/or 750°F is a typical commercial limit. The cost increases rapidly because of material changes at higher pressures or temperatures. The more efficient multistage unit in any horsepower has a cost dividing line at 600 psiG and 825°F, but the increases are not as severe for higher conditions as on the single-stage machines. This type may be commercial over a wider range, depending upon size and steam cost.

Control

For small turbines with initial steam pressure of 150 psiG or more, a single control valve under constant control of a speed governor, pressure controller, or other suitable controller may be used. If there is any appreciable operation at reduced load, however, it is advisable to consider a multivalve turbine in order to obtain improved efficiency at the reduced load points. When the steam flow is in the order of 60,000 lb/hr or greater, it is desirable to use the multivalve design. This is true when constant load is expected as the multivalve design give greater reliability of operation for the larger steam flows.

Efficiency

Fig. 15-O and Fig. 15-P give approximate Rankine Cycle Efficiencies (see page 5-7) for single-stage and multistage turbines at various ratings and steam pressures. Superheat of 100°F has been assumed. These data

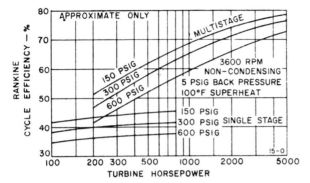

Fig. 15-O. Approximate non-condensing steam turbine Rankine Cycle efficiencies (3600 rpm only).

may be used only for rough estimating. There is considerable variance between manufacturers for a given rating and condition, depending on how the conditions match a particular frame size or design.

Although very large turbines are used for certain types of compressors, a limit of 5000 hp has been chosen for these data since this encompasses the majority of compressor drives where such data would be used. It is to be expected that larger units would have higher efficiencies. For example, a 25,000 hp 3600-rpm turbine at 600 psiG, 750°F and 5″ Hg abs. exhaust, would have an *RCE* of about 82%.

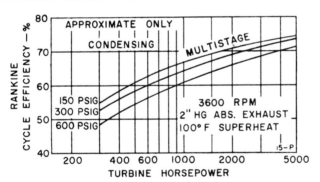

Fig. 15-P. Approximate condensing steam turbine Rankine Cycle efficiencies (3600 rpm only).

Single-stage turbines often operate at some back pressure. The curves of Fig. 15-0 are for 5 psiG back. For back pressures of 15 psiG multiply curve RCE by 1.03 to 1.05; for 30 psiG back, multiply by 1.07 to 1.08; and for 50 psiG, multiply by 1.10 to 1.12. Do not use the last correction when initial pressure is 150 psiG or lower.

Condensing turbines show a small increase in *RCE* for higher absolute exhaust pressure (lower vacuums), but it is not significant for the purpose of these curves.

Superheat Corrections To Curve Rankine Cycle Efficiency

Type of Turbine	Single-Stage	Multistage	
	Noncondensing	Noncondensing	Condensing
Correction Method	Add or Subtract To or From RCE	Multiply	Multiply
Superheat 0°F 100°F 200°F 300°F	add 0.6 .... Subtract 0.6 Subtract 1.2	0.963 1.000 1.012 1.015	0.977 1.000 1.018 1.034

Multipliers For Speeds Other Than 3600 RPM
Multistage Turbine Only

	Noncondensing				Condensing			
RPM BHP	3600	5000	7500	10,000	3600	5000	7500	10,000
500	1.000	1.030	1.036	1.018	1.000	1.000	1.000	1.000
1000	1.000	1.013	1.006	0.982	1.000	1.000	1.000	1.000
2000	1.000	1.001	0.980	0.940	1.000	1.000	1.000	0.957
3000	1.000	0.997	0.968	0.920	1.000	1.000	0.984	0.929
5000	1.000	0.994	0.959	0.902	1.000	1.000	0.955	0.895

Gas Turbines

Although the gas turbine as an industrial driver is relatively new, it has been applied to compressors in a large number of applications. It is most suitable for driving such high-speed types as certain helical-lobe units and centrifugal or axial-flow dynamic machines.

Cycles

The open cycle is the only one so far applied for compressor drive. This is a *once-through* cycle. Fig. 15-Q shows the simplest form, using a compressor (generally of the axial-flow type) to compress air into a combustion chamber or combustor into which a fuel gas or oil is admitted and burned. The resultant high-temperature gas-air mixture flows through an expander turbine. Part of this power is used to drive the axial compressor, the remainder is available as a prime mover.

The simple open cycle is relatively low in thermal efficiency, ranging from 16 to 25%. The principal loss is in the waste of exhaust gas heat.

There are many modifications that may be used to improve the efficiency, the use of a regenerator being the most common. This cycle is shown in Fig. 15-R. The exhaust gas preheats the compressed air entering the combustor, resulting in a lower fuel rate to obtain the same gas temperature to the turbine. An efficiency increase of about 4% may be obtained. An additional refinement is the use of intercooling during compression of the air, thus reducing the power required for a given weight of air.

The gas turbine cycle becomes much more efficient if the hot exhaust gases are used to generate steam, as in a waste heat boiler, or to perform a process function.

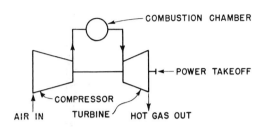

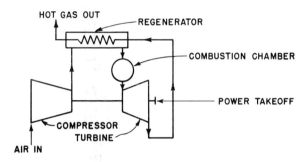

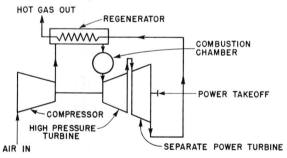

Fig. 15-S. Open-cycle two-shaft gas turbine with regenerator.

General Comments

Gas turbines are essentially constant-speed units, the efficiency falling rather rapidly when speed is reduced. Single-shaft turbines have an efficient speed range of approximately 10%. When driving a centrifugal compressor, this range will usually be sufficient for control purposes. When greater speed variation is needed, the two-shaft arrangement may be used. See Fig. 15-S. Quite wide speed variation is possible. The expander is in two sections; one driving the air supply compressor on one shaft; the other having a separate shaft for connection to the loading compressor.

Operating on gas fuel, the gas turbine is about as reliable as a steam turbine, making possible long continuous runs without shutdown for inspection or maintenance. When using distillate or treated residual fuel, the tips of the burner nozzles must be cleaned periodically.

Basically, the open-cycle gas turbine is a very simple machine. However, because of high temperatures, high speeds, and close tolerances, it must have complex apparatus for control, cooling, lubrication, and emergency protection. It must have a sizeable starting motor or turbine with a disengaging clutch, or a source of compressed air sufficient for starting purposes. It becomes self-supporting at about 55% speed.

Fig. 15-T.   A gas-turbine-driven centrifugal pipeline compressor.

The gas turbine is a lightweight prime mover, capable of rapid start-up and loading, and has no stand-by losses. It can be arranged to require little or no cooling water, making it advantageous for use in areas where water is a scarcity. The gas turbine establishes the speed of any driven dynamic compressor unless gears are used.

Efficiency is closely related to air compression ratio and temperature of gas to the turbine. The latter is primarily limited by presently available turbine materials. As better materials become available and cooling methods are improved, gas turbine efficiencies may be increased.

Air compression ratios of 5 to 7 are quite common and higher ratios have been used for improved efficiency.

The influence of air compressor intake temperature and altitude is considerable since they affect the weight of air (and oxygen) available for combustion. NEMA standards for land-based equipment are 80°F intake at 14.17-psiA pressure.

Aircraft jet engines may be adapted to compressor drive by the addition of a power turbine to drive a loading compressor. The result is a two shaft gas turbine.

A typical centrifugal pipeline compressor driven by a gas turbine is shown in Fig. 15-T.

Applications

Gas turbine applications range widely and in process industries their uses are increasing rapidly. Among the applications are:

1. Driving compressors for
     Pipeline gas transmission
     Oil field repressuring
     Oil refinery processes
     Blast furnaces
     Combustion air for pressurized boilers, the boiler
        being the combustor
     Combustion air for nitric acid plants

2. Miscellaneous
     Generation of electric power (peak and stand-by)
     Driving locomotives
     As a hot gas producer for process

Modifications are possible to permit bleeding low pressure air from the turbine compressor to a process.

The exhaust normally has a high oxygen content (about 18%) and may be useful in a process for this reason, particularly if a hot gas stream is desirable.

Gas Engines

The heavy-duty internal combustion engine, principally the spark ignited gas engine, is the second most popular stationary compressor driver. It is used almost exclusively in natural gas storage plants, natural gasoline facilities, and liquefied petroleum gas plants. The gas engine drives over 90% of the reciprocating and centrifugal compressors in the natural gas transmission industry. The majority of gas lift production compressors are powered by this type of driver. Under certain economic conditions, the gas engine is an attractive driver in oil refineries, petrochemical plants, and refrigeration service in a variety of industries. Some favorable conditions for gas engine drive are:

1. Relatively inexpensive gaseous fuels available;
2. High prime mover thermal efficiency desirable due to a high load factor and/or limited fuel supply, such efficiencies not being available in other types of drivers;
3. Electric power sources limited or undependable; and,
4. Skills for supervising and maintaining engines available.

The integral engine driven compressor, Fig. 6-L and Fig. 6-M, page 6-11, is the predominent reciprocating compressor type, although engines are occasionally direct coupled to separate compressors, usually of the type illustrated on page 6-12, Fig. 6-N. Speed-increasing gears are used when driving centrifugal compressors. Natural gas, principally methane, is the usual fuel, although various process tail gases may be used and, on standby service, liquefied petroleum gas may be the fuel. Currently these engines are available in 120 to 5500 hp sizes.

Engine Types

Two types of engines, the 4-stroke cycle and the 2-stroke cycle, are being built in the U. S. A. Some manufacturers build both in certain sizes.

Each type has a supercharged version. Units of the *4-stroke cycle* (commonly called 4-cycle) in the naturally aspirated version have the familiar intake, compression, power, and exhaust strokes consuming 720 degrees of crankshaft rotation.

In the nonsupercharged *2-cycle* design, the intake and exhaust strokes are essentially replaced by scavenging air compressors of the reciprocating or centrifugal type. These serve to remove the spent gases and to cool and fill the cylinder with a fresh air charge. In order to accommodate the foregoing events near the power cylinder bottom dead center, the power stroke is shortened. A fuel injection valve is used to add fuel after the exhaust valve or port is closed to avoid fuel loss. Power cylinder lubricating oil is likewise injected by a force-feed lubricator.

Supercharging

Supercharging, that is increasing the charge density external to the power cylinder, is widely practiced to obtain improved thermal efficiency and greater power output per unit of space and weight. If the supercharger is powered by expansion of exhaust gases in a turbine, the process is called turbocharging. The engine (including the turbine) becomes a compound machine with the energy balance between the two units under the control of the designer.

Speed Control

Gas engines are variable-speed machines that frequently offer sufficient capacity flexibility, while operating at full torque, to satisfy a compressor application without the need for other control devices. These units are capable of operating at reduced capacity with good economy. The minimum operating speed, as a percent of rating, varies widely with specific designs; however, percentages as low as 50 to 60% are not unusual.

Availability

Availability in *moderate* load factor plants frequently is 100%, and in high load factor plants will average 95-99%, depending upon the over-all excellence of plant design, spare part availability, and the skill of supervisors and maintenance personnel.

Effect of Altitude and Ambient Temperature

Engines, being air consuming machines, are affected by air density. A reduction in ambient air density, either due to altitude or high air temperature, can be compensated for by derating the power output or by the expenditure of additional energy (commonly recovered from the engine exhaust) to compress ambient air and restore sea level (or higher) density at the engine inlet. Because of variations in practice, the effect of altitude on engine ratings should be discussed with manufacturers.

Low ambient temperatures can be utilized to increase the output of gas engines. This is particularly significant on turbocharged engines where cold water for aftercooling becomes available with low ambients. Currently, turbocharged gas engines are offered which permit loading the engine to 124 percent of its normal rating when the ambient temperature is 40°F or lower.

Thermal Efficiency

Fuel consumption is a function of design. The thermal efficiency increases with pressures and the expansion ratio. The thermal efficiency of the naturally aspirated units ranges from 28 to 32%. Turbocharged machines will have efficiencies ranging from 34 to 40.5%. Both are based upon the fuel's lower heating value.

Heat Rejection

Since gas engines are heat engines, thermal energy not converted to useful power must be continually dissipated to prevent unduly high temperatures that would intensify heat stresses and impair lubrication. The amount of heat involved is 59.5 to 72% of the caloric value of the fuel input, and for a given cylinder surface, is termed thermal loading. In conjunction with mechanical stresses, this determines physical size and provides the explanation as to why an engine that fires every crankshaft revolution, as opposed to every other revolution, is not half the size of the latter. Fortunately, the majority of the waste heat can be rejected to the atmosphere by the exhaust gases. This is particularly true of supercharged machines, because the centrifugal compressor exists as a means to pass additional air through the engine accompanied by an incremental increase in horsepower.

The fact that so much heat passes out the exhaust has led to the application of waste heat boilers or heat recovery exhaust silencers in cases where a use existed for the exhaust heat. The system efficiency can thus be raised considerably.

Heat rejection to jacket water approximates 2000 Btu/hp hr on naturally aspirated engines, but is sharply reduced in supercharged engines to about 1200 Btu/hp hr. Interestingly enough, one 4-cycle machine design rejects only 700 Btu/hp hr to the jacket water. Heat rejection to the lubricating oil is 325 to 470 Btu/hp hr, depending upon the design. (All machines considered have oil cooled pistons.)

Heat exchangers requiring relatively cool water are needed to cool the oil and, on supercharged engines, aftercooling of the compressed air charge is frequently required.

Engine Selection

The selection of an engine is usually based upon project and local economic factors, as well as such specific engine features as cylindering and balance. Four-cycle engines have higher thermal efficiency, consume less lubricating oil, are smoother running and easier starting than 2-cycle engines. Two-cycle engines have no inlet valves, may have no exhaust valves, they require less displacement, and therefore may have fewer power cylinders. The differences are usually small, particularly in the turbocharged models. Both types are in extensive use.

Diesel and Dual-Fuel Engines

In the heavy-duty class, diesel engines are used rather infrequently for compressor drive. An integral compressor design is available only in the low range of 200 to 1300 bhp.

Larger sizes are available for coupling to separate reciprocator frames or for gearing to centrifugal units. These engines are usually dual-fuel engines, designed to operate on either diesel oil or a mixture of natural gas and diesel oil with a minimum of 5% oil. Some may be converted rather easily to a standard gas engine with spark ignition.

The dual-fuel arrangement permits use of lower-cost natural gas during off-peak seasons at an interruptable rate, switching to 100% oil when the gas supply is cut off, usually during cold weather. Complete fuel oil storage facilities are, of course, required. There are very few of these compressor drive installations.

Special Problems

Starting

Methods of unloading the main types of compressor for starting have been discussed briefly in Chapters 6, 7, 8, and 9. The starting cycle includes not only the initial breakaway from rest of both driver and compressor but the acceleration of both to full speed. In the case of the synchronous motor, the pull-in requirements are also included.

The reasons for starting compressors unloaded are quite varied, but usually are related directly to driver torque capacities. The following shows generally accepted combinations and their unloading requirements.

Starting Unloading Required

Driver	Reciprocating	Vane Rotary	Helical-Lobe Rotary	Dynamic
Induction Motor	Yes	*	Yes	Usually
Synchronous Motor	Yes	Yes	Yes	Usually
Steam Engine	Seldom	——	——	——
Steam Turbine	Usually	*	Yes	Frequently
Gas Turbine	Yes	——	Yes	Yes
Gas Engine	Yes	——	——	Yes
Industrial Engine	Yes	*	Yes	Usually

*Consult manufacturer. Some units require no unloading.

Acceleration

Of all the drivers listed, only the electric motors have material problems in accelerating the compressor to full speed. Engines and turbines have plenty of accelerating power once a breakaway is made and a reasonable speed has been attained. Acceleration time is not too important. Motors, with the greater-than-normal current flow during the starting and accelerating period, will overheat if the starting cycle lasts too long. Acceleration must therefore occur within a limited number of seconds. This may require the development of other than standard torques.

Following breakaway, the friction load becomes a minor factor. However, as the speed increases, the load imposed by gas flow through the system increases, regardless of whether the compressor is unloaded or not. Unloader systems and methods are designed specifically to keep this factor within satisfactory limits.

The third factor involved in acceleration is the inertia of compressor (and driver) parts to be overcome as the speed is increased. This can be major in certain compressors, particularly dynamic machines and the high speed vane-type and helical-lobe rotary units. The reciprocating unit seldom encounters this problem unless very heavy flywheels are involved.

Squirrel-cage induction motors do not, as a rule, overheat unless the starting cycle must be gone through frequently. In this case, the motor manufacturer should make the selection. (See page 15-7, Duty Cycle). Considering synchronous motor drive, the solution often involves not only the motor, but the switchgear and power supply. Drawing more than normal current for a sustained period can effect all areas. This is the reason no standard can be set. Motor manufacturers are best able to decide on the proper selection. They are supplied compressor inertia values (WK^2), speed-torque curves, and similar information about gears, if used. These data, together with the characteristics of the motor proposed, permit successful analysis.

Motor Current Pulsation

Most compressors have reasonably smooth shaft torque requirements. The power and current demands on the driving motor are relatively constant. The reciprocator is the exception. It has a torque that is quite variable *throughout each revolution,* the extent depending upon the number and arrangement of cylinders, the method and amount of unloading, etc. Unless the proper amount of flywheel effect is provided, this can result in excessive fluctuation in the current drawn by the motor. This will cause overheating of the motor and may loosen the coils in the stator windings. Furthermore, on some power systems, it will cause variations in the voltage sufficient to produce flickering of lights or adversely effect the operation of other equipment supplied from the same system.

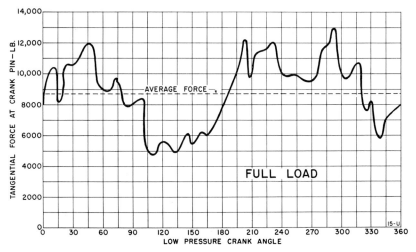

Fig. 15-U. Typical full-load shaft torque effort diagram
for a horizontal-duplex compressor with 90 degree cranks

To prevent this, an analysis is made of the compressor torque characteristics which, together with the motor characteristics, determines how much flywheel effect is necessary to limit the current pulsation to an acceptable value. The usual limit is 66% of motor full-load current. The necessary flywheel effect (WK^2) may either be incorporated in the motor rotor or in a separate flywheel. Occasionally the electrical characteristics of the motor may be changed to reduce the current pulsation.

Fig. 15-U shows a typical full-load torque effort diagram for a duplex horizontal two-cylinder compressor with cranks at 90 degrees. The average torque line represents the basis for the actual motor rating. The diagram shows torque variations for one revolution. On this particular compressor, assuming five-step clearance control, the 3/4-load condition would cause more pulsation than full-load. Hence, the 3/4-load diagram would be used for analysis.

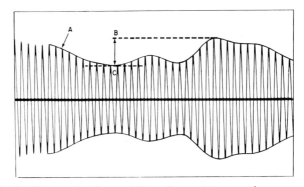

Fig. 15-V. Oscillogram showing variation of current to a synchronous motor driving a compressor as described in Fig. 15-U. Line A is the envelope of the current wave. Difference B-C divided by *rated* full-load current multiplied by 100 is percent current pulsation.

Fig. 15-V shows an oscillogram of line current variation within the motor on a reciprocating unit. Current pulsation is a general problem only with synchronous motors. It may arise with direct-coupled induction motors. With synchronous motors, the application to various arrangements and types of compressors has become quite standardized. Extensive analysis is usually unnecessary. There are, however, special situations requiring co-operation between compressor and motor builders.

Critical Speeds

At certain speeds, known as critical speeds, rotating shafts and systems of shafts may become dynamically unstable with abnormal vibration. This phenomenon is due to resonance when the rotation speed in revolutions per second corresponds to a natural frequency of shaft vibration. Vibration may be *lateral* or *torsional* (twisting).

In both, the complete system is involved, including compressor, gears or belts (if used), couplings, and driver. In the case of torsionals, the coupling stiffness can be altered to change the natural frequency of the systems. In the case of laterals, the coupling weight is of considerable importance.

It should be pointed out that certain systems, such as a gas engine driving a reciprocating compressor, must be designed to prevent excessive speed variation between the driving and the driven units during one revolution, even though resonance as such may not be involved. Excessive swings in comparative speeds may cause structural failure or excessive wear.

For either lateral or torsional critical speeds to be a problem, two conditions must exist *simultaneously:*

1. A natural system resonance within the operating speed range; and,

2. A force input at resonant speed or a multiple thereof.

Lateral Vibration

Lateral critical speeds exist in all machines, but are most important in dynamic units because of their close clearances and higher speeds. It may develop with other types if the system includes a long shaft as in a fire wall installation, or if a turbine driver is used.

The force input for a lateral critical is from some unbalance which system resonance can multiply to dangerous values. In a dynamic assembly, the amount and location of the unbalance and the system construction have an effect on the severity of the critical speed when observed on test or in operation.

Torsional Vibration

Torsional vibration requires that there be some variation in torque during one revolution of the driver or driven equipment. This may occur because:

1. Torque varies throughout the two-stroke compression cycle, as in a reciprocating compressor;

2. Same as (1), except reciprocating engine driver;

3. Motors coming up to speed have torque variations due to slip;

4. Torque varies due to abnormal operating conditions, upsets, and equipment failure;

5. Gear has tooth-to-tooth errors; and,

6. Turbine blades give varying impulses.

A considerable backlog of experience on critical speeds and their satisfactory solution has been developed through the years with all types and arrangements of compressors and drivers. However, there are areas that manufacturers investigate thoroughly unless the system has previously been proven satisfactory.

Power Increase Possibilities

Various possibilities requiring more than rated power must be considered in any driver selection.

Seasonal Temperature Changes

Dynamic compressors experience a marked increase in total pressure developed and in power requirement at full capacity when inlet temperature falls below design. (See page 4-23). This change is most important with air compressors in winter, but is felt in some degree regardless of the gas handled. Positive-displacement machines do not experience this particular problem.

As a practical matter, this seldom requires oversize dynamic drivers if the unit is not intercooled, since the excess pressure is seldom useful and some form of control acts to keep the discharge pressure and power rather uniform.

However, *all* types of *multistage* compressors *with intercoolers* are subject to a considerable increase in power when the intake temperature falls from design and the intercooler water temperature remains constant or changes a lesser amount. Interstage volumes increase relative to intake volume and more power is required in the upper stages. This may cause as much as 5 to 8% power increase on a four stage intercooled machine.

The driver must be selected to take care of these possible overloads or some control must be provided to maintain horsepower at an acceptable limit.

Pressure Conditions

Examination of any theoretical horsepower formula will show that both inlet and discharge pressure have a large part in determining power requirements. Intake is the more influential. Any increase in intake with constant volume and discharge pressure increases power almost proportionately. Hence, it is important that all predictable variations of pressure from design, *particularly the intake*, be studied for their effect on driver sizing.

Gas Composition

There are applications where the gas composition characteristics may change from time to time. These can alter power required severely and must be considered in driver sizing. Changes in molecular weight are particularly important with dynamic machines.

Chapter 16

Compressor Selection

Introduction

Selection implies that there is a choice. Usually this is true, as between various types and arrangements of equipment, although occasionally only one type may be able to meet requirements. As an example, a 20,000-psiG requirement can only be handled by a reciprocator. Alternatively, a single 150,000-cfm, 30-psiG compressor must be a centrifugal or axial dynamic unit.

References

Reference is made to prior information regarding the various main types of compressors, particularly their capacity and horsepower ranges and general characteristics and limitations. These should be reviewed since they can influence selection materially.

Reciprocating - Chapter 6.

Vane-type rotary - Chapter 7.

Helical-lobe rotary - Chapter 8.

Dynamic - Chapter 9.

Two Groups Involved

Compressor applications may be generally placed in two groups; air compressors for power purposes; and compressors for handling process gases, usually in refineries and chemical plants. Requirements may vary materially, but in all cases *selection must stand the test of over-all economics.*

Air Power Compressors

Air power compressors generally operate at pressures of 500 psiG or lower, with the majority in the range of 125 psiG or less. All major types of compressors (reciprocating, vane, and helical-lobe rotary, and dynamic) are used for this service. Choice is limited somewhat by capacity. For example, the reciprocator has a listed top capacity at 100 psiG of about 10,500 cfm but can be built to approximately 26,000 cfm. The vane-type rotary has an upper listed size of 3700 cfm as a twin unit, and the helical-lobe rotary can be used to nearly 20,000 cfm. The centrifugal, on the other hand, can be built to very large sizes. It is currently offered in the proven moderate-speed designs starting at a minimum of about 5000 cfm. High-speed designs are available for even lower capacities.

Today, even in sizes where several alternates are available, the reciprocator is apt to be the more prevalent choice. Reasons are varied. A number of factors influence the choice of *air* compressors.

Power Required

From the power standpoint, the reciprocator will usually be the best, followed by the centrifugal within its sound capacity range, then the vane and helical-lobe rotary units.

Reliability

Properly applied, operated, and maintained, all four basic designs will give years of good service. Heavy-duty units are available in all types. In addition, reciprocators are offered in designs suitable for the many moderate-duty applications. See page 6-4. Moderate-duty units may be expected to require a major overhaul every three to five years of normal operation. Heavy-duty units will require major overhaul very seldom during their life. See *Availability*, page 16-9.

Floor Space

Floor space and its shape will, at times, influence selection. The opportunity for selection will be broadened if the exact dimensions of the space available are given to all manufacturers. Design adjustments or alternate arrangements are often available.

Foundation Needs

Foundation requirements for rotating machinery will almost always be less than for an equivalent reciprocator unless one can utilize the smaller moderate-duty unit. The latter require (generally) limited foundations. Foundations are discussed on page 18-4.

Capacity Control

Variation in demand for air power must be considered. It usually ranges from full compressor capacity to zero. The different types have widely varying abilities to handle this range, some being much more economical at part load than others. The reciprocator is particularly favored in this area. A review of *Capacity Control* in the discussion of each type (Chapters 6, 7, 8, and 9) should be made before a decision is reached.

Variety of Choice

Within the four general divisions of compressors, there is little freedom of choice between arrangements other than with the reciprocator. Many selection problems can be solved by considering more than one of the available designs.

Oil Free Air

Any requirement for oil free air rules out the vane-type rotary. The helical-lobe and dynamic units require no oil in the compression space at any time; the reciprocator can be obtained in a nonlubricated design. See Chapter 14.

Cost of Air

Compressed air is never "free". It costs a considerable sum, and the selection of a compressor should always consider this factor, particularly on heavy-duty service. Costs are discussed briefly in Chapter 27, but two facts should be mentioned. First, power cost is by far the largest item in over-all air cost; second, power cost over the service life will be many times the first cost of any compressor. Therefore, the more efficient unit will usually pay a dividend in power savings, even though it may have a higher installed first cost.

Special Recommendations

Load Factor

Load factor is a consideration largely in the smaller installations where only one or two compressors are to be installed.

Load factor is the ratio of actual compressed air output (while the unit is operating) to the rated full-load output during this same period. It should never be 100%, a good rule being to select an installation for from 50 to 80% load factor, dependent upon the size, type, and number of units involved. Proper use of load factor results in:

1. More uniform pressure, even during peak demand periods;
2. A cooling-off period (extremely desirable for air-cooled units);
3. Less maintenance; and,
4. Ability to increase use of air without immediately increasing plant size.

Load factor is particularly important with air-cooled machines where sustained full-load operation results in an early build-up of deposits on valves and other parts, thereby adding to maintenance. Intermittent operation is always recommended for these units, the degree depending upon the size and operating pressure. Air-cooled units for higher than 200-psiG pressure are usually rated by a rule that states that "pump-up" (compressing) time shall not ordinarily exceed 30 minutes, nor be less than 10 minutes. Shutdown or unloaded time should be at least equal to compression time." This means 50% load factor.

Multistaging

Any *air cooled* compressor for 80-psiG pressure or higher should have two or more stages of compression unless very small. Such a two stage unit for 100 to 200 psiG will run 100° to 150°F cooler than a single-stage unit, thus reducing deposit formation and need for cleaning valves. Two-stage compression of air to 100 psiG also saves 10 to 15% in power over single-stage.

Heavy-duty water-cooled units for the same service are more economical to operate than the air-cooled units and normally run at considerably lower speed and temperatures. Hence, maintenance will consistently be less. They are universally two staged for 100-psiG air service above approximately 125 bhp.

Other Factors

If the unit must be subjected to freezing temperatures, an air-cooled unit may be the answer.

The number of machines installed must be such that the maximum protection against shutdown of air supply is obtained. This must be balanced against the investment required and the cost of a complete plant shutdown.

The driver has an influence and may dictate certain restrictions.

To summarize, selection of the proper air compressor for power services is an economic and engineering problem involving a choice between a number of alternates. It is best to discuss the problems involved thoroughly with manufacturer's representatives before making a final selection.

Process Gas Compressors

The process gas compressor is called upon to handle many and diverse types of gases. Its capacity-control requirements have a lower range (50% being a quite frequent minimum even with reciprocating units where control possibilities are usually greatest), and they are practically never "spared." Twenty-four hours a day, seven days per week operation is the general rule for months at a time. On-the-line continuity of operation is highly important.

Quick Review of Possibilities

For a quick review of possibilities, it is best to consider only horsepower and pressure. The upper limits for each type are summarized from previous references. These columns do not usually apply simultaneously.

Compressor Type	Approx. Max. BHP	Approx. Max. Pressure-psiG
Reciprocating	Over 12,000	100,000
Vane Type Rotary	(Twin unit) 860	400
Helical Lobe Rotary	6,000	250
Centrifugal Dynamic	Over 35,000	5,500
Axial Flow Dynamic	Over 100,000	500

These maximums are subject to certain limitations imposed by other factors and under certain conditions can be exceeded.

Horsepower may be approximated rather quickly for positive-displacement units by using the curves and procedure referred to on pages 34-122 and 34-146, applicable closely to reciprocators and less closely to the two rotary units. Horsepower for the dynamic units may be approximated by using formula 3.45 (page 3-22) and Fig. 3-E, or from the method on page 34-140 and reference curves. Within its range, the latter is probably the more accurate.

Discussion Restrictions

The following discussion is limited to the two principal process compressor types, the reciprocator and the dynamic, usually the centrifugal. The vane-type rotary is not to be written off in certain areas, but its main field is as an air compressor, booster, or vacuum pump. For the latter, see Chapter 20. The helical-lobe rotary is most suitable for vacuum and specialty applications at moderate pressures. Although this type is not as well known as the others, its use in process is growing rapidly. Where it fits, particularly for oil-free service, it should be considered. Most types are well adapted to turbine drive. They are economical with reference to floor space and foundation.

Gas Characteristics

Gas composition and *characteristics* can have a decided influence on compressor type. A low gas inlet density, for example, usually will affect the centrifugal to a greater degree than the positive-displacement machine. A centrifugal handling low density gas will require many more stages (a larger unit) than when handling a high gravity inlet gas. Reciprocating and other positive displacement compressors are not seriously effected by the gas MW, specific gravity, or inlet density.

Other gas characteristics, such as ratio of specific heats, compressibility, or moisture content do not influence choice.

At times, a gas may have certain *limiting conditions* within which it must be kept during compression. These conditions, if exceeded, may cause problems of corrosion, dangerous reaction of the gas or its components, or a cracking of lubricating oil resulting in constituents that cannot always be tolerated by a process. Limiting conditions are usually those of maximum discharge temperature. There is not too much to choose between the two main types, but the process reciprocator with its usually better efficiency, jacketed cylinders, and frequent intercooling usually has a slight edge. The answer may be to lower gas inlet temperature if an otherwise usable type can thus be made satisfactory.

Process Conditions

Data that are established by the process affect the selection of the compressor.

In any compression problem, for a given compression ratio the *flow rate* to be handled establishes the physical size of the equipment under consideration. It must be remembered that the compressors discussed here recognize only volume at inlet pressure and temperature conditions. Exact definition of flow rate is therefore highly important.

If 80,000 cfm of gas must be compressed at near-atmospheric suction conditions, a centrifugal compressor almost certainly would be used for the lower stages of compression. If the final discharge pressure is quite high, for example 5000 psi, the upper stages of compression would be handled by reciprocating compressors. Where the centrifugal leaves off and the reciprocating compressor takes over would depend upon the gas density, type of regulation required, and the like.

If, on the other hand, 100 cfm of gas must be compressed to 5000 psi discharge pressure, a reciprocating compressor would most certainly be used for the whole range.

These extremes are mentioned as examples only and indicate that the quantity of gas being handled is significant in selecting the compressor.

The *variation in flow rate* from maximum to minimum can likewise affect selection. If the process requires a change in flow rate from the maximum down to or near zero, the reciprocating compressor can do it with a reasonable sustained efficiency. With the centrifugal compressor, operation will not be economical below the pumping point which ordinarily is between 50 and 90% of rated capacity.

Each type compressor has some practical limits as to the maximum or minimum *gas temperatures* that can be handled. For example, the centrifugal compressor has been used quite successfully as a hot gas circulator to compress and recirculate gas at temperatures as high as 800°F. In a reciprocating compressor using present known lubricants, such temperatures are impractical. If the flow rates are too low to be practical for the centrifugal compressor and the reciprocating compressor must be fitted into such a process, it can be done only by cooling, compressing, and then reheating the gas.

Lubricated reciprocating compressors are being operated successfully with suction temperatures below minus 100°F. These low suction temperatures again create a lubrication problem. Insofar as mechanical operation is concerned, the centrifugal compressor is less affected by high or low temperature extremes than is the reciprocator.

Inlet and discharge pressures are very important in a compression problem. Yet when they vary, the magnitude of the effect is seldom realized. On reciprocating compressors, particularly multistage machines, the most common error is to assume that a small change in suction pressure makes little difference. It must be remembered that once a multistage reciprocating compressor is proportioned, lowering the suction pressure while maintaining the discharge pressure, will lower the over-all horsepower, lower the differential pressure on all stages except the last, increase the differential and the temperature rise of the last stage.

Conversely, if the suction pressure to the first stage is raised, horsepower of the complete machine is raised, differential in pressure on all stages to the last stage is raised, while differential on the last stage and its temperature rise is lowered.

If a six-stage compressor designed for 15-psiA intake and 5000 psiA discharge had suction pressure raised to 20-psiA, the increase in horsepower would be approximately 25%. All intercooler pressures would exceed the design point and safety valves would blow.

In centrifugal compressors, if suction pressure is raised, the discharge pressure will exceed the design point, the horsepower will increase, and excess pressure will have to be throttled out. If the suction pressure is lowered, the centrifugal will not compress to the desired discharge pressure.

Therefore, it is most important that the suction and discharge pressures, *their variation* and its influence be evaluated accurately.

Low compression ratios with reasonable capacities favor the centrifugal. High compression ratios and higher pressures favor the reciprocating machine. One could not attempt to define the borderline in pressure between reciprocating and centrifugal compressors because there are too many other factors to be considered.

In some multistage process compressors, the *interstage pressure* is set by the process. This may be for washing out undesirable elements, adding gas, or for carrying out chemical reactions that change the nature of the gas between stages. It is important that such interstage pressure restrictions be considered, including the pressure drop involved.

Driver

Generally speaking, if choice of driver is dictated by the available source of power, the heat balance, waste gas use, or any other factors in the plant or process, the compressor that best fits the driver should receive first consideration. In other words, the centrifugal always receives first consideration if the driver must be a turbine. The reciprocating compressor should probably always receive first consideration if the driver is to be an electric motor. The reason is that the majority of motor-driven reciprocating compressors can be direct-driven, whereas, most motor-driven centrifugal compressors require a speed-increasing gear. The converse is true if turbines are used.

Oil Contamination

Oil contamination can have a bearing on compressor type selected. The degree of importance attributed to oil contamination will also influence decisions. *Partially lubricated or nonlubricated* reciprocator designs may be more suitable than the centrifugal (or helical-lobe unit). See Chapters 13 and 14.

Foundation and Floor Space

Soil and foundation conditions must be considered in compressor selection. In a few instances, this dictates the type of machine. A centrifugal compressor operates without producing unbalanced forces. The foundation need only support the dead-weight load with adequate stiffness to maintain alignment. The type of reciprocating compressor most widely applied today in chemical and process plants is designed specifically for a minimum of unbalanced forces. Generally, a foundation that will support the dead-weight load of the compressor and maintain alignment of compressor and driver will have adequate mass to absorb the small unbalanced forces that may be present. See the discussion starting on pages 18-4 and 18-39.

The centrifugal will usually be favored from both the foundation and floor space angles.

Multiple-Service Units

For sound economic reasons, process plants have been installing fewer compressors to do a given job, using larger sizes and no spares. Where a process requires handling of many streams, quite common in some types of plants, it is required that several streams be handled by a single driver.

It is seldom that more than two services are handled in a combination of centrifugal casings having a common driver. There are problems of capacity and pressure control, as well as other factors.

With reciprocators, a greater flexibility is possible in the number and size of streams that can be handled on a single driver. Desired capacity control is also usually more easily attained. As many as six separate streams have been handled on large existing compressors. Fig. 16-A shows the layout of one such compressor in a synthetic ammonia plant. Included in each of two trains in this plant are another unit handling five services and a large multistage synthesis gas compressor.

First Cost

There is no formula for establishing the relative cost of the centrifugal versus the reciprocating compressor. If volume, pressure, k factor, and all other factors are the same, then gas specific gravity can influence the cost of the centrifugal, but it will have little effect on the reciprocator.

If the source of power is steam, the centrifugal is more favorable because the drive is direct from the turbine. The reciprocator must have either a steam engine or turbine-gear drive, both of which are more costly than direct-coupled turbine or electric motor.

As has been mentioned earlier, power cost throughout the service life of a compressor is many times the first cost. While is is possible that the more efficient machine may be higher in original installed cost, the power savings over a period of years usually will quickly pay off the differential and return a profit for the remaining life.

Power Cost

Except at very low ratios of compression, the centrifugal compressor is inherently less efficient than the reciprocating compressor.

Very large volumes, low ratios of compression, and low final pressures favor the centrifugal compressor. No one today would think of using the reciprocating compressor for blast furnace blowing. Conversely, higher ratios of compression and higher terminal pressures favor the reciprocating compressor.

Availability

Availability is the time during a year that the compressor is ready and *available* for operation divided by the total hours in a year (8760) and is expressed in percent. The unit need not be operating to get credit but it must be available. This is a frequently mentioned criterion in any process plant where continuity of production is mandatory. The value of lost production usually exceeds the actual cost of repairs.

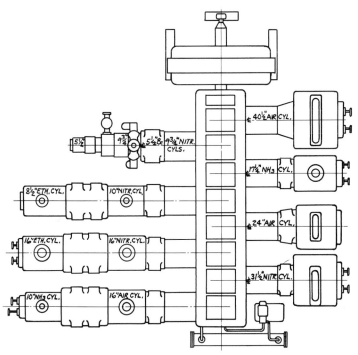

Fig. 16-A. Typical multiple-service reciprocating compressor handling six service streams in twelve cylinders.

In some circles, there has been the mistaken impression that the reciprocating compressor has very low availability when compared to the dynamic machine. It is true that the dynamic unit will often make the longer non-stop runs but total outage per year will not be much less than the reciprocator. It is also true that the outages on the dynamic unit will be more predictable and shutdowns will be less frequent.

Here are a few actual records on the reciprocator.

    (A) Three 1750 hp synchronous-motor-driven 100 psiG air compressors in a large industrial plant had no forced shutdown in three years of operation. Compressor valves are cleaned once a year.

(B) A 125 hp two-stage 100 psiG air compressor ran 30,000 hours without a valve failure and 60,000 hours without a bearing failure or adjustment.

(C) Seventeen 2000 hp gas-engine-driven 900 psiG gas pipeline three-stage machines with a total of 784 valves, ran six months with only two valve failures.

(D) Five synthetic ammonia plants operating 32 large compressors totaling nearly 90,000 hp with synthesis gas pressure of 12,000 to 15,000 psiG had a 1963 recorded average availability of 99.0%. The minimum was 98.3%. The compressors involved were from three to 23 years old.

Maintenance Costs

Many engineers also have the mistaken impression that maintenance costs of reciprocating compressors are very high. Figures used in evaluations have run as high as $12 per horsepower year or higher.

It is generally conceded that when a centrifugal compressor and a reciprocating compressor handle the same gas that is clean, pure, and noncorrosive, under exactly the same terminal pressure conditions, maintenance will be less on the centrifugal compressor than on the reciprocating compressor. As compression problems become more difficult, maintenance on both machines increases and probably becomes more nearly equal. However, within its range the centrifugal should always show less maintenance than the reciprocator.

Actual maintenance figures are not always carefully kept and exact values are difficult to pin down at times. However, the following are three groups in which information about reciprocators is available.

1. Air power compressors operating at 100 psiG provide many accurate case histories of maintenance costs of less than $1 per horsepower year. One example concerns five compressors totaling 4450 HP. These units have operated at least 16 hours per day for 300 days per year for 25 years. Average total maintenance costs for a five year period was $3800 per year or $0.85 per horsepower year. This is not a specially selected example. It is quite typical. A conservative figure of $1 per horsepower year can safely be used for this group.

2. Another group where reasonable figures can be developed is the gas-engine-driven pipeline compressor, usually operating at about 900-psiG discharge pressure. These are on heavy-duty service. All pipeline companies must report detailed annual operating figures to the Federal Power Commission. These are published and the tabulation of Fig. 16-B shows the costs for the latest available *complete station maintenance* expense for a representative group of companies. The average for all listed stations for the years 1961 and 1962 is $3.86 per horsepower year.

This includes expenses on miscellaneous items not allied to compressors. If this is 5%, the engine and compressor maintenance becomes $3.66 per horsepower year. Engine power end maintenance can be conservatively said to be five times the compressor end maintenance. Therefore the compressor maintenance only will amount to $0.61 per horsepower year. If it is assumed that a complete electrically driven compressor (less driver) has double the expense of above compressor end only (a very liberal allowance), the compressor maintenance would become $1.22 per horsepower year.

3. An analysis of 1963 actual maintenance costs on four synthetic ammonia plants with 26 units totaling 75,000 hp gives an average of $2.45 per horsepower year. The compressor complete, less driver, is included in these data. Discharge pressures varied from a few hundred to 15,000 psiG. It is significant that the general effect of increased operating pressure toward increasing maintenance cost is quite evident in certain of the figures in this group.

From Federal Power Commission Reports

Average of 1961 — 1962

Company	Average Station HP	Average Expense $/year	Expense $/HP year
Atlantic Seaboard Corp....................	58,665	223,980	3.81
Cities Service Gas Co....................	186,210	919,985	4.95
El Paso Natural Gas Co...................	706,680	3,065,625	4.35
Equitable Gas Co.......................	27,875	123,380	4.43
Hope Natural Gas Co....................	80,140	328,815	4.13
Lone Star Gas Co.......................	41,450	171,735	4.16
Michigan-Wisconsin Pipeline Co............	186,900	608,330	3.25
Mississippi River Fuel Corp................	111,375	608,270	5.30
Natural Gas Pipeline Company of America..	420,780	1,735,040	4.11
Northern Natural Gas Co.................	560,930	1,725,820	3.08
Panhandle Eastern Pipeline Co............	353,290	1,970,570	5.57
Pennsylvania Gas Co.....................	11,400	63,125	5.52
Southern Natural Gas Co.................	188,700	504,115	2.68
Tennessee Gas Transmission Co............	875,000	2,787,410	3.19
United Gas Pipeline Co..................	147,890	432,750	2.93
Totals and Average..................	3,957,285	15,268,950	3.86

Fig. 16-B. Annual total compressor station maintenance expense for a group of natural gas pipeline operators.

The modern reciprocating compressor is a highly reliable piece of equipment. When evaluating the centrifugal versus the reciprocating compressor, factors other than maintenance and availability should be considered in making the choice for a given job.

Summary

Although this discussion brings out the major factors in compressor selection, the best solution to a compression problem can be obtained by presenting the complete picture to the compressor manufacturer. Then let him offer his best solution, be it reciprocator, centrifugal, vane or helical-lobe rotary, or a combination of types.

Chapter 17

Information Required
by the Manufacturer for Bidding

Introduction

A manufacturer always wants to quote the best offering and to assure the purchaser that it will fulfill requirements when installed. Lacking complete information at the start of a project, some important factors may be omitted or inadequately provided for. Communication between purchaser and supplier should be free and complete.

When the compressor is for air power, often involving standard designs regularly priced, this detail is not normally necessary. For any other service, complete information should always be provided regardless of the compressor type or gas being considered. The supplier having more than one type to offer is then able to make alternate offerings if warranted.

Modern process plants are complex, often with many gas streams. It may be desired to combine certain streams on a single unit or units. In the plant mentioned in connection with Fig. 16-A there are twelve streams divided into two trains of three machines, each train handling half the total quantity. After much study, the final grouping of streams was considered the best arrangement for operation. To do this required close co-operation between supplier and purchaser early in the negotiation.

There are a few special applications where dividing the total gas flow into two equal streams does not permit the plant to maintain operation when one machine is down for inspection or repair. For example, it has been found that some air separation plants required 55 to 60% of rated air capacity to continue operation. It is necessary in such a case to provide each unit with more than 50% of the total stream capacity and to control output as needed when on full load.

At times, purchasers require that there be no negative guarantee tolerance on capacity. In such cases, it is customary to offer a unit larger than specified by the capacity tolerance involved, tolerance still being maintained.

For comments on the various units of measurement which may be used in presenting this data, see page 2-12 and subsequent pages.

Following is minimum data required by bidders, grouped in various categories. Information needed for bidding on ejectors is presented separately.

The Gas to be Handled (Each Stream)

Analysis — state whether by Mol %, volume %, or weight %.
Does composition vary? To what extent?
Molecular weight or specific gravity.
Is gas corrosive and to what?
Are there limits to discharge temperature that will cause problems with the gas?

Quantity to be Handled (Each Stream)

State quantity and unit of measurement.
If by volume, show (1) Whether *wet* or *dry*.
                 (2) Pressure and temperature reference points.
Number of units.
Is quantity total or per unit?

Inlet Conditions (Each Stream)

Barometer
Pressure *at compressor flange*. State whether gauge or absolute.
Temperature at compressor flange.
Relative humidity.
Ratio of specific heats.
Compressibility.

Discharge Conditions (Each Stream)

Pressure *at compressor flange*. State whether gauge or absolute.
Compressibility. State temperature reference.

Interstage Conditions (Each Stream)

Temperature difference between gas out of cooler and water into cooler.

Is there interstage removal or addition of gas?

Between what pressures may this be done? Advise permissible range.

If gas is removed, treated and returned between stages, advise pressure loss.

What quantity change is involved?

If this changes gas composition, advise resultant analysis, ratio of specific heats, relative humidity and compressibility at specific interstage pressure and temperature.

Variable Conditions (Each Stream)

State expected variation in intake conditions — pressure, temperature, relative humidity, MW, etc.

State expected variation in discharge pressure.

It is extremely important that changing conditions be related to each other. For example, if relative humidity varies from 50 to 100% and inlet temperature varies from 0° to 100°F, does 100% RH correspond with 100°F? Variations in conditions are best shown in tabular form with all conditions included in each column.

Flow Diagram (Each Stream)

Provide a schematic flow sheet showing controls involved.

Regulation (Each Stream)

What is to be controlled — pressure, flow, or temperature?

Advise permissible variation in controlled item.

Is regulation manual or automatic?

If automatic, are operating devices and/or instruments to be included.

On a reciprocator, how many control steps are desired?

Cooling Water

Temperature — maximum and minimum.

Pressure at inlet and back pressure, if any.

Whether open or closed cooling system desired.

Source of water.

Fresh, salt, or brackish.

Silty or corrosive.

Heat Exchangers (Each Stream)

Are intercoolers and/or aftercoolers to be included?

Are they to be machine-mounted and piped, or mounted separately by others?

What, if any, construction codes are desired?

Advise of any special materials required, water side and gas side.

Driver

Specify type of driver.

Electric motor — type, current conditions, power factor, enclosure, service factor, temperature rise, ambient temperature.

Steam — Inlet and exhaust pressure, inlet temperature and quality, importance of minimum water rate.

Fuel Gas — gas analysis, available pressure, low heating value of gas.

Geared — AGMA rating if special.

General

Are petroleum lubricants acceptable?

Is the installation to be indoors or outdoors?

Is floor space limited or of special shape?   If so provide a sketch.

What is soil character?   Is there apt to be a foundation problem?

What streams lend themselves best to combination on one driver?

List accessories desired and advise which are to be spared.

Are pulsation dampeners or intake or discharge silencers to be supplied?

Specifications

Provide each bidder with three copies of any specification for the particular project.

Note that *complete* information enables all manufacturers to bid competitively on the same basis and assists the purchaser in evaluating bids.

For Ejectors Only

Application

Specify the type of equipment with which the ejector will be used and any special features involved.   Equipment might be a barometric condenser, surface condenser, evaporator, crystallizer, vacuum drier, still, pump primer, or impregnator.

Suction Conditions

Conditions must be at *ejector inlet* connection and specify clearly units of measurement involved.   Piping pressure losses must be allowed for.

Gas pressure and temperature must be given.   Installation altitude above sea level must be stated.

Capacity or load is preferably to be expressed in lb/hr.   For dry air, molecular weight is not needed but for gas mixtures, the lb/hr and MW of each component are both necessary.

When water vapor is present, the saturated vapor temperature and the composition of the *dry* components must be specified.

When presenting gas mixtures in volume units (SCFM), include percent by volume of each component as well as molecular weight.

Discharge Conditions

Specify the back pressure allowing for any discharge pipe fric ion loss. Standard ejector design is based on 1.0 psiG maximum.

Specify *maximum* water temperature for intercondenser and after-condenser use. Specify whether barometric (direct contact) or surface condenser design is preferred or mandatory.

Steam Conditions

It is important that the *minimum* steam pressure and *maximum* temperature at *ejector steam* inlet be stated. Include in this determination all piping pressure losses to the jet body. Steam may be saturated but must be dry. Some superheat is desirable. Conditions must be at ejector inlet, not at the boiler.

If power medium is other than steam, specify the gas, its analysis, pressure, and temperature.

Additional Design Considerations

Specify whether operating cost is important. If it is, give costs of steam and condensing water for proper study of alternates. Advise whether ejector is to be in operation continuously or for shorter periods. State the hours/day.

For standby, quick pumpdown, and/or control purposes, ejectors are often installed in parallel systems, each element complete in itself. When such a setup is desired, specify the number of systems *and the capacity of each.*

Chapter 18

Compressor Installation, Operation, and Maintenance

(Continued)

Introduction

Within the scope of a single chapter, it is possible to present only a general discussion of the main items involved in installation, operation, and maintenance and to highlight certain of their specific applications to the various types of compressors. Although the final emphasis is on maintenance, both installation and operation influence maintenance to such a great degree that they must be included. A compressor improperly installed is sure to have high upkeep costs; sound operating practices could well be called preventive maintenance.

Much of this discussion is based on air compressors because of their predominance, although most comments apply equally well when other gases are handled.

Selection

The complete success of any installation usually depends upon the care with which the type and size of the compressor is initially selected and how well its characteristics are matched to the specific application. See Chapter 16.

Instruction Books

An instruction book is prepared by the manufacturer and sent with every compressor. This is a very valuable piece of literature and will be referred to frequently in this chapter. It is a detailed guide to proper installation, operation, and maintenance of the machine. What it tells should be diligently studied by both operators and maintenance men. Too often these books are not made available to those persons who are given responsibility for the care and continuity of service of the unit. This is obviously the wrong approach.

Instruction books also usually include spare part lists of great importance when ordering new parts.

Installation

A carefully planned and executed original installation, including all the proper equipment, is of immeasurable value toward making operation simpler and safer and keeping maintenance low.

Location

The preferred location for any compressor is near the center of its load. The choice should, however, be influenced by the cost of operating supervision at this point. Supervision, a continuous expense, may be less expensive elsewhere and overbalance the cost of longer piping. Use of a control system (Chapter 25), applicable to any compressor, may still permit the more central location.

A compressor will always give better service when enclosed in a building. In cold climates, the building should be heated. In certain locations it may be economical to use a roof only, but this is not recommended unless the weather is mild. Even then, special attention must be given by the manufacturer to the compressor construction so that rain or wind-blown sand is prevented from entering any running parts. All such installations should be planned with the manufacturer's representative before purchases are made.

Compressors, particularly smaller and air-cooled units, too often are located in poorly lighted and unventilated corners with insufficient room for proper and safe inspection and maintenance. This is false economy.

Ventilation around a compressor is vital. On a motor-driven air-cooled unit, the heat radiated to air in the room will be equivalent to 65 percent or more of the electrical power input. On a water-jacketed unit with an aftercooler and outside receiver, the heat radiated to the air around the compressor may represent 15-25 percent of the total energy input. This is still a substantial amount. Positive outside ventilation is recommended for any compressor room where ambient temperature may exceed 104°F, particularly if the driver is a motor that is normally designed for 104°F maximum ambient.

Never place the compressor where the atmosphere is dusty or damp or where corrosive vapors may enter the unit or its driver. Otherwise increased maintenance will surely result.

A crane or hoist is helpful in both erection and maintenance and should be provided when machine parts are heavy. However, a crane for handling the heaviest parts for erection is not necessary since these are seldom moved after the initial setting. Manufacturers can advise weights of the heaviest parts for both erection and maintenance so that proper equipment may be selected.

Foundation

Any stationary compresor must be anchored to a solid mounting. Depending upon size and type of unit, the mounting may vary from a simple bolting on a substantial floor to a large and massive special foundation.

Responsibility

Instruction books and foundation plans should be consulted in the design of the mounting or foundation. However, it is impossible for a manufacturer to know all the conditions at the installation site, particularly soil characteristics. The manufacturer's recommendations, even as they may be typically shown on certified foundation plans cannot be guaranteed for a specific installation. *The responsibility for a successful foundation rests with the purchaser.*

Basic Foundation Design Objectives

A proper foundation (1) maintains the compressor and driver in alignment, level, and at the proper elevation, and (2) minimizes vibration and prevents its transmission to adjacent building structures.

There are five steps to accomplish the first objective:

1. The safe *dynamic* soil bearing capacity must not be exceeded at any point on the foundation base.

    Note:—The usually allowable static load, as for building footings, is much too high for dynamic loads. Furthermore, published footings tables vary widely, some giving twice the allowable loading of others.

2. The unit loading of the soil must be distributed over the entire area.

3. Foundation block proportions must be such that the resultant of vertical load due to both machine and block and any unbalanced inertia force falls within the base area.

4. The foundation must have sufficient mass and bearing area to prevent its sliding on the soil because of any unbalanced forces.

5. Temperature variations in the foundation itself must be uniform, else warping will occur.

Involved in the second objective, in addition to the ability of the soil to carry the load, is its elasticity. Soil quality may vary seasonally, being alternately wet or dry. Such conditions must be carefully considered. Piling may even be necessary. If there is any question regarding variables, it is best to employ a foundation expert familiar with the local area. On any sizeable installation, soil tests are recommended.

Whether two or more compressors should have separate or a single foundation depends somewhat upon the compressor type. A combined foundation is recommended for reciprocating units since the reciprocating forces of one unit usually will tend to partially balance out the forces from the others. The greater mass and surface in contact with the ground damps the foundation movement and provides greater stabilization. Rotary compressors may have either a separate or a common foundation, whereas it is generally recommended that dynamic units be separately mounted.

No foundation should rest partly on bed rock and partly on soil. It should rest entirely on one or the other. If placed on ground, make sure that part of the foundation does not rest on soil that has been disturbed. An example is soil that has been excavated near building footings or other machinery and then backfilled. This soil will settle more than undisturbed soil and foundation bearing will be uneven.

Foundation bulk, of itself, is not usually the complete solution to foundation problems. A certain weight is sometimes necessary, but soil bearing area is usually of more value than mass.

Manufacturers will supply weight, center of gravity, and unbalanced force data for any compressor and will give suggested foundation dimensions *suitable for sound, firm, dry ground backed up by bedrock.*

Since it is expensive to repair or replace a foundation once in place, one should never economize.

Foundations for Rotary and Dynamic Compressors

Rotary and dynamic compressors seldom pose serious foundation problems. There is no variable load to be supported since there are no moments or shaking forces. A foundation or mounting of sufficient area and mass to maintain level and alignment and to assure safe soil loading is all that is required. Either of the two rotary types or the dynamic units may be supported properly on structural steel if necessary. Referral of the mounting design to the manufacturer is recommended. For dynamic units, see page 18-39.

Foundations for Reciprocating Compressors

The reciprocating compressor, because of the alternating movement of its pistons and various other parts, develops a shaking or inertia force that alternates in direction, the net result of which must be damped and contained by the mounting. This is in addition to the dead weight load.

There are many compressor arrangements and the net magnitude of the moments and forces developed varies a great deal between them. In some cases, they can be partially or completely balanced out; in others the foundation must handle it all. When complete balance is possible, this machine also can be mounted on a foundation just large and rigid enough to carry the weight and maintain alignment. Some units have been mounted on a structural steel platform. Small units of the Y- or W-cylinder arrangement (see Figs. 6-A and 6-B on pages 6-5 and 6-6) can be bolted to a substantial building floor. However, most reciprocating compressors require attention to foundation design.

Why Foundations Move

A reciprocating piston will tend to move the compressor and its foundation because inertia forces are set up, just as when a man stands in a small boat and moves suddenly in one direction and then the other. Relative to the lake bottom, the boat also changes its position. The heavier the boat or the broader its bottom and therefore the greater the resistance to movement (the heavier the foundation and the broader its base), the less the movement, but movement still occurs.

The Effect of Unbalance

Compressor inertia forces may have two effects, one being a force in the direction of the piston movement and the other being a couple or moment that is developed when there is an offset between the axes of two or more pistons on a common crankshaft. The interrelation and degree of these forces will depend upon such factors as number of cranks, their longitudinal and angular arrangement, cylinder arrangement, and degree of counter-balancing possible. Two significant vibration (movement) periods are set up; the primary at the rotative speed of the compressor and the secondary, at twice the rotative speed. There are others that normally can be neglected.

Any foundation and the soil upon which it rests has a *natural* period of vibration. The soil is elastic (as a spring), the degree depending upon its character. The foundation design, mass, and the soil characteristics must be such that this natural period of vibration is quite far removed from the primary and secondary vibration periods imposed by the compressor. Unless this is so, resonance will occur, vibration amplitude will multiply and the foundation will have to be altered. A good foundation will have a period well above the operating speed.

Magnitude of the Forces

Although the forces developed are sinusoidal, only the maximum is considered in analysis. Without going into details, Fig. 18-A shows relative values of the inertia (shaking) forces for various compressor arrangements. The diagrams are plan views with the exception of the fourth arrangement with cylinders at 90°F, an elevation.

For those who must be responsible for a reciprocating compressor foundation without benefit of expert advice, the following guide lines are offered.

      1. The compressor manufacturer's standard foundation is designed to absorb the unbalanced forces inherent with the particular machine and provide the rigidity necessary to maintain good alignment. However, it is intended only for very firm soil.

CRANK ARRANGEMENTS	FORCES		COUPLES	
	PRIMARY	SECONDARY	PRIMARY	SECONDARY
SINGLE CRANK	F' WITHOUT COUNTERWTS. 0.5F' WITH COUNTERWTS.	F"	NONE	NONE
TWO CRANKS AT 180° IN LINE CYLINDERS	ZERO	2F"	F'D WITHOUT COUNTERWTS. $\frac{F'D}{2}$ WITH COUNTERWTS.	NONE
OPPOSED CYLINDERS	ZERO	ZERO	NIL	NIL
TWO CRANKS AT 90°	1.41 F' WITHOUT COUNTERWTS. 0.707F' WITH COUNTERWTS.	ZERO	.707F'D WITHOUT COUNTERWTS. 0.354F'D WITH COUNTERWTS.	F'D
TWO CYLINDERS ON ONE CRANK CYLINDERS AT 90°	F' WITHOUT COUNTERWTS. ZERO WITH COUNTERWTS.	1.41 F"	NIL	NIL
TWO CYLINDERS ON ONE CRANK OPPOSED CYLINDERS	2F' WITHOUT COUNTERWTS. F' WITH COUNTERWTS.	ZERO	NONE	NIL
THREE CRANKS AT 120°	ZERO	ZERO	3.46F'D WITHOUT COUNTERWTS. 1.73F'D WITH COUNTERWTS.	3.46 F'D
FOUR CYLINDERS CRANKS AT 180°	ZERO	4F"	ZERO	ZERO
CRANKS AT 90°	ZERO	ZERO	1.41F'D WITHOUT COUNTERWTS. 0.707F'D WITH COUNTERWTS.	4.0F"D
SIX CYLINDERS	ZERO	ZERO	ZERO	ZERO

F' = PRIMARY INERTIA FORCE IN LBS.
F' = .0000284 RN²W
F" = SECONDARY INERTIA FORCE IN LBS.
F" = $\frac{R}{L}$ F'
R = CRANK RADIUS, INCHES
N = R.P.M.
W = RECIPROCATING WEIGHT OF ONE CYLINDER, LBS
L = LENGTH OF CONNECTING ROD, INCHES
D = CYLINDER CENTER DISTANCE

Fig. 18-A. Unbalanced inertia forces and couples for various reciprocating compressor crank arrangements.

2. Many soils considered good for static loads, such as building footings, do not provide adequate support for the dynamic loads found in some compressors. These soils include sand and clay and alluvial soils. If the soil at the proposed site is anything less than bedrock or well cemented sand and gravel in thick beds, or, if the soil is wet at times, special precautions must be taken. In such cases, it is generally advisable to extend the foundation horizontally or to use a mat. Increase the area several times if necessary.

Keep in mind that no mistake can be made by spreading the foundation, but that going deeper will increase the tendency to rock.

3. In some cases where bedrock can easily be reached, the foundation may be made deeper. Do not go deeper than the length of the foundation, if unbalanced horizontal forces are involved. (The long dimension of the foundation should be in the direction of these forces.)

If the firm ground is anything less than bedrock, the foundation should be extended or a mat used so as to increase the dimensions of the base in proportion to the depth.

Making a foundation deeper or higher lowers the resonant (natural) frequency. This is objectionable. In the case of bedrock, this effect will be small and may be tolerated; but in the case of less firm ground, a serious vibration problem may result.

4. Make sure that the foundation does not rest partly on firm ground and partly on ground that has been disturbed. Soil that has been disturbed for a building footing or other foundation will settle, allowing the foundation to rock.

5. Piling should be considered only for large installations and should only be used by the experienced compressor foundation designer. One common difficulty with pile supported foundations is that the ground will settle away from the foundation leaving the block resting on limber supports that are relatively flexible in the horizontal direction. If unbalanced horizontal forces exist, resonant vibration in this direction may develop. Batter piles do not always supply sufficient horizontal rigidity to prevent a resonant condition.

6. If two or more compressors are being installed, place them on a common foundation or use a common mat.

Typical examples of improper foundations and their correction are given in Fig. 18-B. The following apply to the figures:

A. Too heavy soil loading; foundation sinks. Solution — expand base or footing surface.

B. Foundation not centered under center of gravity; foundation tilts due to unequal soil loading. Solution — add more area at heavy end.

C. Foundation rocks; resultant of vertical and inertia forces falls outside foundation. Solution — spread foundation bearing as shown.

D. Foundation too light; slides on soil. Solution — make foundation deeper and longer.

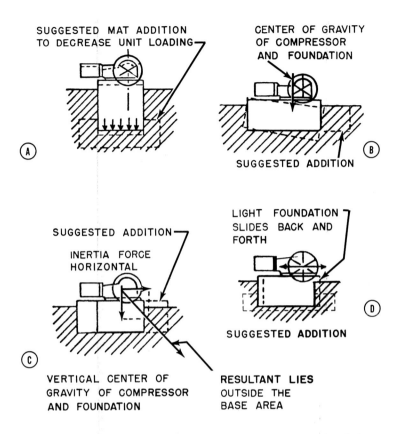

Fig. 18-B. Examples of improper foundation designs and possible solutions.

Compressor Storage

Compressors are protected against corrosion and deterioration during shipment, but are not usually sufficiently protected for an extended period of storage before erection. If there is to be a delay in erection and putting into service, special precautions may be necessary. The manufacturer should be consulted. Minimal action includes storage in a dry building protected from the elements. In a humid climate, all electrical and mechanical equipment should be in a heated enclosure. This may consist of a tarpaulin cover with space heaters or even electric light bulbs.

Erection

Erection cannot be done too carefully. The specific instruction book should be the guide.

Small, vertical air-cooled units are usually mounted on a base with the motor. This assembly is often mounted on the air receiver. These machines can be bolted to any substantial floor or a small concrete pad, but must be set level in both directions. Shims under all points of support should be used to provide a solid tie-down.

Units with a substantial flat base area should be grouted to assure a firm bearing on the foundation. Grouting must be very carefully done. Follow instructions.

Always level before tightening the fastening bolts and check again after pulling them down. If the compressor goes out of level, start over.

Larger units, whether horizontal, vertical, Y, or angle type, will have their particular alignment and leveling procedure presented in detail in the instruction book. Be sure to study and follow these procedures. Particularly follow instructions for the alignment of couplings.

A compressor that is not level and aligned will develop operating problems and extensive maintenance will be required. This job done perfectly at the start should last a lifetime.

V-Belt Drives

When first setting up a V-belt drive, check the alignment of compressor and motor sheaves carefully. Recheck it occasionally to be sure the sheaves have not moved on the shafts.

V-belt-driven compressors require occasional belt adjustment by the means provided on the motor base. Belts that are too tight will overload and wear out compressor and motor bearings. Belts that are too loose will slip, waste power, overheat, and quickly wear out. A good method for checking proper tension of a multi-V-belt drive is by "striking" the belt with your fist. Slack V belts feel dead under this test. Properly adjusted V-belts vibrate and feel alive.

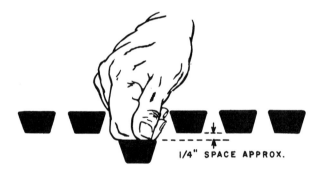

1/4" SPACE APPROX.

Fig. 18-C.　Checking multi-V-belt drive for correct tension.

Another simple test that can be made to check multi-V-belt drives for correct tension is illustrated in Fig. 18-C. Press down firmly on each individual belt. When the top can be depressed so that it is in line with the bottom of other belts on the drive, correct amount of tension has been applied. Each belt should be given this test individually. The drive must be "run-in" before this test is applied.

Some instruction books also show a spring scale method of testing belt tension. This is excellent.

When replacing V belts, always replace the complete set. Never replace just one or two in a multiple belt drive.

In connection with V belts:

1. Do not pry them on or off pulleys — loosen and move the driver.
2. Do not use any belt dressing.
3. Do not let oil or grease get on belts from any source.

Supervisor of Erection

Quotations for large compressors will frequently include or quote the services of a competent supervisor of erection to oversee the initial installation. He is a field-and-factory-trained expert and his services will be repaid many times over. Make the most of his experience during both erection and startup — the most critical periods in the life of a compressor.

Piping

The majority of compressors require the addition of some piping at the installation site. Only inlet and discharge piping is usually involved, interstage piping being shipped completely assembled on the unit. Large machines however, must be disassembled and shipped in pieces. Precautions must then be taken in reassembly to prevent entry of foreign material and dirt that will surely damage the unit.

From the maintenance standpoint, the most important piping factors are cleanliness and alignment, the latter to prevent piping strain on the compressor.

Pipe Cleaning

The importance of starting any compressor with clean piping, particularly on the intake to each cylinder, cannot be over-emphasized. This is particularly important with multistage high-pressure compressors where special metallic packing is required and where all parts are apt to be rather expensive. Any dirt, rust, welding beads, or scale carried into the compressor will cause scored packing rings, piston rods, cylinder bores, and pistons, and pitted and leaky valves.

It is important that the piping be fabricated with sufficient flange joints so that it can be dismantled easily for cleaning and testing. It is better to clean and test piping in sections before actual erection than after it is in place.

When piping is cleaned in sections, before erection, it is possible to do a thorough job of eliminating all acid, neutralizer, water used for flushing, etc. Some carry-over of acid into the cylinders is almost certain when piping is cleaned after erection. This can and has caused extensive damage.

If it is necessary to conduct a final hydrostatic test when the piping is in position, care should be taken to provide vents at the high spots so that air or gas will not be trapped in the piping. Make provision for complete drainage after the test. These connections should be planned in advance. It is also essential that all connections to cylinders be broken and blanked preferably with a spool piece removed between the pipe and cylinder. Complete drainage of the piping is essential if start-up damage is to be prevented.

Use of chill-rings for butt welds in piping is generally recommended. This prevents welding beads getting into the pipe to carry through, not only on the original start-up, but later, during operation.

After hydrostatic tests have been made and the pipe sections have been cleaned as throughly as possible on the inside, the piping should be pickled using the following or a similar procedure.

1. Pickle for 14 hours with hydrochloric acid. Circulate the acid continuously by means of a small pump. Use a 5 to 12 percent acid solution, depending upon the condition of the pipe.

2. Neutralize with caustic.

3. Blow hot air through for several hours.

4. Fill with mineral seal oil and drain.

5. Blow out with hot air.

6. Pipe is now ready to use. If the pipe section is not to be assembled immediately, seal the ends tightly until ready for use. Before installation, pull through a swab saturated with carbon tetrachloride.

On large piping (where a man can work inside), the pickling procedure can be omitted if the piping is thoroughly cleaned mechanically with a wire brush, vacuum cleaned, and then thoroughly inspected to be sure it is clean and coated with a light oil to prevent rusting. Time and trouble taken in the beginning to insure that the dirt is out will shorten the break-in period, and may save a number of expensive shutdowns.

There are companies equipped to do the above chemical cleaning on the job site.

Temporary Line Filters

Even though this cleaning procedure has been carefully followed, a temporary filter should be installed in the suction line to the suction bottle to remove particles 230 microns (.009″) in diameter or larger. If the compressor is of NL (nonlubricated) design, the filter should be designed to remove particles 140 microns (.0055″) in diameter or larger. Provision must be made in the piping to check the pressure drop across the filter and to remove filter cell for cleaning. If pressure drop across the filter exceeds five percent of the upstream line pressure, remove the filter, clean thoroughly, and re-install. The filter cell should be removed and left out only when the inlet line is free of welding beads, pipe scale, and other extraneous matter. *These filters are not intended for permanent installations.* A typical installation, with pressure drop gauge, is illustrated in Figures 18-D-1 and 18-D-2.

The cone type shown is good for any line pressure. For low pressure lines at 7 to 15 psiG, depending upon size, a commercial design (Fig. 18-E) is available. A modified design is available to 300 psiG pressure. The cone type should be installed in a horizontal run of pipe, the commercial filter in a vertical run.

Piping Fitup

Piping should fit easily to the compressor connection without any need to′ spring or twist it to fit. It must be supported independently of the compressor and anchored as necessary to limit vibration and prevent expansion strains. The cylinder or casing may be distorted or pulled out of line if piping is improperly installed. This applies to every element of the machine and to every unit, large or small. It particularly applies to certain rotary units. See page 8-10, for example, and comments on page 18-40 regarding dynamic units.

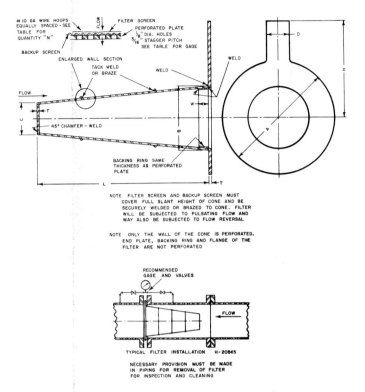

Fig. 18-D-1   Details of a temporary cone-type intake pipeline filter. (Continued on next page).

Air Intake Piping

The intake pipe on an air compressor should be as short and direct as possible. Cool air is preferred since every 5°F lower temperature results in approximately 1 percent more compressed air for the same power input. This is due to the greater density of the intake air at reduced temperature, while the air at the point of use maintains the same density. Guard against supercharging on reciprocating units caused by using a resonant length of intake pipe. See page 6-49. Some small air-cooled reciprocators require use of a surge bottle in any long intake pipe to provide an even flow. Refer to the instruction book.

It is better that air be taken from outdoors, in which case the pipe should be a minimum of six feet above ground, screened or preferably equipped with an air filter. It must be free of drift from steam or gas engine exhausts. It should be hooded or turned down to prevent the entry of rain or snow. Keep it above the building eaves and several feet from the building.

Do not reduce pipe size below that of the compressor connection. If it is unavoidably long, the size should be increased.

NOMINAL PIPE SIZE	A*	B*	C	D	H	L	N	T	W	PERFORATED PLATE MAX DIFFERENTIAL PRESS. ON FILTER			
										14 GA STL STEEL	16 GA STL STEEL	14 GA CARB STEEL	16 GA CARB STEEL
24	27 1/4	19	9 1/2	1 3/4	24	47	7	5/16	3/4	70	55	55	45
20	25	15 3/4	7 7/8	1 3/4	21	39 1/4	6	5/16	3/4	85	65	65	50
18	21	14 1/8	7 7/16	1 3/4	19	35	6	5/16	3/4	95	70	70	60
16	18 1/2	12 1/2	6 1/4	1 3/4	18	31	5	1/4	3/4	105	80	80	65
14	16 1/4	10 7/8	5 7/16	1 3/4	16	26 1/2	5	1/4	3/4	120	90	90	75
12	15	9 7/8	4 15/16	1 5/8	16	24 1/4	4	1/4	1/2	130	100	100	80
10	12 3/4	8 1/4	4 1/8	1 5/8	14 1/2	20 1/4	4	1/4	1/2	160	120	120	100
8	10 5/8	6 5/8	3 5/16	1 5/8	12 1/2	16 1/4	3	1/4	1/2	200	150	150	120
6	8 1/2	4 3/4	2 3/8	1 5/8	11 1/2	13	2	3/16	1/2	250	190	190	160
4	6 3/16	3	1 1/2	1 5/8	8 1/2	9	1	1/8	1/4	325	245	245	230
3	5	2 1/8	1 1/16	1 3/8	7 1/2	7 1/2	1	1/8	1/4	400	325	325	300
2 1/2	4 1/8	1 5/8	13/16	1 1/4	6 1/2	6 1/4	0	1/8	1/4	500	400	400	350
2	3 5/8	1 7/16	13/16	1	6	5	0	1/8	1/4	600	500	500	425

A* – DESIGNED FOR USE WITH FLAT OR RAISED FACE FLANGES

B* – DESIGNED TO FIT INSIDE HEAVIEST WALL PIPE

MATERIALS – STANDARD FILTER – FRAME CARBON STEEL, SCREENS & HOOPS OF BRONZE
BACK UP SCREEN –.017" DIA WIRE 30 MESH – 410 MICRON OPENING
FILTER SCREEN .0075" " 60 " 230 " "
SPECIAL FILTER – ALL PARTS OF STAINLESS STEEL
BACK UP SCREEN –.017" DIA WIRE 30 MESH – 410 MICRON OPENING
FILTER SCREEN –.0045" " " 100 " 140 " "

NOTE SPECIAL FILTERS RECOMMENDED FOR ALL NONLUBRICATED APPLICATIONS AS WELL AS THOSE APPLICATIONS WHERE FILTER ELEMENT MAY BE SUBJECTED TO ATMOSPHERES CORROSIVE TO BRONZE AND CARBON STEEL. ALL OTHER APPLICATIONS USE STANDARD FILTERS.

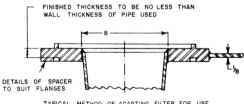

HEIGHT OF RING JOINT GASKET MUST BE SUFFICIENT TO PROVIDE SPACE BETWEEN FLANGES GREATER THAN FILTER DIMENSION "T"

TO SUIT FLANGES

TYPICAL METHOD OF ADAPTING FILTER FOR USE WITH RING TYPE JOINT FLANGE FACINGS

FINISHED THICKNESS TO BE NO LESS THAN WALL THICKNESS OF PIPE USED

DETAILS OF SPACER TO SUIT FLANGES

TYPICAL METHOD OF ADAPTING FILTER FOR USE WITH TONGUE AND GROOVE FLANGE FACINGS

Fig. 18-D-2.　Further details of temporary cone-type line filter (continued from page 18-13).

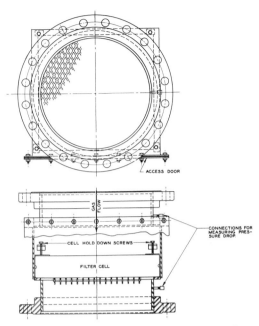

Courtesy of American Air Filter Company, Inc.

Fig. 18-E. Commercial temporary, low pressure, removable cell-type intake pipeline filter. This assembly remains in the line, the cell being removed when line is clean.

Gas Intake Piping

Most contaminants can enter a gas compressor through the first stage intake. This is also the place to prevent entry. Rubbish from improperly cleaned pipe and all condensate must be kept out of the compressor, using filters, receivers, separators, and drop legs as needed. Liquid carry-over destroys lubrication, causes wear, and frequently damages internal parts. It is good maintenance to install piping so these problems are eliminated initially.

Discharge Piping

Discharge piping should be the full size of the compressor discharge connection and should not be reduced until flow is steady and nonpulsating. With a reciprocator, this means beyond the aftercooler and/or receiver. Piping handling nonpulsating flow may be sized by normal methods. Long radius bends are recommended. All discharge piping must be designed so there are adequate expansion loops or bends to prevent undue stresses at the compressor due to the change between the cold and hot conditions.

Drainage

Before piping is installed, the layout should be analyzed to eliminate every possible low point where liquid could collect. Provide drains at those that cannot be eliminated.

A regular part of the operating procedure must be the periodic drainage of separators and piping and the checking of automatic trap operation.

Pressure Relief Devices

All positive-displacement compressors must be fitted with pressure relief devices to limit the discharge or interstage pressures to a safe maximum for the equipment served. Most dynamic compressors must have similar protection due to restrictions placed on casing pressure, power input, and/or keeping out of the surge range.

Two types of pressure relief devices are available, *safety valves* and *relief valves*. Although these terms are often used interchangeably, there is a difference between the two.

Safety valves are used with gases. The disk over-hangs the seat to offer additional thrust area after the initial opening. This fully opens the valve immediately, giving maximum relief capacity. These are often called *pop safety valves.*

With relief valves, the disk area exposed to over-pressure is the same whether the valve is open or closed. There is a gradual opening, the amount depending upon the degree of over-pressure. Relief valves are used with liquids where a relatively small opening will provide pressure relief.

Positive-displacement machines use *safety valves.* There are ASME standards of materials, sizing, etc., and only ASME stamped valves should be used. The relieving capacity of a given size of safety valve varies materially with make and design.

Always install a safety valve capable of passing the full-load capacity of the compressor between any line valve and a positive displacement machine. Too often, a discharge line shutoff valve is installed with no safety valve interposed between it and the compressor. If the compressor is started without opening this valve, or if the valve is accidently closed while the compressor is running, disaster can strike.

Safety devices are set to open at pressures somewhat above normal compressor operating pressures. The following are close to an industry standard as proper settings for pop safety valves for reciprocating and most other positive-displacement machines. Helical-lobe rotary compressors have less tolerance to over-pressure operation and safety valves are usually set to 10 percent of *absolute* discharge pressure *or* 5 psi, whichever is lower.

Pressure Increase Over Working Pressure

Working Pressure psiG	For Interstage	For Final Discharge	Next higher Increment—psi
Up to 50	15 psi	10 psi	—
51 to 125	25%	*10 psi	5
126 to 250	20% but not less than 30 psi	10%	5
251 to 1000	15% but not less than 50 psi	10%	10
1001 to 5000	12% but not less than 150 psi	10%	25
5001 to 10,000	12%	10%	50

*For standard 100 to 115 psiG two-stage air compressor discharge, safety valves are normally set at 125 psiG.

The increment suggested above is the "round out" of odd values. For example, the calculation may show 49.5 psiG, in which case set at 50 psiG; or calculation may show 1012 psiG, set at 1025 psiG.

Safety valves should be located on the cold side of piping where possible; that is, following a heat exchanger. Safety valves should be purchased not only for the required pressure setting but for expected gas characteristics and temperature.

In normal service, safety valves should be popped by hand about once a week to make sure they are in working order. This rule does not hold for valves set 1000 psiG or higher. They often require reseating if they pop. These higher pressure valves should be removed at least once a year and tested for accuracy on a hydraulic tester.

Rupture disks are used in some applications in place of, or supplementary to, pop safety valves. These are special cases where the proper action of a safety valve might be questionable due to corrosion.

Dynamic compressors cannot generally use pop safety valves because of the large volumes involved. There are, however, certain cases where maximum pressures must be limited because of casing strength or other conditions. On air compressors, problems normally arise only during periods of extremely cold weather, when the inlet air density is much higher than usual and the pressure rise is increased above normal for a given volume throughput. The entire characteristic curve is raised. This becomes a matter of controlling the maximum operating pressure. There are various solutions, the most common being a weight loaded *relief valve* to open and vent air to atmosphere to maintain the pressure at the safe maximum limit. Although rupture disks are used in some types of dynamic installations, the majority of over-pressure problems are solved by carefully worked out control schemes tailored to the specific system design.

Accessories

Standard equipment for every *positive-displacement air* compressor installation should be an intake air filter, an aftercooler and, on most types, an air receiver. There are many installations where intake and, possibly, discharge silencers also are required, particularly with certain rotary compressors. See pages 7-6 and 8-11. Reciprocating air compressors may require inlet silencers, but their usual use is for pulsation dampening rather than high-frequency noise abatement.

Dynamic air compressors require no receiver and use of an aftercooler will depend upon the application. Inlet filters should be used. Inlet silencers are required at times, often being combined with the filter.

Compressors handling gases other than air frequently should be fitted with some permanent protection against the entry of rubbish through the intake. Special scrubbers are installed at the entrance of many natural gas pipeline compressor stations and the more conventional filters may be used in other cases. These are usually special applications.

Many gas compressor installations utilize aftercoolers, but their application is subject to more variation than with air compressors. Designs follow usual standards.

Receivers are used less generally on gas compressors than with air units. When omitted, special care should be taken with the location of pressure taps from which control devices are operated. If there is insufficient system volume to this point, the unit may cycle too frequently between control steps. There are many positive displacement gas compressor installations where the inclusion of a receiver or equivalent pipeline volume close to the compressor would improve over-all operation and possibly reduce power requirement, particularly with reciprocating machines.

The following applies only to air compressors.

Intake Air Filter

There is a great deal of dirt in even the cleanest atmospheric air. It will cause unnecessary wear, accelerate the build-up of deposits and can, if neglected, result in a dangerous condition.

There are three basic air intake filters. The *dry* type is made in a number of designs. The filter media is either a felted cloth or a special lightly oil coated paper. These are excellent where pulsations are not severe, such as a reciprocating compressor with a dampener or the rotary and dynamic units. The felt is the stronger medium and may be dry- or vacuum-cleaned occasionally. It may, however, shrink under humid conditions whereas the paper is completely renewed when dirty. These filters function well at air flows below maximum rating.

Viscous-impingement filters have woven or packed wire in cells or frames, the whole being coated with oil to hold dirt. These are *not* recommended for extremely dusty areas or for nonlubricated machines. The latter should always use the dry type.

The third type has an *oil-bath* that removes dirt from air by scrubbing action. Dust is washed down and collects in a sump, from which it is manually removed as necessary. These have good dust-removal capacity between cleanings.

If viscous-impingement or oil-bath filters are used, the oil must be suitable for the range of ambient temperatures involved in summer and winter. Both operate at best efficiency near their design rating.

The choice of filter will depend largely on locality, type and quantity of dust involved, and personal preference. However, manufacturers of

Courtesy of Dollinger Corporation

Fig. 18-F. Typical dry-type intake air filter-silencer.

vane-type rotary units recommend an oil-bath filter for normal service; or for high-dust loads, a dry-type filter.   In severe cases, a series arrangement is best.

Fig. 18-F shows a dry felt type air filter — silencer combination built to 4500-cfm maximum size.   Fig. 18-G illustrates a three-cell viscous impingement filter designed for mounting at the end of an intake pipe.

Courtesy of American Air Filter Company, Inc.

Fig. 18-G.   Typical cell-type viscous-impingement intake air filter.

Louvers over the cells are available for weather protection.   Each cell is removable for cleaning or replacement.   A similar construction is available with dry-type cells.   Dry-type filters of the cellular design are preferred with dynamic units to assure no oil carry-over.   Large sizes are available with either medium.

Fig. 18-H covers a typical moderately sized oil-bath filter.

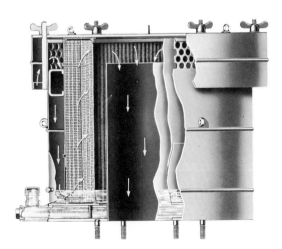

Courtesy of Air-Maze Division, Rockwell-Standard Corporation.

Fig. 18-H.   Typical oil-bath intake air filter.

A section through a large-capacity, automatically cleaned and operated, viscous-impingement filter for use principally under steady flow conditions, as with a dynamic or rotary compressor, is shown in Fig. 18-I.

All air filters require regular and intelligent servicing. Regardless of design there is a continually recurring need that they be cleaned. A dirt-clogged filter is almost worse than none at all. It reduces the amount of air compressed, causes overheating, and, in extreme cases, may break up and be drawn into the compressor.

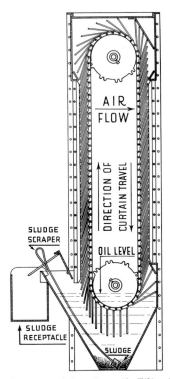

Courtesy of American Air Filter Company, Inc.

Fig. 18-I. Automatic viscous-impingement intake air filter for steady-flow conditions.

Filters must be cleaned on a regular schedule. Environment and operating time will determine frequency. With many types a spare filter element for quick replacement (cleaning the other at leisure) will be advantageous. To assure filter maintenance, locate them where servicing is easily done.

Intake Silencer

Commercial silencers are available for all types of compressors. Some compressor manufacturers offer designs tailored to their specific equipment. Alternates are offered in many cases for varying degrees of silencing. Silencers should always be installed as close to the compressor intake as possible.

Aftercooler

An aftercooler usually is a good investment. It condenses and removes moisture from compressed air before it can get into the distribution system and tools causing wear and operating problems. An aftercooler reduces the fire hazards due to misoperation or improper oil use.

Aftercoolers are best water-cooled. Install indoors, making sure there is plenty of room to pull tube nests for cleaning and maintenance. Slope piping away from the compressor. Routine maintenance is minimal, other than draining the separator as required. An automatic condensate trap should be used on any cooler operating at a pressure of 500 psiG or lower and serving a unit of 25 HP or larger. Piping should be arranged to permit checking trap operation manually. Use manual drains on pressures higher than 500 psiG.

Water cooled aftercoolers are available for all sizes of units. Maintenance will be increased materially if cooling water used is not cool, soft and clean. Dirty water will clog tubes, reducing heat transfer and resulting in power losses and higher operating temperatures. Hot water may accelerate scaling.

Air Receiver

Every reciprocating, and most other positive-displacement, air compressors should be piped to a discharge air receiver. Dynamic units do not require receivers because they have capacity control that always equalizes line output with demand. Positive-displacement units unload in steps and a receiver helps reduce pressure variations. Receivers also provide air storage for sudden heavy demands and act as secondary separators beyond the aftercooler, removing more of the oil and condensate.

A receiver is an unfired pressure vessel, and should be built to the ASME Code and properly stamped. It should meet all local and state legal requirements and be satisfactory to the owner's insurance company.

Fittings should include a safety valve, pressure gauge, and drain valve with necessary piping. Be sure all are installed in accordance with instructions. Check the safety valve setting. It should never be higher than the maximum allowable working pressure stamped on the tank. The safety valve should have a lever or other device by which it can be manually popped to make sure it is operable.

If the receiver is outdoors, pipe the safety valve and pressure gauge indoors to prevent freezing. Slope the piping toward the receiver to provide drainage and eliminate all spots where moisture can collect.

The drain valve should be readily accessible. The receiver will collect condensate plus some oil. Drain it at least once a shift. For small units, weekly may be enough.

The proportion between receiver volume and compressor capacity is relatively greater for smaller machines than for larger units. There are established industry standards for normal compressor service in this regard. For automatic stop-and-start control, it is usual to use about twice the normal receiver volume to prevent too frequent starting.

Cooling Water

Maintenance can be materially affected by the quality, quantity, and temperature of the cooling water used. Water to compression elements themselves removes 15-40 percent of the total heat of compression depending upon machine size, type, rpm, compression ratio, and other factors. Intercoolers on two-stage units will remove 30-40 percent of the total heat of compression plus the Btu's from moisture condensation. If this heat is not removed because of mud or scale in jackets and cooler tubes, temperatures will become excessive and maintenance will increase. Therefore, clean, soft water should be supplied. This may require a separate closed-circuit system, the circulated water itself being cooled by other means.

Information on temperatures, heat removal, etc. has been given in Chapters 6, 7 and 8 on the various units using water cooling.

Water Pressure

Manufacturers prefer an open discharge for water leaving the compressor because this places no appreciable pressure on the jackets and cooler water circuit. This is not always desirable from the operator's viewpoint, however, since he may need to conserve water and reuse it or circulate it over a cooling tower. To do so requires a closed system in which there is back pressure. This should be brought to the manufacturer's attention *before* purchase. There are water pressure limitations on water jackets and coolers that vary considerably between manufacturers, machine types, and size, An average pressure might be 50 psiG, but the maximums vary from 25 to 75 psiG.

Manual control of water flow should usually be from a valve on the inlet. Protection from an excessive system pressure is required if any valve, automatic or manual, is used on the outlet. On closed systems, install sight flow indicators and thermometers located where they can be regularly checked.

Water Temperature

Water should be cool but not cold. It is desirable that water enter the cylinder at a temperature at least 10° to 15°F higher than the gas intake temperature to prevent the initial condensation or sweating of moisture in the gas within the cylinder. This is sometimes difficult. On multistage units, the problem is solved by passing the cool water first through the intercooler and then through the jackets. The same result can be obtained on a single-stage unit which has an aftercooler by using the water first in the aftercooler. In any case, the coldest water should go through the coolers to obtain maximum benefit. If there are no coolers, the only alternative is to cut back on water quantity to raise the *average* water temperature in the compression element. As a guide, keep water outlet temperature not less than 15-20°F above gas inlet temperature.

For proper control, a valve in a small bypass around the main valve should be supplied. Water leaving the unit should generally be between 100° and 120°F. See the instruction book for specific recommendations. If water conditions are such that the exit temperature must be higher, consult the manufacturer. High water temperatures may cause overheating and accelerate the formation of scale in coolers and jackets.

Operation and Maintenance

Responsibility

Operation and maintenance consist of eternal vigilance in checking small items on a regular schedule. Regardless of the type or size of compressor, someone must be charged with those specific duties. The man or men responsible should have free access to all instruction books.

Records

Both operation and maintenance involve routine inspections, sometimes hourly, sometimes daily and sometimes weekly or monthly. Records should be kept. They need not be elaborate. In a large plant, a daily log should include temperature and pressure readings (both interstage and terminal) every one or two hours, with notations regarding all operational functions and checks performed. Analysis of records will usually show the need for maintenance before the situation becomes acute. In a small plant, a formal daily log may not be warranted, but a record should be kept of lubricating oil use, approximate daily or weekly hours of operation, oil changes, cleaning of air intake filter, etc. When trouble occurs due to accident, misoperation, or other causes, adequate records can often explain what happened.

For maintenance involving other than strictly routine items, a special record card is usually set up. This should cover such items as the date of the trouble, what was repaired or replaced, the probable cause, comments on the condition of parts (such as valves), when inspected, and the date for the next inspection. These records permit scheduling preventive and routine maintenance. The man responsible will then know *what* is required, and *when*, and he can make sure needed parts are available. The job is less likely to be overlooked. Some plants may find a detailed valve record helpful for reciprocating compressors. See page 18-27 for valve records and maintenance.

Cleanliness

Internal cleanliness is a function of clean piping, clean gas, properly maintained inlet filters, proper handling and use of lubricating oil, and care to prevent entry of dirt when the machine is open for maintenance.

Heat exchangers must not be neglected. Air-cooled inter- and after-coolers need cleaning of external surfaces at intervals depending upon environment and use; heat transfer to the ambient air depends largely on cleanliness and can easily be halved by severe coatings of dirt, dust, and oil. Normally, use safety solvent and an air jet at least once a month. *Caution* — do not use solvent on hot parts. Follow the instruction book.

About once a year, dismantle any air-cooled inter- and after-coolers and examine the interior for deposits. These machines run much hotter than those with water-cooled exchangers on similar service and deposits may form that require solvent or cleaning compounds for removal.

Water-cooled exchangers require attention on the water side to remove scale or mud that may collect. They also will require cleaning on the air side if dirt enters the machine or there is improper lubrication. The industry almost exclusively supplies exchangers with removable tube nests, so cleaning is simplified. Methods may vary through tube swabbing to elaborate chemical treatment.

External cleanliness is also a part of good operation. A properly cared for unit should be protected from the elements. The surroundings must be kept clear. Dirt, dust, and vapors should not be permitted in the operating room.

Lubrication

Lubrication of any compressor is of such great importance that a separate Chapter 13 has been devoted to it. Remember, only the best oil obtainable should be used, it should be used only in the recommended amounts, and a record of oil used and the running time of the unit should be kept.

Check the instruction book for oil changes during break-in and at other times. The book also discusses the proper oil type to be used.

Safety

Safety should always be paramount in operation and maintenance. The following are basic rules.

1. Before attempting any maintenance, be certain the compressor cannot be started accidently. Tag the switch and then pull the fuses or disconnects.

2. Blow down the receiver and all intercoolers and aftercoolers. Isolate the compressor. Tag the shutoff valve.

3. Be certain there is no pressure in the machine before opening. On a reciprocating unit, loosen (do not remove) all nuts on a discharge valve cover. Pry it loose so that any trapped air may escape. Then remove all nuts and the cover.

4. On a crosshead-type reciprocator, place a wooden block in the cylinder between the piston and each head to prevent its movement. Do this through a valve hole. Sometimes it may be more convenient to block the crosshead in the frame.

5. Always use a safety solvent for cleaning compressor parts and dry them thoroughly before replacing.

6. Pop safety valves manually at least once a week.

7. If a safety valve blows during operation, stop the unit immediately and determine the cause. Safety valves on the receiver will normally blow only if the capacity control is not functioning correctly. An intercooler safety valve will blow when there is unusual leakage in the higher-pressure stage. Any blowing safety valve indicates trouble somewhere.

8. Read the instruction book.

Starting First Time

To start compressor for the first time, the things to be done are listed in the instruction book. These should be carefully followed. They include the following, but may vary with the type of unit.

1. Be sure all oil sumps and lubricators are filled with the *proper* oil.

2. Be sure all lubricator lines are filled and lubricators are functioning properly.

3. Open proper valves in unloader, discharge, and regulator lines. Be sure the unit is unloaded as necessary for starting.
4. Clean the machine, its foundation, and the floor around it. Remove all tools, rags, etc.
5. Be sure intake filters and screens are in place and charged with oil as necessary.
6. Turn on cooling water, if used.
7. Turn machine over several revolutions by hand to be sure everything is free and operates properly.
8. Be sure unit rotates in the proper direction.

Break-in Period

The advantages of proper break-in of a compressor before putting it steadily under load are seldom appreciated.

All machined surfaces have asperities, or hills and valleys. The height of the hills or depth of the valleys is a function of many such variables as metal structure, type of finish machining operation, and machine tool operator experience. During break-in, it is necessary that mating parts establish a satisfactory bearing with each other. To do this, there must be a certain amount of wear, rounding off or bending over of the asperities, etc. This is probably the most critical period in the life of such parts and the demands on the lubricant are the most extreme. During this break-in period, the oil must maintain lubrication, keep the bearings sufficiently cool, and flush away the wear particles and any dirt that comes over. Consult instruction book for proper lubricant for break-in of cylinders.

Most vane- and screw-type rotary compressors, as well as the dynamic units, are shop tested and normally require only a few hours of break-in. Reciprocators generally should be run on part load awhile in the field before going into full-time service. Specific comments on each unit appear in later special sections in this Chapter. See also Chapter 13.

Capacity Control

There are many types and designs of capacity control, depending on the service and type of machine and driver.

Controls are tested and set by the manufacturer before shipment and should operate for long periods without much attention. Two rules are important; don't "fiddle around" with the control any more than necessary; and, read the manufacturer's instructions carefully and follow them closely when maintenance is required.

Regulator and control-operating air should be taken directly from a point near the top of the receiver. Make sure it is clean. Use a small in-line filter or screen ahead of the regulator on the machine if not included as standard equipment. Be sure no moisture can carry over with the control-operating air. Slope piping toward receiver.

Motor manufacturers limit the number of starts per hour because of overheating developed by too frequent starts. This is discussed in greater detail in Chapter 15. Briefly, the combination of operating pressure range and receiver size should be such that the unit will not start oftener than eight times per hour for the 1/2- to 20-hp sizes, ranging down to four times maximum per hour for the 100-hp. See page 15-8.

In connection with automatic start-and-stop on vertical single-acting units, it is best to have the compressor run loaded a minimum of 10 minutes continuously per cycle. This will prevent excessive moisture condensation in the crankcase.

Spare Parts

Discuss the subject of spare parts with your compressor supplier *when buying the unit* and obtain a recommended list of spares. Stocking these few items is insurance against extended down time while parts are obtained. Have them available *before* break-in.

Spares should be greased if necessary, wrapped in a protective coating, and stored in a clean, dry place. When taken for use, they should be replaced promptly.

Trouble Shooting

Troubles may be major or minor. Major difficulties can be corrected only by considerable dismantling and labor, with consequent loss of operating time and replacement of large, perhaps expensive, parts. Major troubles usually can be traced to long periods of operation with unsuitable cooling or lubrication, or careless maintenance. *Lack of proper care of any piece of machinery is bound to result in a succession of minor troubles, developing eventually into a major breakdown.*

Minor troubles are those that can be corrected by making an adjustment or by replacing a small part. Minor troubles are most often traced to dirt, to maladjustment, or to operating personnel being unfamiliar with the functions of the various machine parts. Difficulties of this type can usually be corrected by cleaning, proper adjustment, elimination of an adverse condition, or quick replacement of a relatively small part.

Trouble shooting is largely a matter of elimination based on a thorough knowledge of the interrelated functions of the various parts and the effect of adverse conditions. Instructions books usually develop this subject in detail and their contents should be common knowledge with operating and maintenance personnel.

Detailed Comments — Reciprocating

Break-in Period

Many reciprocating compressors are test-run in the shop and are partially broken in before shipment. However, large units may have not been run prior to erection. There are gradations in shop operating procedure for in-between sizes.

Air-cooled units to 125 hp are universally shop tested and require little field break-in. As a guide, the following is suggested as a minimum running time. Instruction books should always be followed if they contain specific recommendations.

HP Rating	Type	Hours No Load	Hours Gradually Increasing Load
Below 25	Air-Cooled	1	2
25 to 125	Air-Cooled	1	5

See Chapter 13 for break-in recommendations for crosshead type compressors.

Whenever new parts are installed, the break-in procedure must be repeated sufficiently to properly seat the part.

Piston Rod Packing

Most modern crosshead-type units use full-floating metallic packing on piston rods. This requires much less attention than any other type and should be specified. See page 6-37. It is precision-made and, although it requires little routine attention, must be handled carefully and reassembled correctly when repairs or replacements are made. Rings *must* be removed before removing or installing the piston rod. Do not try to use sheet metal cones over the rod threads. Instruction books usually discuss this and must be followed. The piston rod must never be scratched, nicked, or otherwise marred if the packing is to make a seal.

There is a set of oil wiper rings in the end of the crankcase to prevent oil being carried out along the rod. The operation of these rings should be checked frequently. Any excessive replenishment of crankcase oil is an indication that they need attention. When replacing, be sure they are installed in the correct position.

Valves

The valve discussion starting on page 6-16 should be reviewed since valves are the most important parts of any reciprocating compressor. An understanding of their proper care and the steps which can be taken to promote longer service life and reduced maintenance should be required.

A survey of many large synthetic ammonia plants showed remarkable unanimity on the factors in operation and maintenance that are considered as most important in extending compressor valve life. These are arranged below in order of importance.

1. A *limited* number of *well-trained* men on valve overhaul;
2. Clean gas;
3. No liquid carry-over;
4. Proper lubrication; and,
5. Systematic records.

Note the emphasis on "well-trained men". They should be trained by means of the instruction book as well as by guidance from manufacturer's representatives. Continuity of operation *can* be improved if thoroughly trained people take over valve maintenance.

The Importance of Valve Lift

In any valve, lift affects both efficiency and durability. Too high a lift will cause premature valve failure due to impact fatigue. Too low a lift will result in excessive gas velocity, high losses, and consequent inefficiency.

Design valve lift must be maintained. This requires care and understanding during certain maintenance operations. For example, worn seats or stop plates can often be refinished, but the original lift can be altered if the refinishing is incorrectly done. Lift limitation is obtained in different ways in different designs. Manufacturer's instruction books are usually quite detailed in this regard and should be carefully followed. Do not alter the original lift without consulting the manufacturer.

Why Valves Fail

Valve failures can be classified as resulting from:

1. Wear and fatigue;
2. Abnormal mechanical action; and,
3. Foreign materials.

Wear and Fatigue

Wear cannot be completely eliminated. It can be minimized by proper lubrication, design, and selection of materials.

Most valves require some means of guiding. Wear at the guides — if severe — can result in sloppy action, cocking, poor seating, and failure. Wear must never be permitted to develop to this degree.

Fatigue is the result of repeated cyclic stress. However, barring abnormal action, well-designed valves have a good record as far as fatigue is concerned.

Both wear and fatigue are adversely affected by abnormal mechanical action.

Abnormal Action

Detective work is sometimes necessary to spot abnormal action. There are three general causes:

1. Slamming;
2. Fluttering; and,
3. Resonance or pulsation.

Slamming occurs when the valve is either opening or closing more rapidly than it should. Listening will often confirm this; the valve will be more noisy than usual. A change in lift or springing is the usual remedy.

Fluttering is the result of insufficient pressure drop through the valve when open. The valve never lifts firmly against the stop plate, but flutters in an intermediate position. Springs usually fail when this happens. The solution involves using lighter springs or lowering the lift, or both.

Resonance or pulsations can seriously upset normal valve action. This is an external piping problem; the valve designer can do nothing about it. The sole remedy is to alter the intake or discharge piping to eliminate the causative pressure wave.

Abnormal operation is seldom associated with highly standardized 100-psiG air compressors. However, resonance and pulsation problems do occasionally appear. Whenever a problem in this category is suspected, the manufacturer should be consulted before taking any action.

Foreign Materials

Foreign materials may be:

1. Liquid carry-over;
2. Dirty air;
3. Carbonaceous deposits; and,
4. Corrosive elements.

Liquid carry-over from interstage coolers is apt to cause premature failure, particularly in intake valves. A slug is particularly hard on valves and may even break a seat. Liquid also destroys lubrication, accelerating wear on valves and cylinder bore.

It is important that interstage separators be drained regularly. Automatic traps, if used, should have a bypass piped for visual observation to check trap operation at stated intervals.

Examination of the valve plate sometimes will indicate liquid carryover, but liquid in a cylinder is generally discernible otherwise.

Dirty air can cause all sorts of problems. It accelerates wear very rapidly at all guiding points since it is usually a good grinding compound. Foreign matter between the coils of springs is a frequent cause of spring failure and subsequent failure of other parts.

Excessive *carbonaceous deposits* resulting from a particular oil may hinder proper valve action. Too much oil is as undesirable as too little oil. Rate of feed must be determined from experience and should be no more than is necessary to properly lubricate a cylinder and valves. Excessive temperatures will accelerate deposit formation.

Corrosion can cause high localized stress and subsequent failure. Springs are apt to fail first. This should not be a frequent problem with the valves and springs in air compressors because of the materials used. However, the presence of moisture will usually accelerate corrosion. In many cases, simply increasing jacket water temperature will often eliminate this problem.

The problems of *wear* and *foreign materials* can be limited by correct installation and operation and by proper lubrication.

Records Help

Unusual valve problems are apt to have a definite pattern. This is seldom discernible from casual or mental notes. It pays to keep good valve records. They need not be elaborate, but should cover, separately for each cylinder and valve, date of inspection, condition of valve, parts replaced, reconditioning required, and approximate hours of operation since the last inspection. The location of each valve should be noted in the record.

A survey of this record will quickly indicate any valve requiring more than normal maintenance. The reasons then can be investigated. Manufacturers are anxious to assist in remedying all valve troubles. They are proud of their product.

A comprehensive paper on this subject (Form 283) is available from Ingersoll-Rand Co., Advertising Division, Phillipsburg, N. J. 08865.

Inspection

Valves should be removed and inspected at the end of the first three months of service. After the initial inspection, and depending on what is found at that time, schedule the next valve inspection not longer than six months ahead. After that, inspect not less often than once a year. This should be sufficient for a properly operated machine handling clean gas. Multistage compressors usually require less valve servicing than single stage units because of lower temperatures.

If a broken valve is found, locate all the pieces. Otherwise, they might get into the cylinder causing scoring or other damage.

When taking a valve apart, be careful to keep all parts in order so that each one can be replaced *exactly* as it was.

Be careful not to turn leaf or channel valves end for end.

Do not turn leaf valves over.

Inlet valve and discharge valve springs are often of different stiffness. Do not mix them up. Discharge will normally be the stiffer.

Reconditioning

Clean with safety solvent. A soft wire brush may be used on all non-seat parts. Use only a bristle brush on valves and seating surfaces.

Avoid scratching, nicking, or dropping any parts.

Replace valves when inspection shows they are worn. Do not wait till they break.

When springs are arched or of spiral flat stock, be careful not to bend or change their shape.

Do not put new valves on worn seats.

Do not put used valves on new or reconditioned seats.

When resurfacing a seat, finish it smooth — grinding is usually best.

Lapping of a valve to its seat is seldom necessary.

Do not alter the valve lift.

If reconditioned valves are put in storage till needed, apply a protective coating and wrap thoroughly. Check their condition before using.

Reassembly

There are specific correct spring arrangements in most valve assemblies. See the instruction book.

After reassembling valves, use a small piece of wood to check valve freedom and to see that they will open fully.

Replacement In Cylinder

Valves are seated in the cylinder and generally use gaskets to seal the joint. Some, however, are metal-to-metal and others use a sealing compound.

It is always best to use new valve seat and valve cover gaskets, although reuse is sometimes possible provided they are inspected carefully and have no dents, nicks, or breaks. A leaky gasket means another shutdown and repair job.

On certain assemblies, gasket thickness is very important. Use only gaskets furnished by the manufacturer.

Be sure all seating surfaces are clean.

Be sure valve assemblies are seated properly in the cylinder — not cocked.

With leaf or channel valve assemblies, install so that air flow from the cylinder into the valve is along the seat ports, not across them. In a few cylinders this is not possible, but it is a general rule that can result in better flow characteristics to and from the valve.

Be especially careful to replace inlet valves in the inlet side of the cylinder and discharge valves in the discharge side. Many valve assemblies are interchangeable. It is good practice to mark the valves "I" or "D" and to do the same with the cylinder holes when the valves are removed.

After placing valves in the cylinder port, using a small piece of wood, try to depress the valve proper working through the valve cover hole. If it can be depressed, it is an inlet valve. If it cannot be depressed, it is a discharge valve.

Serious damage may result if valves are not properly located.

Preparation for Extended Shutdown

Any compressor, when taken out of service for a long period, will deteriorate rapidly through rust and corrosion if not especially protected. The following are basic precautions to be taken with reciprocating machines.

Air-Cooled Compressors

The crankcase should be drained and refilled with a preservative oil. Such oil contains more inhibitor than normal inhibited oil. The machine should then be operated a minimum of 15 minutes at no pressure for thorough distribution and the driving off of any crankcase condensate. At the same time, fog some of this oil into the compressor intake.

All openings then should be taped or plugged to exclude moisture. Relieve V-belt tension. Drain the receiver and aftercooler. Drain aftercooler cooling water, if used. The driver should be treated in accordance with the manufacturer's instructions.

This will permit storage for a year. However, if the unit can be run for 30 minutes every two or three weeks at full load followed by 15 minutes at no pressure, these precautions may not be necessary. Be sure operational periods are scheduled and that the machine is actually run.

Crosshead Type Compressors

When a three- or four-day shutdown is contemplated, run the compressor at no load for ten to fifteen minutes, simultaneously operating the cylinder and packing lubricator by hand to pump extra oil to those parts.

For a shutdown of several weeks, do the same, then remove the piston rod packing and the oil wiper rings from the rod, coat the rod with grease, grease rings, and wrap them in waterproof paper. Leaving the packing rings on the rod may result in a ring of corrosion that will injure the packing when the unit is restarted. When a unit is to be shutdown for a lengthy period, write to the manufacturer for complete instructions.

If freezing is possible during shutdown, *all* water must be drained from jackets, intercoolers, aftercoolers, separators, drain traps, and oil coolers. If this is neglected, cylinder jackets or cooler tubes might burst and major repairs will result.

When putting the unit back into service, go through every check and procedure required for first starting a new machine.

Routine Checks

Operating and maintenance routine will vary with the size and type of compressor. The manufacturer's instructions should be followed. Following are general routine maintenance checks based on 100 psiG air compressors. Use them in setting up a schedule on which to operate.

Air-Cooled Compressors

When first started — after eight to ten hours of operation, tighten all head, valve cover, cylinder flange, shaft cover, and foundation bolts to recommended torque.

Weekly — check air filters (there may be more than one) for cleanliness. If conditions are bad, clean them. A biweekly schedule may be found adequate later.

Drain air receiver and intercooler. In humid weather, it may be necessary to drain more frequently. On larger units, this should be a *daily* procedure.

Check the crankcase oil level. Replenish as necessary.

Operate all safety valves manually.

Monthly — Clean the machine and driver externally.

Check time required to pump up the receiver with its outlet shut. A record kept of the time required to increase the pressure from, say, 30 psiG to 100 psiG, will provide a check on machine efficiency. Any serious difference may indicate leaky or broken valves.

Run a pipe leakage check. During lunch hour, or any other time when the surroundings are quiet, follow closely all distribution lines beyond the receiver while the compressor is shutdown but pressure is still high. Listen for leaks. Fix those found.

Two to three months — Change crankcase oil. For definite recommendations, read the instruction book.

Tighten all bolts and check V-belt tightness.

Six months maximum — Remove and clean all valves. Do this first after only two to three months, then as needed up to six months maximum. Check air ports, piston, and head for deposits and remove any found.

Crosshead Type Compressors

At Least Once a Shift — Drain receiver. Conditions may warrant more frequent drainage.

Check intercooler and aftercooler condensate trap operation several times. A 1000-cfm, two-stage 100 psiG compressor handling intake air at 70°F and 75 percent relative humidity will condense about 2-1/2 gal/hr of moisture in the intercooler when using 60°F cooling water. This condensate *must* be removed as it forms.

Check cooling water flow and outlet temperature every one or two hours.

Check crankcase lube oil pressure several times if positive pressure circulation system is used.

Check cylinder and packing lubricator feeds. Make sure each feed is pumping oil and that reservoir is filled with correct oil.

Check and record interstage and discharge pressures. If any substantial change is noted, find and correct the trouble immediately. Interstage pressure is normally almost constant for a given discharge. Any abnormality in reading probably indicates leaking valves.

If frame oil filter can be cleaned manually, operate it as directed.

Weekly — Pop all safety valves manually.

Operate regulator manually throughout entire load range to keep free any unloader that may not normally be in regular operation.

Keep the compressor and it surroundings clean.

Check crankcase oil level and add proper oil as needed.

Check cleanliness of intake air filter.

Operate safety shutdown or alarm devices where possible.

After first week, tighten foundation bolts and all other nuts and bolts on the unit. Recheck alignment if there is foundation bolt take-up.

Semiannually — Change crankcase oil (on some machines more often). See instruction book.

Check condition of water side of coolers and jackets.

Tighten all foundation bolts and nuts and bolts on the machine. Recheck alignment if there is any foundation bolt take-up.

Annually — Check clearances in all bearings.

Check clearance between pistons and cylinders.

Adjust crosshead or replace parts to restore piston rod alignment as necessary due to wear on crosshead shoe or piston.

As Experience Dictates (at least annually) — Check condition of all valves.

Check condition of cylinder bore through valve opening.

Check effectiveness of lubrication by observing the degree of oiliness on the cylinder bore and valves.

CAUTION: If for any reason the compressor is operated without water and cylinders become overheated, do not turn on cooling water until they have cooled. A sudden application of cool water may crack the cylinder.

Trouble Shooting

Pages following present charts designed to "tip off" the maintenance man where to look for the cause of some difficulty. These charts, although designed mainly for 100 psiG compressors of all types, apply quite generally. Some items apply only to the vertical air-cooled units, some to water-cooled only and some to two-stage only.

Many categories in the chart refer to *normal* conditions. There is no way to know what normal conditions are except to keep a record of temperatures and pressures. Other items should also be recorded in certain cases.

Temperatures recorded a minimum of twice a day could well include the ambient on air-cooled units a few feet from the compressor and the air discharge temperature. On larger two-stage units, the discharge temperature of the first stage cylinder should be added. Water temperature in and out is desirable on water-cooled compressors.

Pressures recorded should include those taken at discharge or receiver and, on a two-stage compressor, always at the intercooler. It is a particularly valuable norm to have.

On smaller compressors operating either start-and-stop or constant-speed, make a one-hour study (at least once a month) of the number of starts or full-load periods and the total running time. Do this at the same hour each time and select the hour when maximum demand is apt to exist. In most industrial installations this occurs around 10 to 11 a. m. and 1:30 to 2:30 p. m. The purpose of making this study is to discover any trend in operating time that would render a change in control advisable. Also, if the operating time is increasing steadily, there is either increasing system leakage, some compressor deficiency, or an increased demand. The correct reason should be determined, the proper remedy applied.

Valve problems are apt to be the predominant maintenance item. Leaking and broken valves and gaskets should be discovered and repaired quickly. As previously discussed, these lead to many added problems and even to dangers if neglected.

Trouble Shooting

THE CAUSES / THE PROBLEM	Compressor noisy or knocks	Air discharge temperature above normal	Carbonaceous deposits abnormal	Operating cycle abnormally long	Piston ring, piston, cylinder wear excessive	Piston rod or packing wear excessive	Motor over-heating
System demand exceeds rating				•			
Discharge pressure above rating	•	•	•				•
Unloader setting incorrect		•					
Intake pipe restricted, too small, too long		•					
Intake filter clogged		•		•			•
Valves worn or broken	•	•	•	•			•
Valves not seated in cylinder	•	•	•	•			•
Valves incorrectly located		•	•	•			•
Gaskets leak		•	•	•			•
Unloader or control defective	•	•	•	•			•
System leakage excessive			•	•			•
Piston rings worn, stuck or broken	•	•	•	•			•
Cylinder (piston) worn or scored	•	•	•	•	•		
Belts slipping	•						
Speed too high		•	•				•
V-belt or other misalignment	•						
Pulley or flywheel loose	•						
Motor rotor loose on shaft	•						
Foundation bolts loose	•						
Foundation uneven-unit rocks	•						
Piston to head clearance too small	•						
Crankshaft end play too great	•						
Piston or piston nut loose	•						
Bearings need adjustment or renewal	•						•
Liquid carry-over	•		•		•	•	
Oil feed excessive	•		•			•	
Oil level too high	•	•	•				
Lubrication inadequate	•	•			•	•	•
Oil viscosity incorrect	•		•		•	•	•
Intercooler vibrating	•						
Tank ringing noise (1)	•						
Ambient temperature too high		•	•				•
Ventilation poor		•	•				
Air flow to fan blocked		•	•				
Rotation wrong		•	•		•		
Oil level too low		•	•		•		
Check or discharge valve defective		•	•				
Cylinder, head, cooler dirty		•	•				
"Off" time insufficient		•					
Water quantity too low		•					
Belts too tight							•
Water inlet temperature too high		•	•				
Water jacket or cooler dirty		•	•				
Valves dirty		•	•				
Air discharge temperature too high			•				
Wrong type oil			•		•	•	
Air filter defective			•		•	•	
Dirt, rust entering cylinder			•		•	•	
Packing rings worn, stuck, broken						•	
Rod scored, pitted, worn						•	
Motor too small							•
Electrical conditions wrong							•
Voltage abnormally low							•
Excitation inadequate							•
Excessive number of starts							•
Discharge line restricted		•					•
Resonant pulsation (inlet or disch)							•

(1) Consult manufacturer.

Trouble Shooting

THE CAUSES	Delivery less than rated capacity	Discharge pressure below normal	Receiver pressure above normal	Receiver safety valve pops	Intercooler pressure above normal	Intercooler safety valve pops	Intercooler pressure below normal	Compressor parts overheat	Outlet water temperature above normal	Valve wear and breakage abnormal
System demand exceeds rating	●						●			
Discharge pressure above rating	●	●	●	●	●	●		●	●	
System leakage excessive	●	●					●			
Intake pipe restricted, too small, too long	●	●					●	●		
Intake filter clogged	●	●					●	●		
Valves worn or broken	●	●			●H	●H	●L	●		
Valves not seated in cylinder	●	●			●H	●H	●L	●		
Valves incorrectly located	●	●			●H	●H	●L	●		
Gaskets leak	●	●			●H	●H	●L	●		
Unloader or control defective	●	●	●	●	●	●		●		●
Unloader setting wrong	●	●	●	●	●H	●H	●L	●		
Piston rings worn, broken or stuck	●	●			●H	●H	●L	●		
Cylinder (piston) worn or scored	●	●			●H	●H	●L	●		
Rod packing leaks	●	●						●		
Safety valve leaks	●	●						●		
Belts slipping	●	●								
Speed lower than rating	●	●								
Gauge defective		●	●		●		●			
Safety valve set too low				●		●	●			
Safety valve defective				●		●	●			
Control air pipe leaks			●	●						
Intercooler passages clogged					●	●				
Intercooler leaks							●			
Cylinder, head, intercooler dirty								●	●	
Water quantity insufficient	●				●			●	●	
Water inlet temperature too high	●				●			●	●	
Water jackets or intercooler dirty					●			●	●	
Air discharge temperature too high								●	●	
Intercooler pressure too high								●	●	
Speed too high								●	●	
V-belt or other misalignment								●		
Bearings need adjustment or renewal								●		
Oil level too high								●		
Lubrication inadequate								●		●
Oil viscosity incorrect								●		●
Ambient temperature too high								●		
Ventilation poor								●		
Air flow to fan blocked								●		
Rotation wrong								●		
Oil level too low								●		
Check or discharge valve defective								●		
"Off" time insufficient								●		
Belts too tight								●		
Valves dirty					●		●			●
Liquid carry-over										●
Oil feed excessive										●
Air filter defective										●
Dirt, rust entering cylinder										●
Assembly incorrect										●
Springs broken										●
New valve on worn seat										●
Worn valve on good seat										●
Rod packing too tight								●		
Control air line clogged			●							
Resonant pulsation (inlet or disch)					●	●				●

H (in high pressure cylinder).   L (in low pressure cylinder).

Trouble Shooting

THE PROBLEM / THE CAUSES	Excessive compressor vibration	Oil pumping excessive (single acting compressor)	Crankcase water accumulation	Crankcase oil pressure low	Starts too often	Compressor fails to unload	Compressor fails to start
Intake pipe restricted, too small, too long		•					
Intake filter clogged		•					
Unloaders or control defective	•				•	•	•
Unloader setting wrong	•				•		•
Discharge pressure above rating	•						
Piston rings worn, broken or stuck		•	•				
Cylinder (piston) worn or scored		•	•				
Gauge defective				•			
Intercooler, drain more often			•				
Speed too high	•						•
V-belt or other misalignment	•						
Pulley or flywheel loose	•						
Motor rotor loose on shaft	•						
Foundation too small	•						
Grout, improperly placed	•						
Foundation bolts loose	•						
Leveling wedges left under compressor	•						
Piping improperly supported	•						
Foundation uneven-unit rocks	•						
Liquid carry-over			•				
Oil level too high		•					
Oil viscosity incorrect		•		•			
Rotation wrong							•
Oil level too low				•			
Belts too tight							•
Oil wrong type		•					
Crankcase oil pressure too high		•					
Unloaded running time too long (2)		•					
Piston ring gaps not staggered		•					
Piston or ring drain holes clogged		•					
Centrifugal pilot valve leaks		•					
Runs too little (3)			•				
Detergent oil being used (4)			•				
Location too humid and damp			•				
Oil relief valve defective				•			
Oil piping leaks				•			
Oil filter or strainer clogged				•			
Air leak into pump suction				•			
Gear pump worn, defective				•			
Receiver too small					•		
Receiver, drain more often					•		
Demand too steady (3)					•		
Unloader parts worn or dirty						•	
Control air filter, strainer clogged						•	
Regulation piping clogged						•	
Motor too small							•
Electrical conditions wrong							•
Voltage abnormally low							•
Excitation inadequate							•
Motor overload relay tripped							•
Fuses blown							•
Wiring incorrect							•
Low oil pressure relay open							•
System leakage excessive					•		
Bearings need adjustment or renewal				•			

(2) Use automatic start-stop control.   (3) Use constant speed control.   (4) Change to nondetergent oil.

A defective inlet valve can generally be found by feeling the valve cover. It will be much warmer than normal. Discharge valve leakage is not as easy to detect since the discharge is always hot. Experienced operators of water-cooled units can usually tell by feel if a particular valve is leaking. This is not for those who infrequently check their units. The best indication of discharge valve trouble is the air discharge temperature. This will rise, sometimes rapidly, when a valve is in poor condition or breaks. This is one very good reason for keeping a record of the air discharge temperature from each cylinder.

It must be remembered that there will be seasonal variations in temperature, all temperatures rising in summer and falling in winter. These are of no concern — it is the unusual rise that is the indicator. When it appears, act at once.

The recording of intercooler pressure on multistage units is valuable because any variation, when operating at a given load point, indicates trouble in one or the other of the two stages. If the pressure drops, the trouble is in the low pressure cylinder. If it rises, the problem is in the high pressure cylinder.

Detailed Comments — Water-Cooled Vane-Type Rotary
Break-in Period

These machines are run several hours in the factory and require little field break-in before putting on load. Two hours is suggested by one manufacturer. For a period of several days, feed about 25 percent more oil than normal to help flush out dirt and wear particles. The importance of properly cleaned inlet pipe cannot be overstated and a temporary screen at the intake is desirable. See page 18-12. The essential close clearances in this type of compressor make it vulnerable to dirt.

Important Maintenance Items

The most important maintenance items are shaft packing or seals, vanes, and bearings.

Shaft seal leakage should be checked visually once a week or oftener. Leakage may not extend to the outside of the gland and if taken off in a vent, the vent discharge should be arranged for easy inspection. Leakage beyond normal is the signal for replacement. Under good conditions of cleanliness, mechanical seals have a life of 10,000 to 15,000 hours.

Vanes wear continuously on their outer edges and, to some degree, on the faces that slide in and out of the slots. The vane material is affected somewhat by prolonged heat and gradually deteriorates. One manufacturer recommends inspection when operating under good industrial conditions every 8000 hours or oftener. On 100 psiG units, one manufacturer suggests complete replacement be made every 16,000 hours and, on low-pressure units, after 32,000 hours. Another manufacturer recommends replacement every two to three years. These are maximum and should be altered as actual operating conditions and inspections warrant. Vane replacement before breakage is extremely important since breakage while operating can damage the machine severely and usually forces a complete overhaul and realignment of heads and clearances.

Bearings have relatively long life, but replacement after about six years of operation is recommended by one manufacturer.

Cleaning

When inspections are made, the interior of the machine should be thoroughly cleaned, including the rotor slots.

Extended Shutdown Protection

These units should not be left idle for long periods of the time. A minimum operating period of two hours a week is recommended. This keeps the interior dry and well lubricated and prevents absorption of moisture by the blades, which causes swelling. If a unit is to be taken completely out of service, the blades must be removed and specially stored. Consult the manufacturer. Drain all water from jackets and coolers.

Complete Overhaul

A complete overhaul with realignment and check of clearances requires careful attention to details and the instruction book *must* be followed.

Routine Operating Checks

These consist mainly of keeping the lubricator filled with the proper oil, draining the oil separator and receiver at least once a shift, and checking any automatic traps on aftercooler and intercooler to be sure they are operating. There may be several places on the unit itself requiring occasional drainage. Refer to instruction books for details. Unusual vibration or noise calls for immediate shutdown and inspection.

Detailed Comments — Helical-Lobe Rotary
Break-in Period

These units will normally have been run in the factory and need no long break-in. Some types of seals if replaced require a short break-in period. The instruction book will advise specifically.

Operational Note

Dry (not oil-flooded) helical-lobe rotaries on most services will overheat and be damaged severely if the inlet is blanked off. With some arrangements, severe intake throttling, even though not a complete closure, will have the same result. Care must be taken that this does not happen.

Important Maintenance Items

Properly selected, installed, and lubricated, there should be little maintenance on these machines. There is no metallic contact within the casing. Bearings and gears are contact items but with proper lubrication have long life. Shaft seals of the various types require inspection about once a year and occasional replacement. When disassembly is required, be very sure to follow manufacturer's instructions explicitly since maintenance of proper clearances throughout is vital to good performance and long life.

Lubrication

Lubricating system operating instructions must be followed. Proper levels of oil in reservoirs, use of a proper oil, and maintenance of cooling when required are probably the most important daily operations. Lub oil should be changed as the manufacturer suggests. Oil types are discussed in Chapter 13.

Extended Shutdown Precautions

The main problem is internal corrosion. If, as is usually the case, the gas handled contains some moisture, or if water injection has been used, the rotor chamber must be thoroughly dried by circulating a warm dry gas through the machine. The entire rotor area should be spray coated with a rust preventive through intake and discharge openings. Spray rust preventive in all shaft seals. Store in a warm dry room, observing normal precautions dictated by local conditions and length of shutdown time.

Routine Operating Checks

Check lubricating oil level daily and maintain a full reservoir.

Check oil pressure and temperature frequently.

Change oil per manufacturer's instructions.

Maintain cooling water outlet temperature within manufacturer's recommendations.

Check discharge gas temperature frequently. Do not exceed manufacturers' limit.

Do not exceed nameplate operating conditions.

Clean oil filter (if used) frequently.

Check for unusual vibration —a sign of trouble.

Follow instruction book details.

Detailed Comments — Dynamic

Proper installation is the most important requisite for satisfactory operation of high-speed rotating machinery. Although such machinery will operate under somewhat adverse conditions, it is always advisable to provide proper operating conditions if the machinery is to give maximum reliability at minimum operating cost.

This discussion is based on the more comprehensive requirements of the larger units, but applies equally to the smaller units in most details.

Plant Layout

Machinery foundations, piping, electric wiring, and all necessary auxiliary equipment must be carefully arranged in the plant layout. Even though space is limited, skillful placing of the equipment will result in a better installation, more reliable operation of the equipment, and a minimum of maintenance. Machinery that is easy to install, operate, and maintain will generally get better attention from the operating and maintenance personnel.

Foundations

While the foundation for high-speed rotating machinery need not be as massive as that for reciprocating machinery, it must be sufficient to provide a permanently rigid, nonwarping support for the machinery. The user must necessarily take full responsibility for an adequate foundation. In general, it is desirable to have it designed by a competent structural designer with experience in heavy machinery foundations.

The following represent some of the points that should be kept in mind.

1. The foundation must provide a permanently rigid, nonwarping support for the machinery.

2. The foundation substructure should rest on a uniform footing, entirely on bedrock or entirely on solid earth.

3. The temperature surrounding the foundation should be substantially uniform. If it is variable, the variations should be essentially the same for the entire foundation.

4. If more than one machine is to be installed in a given location, each should have a completely independent foundation supported from bedrock or solid earth. The foundation should be entirely free from building walls or other parts of the building that might transmit resonant vibration. Operating platforms must also be isolated from the machinery foundations.

5. If the foundation structure rests on bedrock, and if it is imperative that no resonant vibration be transmitted to adjacent structures, a vibration damping material should be interposed between the structure and the bedrock.

6. Where foundations must be supported from floor beams, whether there be one or more machines so supported, a vibration damping material should be interposed between the beams and each foundation.

7. Where the foundation substructure rests on piling, the piling should be covered with a heavy continuous mat.

Piping

Air or gas piping for a compressor and steam piping for a turbine must be carefully arranged to avoid strains that may throw the machinery out of alignment. Misalignment is a frequent cause of vibration, and most misalignment is directly traceable to piping strains. Although all piping design should have zero loading as its goal, of greater importance is original perfection of alignment between pipe and machine, and maintenance of that alignment in spite of temperature and pressure changes.

Three types of piping strains must be considered:

1. Strains due to dead weight of the piping itself;

2. Strains due to expansion or contraction of the piping as it undergoes temperature change; and,

3. Strains due to internal pressure within the piping.

Adequate piping support is necessary to prevent excessive dead loads on the flanges of rotating machinery. Piping supports should normally be of the flexible type and located as close as possible to the flange connections on the machinery. Fig. 18-J illustrates an acceptable method of supporting piping.

Expansion or contraction due to temperature change can usually be handled by installing an expansion joint, an expansion loop, or a pipe bend adjacent to the flange of the rotating machine. Referring to Fig. 18-K (a), a straight run of pipe between two fixed points will, when subjected to a temperature change, exert a force upon the flange of the machine. For low-pressure applications, a corrugated-type expansion joint, as shown in

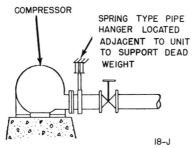

Fig. 18-J. Hanger method of supporting pipe.

Fig. 18-K (b), will normally suffice to relieve excessive strain on the flange. For high-pressure applications, the bellows action of the expansion joint may exert a considerable force owing to the lack of rigidity of the walls of the joint. It may then be desirable to use limiting tie rods to resist this force. Another possibility is an expansion loop such as shown in Fig. 18-K (b). The latter arrangement is normally limited to relatively small piping.

Another method of allowing for thermal expansion is to use a combination of pipe bends and flexible supports. For example, if the header shown in Fig. 18-K is flexibly supported instead of fixed as shown, and if it has sufficient length or bends to permit relatively free movement in the direction of the pipe to the compressor, the header will deflect laterally and relieve the force due to expansion of the pipe to the compressor. In this case, the need for an expansion joint or loop is minimized.

For extremely high pressures, the force exerted on the flange of the machinery may be such that special designing is necessary. Balanced

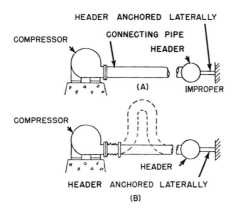

(A) PIPE WILL EXERT A LATERAL THRUST ON COMPRESSOR

(B) PIPING STRAIN MINIMIZED BY USE OF AN EXPANSION JOINT OR LOOP

18-K

Fig. 18-K. Methods of compensating for temperature expansion piping changes.

expansion joints are available, and even though they are sometimes bulky and expensive, their use may be justified by existing conditions. If the machinery must stand the full force of the internal pressure, special treatment of the foundation and mounting of the machinery may be necessary to resist this force.

The direction in which expansion occurs and the magnitude of expansion must be considered in the design of the piping. Unless they are controlled, excessive forces or twisting moments may be exerted on the machinery.

An accepted method controlling the direction and magnitude of expansion is to install one or more anchors in the piping system. For example, for the case shown in Fig. 18-K, with the compressor fixed and the header anchored laterally, the expansion of the connecting pipe can be easily calculated, and it must occur in the direction of the pipe. Provision can then be made for this amount of expansion. If, however, the header is not anchored in an axial direction, or if the header is anchored at some distance from the junction of the pipe and header, axial expansion of the header itself may impose a large twisting moment and shearing force on the compressor flange. The solution is to anchor the header in an axial direction as close as possible to the junction and to allow the expansion of the header to take place in both directions from the anchor.

For best performance, the gas piping should be arranged for reasonably uniform velocity over the entire area of the compressor inlet. To attain this, the minimum condition is that the gas enter through a long sweep elbow. The ideal is an axial inlet, possible on relatively few designs. Where possible, a straight run of pipe with a length of four diameters or more should be interposed between the long sweep elbow and the machine.

It is frequently necessary to reduce the inlet-pipe diameter to match a compressor inlet flange of lesser diameter. Likewise, it is often necessary to increase the pipe diameter just beyond the compressor discharge flange. Where such conversion is necessary, the transition should be gradual.

A summary of satisfactory piping arrangement follows.

1. Provide adequate support for all parts of the piping system.

2. Allow for expansion in a manner that will avoid piping strains on the compressor; individual conditions will determine whether expansion joints, expansion loops, or bends will be required.

3. Install a sufficient number of anchors in the piping system so that the direction and magnitude of expansion are controlled.

4. Design the inlet and discharge piping so as to provide smooth flow with uniform translational velocity over the entire area of the piping.

More specific information on calculating the force and moments from piping is contained in "Standards for Centrifugal Air Compressors" available from Compressed Air and Gas Institute, 122 East 42nd St., New York, N. Y. 10017.

Inspection and Maintenance

The manufacturer furnishes an operating instruction book with each machine. It should be studied thoroughly before the unit is started. To insure successful performance, these instructions should be followed closely. In general, since maintenance is inseparably tied up with operation, preventive maintenance would include proper starting, stopping, and operation of the machine, keeping it clean both inside and out at all times, and *keeping a good set of operating records.*

Successful maintenance of rotating machinery necessitates carrying certain of the machines expendable parts in stock as spares. The extent to which these spare parts may be justified is dependent upon the degree of wear expected, the replacement time and the value of shutdown time. Certain basic items, such as bearing liners and seals, are normally carried in stock, but the manufacturer's list of recommended spare parts should be used as a guide to determine what is or is not desirable.

While the unit is in operation the lubricating oil should receive constant attention by means of tests and analyses to be sure that it remains clean and free from water and that its lubricating properties and viscosity are held to the standard set by the oil supplier. Manufacturers of dynamic compressors normally specify certain fundamental characteristics of the lubricant most satisfactory for the service, such as viscosity, flash point, pour point, etc. The oil supplier selected should be willing to assume responsibility for the successful and continued performance of the lubricant in the service for which it is intended.

The inspection of rotating machinery at definite, predetermined intervals is essential. The frequency of these inspections can be determined only by local operating conditions, and this may range from once a month to once every several years. On a job where reasonably clean air or gas is handled, inspection once a year may be considered satisfactory. However, in certain chemical processes there may be buildup of foreign matter, erosion or corrosion to such an extent that monthly inspection is necessary to be sure that the machine is fit for continued safe operation.

During inspection of rotating machinery, it is always worthwhile to have a manufacturer's supervisor of erection on hand. The following items should be checked under his guidance.

1. All journal bearings should be carefully examined for evidence of wear; the thrust bearing should be checked for axial position, condition of adjustment shims, and evidence of wear; bearings must be replaced or rebabbitted as required.

2. The couplings (if any) should be thoroughly cleaned and examined for evidence of wear; if a coupling is in questionable condition, it must be replaced with a new one. If a gear-type coupling has been used, both halves should be replaced.

3. If the compressor casing is lifted (internal inspection of the compressor may be less frequent than the inspection called for in items 1 and 2 above), the casing should be examined for corrosion, erosion, fouling, condition of the stationary shaft seals (measurement of sealing clearance should be recorded), and the condition of any other stationary parts that might be subject to maintenance. Any unsatisfactory parts should be replaced or repaired. If the casing includes diaphragm cooling, evidence of leaks should be noted and corrected.

4. The compressor rotor should be examined for evidence of corrosion, erosion, or fouling. If any deterioration is in evidence, an accurate record (including photographs, if possible) should be kept of the rotor condition. If there is any indication or suspicion of unbalance, the rotor should be balanced before returning it to service. All rotor clearances should be carefully checked and recorded and corrections made as required.

5. If the turbine casing is lifted, it should be examined for corrosion, erosion, and fouling; the condition of the nozzle ring, diaphragms, reversing buckets (if any), shaft seals (measurement of sealing clearances should be recorded), and any other stationary parts that might be subject to maintenance should be checked. Parts in unsatisfactory condition should be repaired or replaced as required.

6. The turbine rotor should be examined for evidence of corrosion, erosion, and fouling. If any deterioration is in evidence, an accurate record (including photographs, if possible) should be kept of the rotor condition. If there is any suspicion of unbalance, the rotor should be balanced before returning it to service. All rotor clearances should be carefully checked and recorded, and corrections should be made as required.

7. If an electric motor is involved, the interior and exterior of the motor should be cleaned as thoroughly as possible. The motor may be blown out with dry compressed air at moderate pressure. If possible, however, cleaning by suction is preferred because of moisture in compressed air, blowing metal chips, etc. On sleeve bearing motors, the air gap should be checked and recorded.

8. If the gear casing is lifted, the casing, gears, and pinions should be examined for corrosion, erosion, and fouling, and the teeth checked for possible wear (all data relative to the examination should be recorded). Other stationary parts that may be subject to maintenance should be checked and faulty parts repaired or replaced as required.

9. Protective devices should be checked for the correct setting, and adjusted, if necessary.

10. The governing and regulating system, if any, should be thoroughly cleaned, worn parts noted and replaced if necessary, and the governor adjusted for proper operation.

11. The auxiliaries should be checked to make sure that they are in proper working order. All instruments and gauges should be recalibrated. Drain lines, water piping, and heat transfer equipment should be flushed and cleaned.

12. If separate shafts are used for the compressor and driver, the alignment should be checked and readjusted if necessary.

13. The air filter, steam strainer, and other equipment external to the unit, as well as all piping to and from the unit should be checked for cleanliness. The piping should also be checked to be sure that it has not shifted and placed external strains on the unit.

14. When the unit is reassembled, it should be checked carefully for vibration, and, if excessive, this vibration should be traced to determine its cause and necessary correction made.

15. At the conclusion of each inspection, a permanent record should be made of all repairs, photographs, clearance measurements, and a statement on the general condition of each component.

In general, the inspection serves two purposes; first to determine what parts are worn, dirty, or in need of repair; second, to determine the rate of deterioration of the various parts so that proper precautions can be taken to correct this condition or to provide replacement parts so that future operation will be as trouble-free as possible.

Chapter 19

Gas Coolers

Caption Index **Page**

Introduction

Gas coolers are used with all types of compressors. They are heat exchangers used to reduce the gas temperature, either before, during, or after compression. They bear names indicative of their function such as precooler, intercooler, or aftercooler. When used with ejectors the two latter items are called intercondensers and aftercondensers, but their function remains the same.

Cooling of gas has two objectives — to reduce the gas temperature and volume, and to condense and remove water vapor or other condensable constituents insofar as the cooling medium and operating conditions permit. Both of these objectives tend to reduce power requirements when attained during compression, no matter what the compressor type. After the final pressure has been reached, cooling cannot reduce power, but is done to promote safety, to liquefy and remove condensables which might otherwise deposit in undesirable locations, and for process reasons.

There are many types, arrangements and designs of coolers. The choice will depend on factors such as size, pressure, operating temperature, cooling medium (gas or liquid), if water cooled — the water cleanliness and temperature, space limitations if any, construction code requirements, etc. Fig. 19-A shows how they might be divided into certain rather broad categories.

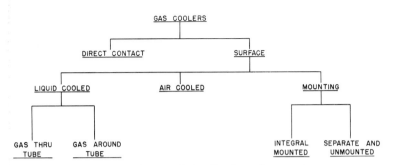

Fig. 19-A.   Diagram of classifications of gas coolers.

Direct-Contact Coolers

Direct-contact coolers are used frequently with ejectors and occasionally as aftercoolers for certain process plants where gas scrubbing is desired as well as cooling.   With ejectors, their use is to condense and remove as much vapor as possible and thus reduce the lb/hr to be handled by the next stage ejector or to eliminate discharge of vapor (steam) directly to atmosphere.   Fig. 19-B shows a typical direct contact intercondenser and aftercondenser as used in a two-stage ejector setup.   The intercondenser

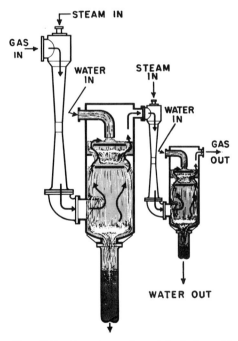

Fig. 19-B. Two-stage steam-jet ejector with direct-contact intercondenser and aftercondenser.

pressure is below atmosphere and the cooler must be fitted with a suitable 34-foot barometric leg or a centrifugal pump to remove the water. The aftercondenser discharges to atmosphere and usually requires no auxiliary means of water removal.

This particular type of counter-current barometric condenser will cool the exit gas to within approximately 5°F of the water inlet temperature.

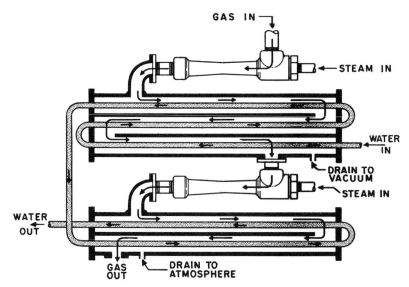

Fig. 19-C. Two-stage steam-jet ejector with surface intercondenser and aftercondenser.

Surface-Type Coolers

These separate the flow of gas from the cooling medium by a wall, usually a round metallic tube. It is diagramatically shown in Fig. 19-C — again using the ejector-type of compressor. There is no intermixing of coolant and the gas being cooled. There are two normal coolants, one liquid, usually water, and the other atmospheric air. Fig. 19-C is liquid (water) cooled.

Liquid-Cooled Designs

There are two general types of so-called shell and tube coolers for water cooling of gases. In one, the gas flows through the tubes as illustrated in Fig. 19-D. In the other the water flows through the tubes and the gas flows around them. See Fig. 19-E. Each has advantages and disadvantages that vary somewhat with size and application. Although the water-tube design has shell pressure limitations, if the cooling water is dirty or corrosive, it is to be preferred because tubes are easy to clean. When water is clean, the gas-tube type may be better. There are no firm rules.

Gas-tube coolers usually have plain round tubes. Water-tube coolers, in some designs, use finned tubes (extended surface) for a better heat-transfer rate on the gas side. These may be of the multiple-section type or they may be assembled into a shell as shown in Fig. 19-F.

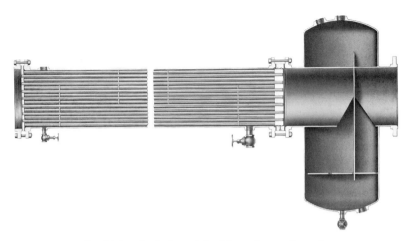

Fig. 19-D. Typical gas-tube intercooler or aftercooler.

For high pressures, a "double-pipe" design is often best. Fig. 19-G shows this. The gas usually flows through the tube, but on occasion these are water-tube coolers with fins on the outside of the inner tube.

Regardless of design, any of these (except very small sizes) should be fitted with removable tube nests for ease of cleaning and repair.

Air-Cooled Designs

The smaller air-cooled compressors, if multistaged, are fitted with air-cooled intercoolers. These are of the fin-tube type with the compressed gas passing through the tube. Coolers may consist of a single finned tube in the smaller sizes or the sectionalized assembly shown in Fig. 19-H for larger sizes.

In the above, the compressors themselves are air-cooled and similarly cooled intercoolers are an advantage. There are numerous cases, however, on larger, normally water-cooled equipment, where water is scarce, non-existent, or of extremely poor quality. Its use must be limited. Direct dry-type intercoolers and aftercoolers, transferring the heat from the compressed gas directly to the atmosphere, are used in many such cases. Portability of equipment and ability to function as a self contained entity is often a factor in the selection of such a design. The engine driver and

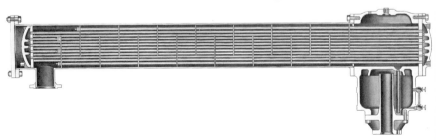

Fig. 19-E. Typical large low-pressure water-tube intercooler with integral separator.

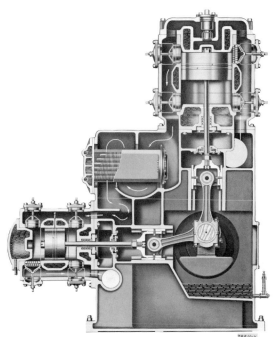

Fig. 19-F. Compact finned-tube intercooler built into a compressor assembly.

certain accessories may remain as water-cooled items, the water being cooled by circulation in a closed system. A radiator is used to discharge the heat to the atmosphere.

Dry coolers are of two general types depending on whether the fans used for air circulation provide forced or induced draft. Regardless of type, selection must be made on an economic basis, taking into account operating costs versus capital costs. The example on page 19-6 is based on an analysis of three designs to accomplish the same cooling results.

This shows that capital investment must increase if the operating power cost is to be reduced and that selection of the most economical cooler on an over-all basis requires study.

Fig. 19-G. Typical double-pipe high-pressure cooler.

Gas-to-Air Cooler Economy Study

Dry cooler design	A	B	C
Fan power ratio	1.0	0.45	0.33
Capital cost ratio	1.0	1.11	1.38

Fig. 19-H.   Typical sectionalized fin-tube cooler as used on some air-cooled compressors.

The gas temperature reduction of dry-type coolers, as compared to conventional liquid-cooled shell and tube exchangers, will usually be less. However, a water-cooled exchanger using a radiator to dissipate the heat in the water may not perform as well as the dry type.

Leakage of the gas to atmosphere is difficult to detect in dry coolers and may create a hazard.   The fan noise level is apt to be high and may be objectionable in certain locations.   Control of gas outlet temperature is sometimes necessary and can be somewhat of a problem where ambient temperatures vary widely.   Snow, wind, hail, and rain can cause difficulties, but as a rule are infrequent where this type of cooler would be used.

In favor of the dry-type cooler is the reduced maintenance, suitability for many locations, lighter weight, elimination of freezing problems in the cooling circuit (although condensate freezing can still be a problem), no loss of water as in a cooling tower, etc.

Fig. 19-I shows an induced-draft dry-type cooler serving a packaged gas engine-driven compressor.   This includes engine water cooling and gas inter- and aftercooling.

Integral or Separate Mounting

Another classification of compressor coolers may be made by the mounting arrangements.   Many compressors include, as an *integral* element of the assembly, intercoolers mounted on, alongside, or under the compressing elements.   Fig. 19-F and 19-H show such assemblies on reciprocating

Fig. 19-I. A dry-type induced-draft cooler serving a gas-engine driven compressor. This discharges to atmosphere the heat from the engine water-jackets, intercoolers and aftercooler.

units. Fig. 19-E also shows a large cooler designed to mount over the cylinders of a reciprocator. Fig. 19-J shows a multistage dynamic compressor with integral intercoolers.

Integral mounting usually makes a more compact arrangement than does *separate* mounting. However, some cooler designs cannot readily be used in the integral assembly because of space and shape limitations.

Integral mounting is common with intercoolers for reciprocating machines but much less frequent with other types of compressors. Aftercoolers are usually separately mounted as are coolers of the dry-type. An exception is on the small air-cooled compressors or packaged arrangements.

Condensate Separators

Since condensation and *removal* of moisture contained in the inlet gas is an important function of many coolers, there must be incorporated, either in the cooler itself or in an auxiliary device, proper means to accomplish this. On very small and particularly on the air cooled units, this is not so necessary. On the larger units having more efficient cooling and greater quantities of condensate, it is highly important. Reciprocating compressors must be protected from water carry-over from any intercooler to the next stage cylinder. This is not quite so necessary with the other main types, such as the helical-lobe or dynamic, but prevention of excessive carry-over is always highly desirable. Separators on large units, particularly reciprocating process compressors, are desirable even if the gas handled be dry and there is no condensate. They trap excess oil, dirt, welding beads, and pipe scale and prevent its carry-over into the next stage where damage could be done. This has been proven by experience.

A typical built-in separator is shown at the right in Fig. 19-E. Fig. 19-F shows the top of the separator chamber below the intercooler in another built-in design. The gas takes a sudden turn to the left at this point, the condensate falling to a sump in the frame where it is automatically drained off.

A separate vessel is used as a separator when it is not possible to build it into the cooler itself, as on gas-tube coolers (Fig. 19-D).

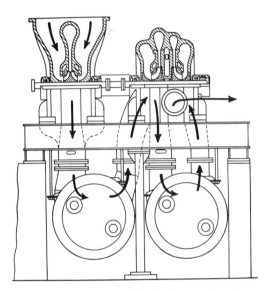

Fig. 19-J. An integral water-tube intercooler assembly with a multistage dynamic compressor.

Separators, whether integral or separate vessels, must be kept drained. It is usual for automatic traps to be used up to 500 psiG gas pressure. Since any trap should be checked occasionally for operation, a manual drain is necessary, the piping being as shown in Fig. 19-K. Above 500 psiG, drainage should be manual, separators being sized to store safely at least one hour's condensate under the most severe moisture condensation conditions to be anticipated. Drainage once an hour will then be sufficient.

Construction Codes

Exchangers to meet specific construction codes may be required by certain states, localities, or industries. This may entail special designs and it is absolutely necessary that the manufacturer be advised of the exact requirements before purchase. One of three principal codes or specifications may be involved.

Section VIII of the ASME Boiler & Pressure Vessel Code covering Unfired Pressure Vessels is the most common. A few cooler designs are not covered by the code, but the majority either meet the code or can be built to meet the code when specified, possibly at increased cost.

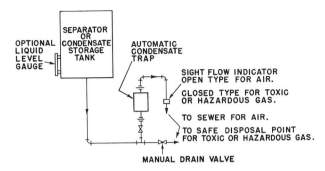

Fig. 19-K. Typical arrangement of automatic condensate trap for separator drainage.

The Tubular Exchanger Manufacturer's Association (TEMA) has written specifications standardizing on certain details of construction, tube size, tube gauge, and length. There are two specifications, TEMA "C" (Commercial) and TEMA "R" (Refinery), the latter being more stringent and expensive.

TEMA "C" or TEMA "R" can be obtained for any separately mounted cooler by special purchase, but neither is normally standard. When intercoolers are to be mounted, it is not always possible to meet TEMA "C" length requirements and TEMA "R" coolers generally cannot be mounted.

The purchaser must carefully spell out any special requirements regarding exchangers, regardless of the type of compressor.

Materials

Exchanger materials must be carefully selected for the service required. In shell and tube coolers, this involves both the gas and water sides. Muntz metal, admiralty, stainless, or carbon steel tubes can generally be obtained. Bimetalic tubes are available for extreme cases. Tube sheets are of steel or muntz metal unless corrosive conditions are unusually severe. Shells are of cast iron or steel as a rule, although brass shells are available for brackish or salt water on gas-tube coolers.

Dry coolers will usually use tube material most compatible with the gas, although consideration such as atmospheric contamination with acid vapors, may take priority.

It is important that there be agreement on cooler materials between the user and supplier. Only the user knows the history of any problems that may have developed or may be expected to develop from the cooling water, atmosphere or other sources. This information should be given to the compressor builder before an order is placed.

Corrosion Allowance

On certain applications an addition is made to the thickness of some parts to allow for possible corrosive action from one or both of the fluids flowing. Corrosion allowance is not usually necessary in compressor work, but should be specified by the user if he feels conditions warrant. It may increase cooler cost slightly.

Corrosion allowance is usually a definite addition to thickness.

Cooling Water

Water for all services on the compressor, regardless of type, should be clean, cool, and available in sufficient quantity. Silty, scale forming and corrosive water should be avoided. When scale-free water cannot be supplied, it is best to limit water discharge temperature to reduce scale deposits. Any condition varying from the above should be specified before purchase so that proper materials and designs can be supplied.

If the cooling water system discharges to a sewer or collecting sump, the outlet will be open and there will be no substantial back pressure in the cooler. If the water system is closed and operates with a back pressure at the water outlet, the pressures involved should be specified before purchase. Most compressor coolers are built for approximately 75 psiG maximum water pressure, but this must not be taken for granted and requirements should be specified before purchase. Added cost may be involved.

Water for closed systems is often treated to reduce scaling, corrosion, and maintenance.

Gas Outlet Temperature

There are no over-all standards on outlet gas temperature as related to coolant temperature. Much depends upon the application and the cooler design. Of course, the lower the coolant temperature, the lower the gas temperature. Coolant selection should bear this in mind.

Within the 100 psiG reciprocating air compressor industry, cooling in intercoolers to within 20°F of the incoming water temperature and in aftercoolers to within 15°F are standard. These do not necessarily apply with other types of compressors or other uses, but can be obtained if specified.

Theory

It is not within the scope of this treatise to cover the ramifications of gas cooler design and sizing. Suffice it to say that although the transfer of heat from a hot gas to colder water or air circulating on the other side of a tube is simple to visualize, it is not so simple to accomplish economically without considerable experience. Among the variables involved are such items as tube size, material and thickness; water or air velocity and type of path; gas velocity and type of path; the gas itself; length of path of both gas and coolant; cleanliness of tubes; and whether counter current or parallel gas and coolant flow or a combination of the two. The rate of heat transfer is affected by all of these. The basic formula for heat transfer is

$$S = \frac{Q}{U \times MTD} \tag{19.1}$$

Surface (S) is the total outside tube surface in sq ft.

Total heat (Q) to be transferred, expressed in Btu/hr, must include not only the sensible heat in the gas, but the latent heat of any vapors which condense. The latter can make a considerable difference.

Mean temperature differences (MTD). See third paragraph below.

Heat transfer rate (U) is expressed in Btu/hr/°F/sq ft and must be determined experimentally for the design and materials used. It is developed from *resistance (R)*. Resistances to heat flow usually include three dependent entirely on design and materials, and two known as *fouling factors.*

R_t is resistance offered by the thin fluid film on the inside of the tube.

R_m is resistance offered by the tube wall metal.

R_s is resistance offered by the thin fluid film on the outside (shell side) of the tube.

R_{tf} is added resistance on the inside of the tube due to fouling in use.

R_{sf} is added resistance on the outside of the tube due to fouling in use.

The heat transfer rate formula is:—

$$U = \frac{1}{R_t + R_m + R_s + R_{tf} + R_{sf}} \tag{19.2}$$

Fouling factors are used to permit a certain degree of tube dirtiness without lowering the cooler performance below the guarantee point. High fouling factor, however, will increase cooler surface and cost materially. Most commercial intercoolers and aftercoolers are designed with a fouling factor of approximately 0.001 to 0.002, divided between the inside and outside of the tube. This is the sum of R_{tf} and R_{sf}.

Mean temperature difference (MTD) is calculated from the *greatest temperature difference (GTTD)* and the *least temperature difference (LTTD)*. In compressor coolers, these are the difference between gas and water temperatures at the gas entrance and exit, respectively. It is quite general to use the *MTD* formula below in calculating these exchangers.

$$MTD = \frac{GTTD - LTTD}{\log_e \dfrac{GTTD}{LTTD}} \tag{19.3}$$

Fig. 19-L is a chart from which *MTD* can be obtained for counter-current flow. Some designs may require a correction factor due to particular multipass arrangements of flow. These correction factors may be found in the *Standards of TEMA*.

$$MTD = \frac{GTTD - LTTD}{Log_e \dfrac{GTTD}{LTTD}}$$

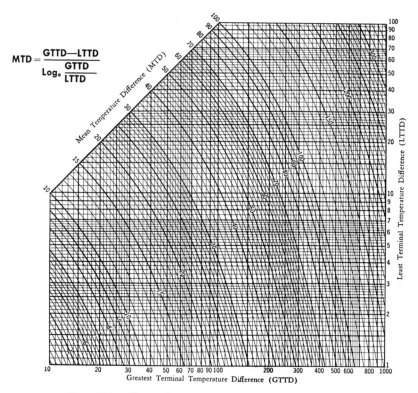

Fig. 19-L. Chart of mean temperature difference as determined from terminal temperature differences for a counter-current cooler.

Chapter 20

Vacuum and Vacuum Equipment

What is Vacuum

A perfect vacuum is space devoid of matter. It is absolute emptiness. The space is at zero pressure absolute. A perfect vacuum cannot be obtained by any known means, but can be closely approached in certain applications.

Uses of Vacuum

Vacuum has a multitude of uses. Those closest to everyday life include the manufacture of electric light bulbs, and television and other electronic tubes; packing of food products; generation of electric power; production of medicines; and, manufacture of paper. Many things that cannot be done under ordinary atmospheric pressure are feasible under vacuum — water will boil even when it's cold, so matter that is frozen solid can be dried; electrons, atoms, and molecules can be made to move in controlled paths; glass, plastics, cloth, and other materials can be coated with metal; metals and paper can be impregnated with oil, wax, or plastics; gas bubbles can be prevented in molten metal; new and purer metals can be produced; and, complex organic substances can be torn apart and their different molecules collected separately.

Vacuum is utilized throughout most of the maximum possible range from just below atmospheric pressure to near absolute zero. Fig. 20-A illustrates many of the applications of vacuum and their approximate pressure level. Recent years have brought the lower range into sharper focus and chambers designed to test space components and similar equipment are now available for operation at pressures lower than 10^{-9} mm Hg abs.

What is a Vacuum Pump

Vacuum pumps are used to produce and maintain a vacuum in a system by removing matter from the space involved to a degree dependent upon the type of system, the leakage into the system and the capabilities of the vacuum pump equipment. A *vacuum pump* is a *compressor* having an intake below atmosphere and usually compressing no higher than the atmosphere, often to a pressure considerably below atmosphere. Certain applications involving low and very low intake pressures may use two or more vacuum pumps in series, often of different types, to achieve the desired inlet and discharge pressures.

Dead-End Pressure

Except for dynamic units, all vacuum pumps have a certain minimum intake pressure (with constant discharge) called *dead end*. The capacity handled becomes zero at this point. The intake pressure at dead end will depend upon the size and type of compressor and the pressure to which it must discharge. Multiple staging lowers the dead end of almost any type. Dead-end intake pressures are often difficult to obtain in practice because leakage into the system cannot be eliminated.

Dynamic machines have a minimum operating intake vacuum at the surge limit or pumping point.

With a constant discharge pressure, vacuum pumps have a capacity that will vary with the intake pressure along a curve. The shape of this characteristic curve varies with machine type.

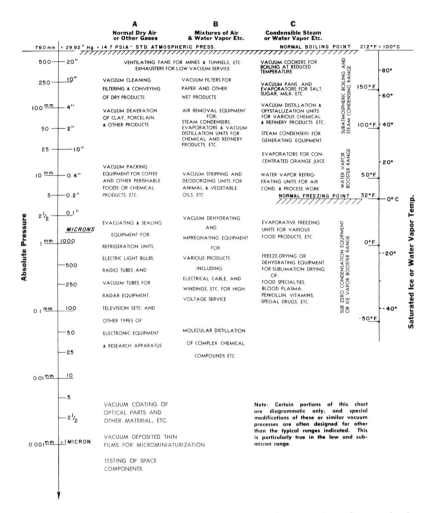

Fig. 20-A. Many of the principal industrial processes that necessitate the use of sub-atmospheric pressures are listed here, together with the typical pressure range for each. The processes involve the evacuation or removal of various combinations of air, other gases, and water vapor, as shown under the three headings A, B, and C. Chart compiled by J. F. Plummer, Jr., of Ingersoll-Rand Company, Phillipsburg, N. J.

Vacuum Systems

Systems involving vacuum may be divided into six types. See ejectors on page 4-37. Comments apply regardless of compressor (vacuum pump) type.

Leakage into the system from atmosphere or other surroundings will be at relatively constant rate and will influence the results. Leakage *must be estimated* by the user and made a part of the *original equipment specifications.* Proper vacuum pump selection cannot otherwise be made.

The Measurement of Vacuum

Vacuum is measurable in any unit of pressure per unit area, but is most often measured in inches of water (H_2O); inches of mercury (Hg); mm Hg (1 mm Hg is known as the Torr); or the micron (0.001 mm Hg). Measurement may be taken with a water or mercury column indicating the difference between atmospheric pressure and the vacuum system pressure. This method is satisfactory over a range down to near 1" Hg absolute for most applications if carefully used. To measure pressures lower than this with accuracy requires more sophisticated equipment and absolute pressure gauges are used. The McLeod gauge is standard, being good to 1 micron. Modified McLeod and other special gauges can measure absolute pressures to 10⁻⁷ mm Hg or lower.

Two methods of specifying vacuum are usable and there is little standardization. See Fig. 2-A and page 2-14. Too often necessary information to correlate these methods is not provided and, in many cases, factors that influence and *limit* production of vacuum are not understood.

The Barometer

A barometer measures the atmospheric pressure. Normally a barometer is a column of mercury in a closed tube, the closed end being so close to a perfect vacuum that it is considered as such. The mercury must be chemically pure and corrections must be made for ambient temperatures. See Fig. 20-B.

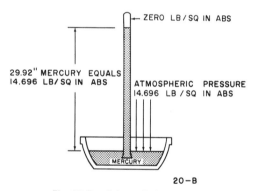

Fig. 20-B. Schematic barometer.

The barometer measures weight of the earth's atmosphere as exerted on the surface of the mercury in the open dish and varies with altitude. The barometer reading is the *absolute* pressure existing at a particular point on the earth's surface at a given time. It never has a fixed value and changes from hour to hour, depending upon weather conditions. In the specification of vacuum by either of the following methods, the average *and* extreme barometer reading *must* be given so the vacuum pump system can be properly selected or designed. This is often forgotten.

Specifying Vacuum by the Vacuum Method

The oldest method of specifying vacuum is the *vacuum* method. It tells the difference between absolute pressure in the vacuum system and absolute atmospheric pressure as it exists at a particular time. It is measured almost exclusively by a mercury column, one end of which is open to the atmosphere, the other being connected to the vacuum system. See Fig. 20-C. Barometric pressure must be specified. This method is used in the lower range of vacuum.

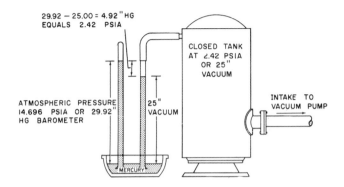

Fig. 20-C. Schematic vacuum system and barometer.

Specifying Vacuum by the Absolute Pressure Method

The specification of vacuum using *absolute pressures* is the only accurate method of expressing pressure to be attained in any system. It is extensively used in scientific circles and should be more widely adopted. This provides the intake pressure to be maintained without subtraction or mental arithmetic. It must be known to select a machine or predict its performance. Training oneself to think only in absolute terms will assist greatly in understanding vacuum problems.

The average barometer must be known since that is usually the pressure to which the vacuum pump(s) must discharge.

Vacuum Referred to 30″ Hg Barometer

A frequent problem is the interpretation of what is meant by a vacuum, for example, of *26″ Hg referred to a 30″ barometer*. For a sea level installation where the average barometer is close to 30″ Hg, there is no problem. Suppose, however, the actual barometer has been given as 27.0″ Hg. Is the absolute pressure still to be 4″ Hg as it would be at sea-level or is it some other value and if so what value? In some applications (vacuum evaporators, for example) the use of 4″ Hg abs (now 23″ vacuum) would not alter the desired conditions within the vacuum system. Actually, the vacuum pump might be smaller than the sea-level size.

In other applications (vacuum filters, for example), the vacuum would probably have to remain at 26″ (now 1″ Hg abs) for the equipment to operate as well. The vacuum pump would be substantially larger than for sea-level operation, because its compression ratio has increased from a sea-level value of 7.5 to an altitude value of 27.0.

Use of this phraseology tells nothing and is confusing. Vacuum should be expressed in terms of absolute pressure or in terms from which absolute intake and discharge pressures may be positively derived. The *actual intake capacity and barometer* should be specified.

COMPRESSED AIR AND GAS DATA

Compression Ratio

The effect of compression ratio on a *reciprocating* compressor is discussed on page 4-6. The same effect, although not always for the same reason, occurs in all vacuum pumps (compressors). They have a reduced capacity over all or part of their operating range when the compression ratio is increased. The following table illustrates the variation in effective operating conditions imposed upon a vacuum pump under typical conditions.

Barometer		Vacuum		Absolute Pressure		
in Hg	mm Hg	in Hg	mm Hg	in Hg	mm Hg	Compression Ratio
30	762	25	635	5	127	6.0
27	686	25	635	2	50.8	13.5
30	762	29	737	1	25.4	30.0
29.2	742	29	737	0.2	5.08	146.0

Factors Limiting Vacuum Obtainable

Four factors limit the degree of vacuum commercially obtainable. These factors do not necessarily influence all types of pumps in the same degree or manner.

1. The capability of the pumping system
2. Leakage
3. The matter being removed
4. The presence of liquid that may evaporate

The first two items are self-evident. The third, although not of great importance, influences certain types of units. The fourth is not always appreciated. See page 3-4 (Gas and Vapor) and page 4-37, Cases 3, 5, and 6. The *minimum partial vapor pressure* of the liquid determines the vacuum obtainable in such cases.

Vacuum Pump Theory

Theory, with most types, does not differ from the standard for compressors. Effect of moisture or the vapors of other materials become more of a factor in many applications and must be given specific attention. Horsepower at peak intake conditions must be considered for certain units. See page 4-9 which applies to most positive displacement units.

Types of Vacuum Pumps

Fig. 20-D charts ten types of vacuum pumps and their *commercial* operating pressure ranges. Dead end absolute pressures will be lower than those shown. In the last three, the absolute pressure shown are typical. There is considerable variation between units dependent on make, size, and gas composition, particularly moisture content.

Rotary Liquid-Piston Unit

The rotary liquid-piston vacuum pump operates on the same principle as the compressor discussed on page 1-8. The liquid is usually water, but other fluids may be used for process reasons. These machines can handle

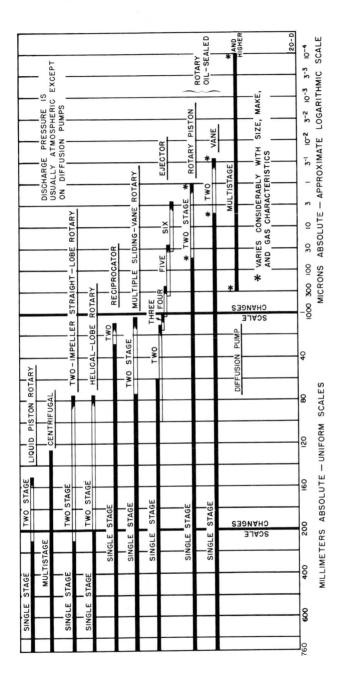

Fig. 20-D. Representative operating ranges of vacuum pumps. Dead-end will be lower than limits shown.

considerable liquid carry-over making them useful in serving paper machines and similar applications. Multiple staging requires two separate units. Performance is influenced by temperature and vapor pressure of the liquid circulated within the casing. Ratings are at 60°F.

The Dynamic Vacuum Pump

The centrifugal compressor (Chapter 9) has not been as widely applied for vacuum as most other types of machines, but has been used in vacuum service for relatively high absolute intake pressures in such applications as exhausters in manufactured gas production. Axials and centrifugals have been used in the operation of wind tunnels. Pressures to $2''$ Hg abs have been attained on some dynamic units with atmospheric discharge.

The Fourdrinier papermaking machine requires several levels of moderate vacuum. The multistaged centrifugal lends itself well to removing air and vapor from the paper machine at different pressure levels. Combining all normal Fourdrinier services into one vacuum pump and driver, can, on large installations particularly, save an appreciable amount of power over the use of a separate machine on each service. With good liquid separation, the discharge is hot and dry and is available for drying paper. If the unit is turbine-driven, the exhaust steam can also be used for the drying section of the paper machine.

Fig. 20-E shows how the pump may be tied into the various vacuum levels on the paper machine. All pressures are inches Hg abs. Efficient water separation ahead of the compressor is essential.

Because of the relatively large rotating mass, as compared to the low horsepower of the driver in vacuum service, acceleration problems are encountered with motor drives and must be carefully studied to assure that sufficient torque will be available.

Two-Impeller Straight-Lobe Type

This unit has been described and illustrated on page 1-9. There is no essential design difference between compressors and vacuum pumps. These are moderate vacuum machines. Two machines in series may be used to obtain somewhat lower pressures. Closely controlled liquid injection is used to provide cooling and sealing. These machines should not handle large quantities of liquid. Separators may be required.

Special units of this design, operating dry, are built for a first stage of a two- or three-stage combination including the rotary (oil-sealed) vacuum pump for the fore-pump or second stage.

Helical-Lobe Rotary Unit

The helical-lobe rotary compressor is frequently used as a vacuum pump. See Chapter 8. For intake pressures below $15''$ Hg abs, it is usual to use water injection, there being a resultant gain in capacity as with the straight-lobe design. Although these units can handle a substantial amount of water, inlet separators must be used if the liquid load is extremely heavy or may carry over in slugs (as in paper machine service). They are often used in a *forepump* or the first stage of a system using an oil sealed rotary as the second stage.

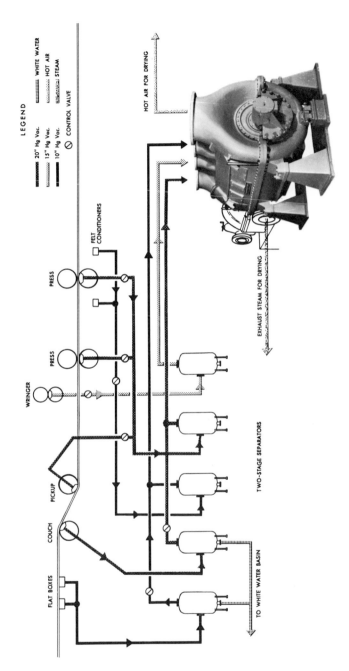

Fig. 20-E. Diagram of the central vacuum system application of a centrifugal compressor, combining service at three pressure levels in a single unit.

Reciprocating Vacuum Pumps

Reciprocating compressors for vacuum service are probably the oldest and were, for years, most widely used. They have been superseded in some areas by other types, but are still available in a wide line of sizes and arrangements and to much larger sizes than most others. They are not designed to handle liquid and adequate inlet separators must be provided. The vacuum pump uses standard frame and running gear designs with a larger-than-normal cylinder of standard construction. The large cylinder is used because horsepower per unit displacement is so much lower under vacuum pump service than for elevated pressures. See Chapter 6.

Sliding-Vane Rotary

Modifications are slight when it is used on vacuum service. These units (Chapter 7) must be protected from liquid carry-over. This design must not be confused with the vane type described below.

Ejectors

The ejector, almost always operated by steam, is a major producer of vacuum. It is available in from one to six stages and in sizes from the very small to those so large as to require special consideration to shipping and erection methods. See page 1-16 and page 4-31.

Regular liquid carry-out will cause throat erosion and should not be allowed.

Rotary (Oil-Sealed) Units

This mechanical unit is designed specifically to produce commercial absolute pressures in the low micron and partial-micron range. These pumps compress to atmosphere. They are of relatively small size, 50 HP motors being about the maximum required. There are a number of makes, both single- and multistage units being available. The compression ratios achieved are extremely high. All pumps are oil sealed and discharge some oil with the gas. Oil is separated and reused. The maximum vacuum (dead end) is influenced greatly by pressure of any vapor contained in the gas and by the vapor pressure of the sealing oil. A discharge plate or poppet valve is used.

There are two oil-sealed pumps. The *rotary piston* is shown schematically in Fig. 20-F. The piston is rotated by an eccentric so there is an increasing volume on one side of the slide valve through which the gas flows into the machine and a decreasing volume on the other side, compressing the contained gas and eventually discharging it to the upper chamber.

The other type is a *vane* machine, one design of which is diagrammed in Fig. 20-G. The two vanes may be spring-loaded or may use another construction in which they act as one piece, sliding back and forth through the rotor. The net action of the vane type is essentially the same as the rotary-piston design.

These units are offered in some sizes for two staging within one casing; otherwise two casings must be used.

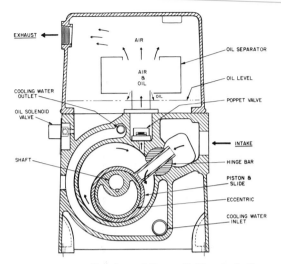

Courtesy of Pennsalt Chemicals Corp.

Fig. 20-F.   Typical oil-sealed rotary-piston vacuum pump.

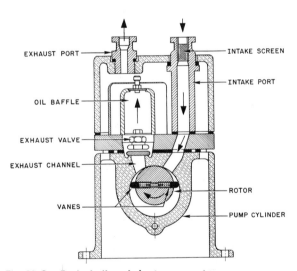

Fig. 20-G.   Typical oil-sealed rotary vane-type vacuum pump.

Diffusion Pumps

Figure 20-H illustrates the action of a diffusion pump. A liquid of low absolute vapor pressure is boiled, the vapor is ejected at a high velocity in a downward direction through the multiple jets and is condensed on the cold wall of the pump. Molecules of the gas being pumped enter the vapor stream and are given a downward velocity component by collisions with

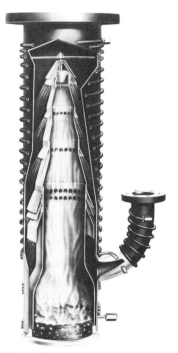

Couresty of Kinney Vacuum Division-New York Air Brake Co.

Fig. 20-H. Typical diffusion pump.

the vapor molecules. The gas molecules are removed through the discharge line by means of a backing pump such as one of the rotary oil sealed pumps.

These pumps operate only at quite low pressures. The discharge, or backing, pressure usually required is 25 to 300 micron Hg abs. Ultimate vacuum attainable depends somewhat upon the vapor pressure of the pump liquid at the temperature of the condensing surfaces. By providing a cold trap or condenser between the diffusion pump and the region being evacuated, pressures far below the vapor pressure of the pump liquid may be achieved. When vacuum is to be used for insulating purposes, the required final pressure may be from 10^{-5} to 10^{-7} mm Hg abs.

The first liquid used for diffusion pumps was mercury, but most commercial pumps now use an oil of low vapor pressure. Silicone oils have excellent characteristics.

Approximate Maximum Capacities-CFM

The following table gives the current approximate maximum capacities of the various types of vacuum pumps. This is not to infer that larger sizes may not be built if the market warrants. Except for the dynamic, reciprocating, and diffusion types, multistage ratings are based on the use of two or more casings (separate units in series).

Type	Single-Stage	Multistage
Liquid-Piston.....................	9,000 (A)	2,500 (A)
Centrifugal.....................	650,000 (A)	200,000 (A)
Axial.......................	——————	2,000,000 (A)
Two-Impeller Straight-Lobe.........	40,000 (D)	20,000 (D)
Helical-Lobe....................	20,000 (D)	20,000 (D)
Reciprocating..................	62,000 (D)	31,000 (D)
Sliding-Vane Rotary.............	6,000 (D)	6,000 (D)
Ejector........................	Limited only by shipping facilities	
Rotary Oil-Sealed		
Rotary-Piston Type.............	780 (D)	780 (D)
Vane Type....................	1,100 (D)	1,100 (D)
Diffusion (very approximate).......	——————	60,000 (A)

(A) Actual at intake conditions   (D) Displacement

The Atmospheric-Air Powered Ejector

Ejectors may use any motive fluid having sufficient pressure. Steam is the most prevalent. In vacuum service, a single first-stage ejector powered by atmospheric air and discharging into a mechanical pump is sometimes used. The ejector will operate very effectively in this area, its motive fluid is always available and makes possible on some services the use of mechanical pumps that otherwise could not develop the necessary vacuum.

Combinations of Vacuum Pumps

Many combinations of pumps are possible, and, other than those already mentioned, include a steam jet primary discharging into a reciprocator, an axial in series with a centrifugal, and a helical- or straight-lobe rotary compressing into a rotary oil-sealed unit or units.

The latter has been done to reduce the number of upper-stage pumps required. Some applications require a considerable number of these oil-sealed units in parallel to obtain sufficient capacity. Boosting the intake level increases the capacity of the battery materially and permits fewer units at less total expense.

Pump-Down Time

There are many applications where ultimate or near-ultimate vacuum is to be attained as quickly as possible consistent with the economics of equipment cost. This is particularly true with power plant surface condensers, sugar pans (evaporators), and such batch processes (cyclic) as impregnation, molding, and fumigation. Pump-down is frequently known as *hogging* or *roughing*. Some space component testing facilities require rather rapid initial evacuation. Pump-down may be proportional to the rate of climb to which the component will be exposed.

The time for pump-down is proportional to the volume to be evacuated and is a function of the performance curve of the vacuum pump based on actual intake volume at intake pressure versus absolute intake pressure. See Fig. 20-I.

This calculation is applicable when the curve of intake volume versus intake pressure is known. This is called the capacity curve for some types of pumps. On the oil-sealed rotary and diffusion types, it is known as "speed" and is often expressed in liters/sec, easily translated to cfm.

$$T = 2.30\,V \left(\frac{1}{S_{(1,2)}} \text{Log}_{10} \frac{P_1}{P_2} + \frac{1}{S_{(2,3)}} \text{Log}_{10} \frac{P_2}{P_3} + \frac{1}{S_{(3,4)}} \text{Log}_{10} \frac{P_3}{P_4} + \text{-----} \right)$$

T = Evacuation time — minutes   V = System volume — cu ft
S = Average actual intake capacity between initial and
final pressures of each term — cfm

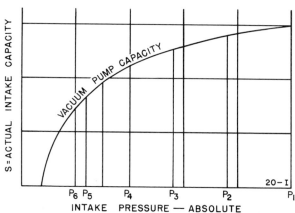

THE GREATER THE NUMBER OF INCREMENTS, THE GREATER THE ACCURACY.

**Fig. 20-I. Incremental method of calculating pump-down time.
Inward leakage and effect of vapor evaporation must be added.**

Fig. 20-I is based on the unit handling a dry gas and does not allow for leakage into the system during pump-down. This will lengthen time required.

A very approximate theoretical formula, suitable *only* for *reciprocating* pumps is

$$PD = \frac{Q}{T} \log_e \frac{p_2 - p_c}{p_1 - p_c} \tag{20.1}$$

where PD = piston displacement — cfm.
Q = volume of system to be evacuated — cu ft.
T = time to evacuate tank — min.
p_2 = pump discharge pressure — in Hg abs.
p_1 = pump intake pressure — in Hg abs.
p_c = pump dead end pressure — in Hg abs.

This assumes no leakage, which may approach 100% in small systems. Allowance must be made.

Vacuum pumps of differing types have widely varying intake volume — intake pressure curves. Fig. 20-J illustrates four types. All units are presented on the basis of percent volume handled as referred to the *air* volume handled at 30″ Hg abs. intake and discharge (zero vacuum and a compression ratio of 1.0). All units discharge to 30″ Hg abs. at all times. The oil-seal rotary has a very flat curve to very low final pressures. See the table. Note that the capacity of ejectors, normally in lb/hr, is presented here in intake cfm.

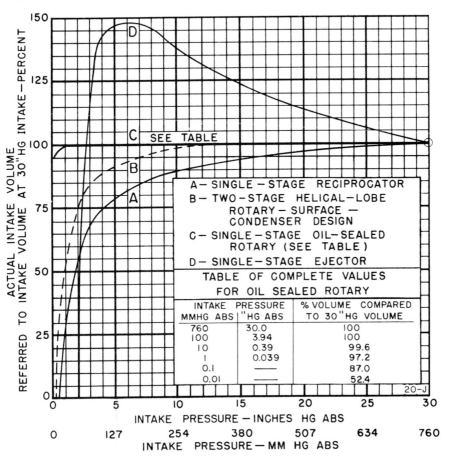

Fig. 20-J. Characteristic actual volumetric capacity curves of various types of vacuum pumps.

Pump performance data are generally on the basis of handling dry air. Inclusion of vapor will influence the performance curves in some instances. If a liquid is evaporating in the system during pump-down, due allowance must be made for this added volume.

HEI Condenser Standards

Standards for pump sizing for various types of steam condensers are contained in literature published by the Heat Exchange Institute, 122 East 42nd St., New York, N. Y. 10017.

System Leakage

Since system leakage is almost impossible to prevent and some method of allowance must be used in pump selection, two criteria are presented. Note — They are not entirely consistent since they come from two entirely different fields of application. In both cases the air is assumed dry.

The HEI Leakage Standard

This is a part of the Heat Exchange Institute Standards and applies to vacuum systems at moderate levels. Fig. 20-K shows the maximum leakage permissible for a system to be considered commercially tight. These values are for a system without any agitator. With an agitator having an ordinary commercial shaft seal, a reasonable amount of maintenance will keep shaft leakage to 5 lbs/hr. With a special high vacuum seal and good maintenance, shaft leakage can be kept to a negligible amount.

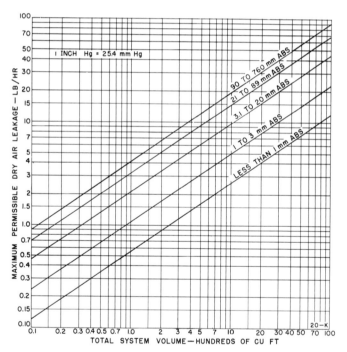

Drafted from data in STANDARDS FOR STEAM JET EJEC-
TORS, Third Edition. Copyright 1956 by the Heat Exchange
Institute, 122 East 42 Street, New York, N. Y. 10017.

Fig. 20-K. Maximum permissible air leakage for a commercially tight system in accordance with HEI Standards.

The values of maximum air leakage should not be used for selecting capacity of the air removal equipment. It is recommended that the design capacity of the air removal equipment be double the maximum estimated air leakage. To this should be added the noncondensable gases produced in the process and any associated condensable vapors.

The vacuum system includes all vessels and piping downstream of the air removal equipment. If there is a barometric condenser or raw water scrubber in the vacuum system, allowance must be made for the air liberated from the water upon admission to the vacuum space. As a guide to this allowance, Fig. 20-L shows recommendations for barometric condensers from HEI Standards.

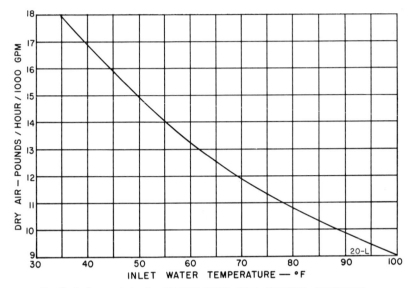

Drafted from data in STANDARDS FOR DIRECT CONTACT, BAROMETRIC, AND LOW LEVEL CONDENSERS. Fourth Edition. Copyright 1957 by the Heat Exchange Institute, 122 East 42 Street, New York, N. Y. 10017.

Fig. 20-L. Allowance to be made for air removed from water used in a direct-contact gas scrubber or barometric condenser.

High Vacuum Leakage Standards

Standards in the areas where the oil sealed rotary and diffusion pumps are used are shown below. After selecting the theoretical size of pump or pumps by the method of Fig. 20-I or otherwise, multiply by the factor shown to obtain the size to install.

Inlet Pressure Range		Multiplier
mm Hg abs	In. Hg abs	
760 to 100	30 to 4	1.0
100 to 10	4 to 0.4	1.25
10 to 0.5	0.4 to 0.02	1.5
0.5 to 0.05	——————	2.0
0.05 to 0.0005	——————	4.0

Leakage Tests

Leakage into a system can be measured with a reasonable degree of accuracy. The following is quoted from HEI publications which apply to moderate vacuum applications.

"The air leakage in an existing vacuum system may be determined by a drop test. This test is based on the fact that air leaks into the system at a constant rate as long as pressure within the system is less than 0.53 times atmosphere pressure (about 15" Hg abs with a 30" barometer). It is usually run with the system empty but with all agitators and other moving equipment in operation to duplicate leakage through seals and glands. The test should be run with the system at normal atmospheric temperature and the system should be free of any liquids.

Procedure

1. Evacuate system to about 5 in Hg abs using available pump.

2. Close off isolating valve between system and pump; then shut down pump.

3. Record elapsed time for pressure in system to rise from one observed pressure to a higher observed pressure. If leakage is low, a rise of one or two inches Hg may take a long enough time to give an accurate estimate of leakage. However, do not permit pressure to rise above 15 in Hg abs.

4. Knowing system volume, initial and final pressure and elapsed time, the total leakage rate into system may be calculated from the following equation. This gives the weight of dry air.

$$\text{Leakage (lbs/hr)} = \frac{0.15 \times \text{Volume (cu ft)} \times \text{Pressure Rise (in Hg)}}{\text{Time (min)}} \tag{20.2}$$

5. In order to prove tightness of the isolating valve between system and pump, the test should be repeated with valve closed and pump operating. If the isolating valve is tight, the total calculated leakage for both tests will be identical. If the isolating valve is not tight, the two values will differ by an amount equal to the leakage through the valve plus the air removed by the pump under the pressure conditions existing across the leaking valve. For reliable tests of air leakage using the drop test, leakage through isolating valve in closed position should be proven negligible. The test may be run using a reliable vacuum gauge or mercury column without correction for barometer pressure."

Pressure Loss in Vacuum Lines

The calculation of pressure loss in vacuum lines is frequently a problem since there is little available data. However, the HEI has developed some information of value which is presented in Chapter 26, Gas Piping.

Atmospheric Pressure versus Altitude

For many years, altitude versus barometric pressure data up to about 15,000 ft altitude were all that were needed. The advent of space studies has aroused much interest in barometric pressures at extreme altitudes. Page 34-158 presents the best available data to an altitude of nearly 400 miles. The temperatures are the average existing at the specific altitude and 40° latitude. These data are from the NASA Standard Atmosphere (1962).

Chapter 21

Expanders

Introduction

Expanders may be defined as those mechanical devices that produce mechanical work through the expansion of gas or vapor from an existing pressure level to a lower pressure level. There are many machines that may be used as expanders. The most common are the steam engine and the steam turbine. Most rotary compressors will operate in reverse as engines or expanders and may be used to produce power. The gas turbine is an expander, but is a completely integrated device as a rule and is not discussed. See page 15-28.

The expanders that this discussion particularly covers are those handling gases other than steam and utilizing available energy for the production of power or for the cooling effect of expansion. In some of the latter systems, power produced may not be put to productive use. In all cases, power must be produced and work must be done.

Energy in many otherwise waste gases may be at too low a pressure to be used in an expander direct. If the temperature is high enough, it may be used in a waste heat boiler to generate steam that drives a turbine and thus recovers the energy.

Fields of Use

Expanders designed primarily for *power recovery* are found in relatively large sizes in nitric acid plants, fluid catalytic cracking of petroleum products, fuel gas mixing, and the Zimmerman sewage sludge disposal system. These are not exclusive, since an application for a power-recovery expander requires only a situation where a gas is to be reduced in pressure or throttled.

Expanders designed for *cooling* (refrigeration) of the expanded gas (or of another gas by heat transfer) are found largely in cryogenic applications for the liquefication of air, hydrogen, helium, and methane. Air is liquefied to permit separation of its components, principally oxygen and nitrogen for process uses. In large plants, power recovery may be significant, but still secondary to refrigeration effect.

Gas Conditions

The inlet gas to any expander should preferably be clean and non-corrosive. Low condensable content is desirable since the cooling effect of expansion may cause condensation.

These conditions do not always exist, particularly on power recovery applications and special designs and/or materials may be necessary. Some liquid in the exhaust may be unavoidable on certain applications and the machine must be designed to handle it. Some liquid can often be tolerated, particularly in axial-flow dynamic expanders.

Conspicuous examples presenting problems are the expansion of tail gas from a nitric acid tower, this being quite corrosive; expansion of flue gas from the fluid catalytic cracking process which may contain erosive particles of catalyst; and, the Zimmerman sludge disposal process where the inlet gas is a mixture of steam, nitrogen, and other gases. It is dirty and good solids separation ahead of the expander must be the rule.

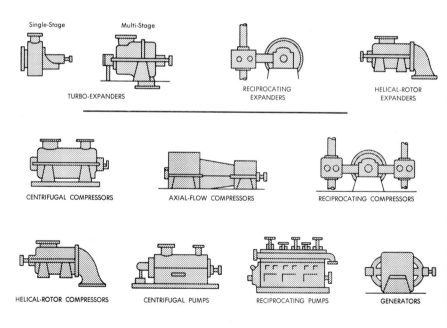

Fig. 21-A. Types of expanders and the machines they may drive.

Expander Types

Any device that actually does work by expanding the gas can be used as an expander.

The rotary positive displacement machine has not been widely used as yet, but there are fields where it may be advantageously applied. Permissible inlet pressures and temperatures will approximate the discharge conditions of the same size compressor. Refer to the appropriate chapter for this information.

Expanders can be used to drive almost any power device (Fig. 21-A), but the more usual are some form of dynamic compressor, centrifugal pump, or generator. On small units, often found in cryogenic applications, the driven device may act only as a brake and the power developed is not used.

Most expanders are of the dynamic or reciprocating types. They may be classified as high- or low-temperature, depending upon inlet conditions and the purpose of expansion. Most power recovery units are high-temperature with inlet conditions varying to above 1350°F maximum. Materials usually set the limit. Low-temperature expanders are used almost exclusively within the cryogenic group. Their inlet temperature is usually below ambient and at times much lower. Exhaust approaches absolute zero in some cases.

The Dynamic Expander

For high-temperature service, expanders are of normal turbine designs, altered in materials and details as required by the gas and its conditions. Both impulse- and reaction-turbine designs are used as well as combinations of the two. The choice depends upon many variables — flow quantity, expansion ratio, gas cleanliness, etc. There is no real limit to size.

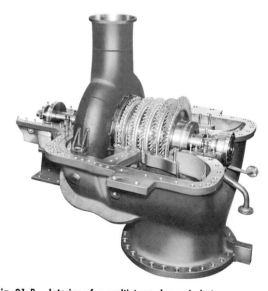

Fig. 21-B. Interior of a multistage dynamic hot-gas expander.

In the fluid catalytic-cracking process, a single-stage expander is usual because of the low inlet pressure. Other processes may use multistage. Nitric acid and ethylene oxide plants providing initial pressures of approximately 100 and 270 psiA, respectively, will have up to five stages.

Fig. 21-B shows a single-stage fluid catalytic-cracking unit; Fig. 21-C illustrates a complete outdoor nitric acid plant installation consisting of an expander (far end) driving an air compressor consisting of axial flow and centrifugal compressors in series.

The steam turbine at the near end (Fig. 21-C) is used during start-up to provide power for pressurizing the process sufficiently for hot gas production to begin. The expander then takes most of the load, the steam turbine supplying only the balance. Electric motors may also be used to supply the necessary differential power during start-up and operation. Some nitric acid processes are self-sustaining and use other methods of starting.

Dynamic machines are also used as expanders in the low-temperature field. These are relatively small units, usually of the axial flow or the centripetal (radial-inflow) types. The latter are essentially centrifugal compressors operating with reverse flow. These are both quite special because of the low temperatures involved. The axial-flow machine will handle more liquid in the exhaust but is considerably less efficient at the lower flow rates of this service. Dynamic machines are basically for the lower expansion ratios and the higher volumes as compared to reciprocators.

Fig. 21-C. A complete outdoor nitric acid power plant consisting of hot-gas expander (far end) driving axial-flow and centrifugal compressors in series, and, at the near end, a steam turbine to start the process and supply make-up power as needed.

The Reciprocating Expander

Reciprocating expanders once were the only type used in nitric acid plants (at 100 psiA) and became highly standardized during World War II. As nitric acid plants increased in size, the dynamic expander came into use and now predominates because of its superior economic and process suitability. In power recovery, reciprocators are adaptations of the integral steam-engine-driven compressor in most cases.

Reciprocators are limited in their economics by the maximum inlet temperature allowable. Lubrication is difficult at high temperatures. The maximum is about 725°F and for some types the limit is lower. Since many power recovery processes have gas available at higher temperatures, the dynamic expander tends to be the more acceptable. In moderate sizes at moderate inlet conditions, the reciprocating unit is reliable and efficient.

For high-ratio work in low-temperature services, particularly in cyrogenics, the reciprocator is available to about 3000 psiA inlet pressure. It generally handles lower volumes than the comparable dynamic unit on this service.

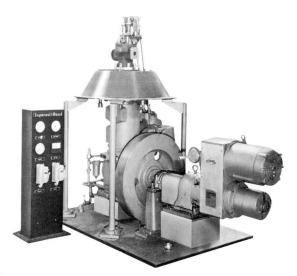

Fig. 21-D. A vertical reciprocating expander for cryogenic service showing complete dome removed. It exhausts at minus 440°F.

Low temperature expanders, both vertical and horizontal, are highly specialized units. Both single- and double-acting designs are available to more than 400 hp output. They normally handle air, helium, hydrogen, or nitrogen. Many designs are nonlubricated, utilizing some of the techniques and materials of the NL compressor.

Fig. 21-D is a vertical helium expander operating in a process to liquefy helium. Fig. 21-E shows the same unit installed with a cryostat surrounding the cylinder to limit heat leakage inward. It operates at *minus* 440°F exhaust temperature.

Fig. 21-E.   The unit of Fig. 21-D with cryostat installed to prevent inward heat leakage.

Location of the Expander

Any process utilizing an expander should be thoroughly studied for the optimum expander location and the possibility of combining it with other methods of energy recovery.   An example is given below, based on handling flue gas from a fluid catalytic cracking process.   Figures are conservative and allow for the power required by auxiliaries.   Pressures and temperatures, other than initial, are typical and may not represent the optimum for the selected process.   Flue gas is available at the following conditions.

Flow - lb/hr	500,000
Inlet - psiA	30.2
- °F	1000
Exhaust - psiA	15.2
Molecular weight	28.0
Ave. adiabatic exponent (k)	1.313

It is assumed that power developed can be used to compress air for this or another process.

Fig. 21-F illustrates at A and B two possible methods of energy recovery. A uses only an expander, B only a waste heat boiler.   To keep the boiler cost to a minimum, the gas pressure is reduced through orifices. The slight Joule-Thompson effect involved is neglected.   Steam is generated for the turbine at 400 psiG and 550°F.

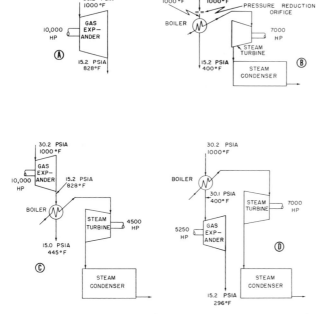

Fig. 21-F.   Diagrams showing the influence on power recovery of expander location and the use of added auxiliary methods of heat usage.

Comparison of A and B shows that the hot gas expander develops nearly 50% more power, but that an appreciable amount of heat energy remains in the exhaust.   Although the boiler has a lower gas outlet temperature, the gas expansion energy has been wasted.

This suggests that a combination of A and B might be better, but which element should come first?   Fig. 21-F, C and D, shows both combinations. It is found that C is the better from a thermodynamic viewpoint.   There is little difference in first cost.

Arrangement	Equipment	Shaft Power	
		Per Unit	Total
A	Expander	10,000	10,000
B	Boiler and Turbine	7,000	7,000
C	Expander, then Boiler and Turbine	10,000 4,500	14,500
D	Boiler and Turbine, then Expander	7,000 5,250	12,250

Assuming that the alternate to waste gas usage is the compression of the air by steam turbine drive with steam at $0.45/1000 lb, the annual saving will be $613,000 and the installation will pay out in less than 30 months.

Expanders for Moderate Temperature Refrigeration

Mechanical expanders are used for refrigeration primarily in cryogenics. See Chapter 23. There are other applications involving only moderately low temperatures. Among these is the *refrigeration-extraction cycle* as applied to casing-head natural gas. The object is to remove valuable condensables.

Utilizing the cycle shown in Fig. 21-G and knowing the initial pressure and temperature at the well-head, a gas expander can be designed to achieve the reduced temperature required for the refrigeration-extraction process. The power developed by the expander may then be used to recompress the gas to the outgoing line pressure for distribution. After going through the process, the gas is substantially pure methane. This requires no conventional refrigeration equipment.

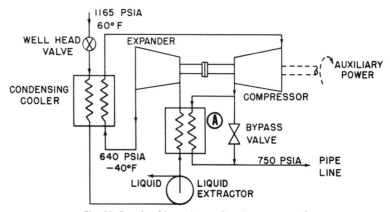

Fig. 21-G. A refrigeration cycle using an expander for extracting condensables from natural gas.

In Fig. 21-G, raw gas immediately flows through the condensing cooler where its temperature is reduced by the cold gas leaving the expander and condensables are removed in the extractor. The gas then flows through the tempering exchanger A and to the expander. After the pressure is reduced in the expander, the cold gas flows through the condensing cooler to the compressor which recompresses the gas as need be to line pressure. Depending upon the relation of well pressure to line pressure, auxiliary power may be required, or, alternatively, power may be generated. The gas conditions shown on the diagram are typical.

The combination of exchanger A and bypass valve permits control of the gas temperature going to the expander, and therefore its outlet temperature.

Chapter 22

Compression Refrigeration

What is Refrigeration

Refrigeration is the cooling of a space or a substance below environmental temperature. A generally acceptable lower limit for *refrigeration* is a temperature of approximately minus 200°F although there are some differences in opinion on this particular value. Below this, the process is considered cryogenics. See Chapter 23.

Only the compression refrigeration system and the use of expanders are considered here.

The compression system involves a thermodynamic cycle wherein a cooling medium, *refrigerant,* circulates through an evaporator, compressor, and condenser in a closed system. There is no physical contact between the refrigerant and the material being cooled.

The *direct evaporation* system differs in that the refrigerant is also the material cooled. This system is used in water vapor refrigeration and often for refrigerant or material storage at temperatures below ambient where pressures are much reduced. Examples of the latter are storage of liquid ammonia and storage of liquefied natural gas (methane).

In the latter two cases the condensed "refrigerant" is returned to storage. In the water vapor system, the vapor, compressed almost exclusively by steam-jet ejectors, may be wasted or saved, depending on the type of condenser used.

Scope of Discussion

This discussion is limited to the basic processes and compressors as applied industrially. It does not attempt to cover certain compressor types or applications as developed specifically for the air conditioning industry, although many of these latter designs and refrigerants have also been applied industrially. Compressors for the various carbon-chlorine-fluorine-refrigerants are quite special and are not discussed.

Units of Refrigeration

The unit of refrigeration in the United States is known as the Ton. It is historically developed from the heat required to melt one ton (2000 lb) of ice at 32°F to water at 32°F during 24 hours. Since the heat of fusion of water is approximately 144 Btu/lb, a US ton of refrigeration equals 288,000 Btu/24 hr, or 12,000 Btu/hr, or 200 Btu/min.

In England, the ton is also used but the standard is different. The English ton equals 237.6 Btu/min or 1.188 US tons.

In Europe, the frigorie is used. This is 1000 gr-cal. One US ton equals 50.43 frigories/min.

The ton and the frigorie are quantities of heat, the value of which does not change whatever the operating conditions. On the other hand, the *standard ton* as a method of rating industrial compressors includes not only the basic heat quantity but standardized operating conditions as well. In the United States, this is evaporating at 5°F saturation pressure and condensing at 86°F saturation pressure. A compressor rated in standard tons would give quite different tonnage capacities at any other conditions. This method is seldom encountered in industrial applications. In England the specific conditions are respectively, 23°F and 59°F saturated pressures.

Applications

Refrigeration is an extremely broad subject involving everyday living as well as a multitude of manufacturing and allied processes. The following brief outline includes many of the principal applications. The first two items under the first category are especially broad.

1. Industrial, refining and chemical.
   Controlling vapor pressure of volatile constitutents during distillation, separation or processing.
   Shifting solubility relationships to permit segregation and removal of such undesired constituents as asphalt or wax in lubricating oils.
   Production of selective chemical reactions.

2. Food
   Manufacture
   Freezing
   Preservation
   Distribution

3. Air conditioning
   Comfort
   Industrial

4. Medicine and drugs
   Manufacture
   Preservation

5. Enviromental testing chambers
6. Cold treatment of metals
7. Construction
   Dams
   Excavations

Refrigerants

There are many refrigerants in industrial use. Selection depends principally on physical characteristics and suitability to the particular evaporation and condensing conditions involved. There are some cases, particularly in refinery applications, where on-the-job availability of a refrigerant may dictate its use. Safety is also at times a criterion.

The physical characteristics or properties that are important include:

1. Pressure at evaporating temperature,
2. Pressure at condensing temperature,
3. Total heat of gas at evaporating conditions,
4. Heat of liquid at the liquid control valve, and,
5. Specific gas volume at evaporation temperature and pressure.

Consider a basic compression refrigeration cycle using ammonia. See Fig. 22-A. The refrigerated material is circulated through a coil immersed in liquid refrigerant. The material in the coil provides the heat to boil

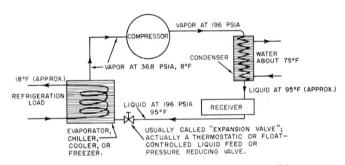

Fig. 22-A. Diagram of basic compression refrigeration cycle using ammonia as the refrigerant.

(evaporate) the refrigerant. The resultant vapor is drawn off by the compressor as fast as it is developed. The evaporator liquid level is properly maintained by the liquid feed valve. The compressor increases the pressure of the vapor until it condenses (liquefies) when cooled by some medium, usually water. The liquid refrigerant from the condenser is stored in the receiver, ready for recirculation. This system is really a heat pump, receiving heat at a low level and discharging it at a higher level.

The desired outlet temperature of the refrigerated material sets the refrigerant evaporating pressure and temperature. The latter will be approximately 10°F lower than the former in most industrial designs. The condenser water temperature obviously determines the refrigerant condensing temperature and its pressure. The differential between water at inlet and the liquid refrigerant out will approach 20°F. These temperature differences are approximate and are influenced by equipment design and other factors.

The operating pressures, both evaporating and condensing (items 1 and 2), may influence the type of compressor used. The condensing pressure will determine the structural strength of the high-pressure side, but the *settling-out* pressure will usually determine the required strength of the evaporating side. This is the pressure at which the entire system balances out when an emergency shutdown occurs and the various items cannot be valved off or isolated.

The difference between the total heat of the gas at evaporating conditions (item 3) and the heat of the liquid at the liquid control valve (item 4) determines the refrigerating effect per pound of refrigerant evaporated and the pounds to be circulated to obtain the desired tonnage of cooling. The latter, when joined with the specific gas volume at evaporation temperature and pressure (item 5), determines the inlet volume to the compressor. Further, a combination of the inlet pressure, the ratio of compression, and the total inlet volume determines bhp.

The performance of refrigerants using these criteria varies considerably. Fig. 22-B shows data about the more generally used industrial refrigerant at theoretical evaporating and condensing refrigerant temperatures of 5° and 86°F, respectively. These conditions are in an excellent range for certain refrigerants — however, the table must be considered as very approximate and not applicable to other conditions in the same degree. The effect of compressibility has been neglected.

Refrigerant	Ammonia	n-Butane	Ethane	Refrigerant 11	Refrigerant 12	Propane	Propylene
Specific Gravity at 60°F & 14.696 psiA	0.594	2.071	1.047	4.78	4.27	1.547	1.453
Evaporating Pressure-psiA (p_1)	34.27	8.25	237.0	2.93	26.48	41.68	52.9
Condensing Pressure-psiA (p_2)	169.2	41.7	679.4	18.28	108.0	156.2	189.7
Compression Ratio	4.93	5.50	2.86	6.25	4.09	3.75	3.58
Total Heat of Vapor-Btu/lb at p_1	613.3	172.3	404.2	92.88	77.81	378.6	468.8
Heat of Liquid-Btu/lb at p_2	138.9	48.4	340.0	25.34	27.77	255.6	344.0
Refrigeration Effect-Btu/lb	474.4	123.9	64.2	67.54	50.04	123.0	124.8
Lb/min/ton	0.422	1.615	3.11	2.96	4.00	1.627	1.603
Cu ft/lb at Evaporating Condition	8.150	10.03	0.53	12.27	1.458	2.515	2.070
Compressor Inlet cfm/ton	3.44	16.2	1.66	36.3	5.82	4.09	3.32
bhp/ton	1.172	1.193	2.35	1.111	1.230	1.257	1.262

Fig. 22-B. Comparative operating conditions and performance of various refrigerants at conditions of 5°F saturated evaporation and 86°F saturated condensation.

The wide variation in operating pressures should be noted. Ammonia is about average, with Refrigerant 11 very low and ethane quite high.

Not all refrigerants are listed in the table. Ethylene, methane, and water cannot well be used at the operating temperatures selected. Ethane, although shown, is condensing so close to its critical pressure that its characteristics are distorted. It would normally be used in a cascade system (described later) where it would be condensed by another refrigerant at a lower pressure. Two others formerly quite common, carbon dioxide and sulphur dioxide, are infrequently used. The bhp/ton is the probable power required based upon the efficiencies of a 500 hp reciprocating compressor.

In an actual cycle, pressures, volumes, and bhp required would vary somewhat due to such factors as inlet superheat, presence of noncondensables, and pipeline pressure loss.

Vapor pressure versus temperature data are of value in refrigerant selection. Page 34-166 presents this information for principal refrigerants. It includes some gases involved in cryogenic work.

Determining Refrigerating Effect and Inlet Volume

Refrigerating effect per lb of refrigerant evaporated is the difference between the total heat of the vapor at the evaporator exit conditions and the heat of the liquid ahead of the expansion valve.

With the simple system of Fig. 22-A, which has a broad usage, the values with ammonia as the refrigerant are.

Total heat of saturated gas at 8°F (Btu/lb).................	614.3
Heat of liquid at 95°F (Btu/lb)...........................	149.3
Net refrigerating effect (Btu/lb).........................	465.0

One ton/day = 200 Btu/min

$$Lb/min \text{ of refrigerant to be evaporated}/ton = \frac{200}{465.0} = 0.430$$

To obtain the inlet cfm to be handled by the compressor for 100 tons/day:

Cu ft/lb at 8°F saturated = 7.63

Compressor inlet cfm/100 tons = 100 × 0.430 × 7.63 = 328

There should be some allowance for piping pressure losses and superheating of the gas as it travels to the compressor.

Cycle Modifications

There are many modifications that may be made to the basic cycle to accomplish specific objectives, two of which stand out particularly.

1. Reduction in power; and,
2. Use of refrigerants in series (cascade) to make use of the properties of some refrigerants that otherwise might not be suitable. This is found primarily in the lower-temperature ranges.

The first group requires multiple staging, either by the use of different machines or by multistaging within a single unit. The second group requires separate compressing compartments for each refrigerant.

The first group is often applied to two stage units and more frequently to ammonia refrigerant than to others.

Among common cycle variations may be;
1. Water intercooling;
2. Liquid intercooling;
3. Liquid precooling;
4. Liquid precooling combined with liquid intercooling; and,
5. Use of a booster.

Water Intercooling

The effect of two staging with intercooling has been discussed on page 3-17. Water intercooling is common when compressing many gases, but is less frequently applied to refrigeration systems, because the gas temperature at inlet is usually well below ambient and the discharge gas temperature is correspondingly reduced. The temperature reduction possible with water intercooling is therefore less than normal and the power saving is not as great. For example, on a 100 psiG air compressor, two staging with a water intercooler will normally save about 15% in power over single stage. On the conditions of the typical ammonia cycle of Fig. 22-A, two staging with 80°F water intercooling will reduce power only about 3%.

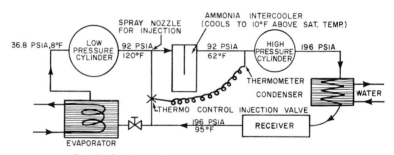

Fig. 22-C. Flow diagram of a two-stage compression refrigeration system using liquid ammonia intercooling.

Liquid Intercooling

Interstage temperatures are sometimes reduced by injecting controlled amounts of the liquid refrigerant ahead of the second stage. Fig. 22-C shows the diagrammatic arrangement and typical conditions for ammonia.

As with water intercooling, the power saving is rather small — for the conditions shown being about 3%.

Liquid Precooling

Where the liquid lines are short and subcooled liquid can be kept cold on its way to the evaporator, use of liquid precooling can save power. Fig. 22-D shows the layout, the liquid being cooled to about 5°F above the interstage saturation temperature. The vapor required to precool the liquid is handled by the high-pressure stage only. Less vapor is required in the low pressure stage to produce the required evaporator refrigeration and power is lowered. At the typical ammonia conditions shown, a saving of about 4% may be expected.

With various types of *intercooling only,* lower evaporator temperatures tend to reduce power saving. With *liquid precooling,* the saving will tend to increase at lower evaporating temperatures.

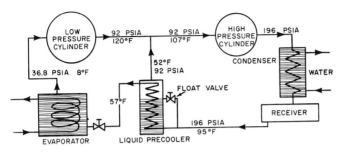

Fig. 22-D. Diagram of a two-stage compression refrigeration system using a liquid precooler.

Liquid Intercooling and Liquid Precooling

When operating conditions warrant the use of liquid precooling, it is usually practical to include liquid injection for intercooling. Equipment cost will not increase materially. This results in a power saving over single stage of about 6% for the selected typical ammonia cycle, the saving being greater as the evaporating temperature drops.

Boosters

Many installations have a large base refrigeration load at one temperature and a smaller load at a considerably lower level. It is most economical to go to two or even three stages of compression in such cases, the low temperature service being one stage discharging into the gas stream going to the main compressors, which may themselves be multistage. Liquid intercooling and precooling may also be incorporated into this cycle. Fig. 22-E diagrams a simple ammonia arrangement.

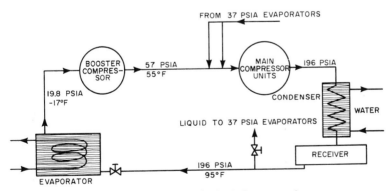

Fig. 22-E. Diagram of the basic booster cycle.

Cascade Refrigeration

Cascade refrigeration uses several refrigerants in series to obtain the desired final low temperature. One such cycle, involving temperatures considered in cryogenics, is shown in Fig. 22-F. In this case, natural gas is being liquefied. The refrigeration process includes cooling the gas, first by a propane system, then by an ethylene system, and finally (through self-refrigeration) by methane. The ethylene is condensed by the propane system. The propane is condensed with water.

Note that in this cycle the Joule-Thomson effect of cooling by throttling is also used at the final methane (natural gas) pressure reduction.

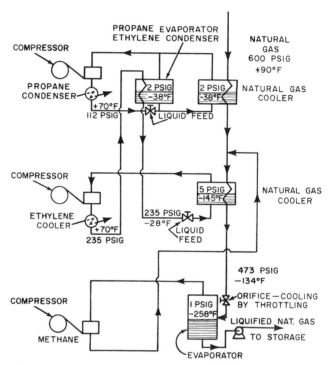

Fig. 22-F. Cascade system for natural gas liquefaction, using two refrigerants in addition to the methane in the natural gas.

Compressor Types

Reciprocating, helical-lobe, and centrifugal compressors predominate in all the above cycles, although the rotary vane-type is frequently used as a booster.

Refrigerants offer no major problems when handled in compressors. They are clean and pure. Care must be taken with most compressor types to prevent carry-over of liquid from the evaporator.

With some compressors, the gas from a low-temperature system may require heating above the evaporator exit temperature to permit use of lubricated units or to reduce the need for special materials. This heat may often be obtained regeneratively from the liquid going to the evaporator, the liquid being cooled in turn. Lubricated reciprocators are available down to about minus 75°F inlet gas temperature, NL-type reciprocators to minus 250°F, centrifugals to minus 300°F, and helical-lobe rotaries to approximately minus 50°F.

Water Vapor Refrigeration

Where steam is available and water is economically obtained, water vapor refrigeration provides the simplest means of economically providing cold water for comfort cooling, manufacturing processes, and industrial

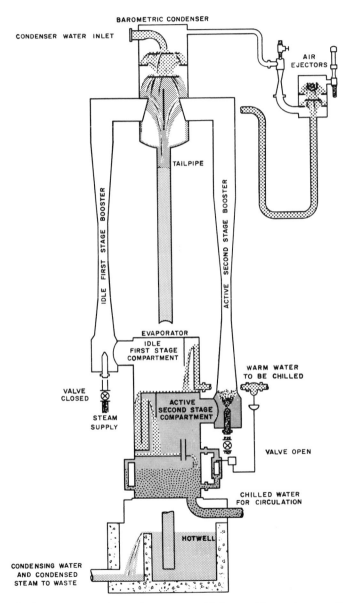

Fig. 22-G. Water vapor refrigeration system with barometric condenser. This has two evaporating (chilling) compartments, each with its own ejector for improved control.

usage. Its principal drawback is the relatively high water consumption. This can be reduced materially through the use of a cooling tower.

Water vapor refrigeration utilizes steam-jet ejectors for vapor compression and can be designed to provide chilled water at any desired temperature to a minimum of 35°F. This system is particularly suitable where:

1. Continuous operation is required;
2. Low maintenance and high availability are desired;
3. Noise and vibration must be avoided;
4. Safety is a paramount consideration;
5. Overload capacity is desirable;
6. Part load economy is needed;
7. First cost must be a minimum; and,
8. Outdoor installation is an advantage.

Fig. 22-H.   Three 850-ton coolers air condition a University Medical Center.

Individual systems are available for from 30 to 1200 tons refrigeration. In addition to commercial building cooling, water vapor refrigeration is used in chemical plants, distilleries, rubber mills, hospitals, food processing plants, gas plants, refineries, and aboard ship.

This system contains no moving parts and uses the water being cooled as the refrigerant. Approximately 1000 Btu of cooling effect are available for each lb of water evaporated and compressed by the ejector to the condenser pressure. Thus almost five tons of refrigeration are available for each lb/min boiled off. This heat removal cools the water flowing into the chamber.

Fig. 22-G shows this system in its basic form using a barometric condenser. Water to be cooled flows over a weir at a rate determined by the usage from the water reservoir below. The ejector maintains the vacuum required to produce the desired temperature and compresses the vapor evaporated, plus air and other noncondensables brought in by the water or leaking into the system. The main or booster ejector or ejectors discharge into a condenser that may be either the barometric or surface type. Small supplementary ejectors serve to remove noncondensables from the main condenser.

Fig. 22-H shows an installation of three 850-ton water coolers with surface condensers for air conditioning of a health center in a southern university.

Chapter 23

Cyrogenics

Caption Index

Introduction

Cryogenics is the science of very low temperatures. Opinions vary as to where refrigeration ends and cryogenics begins; some authorities say minus 150°F (−101°C) and others minus 200°F (−129°C).

Cryogenics is concerned with all problems in this area including construction materials, which may have highly different characteristics when very cold; superior insulation methods and materials required; gas compression and expansion equipment; processes; product storage and transport; and finally, use of the product.

Basically, cryogenics involves liquefaction and use of various gases that have very low condensing temperatures. These can be liquefied only when cooled to or below their critical temperature, regardless of the pressure involved. Cryogenic gases all have low critical temperatures, and since they are normally stored as liquids at or close to atmospheric pressure, temperatures lower than critical are usually involved.

The following shows pertinent information about the more prominent cryogenic gases.

Gas	Critical Temperature		Boiling Point at 14.696 PSIA (1.0333 Kg/sq cm)	
	°F	°C	°F	°C
Methane	−116	−82	−259	−156
Oxygen	−182	−119	−297	−183
Argon	−188	−122	−303	−186
Fluorine	−201	−129	−307	−188
Air	−221	−140	−318	−195
Nitrogen	−233	−147	−320	−196
Neon	−380	−229	−411	−246
Hydrogen	−400	−240	−423	−253
Helium	−450	−268	−451	−269

Applications

Use of these liquefied and very cold gases is burgeoning and any tabulation will soon be incomplete. The following attempts to show the principal uses as well as areas where cryogenics may have greater application in the future.

Liquefaction

The most common gases commercially liquefied are:

Air	Hydrogen	Fluorine
Oxygen	Helium	Argon
Nitrogen	Natural Gas (Methane)	Neon

In many cases, these are liquefied to purify and/or to simplify storage and transportation.

Separation

Mixed gases are often liquefied to permit separation into their components. Air is the most important of these gases, accounting for 80 percent or better of the present total activity in cryogenics. Dry air at sea level has the following closely accurate composition. (Data from different sources vary slightly.)

	By Volume—%	By Weight—%
Nitrogen	78.03	75.47
Oxygen	20.99	23.19
Argon	0.94	1.30
Carbon dioxide	0.03	0.04
Hydrogen	0.01	Trace
Neon	Trace	Trace
Helium	Trace	Trace
Krypton	Trace	Trace
Xenon	Trace	Trace

Nitrogen and oxygen are the principal gases obtained from liquid air by fractional distillation, although some plants also produce argon, neon, krypton, and xenon.

General Uses of Cryogenic Gases and Liquids

By far the largest use of cryogenics is in the production of oxygen and nitrogen, the uses of which are expanding rapidly. The steel industry is a major user of oxygen.

Refrigeration at ultralow temperatures is a large user of cryogenic gases (usually in liquid form). Helium and nitrogen are prominent in this field, applications including:

Research in many areas
Missile fuel
Cryobiology
Atomic studies
Cold working of metals
Construction (freezing of ground)
Space age studies
Electronics (especially computers)
Purification of other gases
Production of superhigh vacuums
Magnetohydrodynamics (electric power generation)

Compressor Equipment Used

In all of these applications, compressor equipment is used. It is the basic tool; air and gas technology, the basic text.

Compressors are principally reciprocating or centrifugal, although axial-flow dynamic or the helical-lobe units may be selected when suitable. The reciprocating or centrifugal expander is a necessary part of many cryogenic processes.

Processes

There are many processes and variations of processes depending upon the raw material supplied and the end product desired.

Use of Expanders Versus Throttling

Expanders and their operation are discussed in Chapter 21 and the Joule-Thomson Effect (cooling of gas by throttling) is discussed in Chapter 5, page 5-6.

Both methods are used to cool gases to very low temperatures; the expander method is the more effective. The reason for this is illustrated by a theoretical comparison on a temperature — entropy chart. Fig. 23-A is based on nitrogen starting at 3000 psiA, minus 10°F and 90 Btu/lb at Point A. Pressure reduction is to 100 psiA.

Joule-Thomson throttling takes place at constant enthalpy, consequently the line AD represents the action and point D the terminal point. The heat content does not change but the temperature falls from minus 10° to minus 90°F, a drop of 80°F.

In an expander, expansion is theoretically at constant entropy and would proceed from point A to C-1 where the temperature at 100 psiA would be minus 283°F. However, losses reduce the heat drop somewhat. An efficiency of 80 percent is frequently obtainable and on this basis the drop in enthalpy will be to point C-2, 80 percent of the enthalpy drop between A and C-1. This gives a final temperature of minus 262°F, a drop of 252°F versus only 80°F by throttling.

Not all gases would show similar results. For example, hydrogen and helium have *temperature-entropy* curves that slope upward, except at very low temperatures, and their Joule-Thomson cycle temperatures would actually rise under the conditions of the above example. See page 5-6. Efficient cooling by throttling of these gases is possible therefore, only when they are subcooled well below their inversion temperature. (Note that Fig. 5-B is a temperature-*pressure* diagram not temperature-entropy).

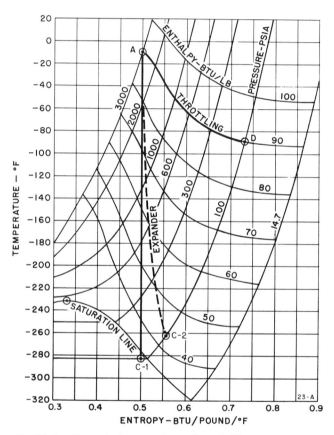

Fig. 23-A. Theoretical comparison of Joule-Thomson cooling effect with nitrogen versus use of a mechanical expander.

Liquefaction of Natural Gas

A typical cascade refrigeration process for the liquefaction of natural gas (methane) has been presented in Fig. 22-F, page 22-8. The expansion process may be practical here for small flows, but it requires more power per pound of gas liquefied. Natural gas is liquefied principally for storage and transportation. The use of this process is growing rapidly throughout the world.

Liquefaction and Separation of Air

Although large air separation plants may use a form of cascade refrigeration for cooling, the expansion process is more commonly used. Fig. 23-B is a much simplified cycle of such a plant designed to produce gaseous oxygen as the primary product. Actual cycles usually are considerably more sophisticated. There are four definite steps.

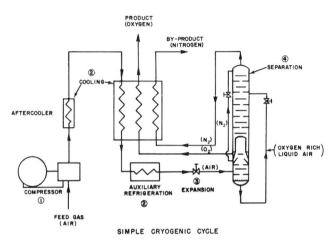

SIMPLE CRYOGENIC CYCLE

Fig. 23-B. Simple cryogenic cycle for air separation.

1. *Compression.* Air is compressed to pressures varying from about 75 to 3000 psiG. This uses a conventional compressor.

2. *Cooling.* The air is cooled to within 10 to 20° of water temperature in an aftercooler. It is cooled further with cold product gases (oxygen and nitrogen) and with auxiliary refrigeration. Contaminants, such as water and carbon dioxide, that would freeze and clog valves, heat exchangers or expanders must be removed at this point.

Large cryogenic plants use regenerators. Incoming gas (or air) is passed through one of two beds of cold packing on which moisture and carbon dioxide is frozen out and the temperature of the incoming gas is reduced at the same time. At fixed time intervals, valves are automatically switched and the cold waste gas (such as nitrogen in an oxygen plant) is passed through the "hot" bed, carrying away the water (ice) and carbon dioxide to atmosphere. At the same time, packing is cooled so the beds can be alternated again and the cycle repeated to continuously cool and remove contaminants from the incoming gas.

Smaller plants, especially in high-pressure cycles, pass the incoming gas (air) through caustic scrubbers (usually between the second and third stages of a reciprocating compressor) to remove carbon dioxide and then through silica gel or another desiccant to remove water. Oil introduced by compressor lubrication (if any) is also removed here. Then the gas (air) is cooled in a heat exchanger by the cold waste gas (nitrogen) and the cold product gas (oxygen) which are warmed to within a few degrees of the incoming air.

3. *Expansion.* Further cooling is accomplished by throttling the gas through a reducing valve, in which process the Joule-Thomson effect (while neither adding nor taking away heat) lowers the temperature. Greater decrease in temperature can be obtained by using an expansion engine or turbine to remove work or heat from all or part of the gas at the same time the pressure is reduced. Efficiency of the turbine or engine is important, not because of useful work obtained, but because the greater the expander efficiency, the greater the amount of heat removed. In this application, the expander is a refrigeration device and the mechanical work developed is normally wasted.

4. *Separation.* As a result of this cooling, air is liquefied and sent to a distillation column, where the higher boiling point constituent (oxygen) collects at the bottom as a liquid and the lower boiling point constituent (nitrogen) leaves from the top of the column as a gas.

In an air separation plant this is normally done in two steps. See Fig. 23-C. Where 90 to 95 percent oxygen purity is acceptable, one step

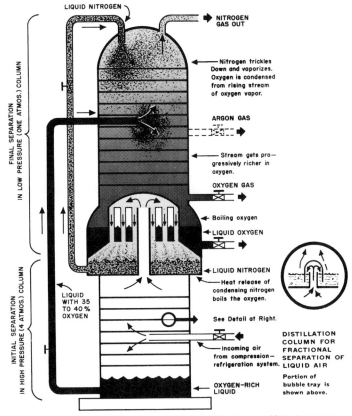

Courtesy of Electric Machinery Mfg. Company.

Fig. 23-C. Typical distillation column for fractional separation of liquid air. Portion of bubble tray shown in the insert circle.

may be sufficient. The partially liquefied air enters the lower or high-pressure column at a pressure of 70 to 85 psiG and a temperature of minus 276° to minus 285°. The rising nitrogen vapors are condensed by contact with the bottom of the upper or low-pressure column that contains liquid oxygen at a pressure of 2 to 5 psiG and a temperature of approximately minus 300°F. The condensed nitrogen is expanded into the top of the low-pressure column to aid in final separation. The oxygen-rich liquid from the bottom of the high-pressure column is introduced into the low-pressure column where remaining nitrogen boils off and liquid oxygen is removed from the bottom of the low-pressure (upper) column at 99.5 percent purity. The impurities are largely xenon, krypton, and argon. In a gaseous oxygen plant, this liquid oxygen is warmed and gasified in exchangers, cooling incoming air.

Miscellaneous Notes

Temperature Conversion Table

See page 34-167, for temperature conversion tables for the sub-zero temperatures encountered in cryogenic work.

Economic Factors

It takes approximately 24 hours to get an air plant (for example) cooled down and into production. After that, continuity of operation is extremely vital. Contracts for output must be met and even a short shutdown for machinery repair may mean a much longer time to get gas purity reestablished. There must be a minimum of compressor and expander down time. Reliability must be a major consideration in selection. An increase in on-stream time of 1 percent (or even ½ percent) is worth a large sum in product value, especially when compared to compressor first cost.

Compressor efficiency is also an important factor since power cost is a large proportion of product cost.

Oxygen Compressors

Oxygen may be handled from the air plant as a liquid or as a gas. The delivery pressure is usually too low for distribution and it must be pumped or compressed for this purpose. Gaseous oxygen has been handled successfully in special nonlubricated reciprocating compressors and in centrifugal units. Special precautions to ship a grease-free unit are required in both cases. See Chapter 14 for a typical degreasing procedure used following manufacture.

Chapter 24

Natural Gas Compression

Introduction

It is probable that compression of natural gas requires more power than is used for handling any other gas except air. Compressors are required in most fields of natural gas utilization and processing. Among these are:

Gas lift

Gas gathering

Natural gasoline and LPG recovery

Helium recovery

Transmission

Distribution

Repressuring (injection)

Gas condensate recovery

Gas storage

Liquefaction for transport

Petrochemical manufacture

What Is Natural Gas

Natural gas is a mixture of many gases, most of which are usually hydrocarbons. The composition is extremely variable and no two areas have the same mixture. Natural gases usually have methane as their principal constituent with ethane as the hydrocarbon next most prominent. Many contain nitrogen and/or carbon dioxide in appreciable to large amounts.

Location	Methane	Ethane	Higher HC	Nitrogen	CO_2	Other
Alaska	98.9	0.2	——	0.7	0.1	0.1
California	82.4	7.7	8.6	0.5	0.8	——
Colorado	68.0	7.2	5.9	18.2	0.1	0.6
Kansas	78.1	6.1	5.0	10.0	0.2	0.6
Montana	79.9	8.5	4.6	4.5	2.3	0.2
New Mexico	72.9	11.0	12.1	3.5	0.2	0.3
Ohio	86.8	5.9	3.3	3.6	0.2	0.2
Oklahoma	85.0	6.7	6.4	1.5	0.2	0.2
Pennsylvania	97.1	2.0	0.1	0.5	0.1	0.2
Texas	81.6	6.5	3.8	7.7	0.1	0.3
Texas	91.8	4.5	1.8	0.5	1.3	0.1
Utah	42.0	8.0	7.5	15.2	25.8	1.5
West Virginia	75.3	14.2	9.3	0.8	0.2	0.2
Wyoming	86.2	7.8	4.1	0.3	1.5	0.1
Australia	95.6	0.2	1.4	0.8	2.0	——
Canada	88.5	2.5	2.6	6.2	0.2	——
Venezuela	73.7	13.8	10.3	——	2.2	——
Transmission Line						
Linden, N. J.	94.5	3.3	1.2	0.3	0.7	——

Fig. 24-A. Typical composition of natural gases from various sources.

Fig. 24-A illustrates variations to be found in the composition of natural gas in a random selection of producing areas. The examples are for one well only and are not to be considered representative of the entire area cataloged. All U. S. well-head analyses are from Bureau of Mines Circular 8221 (1964).

The specific gravity of natural gas as produced varies from 0.55 referred to air at 60°F and 14.696 psiA to 1.00 or, at times, higher. The gravity, of course, depends on the quantity of the heavier components as compared with the basic gas, methane. Since many heavier compounds and impurities are removed for other purposes before the gas is used as a fuel or a chemical raw material, gas at the final market is apt to run higher in methane than as found at the well-head.

There are *wet* and *dry* natural gases based on their content of condensable components heavier than ethane. One classification follows. *Wet* gases contain more than 0.3 to 0.4 gallon of condensables per 1000 standard cubic feet of gas. *Lean* gases contain between 0.1 and 0.3 gallon per 1000 standard cubic feet, while *dry* gases contain less than 0.1 gallon per 1000 standard cubic feet. This may not be acceptable in all areas and local usage will often set the standard. Condensable liquids are the LPG (liquefied petroleum gases) propane and butane, and natural gasoline consisting of the pentanes and heavier components. Wet gases are more commonly associated with oil production.

The ratio of specific heats will vary with composition, averaging 1.26 to 1.30 for a dry gas and near 1.15 for a wet gas.

Natural gas is *sweet* or *sour* depending upon the sulphur content, chiefly found as H_2S. Sour gas must be made sweet or substantially sulphur-free before it may be marketed for most uses. The allowable sulphur content is often regulated by state laws. Sour gases are apt to be corrosive, particularly when water and oxygen are present. Another potentially corrosive agent found in many natural gases is CO_2 which may be removed before marketing. Most modern treatment systems eliminate both H_2S and CO_2 in a single process.

Gas Lift

This is an artificial "air lift" type of system for bringing oil to the surface when it does not flow by natural underground pressure. Widely used today where natural gas is available for providing the lifting power, it has advantages over other means of pumping when very large volumes are to be handled. It should be pointed out the gas lift (see Chapter 31) may be less economical from a power point of view than the normally used beam pump. If the well must be self-sufficient and a closed system is required, there must be sufficient gas associated with the oil to permit its recovery and recompression to pump more oil.

Gas Gathering

Compressors are often required to gather gas from a well or field of wells and deliver it to a transmission line or point of use. Gas from oil wells (after lease separation) is at a relatively low pressure (say 20 to 60 psiG) while gas wells have a considerably higher well-head pressure. Original gas well flowing pressures vary up to 10,000 psiG but fall as the field is depleted. Compression will eventually be required. Compressors for gas gathering are often required to have cylinders good for 1500 psiG discharge to assure delivery into present or future transmission lines.

Gasoline and LPG Recovery

Pipeline gas is normally purchased on a specification calling for a maximum hydrocarbon dew point at the delivery pressure that will be below the expected minimum winter temperature in the pipeline. This prevents condensation of hydrocarbons during transmission. The seller therefore installs extraction equipment to remove these LPG and natural gasoline constituents. This is advantageous to the seller since their value as liquids is much greater than as gas.

Extraction processes include (1) absorption in oil and subsequent separation, (2) condensation by refrigeration, and (3) a combination of these two. Compressors usually are required for refrigeration and may or may not be needed to compress the natural gas ahead of the extraction plant. This will depend upon the incoming pressure.

Many large absorption plants now reduce the pressure of the rich oil through liquid turbines to recover power otherwise wasted by throttling the oil between the absorber and oil rectification section of the plant. The oil turbines may drive liquid pumps or gas compressors.

Gas Transmission

Gas transmission by pipeline requires a tremendous compressor capacity and is the largest segment in the natural gas industry involving compressors. These units are set up in stations that may be spaced 100 miles apart, the size, operating conditions and spacing having been based on extensive economic studies. Most stations are gas engine powered using gas from the line, but electric motors and steam or gas turbines also are used. Jet aviation engines (gas turbines) have been adapted for driving dynamic compressors.

Compressors on this application are generally characterized by operation at low single stage compression ratios of approximately 1.1 to 1.5. This is true with both reciprocating and dynamic units, although higher ratios are available in both types when necessary. In transmission service, compressors restore the pressure lost by the friction of the flowing gas. The above ratios represent the most economical over-all conditions. Line pressures are usually in the range of 500 to 900 psiG, but are increasing.

Reciprocating compressors are extremely flexible in operation, particularly when the quantity and/or pressure of the gas being handled is subject to wide variations. The investment, attendance, and maintenance expense of the reciprocating machine is usually higher than for the dynamic compressor in this service, but its cost for fuel or power generally will be considerably less.

The centrifugal compressor is particularly adaptable to steady output conditions as found on long-distance, large-volume, high-pressure lines. It is also adaptable for growth since it can start with a high ratio — relatively low volume impeller and as throughput increases change to a low ratio — high volume impeller with no change in power.

Local Distribution

Natural gas is usually delivered to the local marketing and distribution systems at relatively high pressure and auxiliary compressors for distribution are rather seldom required.

Repressuring or Injection

Repressuring is associated with the production of oil. It involves separating the gas from the oil which flows from the well, then compressing the gas to force it back into the underground reservoir. This is done through injection wells some distance from the producing wells in order to maintain reservoir pressure and obtain a more complete recovery of the oil from the producing formation.

Both reciprocating and dynamic units are used in this service, some plants being very large. Fig. 9-N, page 9-14, shows ten large centrifugal units in series for repressuring in a Venezuelan gas field.

Gas Condensate Recovery

Gas condensate recovery (cycling or recycling) is a process involved in the production of gas-condensate from certain natural gas wells. These wells tap a reservoir in which the hydrocarbons are in a gaseous state but in which, if the pressure is allowed to fall to a certain point, a phenomenon known as retrograde condensation will take place. The result is a loss of recoverable condensate. The minimum pressure is related to the dew point of the gases. This phenomenon is opposite to the normally expected effect of a pressure reduction on a vapor mixture. In a cycling operation, the high-pressure gas is withdrawn from the formation through the producing wells and is processed to remove the condensable fraction. The residue is compressed and forced back into the reservoir through other wells to maintain the pressure. Sometimes an additional source of gas must be used to supplement the residue, taking the place of the condensate removed.

Gas Storage

Most of the natural gas produced in the United States comes from the southwestern area — principally Texas, Louisiana, Oklahoma, New Mexico, and Kansas. New fields are being discovered frequently. These are often far — maybe 1000 miles — from many major markets. Much of the load in these markets is space heating, which has a seasonal demand far above the average. Transmission lines are at times unable to provide for this demand without cutting off some industrial load. Therefore, better rates are available to those distributing companies that can reduce the winter peaks and distribute their gas purchases more evenly through the year.

This has led to gas storage usually in underground formations, mostly depleted oil or gas fields, or aquifers (gas-tight dome-shaped formations from which the contained water may be forced). Some surface or buried high-pressure tank storage is used, but this is minor because of economic factors. Underground storage is by far the less expensive. Storage is selected to be relatively close to the market, say within 100 miles or so. There are about 300 of these storage areas now in operation, situated in about 25 continental states. Gas is normally put into storage during April through October and removed November through March. Storage may be developed and operated by either the pipeline company, the distribution group, or jointly.

Compressors are required, designed for two functions: first, to compress the gas into the storage where the pressure may be upwards of 2500 psiG; and second, to take it out of storage and provide the pressure (if an increase is necessary) to deliver it to market.

Methane also can be stored as a liquid. This method is increasing in use. Both above-ground tanks and covered pits in frozen earth are being used. The liquid is kept cold by auto-refrigeration, the evaporated methane being compressed and recondensed for return to storage.

Surface storage of natural gas in low-pressure holders is still used in some areas by local distributing companies. LPG gases also are stored as liquids in pressure tanks, mixed with air to provide the proper Btu content, and compressed for local distribution when needed. These methods are for shaving short-term peaks.

Liquefaction for Transport

A great deal of natural gas is produced or available in world areas where markets are extremely limited. There are many good markets that would be happy to have natural gas but have none available locally. This has led to construction of water transport varying from river barges to ocean vessels to carry liquid natural gas — actually liquid methane. Liquefied methane was first shipped to England from the United States in 1959 and, as more vessels have been built, its use to supplement manufactured gas in a number of locations has grown, principally in Europe.

Fig. 22-F, page 22-8 illustrates one process for the liquefaction of methane and the location of the compressors in the system.

Petrochemicals

Natural gas is used widely as a raw material in manufacturing many petrochemicals. Compressors play a large part in these processes.

Compressor Types

All types of compressors are used in the natural gas industry, but the reciprocating and dynamic units predominate. The gas engine and gas turbine frequently are prime movers because of the availability of the fuel.

There are a few special designs involved in handling natural gas or its derivatives. One case is the noncooled reciprocating cylinder design mentioned on page 6-22. This permits better valving and improved efficiency for the low compression ratios involved. Cylinder cooling would be of little advantage. The cylinders also include special capacity-control designs to permit utilizing the full engine power (100 percent load factor) over a wide range of operating conditions. Another special unit is the pipeline centrifugal illustrated in Fig. 9-K, page 9-11.

Chapter 25

Control Systems

Introduction

Compression machinery, regardless of type or driver, requires protection and "operation." These normally have been provided by an operator, who endeavors to give each unit the necessary attention. Location of compressors in remote areas, installation of related "package plants" involving compressors, and growing use of unattended compression stations have brought demands for control systems providing the highest degree of reliability and protection with reduced requirement for operator involvement. This has carried over into the field of compressed air and gas utilization.

Many large dynamic compressors handling air or other process gas, for example, must have controls that will respond almost instantly to a change in the process, either to regulate the compressor or to keep it out of surge. It is almost impossible for an operator to exercise the continuous attention required. Control systems can provide the necessary constant review of operating conditions — and act on them.

The following mentions only what may be classed as *simple* systems.

Definitions

The following definitions will clarify terminology *as used with control systems.*

A PROCESS may involve the functional operation of a compressor or its driver, the operation of an ejector or a pneumatic device, or it may involve a chemical or manufacturing process or a complete plant.

REGULATION fixes the amount, value, degree, or rate involved.

CONTROL exercises direction, guidance, and restraint. Control *includes* regulation. Within the compressor industry, *control* has long been synonymous with *regulation.* In control systems, control has the broader meaning.

Levels of Control Systems

The level of control utilized in industry varies from simple manual systems to highly complex systems under computer control that involve very little human initiation. In the control field, these levels of automation have become known as "levels of increasing sophistication."

Restricting materially the number of levels, the following categories could represent the range of process control.

1. Manual control;
2. Sequence control, routines from simple to complex;
3. Process variable measurement and regulation;
4. Decision-making control by logic action, decisions from simple to complex; and,
5. Optimizing control, adjustment of variables to achieve maximum efficiency.

Manual Control

Whether the application is simple or the manual operation of a fairly complex chemical process, manual control is dependent on the decisions of a human being. Based on the relative complexity of the task, a set of instructions may be available to the operator so that he can satisfactorily command the process, thus operating it safely.

Sequence Control

Sequence control utilizes automatic equipment to follow a prescribed sequence of operations, originally defined by an instruction sheet. This programmed sequence control has at its lower level the performance of a prescribed task (simple or complex sequence) *initiated* by a local operator. The next step is to command the sequence from a remote location with controls that actuate the sequence without assistance. Simple examples of this level of automation are (1) automatic start-up with sequencing of air compressors to maintain plant air pressure at a set pressure, and (2) automatic start-up of emergency electric power generators on decay of voltage caused by utility outage.

Process Variable Measurement and Regulation

A level termed "the controlled process" is achieved by measuring and regulating process variables. The process is examined and regulated because measurements are being taken and a control system is adjusting operation. At the measurement level, information is available so that an operator can, based on his best judgment, make adjustments to obtain better performance. As added assistance to the operator, out-of-limits variables can be signaled by warning lights, a bell, or horn. Another aid in improving the over-all process performance is to record the measurements of specific variables. The operator here supplies the intelligence to utilize available data for improvement in operation. By incorporating certain additional control components, correction of the wandering variable is taken from the operator.

Decision-Making Control By Logic Action

Often it is valuable for the process control to make decisions based on its knowledge of the process being controlled. Systems can be provided to take any number of selective actions based on happenings in the process. In its simplest form, this logic action is a "yes-no" decision on product quality. In complex material-handling systems, the logic action might identify, separate, package, and prepare products from the line for shipment.

An example of a logic decision system applied to a prime mover is one used in gas engine compressor pipeline stations. The logic circuit provides the method to maintain station discharge pressures by starting and stopping compressors. The logic circuit selects a specific unit to be started or stopped based on certain factors; (1) actual unit availability (presently operating, shutdown and available, or shutdown and unavailable) (2) operating hours on various units (selection based on minimum operating hours), etc.

Optimizing Control

Having achieved (1) automatic sequence for the process, (2) complete protection against abnormal conditions, and (3) a regulating control to measure and control process parameters, the ultimate in control would be to optimize process performance. The depth of this level of automation is probably the greatest of all others discussed. At this level, the system examines its own performance and adjusts parameters to improve performance and obtain a more perfect product. During operation there is a continual resetting of the control system to optimize primary parameters to maximum levels. This control senses the changes taking place in variables, anticipates the series of changes that will result, and adjusts the process variable(s) to optimize performance. Optimizing controls in their simplest form might maximize or minimize one parameter that is primary to the performance of the specific process. A truly optimum system when related to a complex process would be required to control a half dozen variables so that optimum system performance is achieved.

Summary

Each specific control system applied to a machine or to a process contains several of the levels of automation just discussed. The various subsystems of the over-all control can usually be categorized as specifically accomplishing certain functions contained within these five levels of automation. An understanding of the "levels of automation" provides a basic insight into the over-all purpose of all process control systems.

Elements of Control Systems

To present control systems in a somewhat different manner, the following elemental operations may be involved.

Sensing

Sensors are measuring devices that gauge the critical variables and transmit signals representing them to other control elements. They may use pneumatic, hydraulic, or electric transmission.

Monitoring

A monitor is a "warning or reminder." As such, monitors are actuated by the sensors to warn the operator if any abnormal operations or conditions occur. The action may be to sound an alarm, to light a warning light, or to actuate a protective or shutdown device.

A typical standard (and simple) monitoring panel for a 100 psiG motor driven plant air compressor will include sensors and monitors for the following operating items.

1. High frame lubricating oil temperature;
2. High intercooler outlet air temperature;
3. High final discharge air temperature;
4. High air discharge pressure;
5. High intercooler condensate separator level;
6. Excessively high frame lubricating oil temperature;
7. Excessively high intercooler air outlet temperature;
8. Excessively high air discharge temperature;
9. Excessively high air discharge pressure;
10. Excessively high intercooler condensate separator level;
11. Low frame lubricating oil pressure;
12. Low cylinder lubricating oil level;
13. Cylinder lubricator rotation stopped; and,
14. Excessive vibration.

In addition, this particular panel includes an hour meter with a range of 10,000 hours before repeating. This registers only when the unit is running and provides information that greatly facilitates sound maintenance practices.

Items (1) through (5) above are monitoring only. When any of these conditions occurs, a warning is given by an amber light and a horn. When any one of items (6) through (14) occurs, the monitor actuates a unit shutdown device and energizes a red light and horn.

Monitoring is available for on-site or off-limits (remote) observance and operation, or both.

Protecting

Protective devices take action to prevent damage to the process or equipment involved in the process whatever they may be. This usually entails an automatic shutdown. However, the extent of the action will depend upon the process being protected and the condition to be protected against.

A monitoring and protective panel (as typically outlined for a motor-driven compressor) will reduce attendance requirements, increase reliability and materially reduce over-all costs. A panel for a steam- or gas-engine-driven unit could vary considerably and would include additional monitoring and protective devices. The more complex the machinery or process involved, the more complete the protection provided.

Sequencing

Virtually any procedure can be carried out by control systems. This presently extends to start-up of a large steam-electric power station, using a computer for the "logic" element. Similar action is being used for compressors, engines, and process equipment. Fortunately the control system is much less complex.

Sequencing systems normally apply to machines in a single location, but they can control widely separated units. Controls for compressors of a 100 psiG air plant form a good example of a fairly simple sequencing system (see Fig. 25-A and Fig. 25-B). These show central point control systems for sequencing and monitoring two types of large plant systems. One is a centralized arrangement of three compressors that are started, loaded, and stopped by the control to match compressor output to plant demand. The other is a decentralized system with five widely separated units, up to several miles apart. In each case, these controls make it possible to provide plant air at the lowest cost.

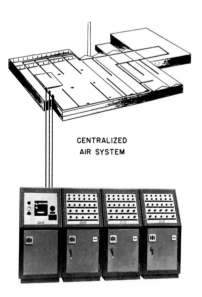

CENTRALIZED
AIR SYSTEM

Fig. 25-.A   Controls for an automated three-unit compressor plant, centrally located.

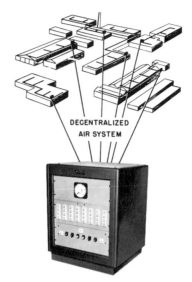

Fig. 25-B. Controls for a decentralized air system have six compressor locations.

Fig. 25-C. Two control systems serving a 4500-horsepower gas-engine compressor. One panel automatically measures demand and regulates the unit; the other starts and stops the compressor and protects it from abnormal conditions.

Fig. 25-C is a large gas engine installation with controls for starting, stopping, and regulation. Engine sequence control is available in several degrees of sophistication as illustrated in the table of Fig. 25-D. Not tabulated but included, are certain safety shutdown features. Others are op-

AUTOMATIC STARTING SEQUENCE	AUTOMATIC OPERATING CONTROLS	AUTOMATIC SHUTDOWN SEQUENCE
● Starting Permissive Check ● Starting & Control Air Supply Check ● Safety Check for All Monitors ● Unit Valve Position Check ● Start Pre-lube Pumps ● Crank Engine & Monitor Speed ● Purge Cylinders ● Apply Ignition ● Ignition Ungrounded Check ● Open Fuel Valve ● Starting Time Check	● Warm Up Check (oil & water temp) ● Start Warm-Up Timer ● Position Unit Valves ● Complete Warm Up Timing ● Governor on Automatic ● Load Engine ● Regulate Engine Speed and Pockets to hold the selected process variable within pre-set limits.	● Unload Compressor ● Move Unit Valves to Shutdown Position ● Reduce Engine Speed ● Start Cool Down Period ● Shut Off Fuel ● Ground Ignition ● Initiate Post Lube ● Reset Monitors

Fig. 25-D. Typical degrees of sophistication available for gas-engine sequence control.

tional. To make use of these controls, a few necessary accessories not normally required must be supplied. To the controls of this table may also be added a torque control panel to automatically control cylinder loading.

Regulation

Regulation is the control of a variable to achieve certain prescribed performance from a process. It may be regulation of compressor loading to maintain constant plant pressure, or it could be regulation of turbine and turbocompressor speed to match discharge pressure or gas weight output to process requirements. This regulation may be performed in steps or it may be continuous, in which case the corrective action is proportional to deviation of the process variable from a "setpoint." Regulation for a complex system might include not only normal regulation, but also several protective controls necessary to integrate the equipment into the process. As complexity increases, a higher degree of understanding of the process operation must be made available to achieve proper performance.

Optimizing

There are many areas where maintaining maximum plant efficiency under varying conditions will result in worthwhile operating cost savings. One typical case is the gas-engine-driven pipeline compressor where controls are often manual. The idea is to maintain, under varying intake and discharge pressure conditions, the maximum load or output the engine will carry. Applicable to four-cycle engine and electric-driven compressors, optimizing will, within the capabilities of the regulating devices, maintain a constant shaft torque. Shaft torque multiplied by speed and a constant equals horsepower, therefore an approximately constant power load is maintained for any given set speed. This permits the operation of a minimum number of units at all times to obtain the desired output. Computer functions are sometimes included.

Optimizing is the broadest category of controls, from the relatively simple applications outlined previously to the computer designs controlling entire industrial processes.

Summary

The word picture so far has shown the capabilities of control systems as applied mainly to reciprocating compressors. Control systems also are applicable to other types of equipment and a summary in pictorial form is useful.

Fig. 25-E illustrates the simplest system where the sensing elements transmit information to the operator who must initiate any operating changes regardless of their purpose.

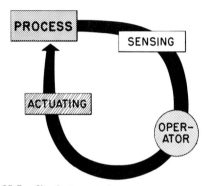

Fig. 25-E. Simplest control system. Operator must initiate operating changes from transmitted information.

Fig. 25-F illustrates a much more complete system where monitoring, protecting, and sequencing are automatic but the regulation and all other actuation are operator controlled.

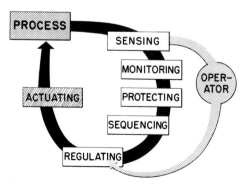

Fig. 25-F. Control system designed to automatically sense, monitor, protect, and sequence, but operator still regulates.

Fig. 25-G places the operator remote from the process installation which often is unattended, an operator spending time at the station only for routine checks. The distance from the central control point is immaterial and may be hundreds of miles. Data is transmitted in code through the use of leased telephone circuits or microwave.

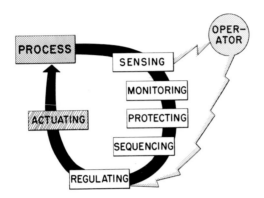

Fig. 25-G. Same control system as Fig. 25-F, except operator may be hundreds of miles away.

Control System Power

The motivating power for control systems is generally pneumatic or electric. Standard *regulating* mechanisms on compressors may be pneumatic, electric, or hydraulic. Complete pneumatic control systems are available where required or desired.

Enclosure of a control system can be a vital factor. Air compressor controls normally are built in general purpose enclosures. Since many applications involve hazardous atmospheres or require that controls be outdoors, explosion-proof or weathertight enclosures are available, generally at higher cost.

Applications to Other Equipment

Only a few of the many possible applications can be mentioned; they are growing in number and variety daily.

Dynamic Machinery

Control systems are available for all types of dynamic equipment including centrifugal and axial-flow compressors and steam and gas turbines.

A typical system for a large steam-turbine-driven axial-flow blast furnace turbocompressor includes the following components and subsystems.

1. Sequence control for the compressor and turbine, including control of air output to match furnace demand (this may be set for either manual or automatic operation);

2. Compressor air weight regulation with ambient pressure and temperature compensation, surge control to prevent unstable operation, and an optimizing control for maximum compressor efficiency over a wide range of flow conditions;

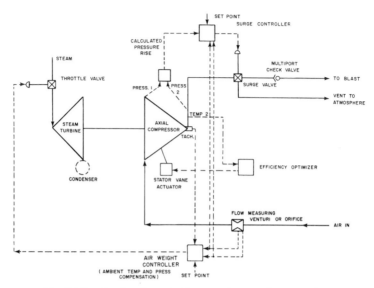

Fig. 25-H. Simple schematic diagram of a complete control system for a steam-turbine-driven axial-flow blast furnace blower.

    3. A battery of instruments for visual indication of the condition and magnitude of various operating variables; and,

    4. A complete monitoring and protective system plus protection against certain off-limit variables.

    Fig. 25-H shows a simplified schematic diagram of this control system.

Pneumatic Hoists

    Control systems can be applied to many functions of hoist operation, particularly where repeated cycles are involved and precision and safety are paramount. One of these is use of controls on a hoist handling automobile bodies from their conveyor on one level to accurate placement on the car frame at a lower level. The body is carried in a cradle. Various protective devices are built in. Final adjustment of location is made by manual push-button controls operative only from the floor. Fig 25-I shows such an installation.

    Another hoist application involves a scraper or slusher type hoist, frequently used underground in mines to move loose ore in a drift to a car loading point. The system controls automatically the direction and distance of travel of the bucket, shows the location of the bucket by lights, shuts the unit down after a preset number of trips, and has a number of safety features.

    This system could be applied to grain handling, bulk cargo, and other work.

Fig. 25-I. A control system takes over operation of this air-operated body hoist in a car assembly plant.

Ejectors

Ejectors are used for many services, a rather unusual application being the use of high pressure gas to power ejectors that compress an exactly proportioned amount of air to blend with the outlet gas and provide the exact Btu content desired in the final mixture. This can be done under system control. This particular application is found in a gas distribution peak-shaving operation.

Water Flood Wells

Water flood wells for secondary recovery of oil are used for putting water under pressure into an underground strata to force oil up producing wells, usually centrally located. The water pumping station may serve a group of 30 or more of the flooding wells. Flow of water to each well must be adjusted frequently for best results.

A control system is available to show in the pumping station the flow to any well, adjustments as desired being made by the operator through remote control of motor operated valves. The entire system is centrally supervised and operated over distances up to 10 or 12 miles.

Summary

The application of systems control is limited only by the desires of the user. Any variable can be sensed, monitored, and regulated. Any equipment or process can be protected, sequenced, or optimized.

Chapter 26

Pressure Losses in Gas Piping

Introduction

A pressure differential must exist between the terminal points in a pipe to start and maintain a flow of gas. Therefore, a pressure loss or drop occurs along the pipe, roughly proportional to the length of gas travel. This loss is due to wall friction and, in most cases, to gas turbulence causing internal gas friction. The energy lost shows up as heat in the gas to no normal advantage.

Pressure loss is an operating cost and continues throughout the life of the installation. Any proper piping design must balance this against the first cost to insure that the most economical pipe size is selected. Piping economics can become quite complex and are not within the scope of this book.

Restrictions

In all cases, round pipe is to be used and flow is steady and nonpulsating. Pulsating flow can cause dramatic and unpredictable increases in pressure loss.

Accuracy

Rational mathematical means can be used to solve only a few seldom-encountered problems in gas flow. Normally-used formulas have been derived from basic theory modified into empirical form. Coefficients are usually obtained from special tests and actual field experience. Each formula is apt to be reasonably sound if used under the conditions for which it was developed. However, there are variables that often cannot be accurately evaluated and *results from any formula should be considered as somewhat approximate until proven otherwise.*

The principal variable is pipe roughness. This can, at best, only be estimated and may tend to exert a greater influence in time due to corrosion and deposits. The probable effect of the gas and any contaminants on this factor must be given serious consideration. Some gases will cause more rapid pipe deterioration than others. Out-of-round pipe, poor alignment, obstructions at welds, and similar irregularities can also cause inaccurate predictions.

It follows that piping design should be based on an intelligent appraisal of probable present and future conditions. A conservative approach should be used, particularly when the pressure drop is a critical item.

Energy required to accelerate the gas mass as the pressure falls is normally neglected.

Factors Involved in Estimating Friction Losses

Types of Flow

There are two basic types of flow of fluid in a pipe. *Laminar* flow is characterized by streamline concentric cylindrical layers of fluid (in this case, a gas) flowing past one another in orderly fashion. The velocity is greatest in the center of the pipe and decreases sharply to zero at the wall or boundary layer. Laminar flow is also known as *viscous, steady,* or *streamline* flow.

The second definite type is *turbulent* flow. There is an irregular random movement of fluid particles across the main stream without an observable frequency or pattern. The velocity distribution over the cross section is more uniform, but if the wall is smooth there is always a boundary layer moving in laminar flow.

Between laminar and turbulent flow lies a critical zone where flow losses cannot be predicted. The exact limits of laminar and turbulent flow can be only loosely defined. They depend somewhat on pipe roughness and the existence of bends and fittings.

In pressure piping practice, turbulent flow is the normal condition.

Symbols

A	Actual internal cross section pipe area	sq in
d	Actual internal pipe diameter	inches
D	Actual internal pipe diameter	feet
f	Friction factor	dimensionless
g	Acceleration of gravity (32.2)	ft/sec²
G	Specific gravity referred to air at 14.696 psiA and 60°F	dimensionless
L	Pipe length	feet
L_m	Pipe length	miles
p_1	Initial pressure	psiA
p_2	Final pressure	psiA
p_m	Mean pressure	psiA
p_o	Standard reference pressure	psiA
Q	Volume flow rate at flowing conditions	cfm
Q_o	Volume flow rate at T_o and p_o	SCFD
R_e	Reynolds number	dimensionless
T_f	Flow temperature	°R
T_o	Standard reference temperature	°R
V	Mean velocity	ft/sec
ρ	Average density at flow conditions	lb/cu ft
Δp	Pressure drop	psi
μ	Absolute viscosity	centipoise
μ_e	Absolute viscosity	lbs mass/ft sec
ε	Absolute roughness	feet

Velocity

Velocity is always figured as the average over the entire actual internal pipe area. It is normal to figure velocity based on Q at entrance conditions, but if pressure drop is high relative to initial pressure, the influence of the velocity increase should be considered.

The maximum velocity obtainable in any flowing gas is the velocity of sound at the conditions of the flowing gas. This condition is seldom involved in commercial installations. See page 5-15 for velocity of sound formulas.

Viscosity

Absolute viscosity is the shear resistance offered by a fluid to relative motion of its parts. This is also known as dynamic viscosity. Absolute viscosity is expressed in centipoise (μ in the metric system) or in lb/ft sec (μ_e in the English system).

$$1 \text{ centipoise} = 0.000672 \text{ lb/ft sec.} \tag{26.1}$$

Fig. 26-A and 26-B give centipoise values of absolute viscosity versus temperature for steam and various gases. Unlike liquids, the viscosity rises with temperature. Pressure does not influence gas viscosity more than 10 percent within moderate ranges (to 500 psiG).

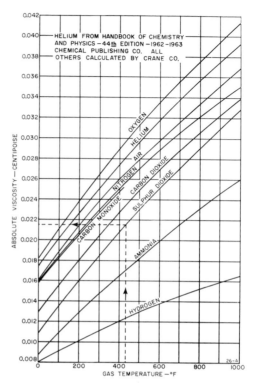

Reproduced with permission of Crane Co.
(Technical Paper No. 410 Flow of Fluids).

Fig. 26-A. Absolute viscosity of various gases.

Reynolds Number

Reynolds' ratio (inertia force versus friction force) shows that the nature of flow in a pipe depends on

    1. Pipe diameter:

    2. Fluid density;

    3. Velocity of flow, and,

    4. Fluid viscosity.

A dimensionless number has been set up to correlate these four factors and is known as the Reynolds number.

$$R_e = \frac{DV\rho}{\mu_e} \tag{26.2}$$

Since gas viscosities are most often given in centipoises and pipe diameters in inches, the following formula will be convenient.

$$R_e = 123.9 \, \frac{dV\rho}{\mu} \tag{26.3}$$

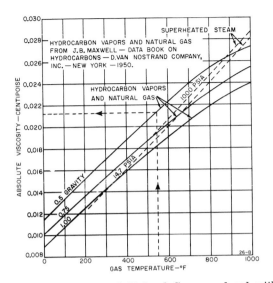

Hydrocarbon Vapors and Natural Gas reproduced with
permission of Crane Co. (Technical Paper No. 410, Flow
of Fluids). Steam based on data in STANDARDS FOR
STEAM EJECTORS, Third Edition. Copyright 1956 by
the Heat Exchange Institute, 122 East 42 Street, New
York, N. Y. 10017.

Fig. 26-B. Absolute viscosity of steam, hydrocarbon vapor, and natural gas.

Above a Reynolds number of 4000, flow is considered to be turbulent.
Below 4000 and to a value that varies with the steadiness and smoothness
of initial flow (together with the existence of disturbing features such as
abrupt bends, etc.), the flow pattern is unpredictable. It is generally considered that flow becomes laminar at a Reynolds number of 2000, although
a strong initial turbulence may lower the limit as far as 1200.

Pipe Roughness

The absolute roughness (ε) of many types of pipe materials has been
approximated and a factor known as relative roughness is used to relate
internal surface conditions to diameter, using the ratio ε/D (both in ft).
For new clean pipes, the value of as developed by Moody in 1944 is shown
in Fig. 26-C. These values have been widely accepted and successfully
used in the design of piping systems. Since most pipe is commercial steel,
the absolute roughness value of 0.00015 is quite standard. Since Moody's
outstanding paper, however, other researchers have reported on their work.
One well executed series of tests and studies on the flow of natural gas in
pipelines is reported in Bureau Of Mines Monograph 9 (1956), published by
the American Gas Association. This found, for commercial steel pipe as
used in gas transmission lines, an absolute roughness of approximately
0.00006. This may reflect improvements in the manufacture of pipe.

A survey of several contractors for refineries and chemical plants
determined that all considered 0.00015 absolute roughness as a safe value
that provides some allowance for future fouling. One company suggests
variable lower values, depending upon the split in pressure loss between

the pipe and the pipe fittings. For example, a lower roughness value was used when fittings losses are more than 30 percent of the total loss. This was done to counterbalance the effect of fitting losses, existing data about which were considered to be high.

The value ε/D is used in the determination of friction factor in the basic Darcy formula.

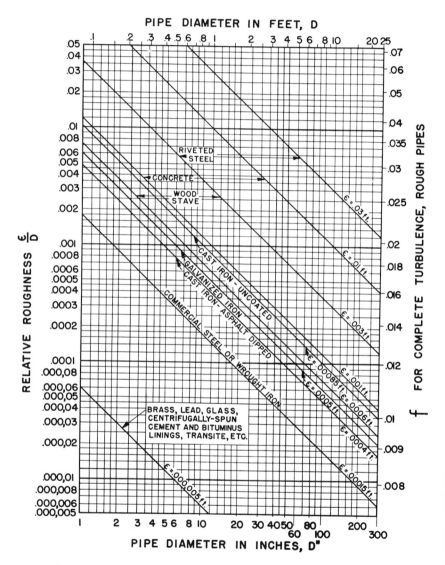

Reproduced by permission. By Lewis F. Moody and published in TRANSACTIONS of the American Society of Mechanical Engineers, Vol. 66, pages 671-677, November 1944.

Fig. 26-C. Relative roughness factors for new clean pipe.

Flow Formulas

Generally accepted formulas are presented in four categories.

1. Low pressure for air (to about 15 psiG);
2. A general formula for any gas;
3. Natural gas pipeline formulas; and,
4. Vacuum.

Low Pressure Air Flow

A formula frequently used for *air* at pressures of 2 to 15 psiG in relatively large pipes is given below. It is based on a flow formula developed by Fritzsche and uses Moody's friction factors for *smooth* steel pipe. It is applicable to tunnel ventilation and similar problems.

$$\Delta p = \frac{CL}{p_m} \tag{26.4}$$

The value of C versus nominal pipe diameter and air flow expressed in cfm at 14.7 psiA and 70°F is shown in Fig. 26-D.

Note that p_m is the average pressure in the line. This must be estimated for the first approximation. Two or three calculations may be required to obtain an accurate value of Δp.

When the piping is crooked and/or rough, the friction factor C may be increased up to 75 percent.

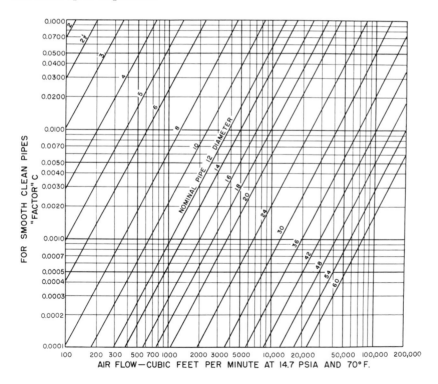

Fig. 26-D. Factor "C" in formula for low pressure air flow.

General Formula

The basic general formula used for pressure drop in piping is as developed by Darcy. Expressed in a form to give pressure drop in psi, the formula is

$$\Delta p = \frac{f \rho L V^2}{144\ D2g} \qquad (26.5)$$

$$\Delta p = 0.00129\ \frac{f \rho L V^2}{d} \qquad (26.6)$$

Laminar Flow

In the range of Reynolds numbers greater than zero and less than approximately 2000 (laminar flow), the friction factor becomes

$$f = \frac{64}{R_e} \qquad (26.7)$$

In this area, flow is independent of surface roughness.

Turbulent Flow

For turbulent flow, the friction factor may be found by the use of Fig. 26-E. The proper roughness factor (ε/D) for the pipe involved is selected from Fig. 26-C and R_e is calculated from formula (26.3).

Application Limitations

The Darcy formula has limitations when used with compressible gases and cannot be applied indiscriminately. As the flow pressure drops, velocity increases while density (lb/cu ft) decreases. The net effect is to cause an actual increase in Δp which is not registered by the formula without some adjustment (note that p_1 is in psiA):

1. Δp less than 10 percent of p_1 — reasonable accuracy will be obtained if ρ and V are based on upstream or downstream conditions, whichever are known;

2. Δp is between 10 and 40 percent of p_1 — the Darcy equation will give reasonable accuracy by using ρ and V based on the average of upstream and downstream conditions $(p_1 + p_2)/2$ Several trials may be required; and,

3. Δp greater than 40 percent of p_1 — the Darcy formula cannot be applied in a single step. It is necessary to divide the total length into shorter sections in which each Δp will be less than 40 percent of p_1 (per section). Then add the sectional drops to obtain the total.

Air Piping Tables

The air pressure drop in pipe has been tabulated for various flows, pipe sizes, and pressures in tables starting on page 34-77. Standard-weight pipe sizes are used. Tables cover pressure drops/100 feet and are calculated directly from formula (26.6) based on initial pressure with no allowance for average pressure. These tables use ε of 0.00015, which, considering the many variables involved, is felt to be an approach giving reasonable values, possibly on the higher side.

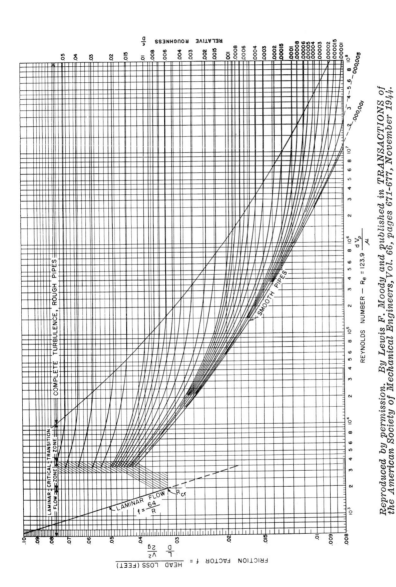

Reproduced by permission. By Lewis F. Moody and published in TRANSACTIONS of the American Society of Mechanical Engineers, Vol. 66, pages 671-677, November 1944.

Fig. 26-E. Friction factor for turbulent and laminar flow in piping based on Reynold's Number and relative roughness.

These tables cover pipe only. The drop through fittings must be included by using the table on page 34-78 which converts the loss through each fitting into the loss in an equivalent length of straight pipe. A *total* effective pipe length can thus be approximated and the pipe pressure drop table used.

Lengths Over 100 Feet

The tables are based on 100 feet of pipe. Longer lengths are frequently involved. First, estimate the total pressure loss by multiplying the drop/100 feet by the number of 100 feet involved including fittings equivalent. If the result is less than 10 percent of the initial pressure (psiA) no correction need be made. If the result is greater than 10 percent of p_1, the following formula may be used or the total calculation may be made in two or more sections, each of which will keep within the 10 percent limit.

In the following formulas, Δp_L is the required total pressure drop. Δp_{100} is the tabulated value per 100 ft.

$$\Delta p_L = P_1 - \sqrt{P_1^2 - 2KL} \tag{26.8}$$

$$K = \frac{\Delta p_{100}}{100} \left(P_1 - \frac{\Delta p_{100}}{2} \right)$$

Interpolating in the Tables

Interpolation for pressure may be made by multiplying Δp at a tabulated reference pressure by the ratio

$$\frac{p_1 \text{ (reference)}}{p_1 \text{ (actual)}} \quad \text{(pressures are psiA)}$$

Interpolation for volume flowing is done by multiplying the reference Δp by the ratio

$$\frac{Q^2 \text{ (actual)}}{Q^2 \text{ (reference)}} \quad \text{or} \quad \frac{V^2 \text{ (actual)}}{V^2 \text{ (reference)}}$$

Gas Pipeline Formulas

In the pipeline transmission of natural gas, the lines are long and pressure drop is relatively high. Formulas are presented as flow formulas with specified initial and terminal pressures. Most generally accepted is the Weymouth formula.

$$Q_o = 433.45 \frac{T_o}{P_o} d^{2.667} \left(\frac{P_1^2 - P_2^2}{L_m G T_f} \right)^{1/2} \tag{26.9}$$

This does not correct for the compressibility of natural gas which, being less than 1.0, reduces the actual volume, velocity, and pressure drop required for flow of a given SCFD. Q_o should therefore be increased by a factor related to the compressibility of the gas at the average pressure. The average pressure may be found by

$$P_m = 2/3 \left(P_1 + P_2 - \frac{P_1 P_2}{P_1 + P_2} \right) \tag{26.10}$$

Fig. 26-F shows multipliers that will usually give satisfactory results.

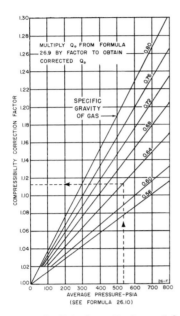

Courtesy of The Petroleum Engineer, July 1945.

Fig. 26-F. Natural gas compressibility correction factors for Weymouth formula.

A more recently developed formula for large lines is the Panhandle formula. It has been modified to allow for elevation and compressibility. Readers are referred to the May and June 1956 issues of *The Petroleum Engineer* for this. Eliminating the two special factors mentioned above, the formula becomes

$$Q_o = 737 \, \frac{T_o}{P_o} \, d^{2.53} \, E \left(\frac{P_1{}^2 - P_2{}^2}{L_m G T_f}\right)^{0.510} \tag{26.11}$$

    $E = 1.00$ for new straight pipe without bends, valves, elbows, change in diameter or elevation;

    $= 0.95$ for typical very good operating conditions;

    $= 0.92$ for average good operating conditions;

    $= 0.85$ for unusually unfavorable operating conditions.

The Panhandle formula will usually give greater flow than the Weymouth formula for a given pressure drop.

Vacuum Piping

Turbulent Flow

These data are applicable only for the turbulent flow of air or steam (vapor) at subatmospheric pressures. This does *not* cover flow in the laminar range. The ratio of weight flow in lb/hr to actual inside pipe diameter in inches *must be equal to or greater than 20* for these data to be used. These data may be used for air-water vapor mixtures by interpolation.

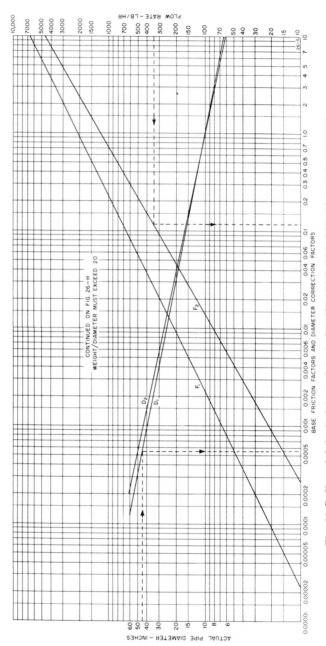

Fig. 26-G, H, and I drafted from data in STANDARDS FOR STEAM JET EJECTORS, Third Edition. Copyright 1956 by the Heat Exchange Institute, 122 East 42 Street, New York, N. Y. 10017. Based on a paper by W. C. Knapp and J. W. Metzgar, ASME TRANSACTIONS, Vol. 77, No. 15, July 1955, pages 675-681.

Fig. 26-G. Basic friction factors and diameter correction factor for vacuum piping. See also Fig. 26-H.

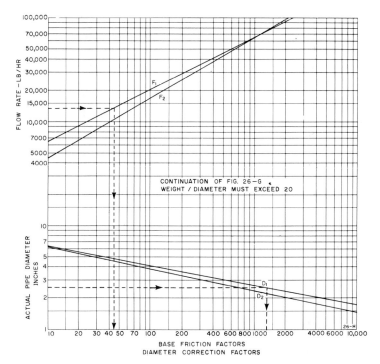

Fig. 26-H. Basic friction factors and diameter correction factor for vacuum piping. See also Fig. 26-G.

The following symbols apply to this particular formula.

F	Pressure drop/100 feet of pipe (13.6 inches water $=$ 1 inch Hg)	inches water
F_1 & F_2	Basic friction factors based on flow rate	dimensionless
D_1 & D_2	Correction factors based on pipe diameter	dimensionless
T_1 & T_2	Correction features based on gas temperature	dimensionless
p_1	Initial pressure	in Hg abs

$$F = \frac{(F_1 \times D_1 \times T_1) + (F_2 \times D_2 \times T_2)}{P_1} \qquad (26.12)$$

The various factors are determined from Fig. 26-G, 26-H, and 26-I.

Pressure losses must be limited to 10 percent of the *final* pressure for accuracy in using this procedure. If the first result indicates a greater than 10 percent drop, calculations must be done in several steps, dividing the pipe into appropriate shorter sections and figuring each separately. These data apply to clean commercial steel pipe.

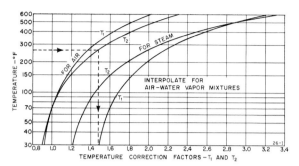

Fig. 26-I. Temperature correction factor for vacuum piping.

Streamline Flow — High Vacuum

This is an adaptation of the Fanning formula, developed with special friction factors (Fig. 26-J) for *laminar* flow only in high-vacuum (low-absolute-pressure) lines. It applies exclusively to the range from 50 microns (0.050 mm) to 1.0 mm absolute.

$$\Delta p = \frac{4f\rho LV^2}{144D2g} \qquad\qquad (26.13)$$

The Reynolds number can be calculated from formula (26.3) using Fig. 26-A for air viscosity. This formula is valid only for air. Note that the maximum Reynolds number plotted in Fig. 26-J is 1000, well within the laminar range.

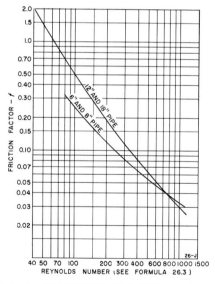

Drafted from data in STANDARDS FOR STEAM JET EJECTORS, Third Edition. Copyright 1956 by the Heat Exchange Institute, 122 East 42 Street, New York, N. Y. 10017. Based on a paper by W. J. Bohnet and L. S. Stinson, ASME TRANSACTIONS, Vol. 77, No. 15, July 1955, pages 683-692.

Fig. 26-J. Friction factors for high-vacuum piping.

Pressure Losses In Fittings

Any pipe fitting causes an additional disturbance in the pipe flow pattern, thus producing an additional pressure loss. This consists of three parts: (1) a minor disturbance upstream of the fitting; (2) the drop through the fitting itself; and, (3) an increased pressure drop downstream due to abnormal turbulence. Page 34-78, is based on the results of many tests and presents the length in feet of straight pipe having an *equivalent* pressure loss. For each fitting involved in the piping system, this length must be added to the total actual length of straight pipe to obtain the equivalent length for calculating total pressure drop, either by formula or from a table.

Losses in Hose

Pneumatic tools and rock drills receive their air supply through flexible hose. The flow is pulsating, hose couplings or spuds of various designs are used, hose condition varies from smooth to poor or badly deteriorated, and the condition of the air may vary. Tests have shown a marked increase in friction loss when an air-line lubricator is used at the hose inlet. For these many reasons, steady-flow clean-pipe tables for pressure loss cannot be used.

An analysis of the test data available, and logical methods of extending them, has resulted in tables for hose pressure drop believed to be within plus or minus 10 percent of a reasonable value. Two tables are presented. One, Fig. 27-F on page 27-10 is designed for pneumatic tools which most often do not use air-line lubricators. The air is considered to be oil and moisture free. The second, on page 34-161, etc., applies especially to rock drills which most often utilize air-line lubricators. These include data for both clean, dry air and for air with oil fog.

All tables are based on a smooth hose lining. Rough or deteriorated lining will increase pressure losses up to 50 percent.

For longer hoses, adjust proportionately. Note that long hoses should, however, be used only under abnormal conditions. It is better to use steel pipe.

Air Mains to Underground Mines

In the design of mains to deliver air to underground workings, it may not always be realized that the weight of the column of compressed air in the main is considerable and causes a continuing increase in the air pressure as the main drops below the shaft head. The principle is exactly the same as the variation in the atmospheric pressure between an altitude and sea level, except that in this case compressed air of a much greater density is involved.

The pressure increase due to compressed air weight varies with depth at an increasing rate. Assuming 90 psiG at sea level (105 psiA) at the shaft head, the pressure will have increased 3.8 psi at the 1000 foot level and 24.6 psi at the 6000 ft level. The average rate of increase is 4.1 psi/1000 ft.

This pressure rise is valuable in helping to offset friction losses in the downtake main and in maintaining proper drill pressure at the face.

References

Among the principal references used in the compilation of this chapter are:

The Pipeline Tables (1957) published by
The Petroleum Engineer Publishing Co.

Flow of Fluids (1957) Technical Paper No. 410 published by
Crane Co.

Compressed Air Data—5th Edition, published by
Ingersoll-Rand Co.

Engineering Data Book (1957) published by
Natural Gasoline Supply Men's Association

Marks Handbook (1958) published by McGraw-Hill Company.

Standards for Steam Jet Ejectors (1956) published by
Heat Exchange Institute

Pipe Friction Manual (1954) published by
Hydraulic Institute

The assistance of many friends in industry is also acknowledged.

Chapter 27

The Air Power System

Caption Index **Page**

Introduction

Compressed air is a major source of industrial power possessing many advantages. It is safe, economical, easily transmitted, and adaptable. Its adaptability is evidenced by the many applications listed in Chapter 32. Some applications would be almost impossible with any other power medium.

Its cost is usually very small relative to the labor saved. For example, when driving hand-held pneumatic tools, a major use in industry, the cost of compressed air *plus the life cost* of the tool will be only 2 to 5 percent of the total cost of doing a given job. In other words, labor accounts for more than 95 percent of the usual job expense. Any action taken to enable the worker to utilize the tool to greater advantage, to produce more in a given time, will pay off in reduced total costs even though the compressed air cost itself is increased materially.

This chapter shows how the best possible air power system may be developed, checked and maintained. Discussion is confined to the nominal 100-psiG service.

Compressor selection, installation, and the accessories required in the compressor plant itself have been discussed in Chapters 16 and 18.

Actual Cost of Compressed Air

The total cost of compressed air includes several main groups.

1. Fixed charges on the compressor installation including drivers; Depreciation, insurance, and taxes;
2. Repairs;
3. Operation; Attendance, lubrication, and cooling water; and,
4. Power.

On the basis of electric-motor-driven 100-psiG reciprocating air compressors in the 125- to 500-bhp range with power (including both energy and demand) at 1.5 cents/KW hr, the proportion of the above items in the cost of air, when operating at full load, will be approximately:

Fixed charges and repairs	15%
Operating charges	20%
Power	65%

These ratios would be altered materially at other net power rates.

Actual compressed air cost figures may vary from 5 to 10 cents/1000 cu ft free air compressed to 100 psiG. The *Compressed Air and Gas Handbook* states that 7 cents/1000 is a reasonable national average.

Compressor Capacity Required

Many industrial air loads are relatively small items that may have widely varying demand characteristics. A study of air-operated devices will show that while a few operate continuously, the percentage of actual operating time will depend more on the type of operation than on the device itself.

A variable known as *use factor* is therefore involved in the determination of the net air use of each device. Use factor is the percent of an average hour the device operates. Use factor can seldom be precisely determined. It must be based on a study of typical operations plus experience and may vary individually from 10 to nearly 100 percent. Tool and compressor manufacturers can be helpful in the setting of sound use factors on their products. See also data in Chapter 29 about Pneumatic Tools.

Occasional loads may be found that require a large amount of air for a short period of time. These warrant careful analysis since quite often the air system demand can be spread over a longer period by the judicious use of air storage in receivers at the point of use. This will reduce average quantity to be supplied, but usually is limited by the allowable receiver pressure drop to rather short term peaks. See *The Engineered Air Receiver* in Chapter 5.

Pneumatic cylinders are used widely in production operations involving automatic machinery. Most of these use only a small amount of air per stroke, but, when totalled, a considerable quantity may be involved. Analysis of each operation is necessary. Cylinders may operate at various cycling speeds. This may influence the air consumption, since at high speed the cylinder pressure may not reach line pressure because of pressure drops through the control valve and piping. This can be quite a complex subject and is not covered here. The simple cylinder which has a relatively slow cycle provides time for full filling. To such cases Fig. 27-A applies. For complex operations, refer to the cylinder manufacturer.

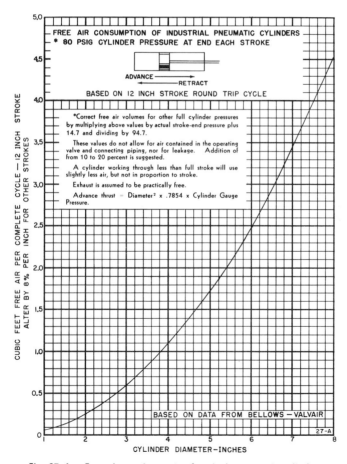

Fig. 27-A.   Free air requirements of typical pneumatic cylinders.

For automotive and tire service stations, recapping plants, etc., analysis of the various operations involved must be made. Obtain the assistance of the compressor manufacturer. If continuity of air supply is a must, and it usually is, the answer, even in a small installation, can well be two units each able to supply a substantial portion, say two-thirds, of the air requirement.

It follows that to properly evaluate compressed air requirements, a complete inventory of all uses must be made. To assist in evaluating various types of tools, the table on the following page is presented. This shows approximate maximum air requirements of various tools. This may be used only as a guide because there are variations of consequence between different makes, sizes, and designs of tools. Devices other than operating cylinders should preferably be based on manufacturer's recommendations.

Low use factors should be applied with caution to sand blasting and other relatively steady and heavy demands.

Cubic Feet of Free Air Per Minute Required By Sand Blast

| Nozzle Diameter | Compressed Air Gage Pressure | | | |
	60 lbs.	70 lbs.	80 lbs.	100 lbs.
1/16''	4	5	5.5	6.5
3/32''	9	11	12	15
1/8''	17	19	21	26
3/16''	38	43	47	58
1/4''	67	76	85	103
5/16''	105	119	133	161
3/8''	151	171	191	232
1/2''	268	304	340	412

Fig. 27-B shows the analysis of a typical foundry and machine shop. The total of column (E) determines the expected net productive air needs. However, this does not represent a recommended air compressor size, since allowances must be made for the inevitable leakage. Every new plant should also provide amply for growth. Leakage allowances should not be less than 10 percent, although a properly maintained plant will be nearer 5 percent. Provision for expansion will vary materially, being greater, even to 100 percent when only one small compressor is being installed. A large multiple compressor plant may reduce this allowance to 20 percent. The availability of air power always extends its use.

Number and Location of Compressors

The number of compressors to be installed in any given situation is not subject to generalization. The most important question to be considered is, "What happens if compressed air is not available?"

There are two possibilities for compressor location. One is the centralized arrangement, with all compressors at one location, the air being distributed from this point. The other is the decentralized system with compressors at the various centers throughout the plant. The various load centers may or may not be interconnected.

FREE AIR REQUIREMENTS OF TOOLS

Tool	Free Air—cfm 90 psiG at Tool 100% Use Factor
Grinders—horizontal	
6″ and 8″ wheels	50
2″ and 2½″ wheels	14-20
1½″ wheels and under	10
Grinders and Sanders—vertical	
Large	53
Medium	30
Small	22
File and Burr Machines	18
Screwdrivers	
Nbr. 2 to Nbr. 6 screw	5
Nbr. 6 to 5⁄16″ screw	10
Impact Wrenches	
To ½″	5
½″ to ¾″	10
¾″ to 1¼″	20
1¼″ to 2″	30
2″ to 3″	55
3″ to 12″	100
Concrete Vibrators	30
Air Hoists	
1000 lb and under	1 cu ft/ft lift
2000 lb to 10,000 lb	5 cu ft/ft lift
10,000 lb and larger	15 cu ft/ft lift
Sand Rammers and Tampers,	
1″ x 4″ cylinder	25
1¼″ x 5″ cylinder	28
1½″ x 6″ cylinder	39
Chipping Hammers, weighing 10-13 lbs.	28-30
heavy	39
weighing 2-4 lbs.	12
Angle Nut Setters to 5⁄16″ weighing 8 lbs.	20
Angle Nut Setters ½″ to ¾″ weighing 18 lbs.	30
Sump Pumps, 145 gals. (at 50 foot head)	70
Paint Spray, average	7
varies from	2-20
Bushing Tools (Monumental)	15-25
Carving Tools (Monumental)	10-15
Plug Drills	40-50
Riveters, 3⁄32″-1″ rivets	12
larger weighing 18-22 lbs.	35
Rivet busters	35-39
Wood Borers To 1″ diameter weighing 4 lbs.	40
2″ diameter weighing 26 lbs.	80
Steel Drills, Rotary Motors	
Capaicty up to ¼″ weighing 1¼-4 lbs.	18-20
Capacity ¼″ to 3⁄8″ weighing 6-8 lbs.	20-40
Capacity ½″ to ¾″ weighing 9-14 lbs.	70
Capacity 7⁄8″ to 1″ weighing 25 lbs.	80
Capacity 1¼″ weighing 30 lbs.	95
Steel Drills, Piston Type	
Capacity ½″ to ¾″ weighing 13-15 lbs.	45
Capacity 7⁄8″ to 1¼″ weighing 25-30 lbs.	75-80
Capacity 1¼″ to 2″ weighing 40-50 lbs.	80-90
Capacity 2″ to 3″ weighing 55-75 lbs.	100-110

Type of Tool	Location	Num- ber of tools (A)	Use factor (per cent of time tools actually operated) (B)	Free Air Cfm required	
				Per tool when oper- ating (C)	Total actually used (A x B x C) (E)
Blowguns, chucks and vises	Machine Shop				25
8-in. Grinders	Cleaning	10	50	50	250
Chippers	Cleaning	10	50	30	150
Hoists	Cleaning	2	10	35	7
Small Screwdrivers	Assembly	20	25	5	25
Large Nutsetters	Assembly	2	25	30	15
Woodborer	Shipping	1	25	40	10
Screwdriver	Shipping	1	20	10	2
Hoist	Shipping	1	20	40	8
Total		47			492

Fig. 27-B. Typical analysis of compressed air requirement for a foundry and machine shop.

The principal advantages of the central plant include the possibility of using larger, more efficient units; reduced cost for bringing in the various utilities; better maintenance and supervision at lower cost; and, better balance between air supply and demand. The central plant may be at a greater disadvantage in the maintenance of proper air pressure, although this should be no problem with a properly designed distribution system.

The principal advantage of the decentralized system is its flexibility. It is simple to add units where needed and piping runs are short.

Fig. 25-A and Fig. 25-B, pages 25-5 and 6, illustrate typically the two systems.

Separate smaller units are frequently used to supply necessary or emergency services during weekends and at night, thus permitting shutdown of the larger units during periods when their load factor and efficiency would be materially lowered.

The Distribution System

The aim of the distribution system is to carry the 100-psiG compressed air from the compressor receiver to the tool or other air-powered device with a limited pressure loss. A well laid out and maintained system should deliver air to the point of actual use at a pressure *close to 90 psiG*.

Most distribution systems will consist of a main line from which branch mains take off to different buildings, departments, or sections. From these in turn are taken the feeder lines to tool stations or individual pieces of air-powered equipment. When tools are being operated, the connection *from* the feeder will be by flexible hose. See Fig. 27-C and D.

Since the flow through the main line will be at the average rate of all air uses, it may be sized directly from the tables starting on page 34-77. Corrections for long runs should be by formula 26.8, page 26-10. Pressure drop in this section should be less than 3 psi. Be sure to include losses through fittings.

Fig. 27-C. Various types of compressed air distribution systems.

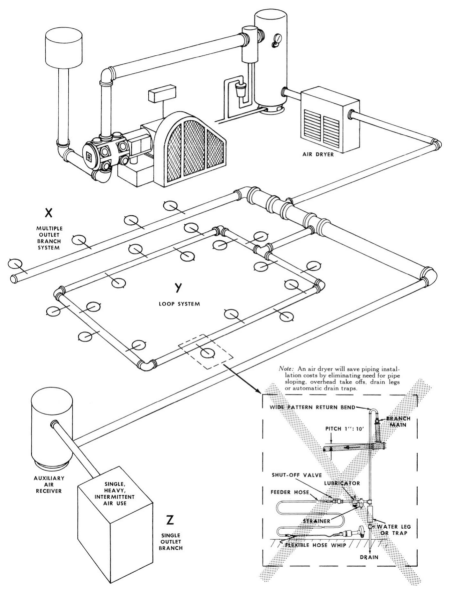

X
MULTIPLE
OUTLET
BRANCH
SYSTEM

y
LOOP SYSTEM

AIR DRYER

Note: An air dryer will save piping installation costs by eliminating need for pipe
sloping, overhead take offs, drain legs
or automatic drain traps.

WIDE PATTERN RETURN BEND
BRANCH MAIN
PITCH 1″: 10′
SHUT-OFF VALVE
LUBRICATOR
FEEDER HOSE
STRAINER
WATER LEG OR TRAP
FLEXIBLE HOSE WHIP
DRAIN

AUXILIARY
AIR
RECEIVER

SINGLE,
HEAVY,
INTERMITTENT
AIR USE

Z

SINGLE
OUTLET
BRANCH

Fig. 27-D. The proper method to connect a
pneumatic tool to a distribution system.

Branch mains do not have as great a diversification of demand as main lines and must therefore be sized for their maximum flow. This may run 150 to 175 percent of the average, depending upon the number of outlets to be in use at any one time. Pressure losses in this section should also be less than 3 psi and may be based on the above tables.

Feed lines from the branch main to the floor should be sized for the maximum flow of as many tools as may be connected at any time. These lines are usually short and pressure drop should be less than 1 psi.

Fig. 27-C illustrates various piping arrangements. Section "X" shows a branch main with air feeding in one end and outlets at intervals. This type is frequently overloaded by over-extension at the far end or by addition of too many outlets. A good way to relieve the condition is to either extend the main to the midpoint of the branch or, better yet, to run a parallel branch and take half the outlets off the new line. Tie both lines together at the far end.

Sometimes there is a line of this type down each side of a building. Better distribution can be obtained if the ends of the lines are joined to form a loop (see section "Y"), thus giving two-way air flow to feed a point of heavy demand.

For heavy intermittent demands, possibly at the end of a long and small line (see section "Z"), reduce serious pressure losses by installing a simple air receiver as near as possible to the demand point, thus storing power where it is needed. For example, say 200 cfm free air is required for two minutes every 10 minutes. It would overload the feeder line and cause excessive pressure loss to draw at a rate higher than 75 cfm. Therefore 125 cfm, or a total for two minutes of 250 cfm *free* air, must be stored. Line pressure (that which is in the receiver when the equipment is not running) is 96 psiG and allowable maximum pressure drop in the receiver when equipment operates is 10 psi. The 250 cfm *free* air must be taken from the receiver storage within this pressure drop. The receiver volume in cubic feet is

$$V = \frac{250 \times 14.7}{10} = 368 \text{ cu ft}$$

This receiver would be about 60 inches diameter by 18 feet long. The receiver pressure would be restored during the period the equipment was idle without appreciable effect on the main line. Without the receiver, the pressure at the equipment would fall too low and its operation would be impaired. For more about *The Engineered Air Receiver*, see page 5-8.

Selection of Pipe Sizes

The tables referred to (page 34-77) provide a means of selecting pipe sizes to keep within a limiting pressure drop under the design conditions. It must be pointed out, however, that most of the cost of installed piping is labor and that the use of the next larger pipe will increase costs but little. This action protects the future, providing automatically for expansion, and pays immediate and continuing dividends in better pressure maintenance.

Importance of Proper Hose

Almost without exception the largest single pressure loss in any system serving portable tools is found in the hose and its connections to the tool. A system with 100 psiG at the compressor receiver should provide 94 to 95 psiG at the entrance to the hose, thus allowing for 4 to 5 psi further loss in the hose. Unfortunately, hose selection does not always receive the attention it deserves and hose losses are extreme. This robs the tool and the worker of potential production.

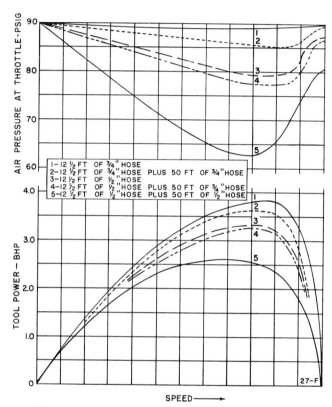

Fig. 27-E. The effect of various hose sizes on the air pressure at the throttle and the power of a typical rotary drill.

These losses occur in two areas. The use of hoses that are either too long or too small (or both) is the more important area. Fig. 27-E shows the effect of various hose combinations on the throttle pressure and power available at a multi-vane type rotary drill at various speeds. Obviously this tool, requiring 75 to 85 cfm of air, should be fitted with a 3/4" hose. Where hose flexibility is essential, a short (12-1/2 foot) length of the full size extra flexible type of hose may be used without serious increase in loss. The use of 1/2" hose, even in short lengths, on a tool of this size is not recommended.

Fig. 27-F will be helpful in selecting hose sizes for smaller tools. Air flow should be the full-load rating at maximum power. Selections should be above the heavy line for best economy. See also page 26-15.

CFM Free Air Flowing	6'—1/8"	8'—5/32"	8'—1/4"	8'—5/16"	8'—3/8"	12½'—1/2"	25'—1/2"	50'—1/2"	25'—3/4"	50'—3/4"	8'—5/32" Plus 25'—1/2"	8'—1/4" Plus 50'—1/2"	12½'—1/2" Plus 25'—3/4"	12½'—1/2" Plus 50'—3/4"
2	3.5	1.2									1.3			
3	7.3	2.7									2.8			
4	12.5	4.4									4.6			
5		6.7									6.9			
6		9.3									9.7	1.2		
7		12.4	1.3								12.9	1.6		
8			1.6									2.1		
10			2.5									3.2		
12			3.5	1.3								4.5		
15			5.3	2.0				1.1				6.9		
20			9.0	3.4	1.4		1.0	1.9				11.8		
25			13.8	5.1	2.2		1.5	3.0					1.3	1.5
30				7.3	3.1	1.1	2.1	4.2					1.8	2.1
35				9.8	4.1	1.5	2.9	5.6					2.5	2.8
40				12.5	5.3	2.0	3.7	7.1		1.0			3.2	3.7
45					6.6	2.5	4.6	8.9		1.2			4.0	4.6
50					8.1	3.0	5.6	10.9		1.5			4.9	5.6
55					9.7	3.6	6.7	13.0		1.8			5.9	6.8
60					11.5	4.3	7.9		1.1	2.1			7.0	8.0
70						5.7	10.6		1.4	2.8			9.4	10.7
80						7.3	13.6		1.9	3.6			12.1	13.9
90						9.2			2.3	4.5				
100						11.2			2.8	5.5				
120									4.0	7.7				
140									5.4	10.3				
160									6.9	13.3				
180									8.7					
200									10.6					
220									12.7					

Based on 95 psiG air pressure at hose inlet end and includes normal couplings. Use of quick-connecting type couplings will increase pressure losses materially. The hose is assumed to be smooth.

Air is clean and dry. If an air line lubricator is used ahead of hose, the pressure loss will be considerably higher.

Pressure loss varies inversely as the absolute pressure (approximately).

For rock drill hose, see tables starting on page 34–161.

Probable accuracy is believed to be plus-or-minus 10 percent.

Fig. 27-F. Recommended hose sizes and pressure drops for air-operated tools.

The second area where excessive hose pressure losses are encountered is in the use of improper couplings, menders, nipples, etc. Considering nipples connecting immediately at the tool, standards are different between percussive and rotary tools, the former having a smaller air passage for a given connection size. This is due to the rougher treatment these tools usually receive and to the fact that they use considerably less air. The nipple selection should always be correct for the tool. Interchanging is to be guarded against.

Couplings and menders should be those recommended by reputable suppliers, not only for safety reasons, but also to obtain the least restriction to flow.

Value of Proper Air Pressure

It has been pointed out earlier that air tools are designed to operate most effectively with 90-psiG pressure *at the tool*. The penalty for not maintaining this pressure is frequently unrealized and there are many plants where production would be increased and over-all costs reduced if proper attention were paid to this factor.

A study of eight makes and sizes of rock drills indicates that operating them at 90 psiG instead of at 70 psiG will increase their drilling speed an average of 41 percent. A given hole can therefore be drilled in less time, with lower labor costs. True, the cost of compressed air will increase about 32 percent, but the air and tool cost in any case does not exceed 5 percent of the total job cost so the net result is a substantial saving.

A similar study with portable pneumatic tools shows an average 37 percent increase in productive work possibility using air a pressure of 90 instead of 70 psiG. The air consumption will increase about 30 percent.

Consider specifically 20 medium duty grinders and air at 7 cents/1000 cu ft. These machines, on a 33 percent use factor, will use 51,200 cu ft more air per day when running at 90 psiG. This is worth about $3.60. Assuming that only one-third of the 37 percent productivity increase can be translated into actual labor productivity, the labor costs to do a given job will obviously be cut by 12 percent. At $21.00/day for each man, this reduces the cost for 20 men to do the job by $50.40.

To present a typical picture in more easily evaluated ratios for the same work output.

Pressure at tool—psiG.....................	70	90
Air and life tool cost—Percent of 70 psiG total....	5	6.5
Labor—Percent of 70 psiG total...............	95	83.5
Total cost—Percent of 70 psiG total............	100	90

Obviously, every plant should make strenuous efforts to maintain proper air pressure. It will pay off.

Causes of Low Air Pressure

Low air pressure has three principal causes, in the usual order of importance:

1. Inadequate piping and hose;
2. Excessive leakage; and,
3. Insufficient compressor capacity.

Inadequate Piping and Hose

To study an existing layout for correction requires the simultaneous recording of pressures throughout the system from the compressor to the tool. It is suggested the system be divided into specific areas and that pressures *when operating at full load* be recorded at the ends of all feed lines, leaving hose and tool fittings for separate study. The pressure drop from the receiver to these points should not exceed 5 or 6 psi. A recording of these terminal readings on a chart of the piping will quickly show bad spots. Study will indicate remedial action.

To check pressure *at the tool*, it is usual to use a needle gauge (Fig. 27-G). The hypodermic needle is inserted in the hose as in Fig. 27-H. In taking readings, the tool must be operating at maximum load. It must be noted that the gauge is for use only on rubber hose. The hole will not be self-sealing on plastic hose. Pressure drop from feed line through the hose should not exceed 4 to 5 psi.

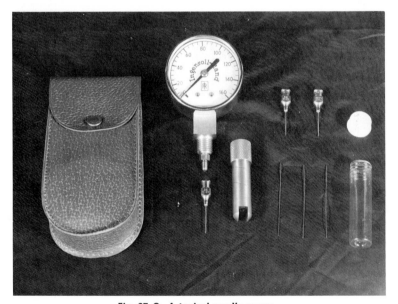

Fig. 27-G. A typical needle gauge.

Leakage

Leakage is a serious power loss in many plants. Because air leakage is not unsafe, it is often tolerated in situations where leakage of other power mediums would not be permitted. Leakage tests have shown wastage to 20 percent of the air compressed, although this is an extreme. Ten percent is more common.

Leakage usually occurs in a multitude of small openings. Each is minor, but the cumulative effect is great. An approach to stopping leaks is outlined below. See page 27-14 for a method of determining system leakage quantity.

      1. Inspect the stem packing of every valve in the system, repack-
         ing when necessary;

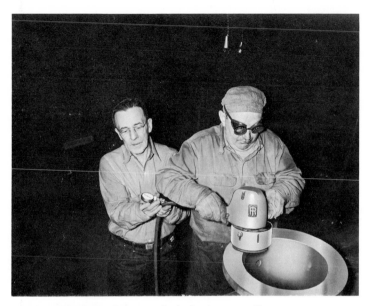

**Fig. 27-H. Proper method of using a needle gauge.
The tool must be operating at maximum power output.**

2. Replace leaky shutoff valves;

3. Repair leaking valves on tools; tools should not be, but often are, left live on the line when not in use, even though used only occasionally;

4. Standardize on good hose clamps; leaks are frequent when make-shifts are used (See Fig. 27-I);

5. Standardize on good blow guns — homemade types usually leak. Also reduce air pressure for blow guns to increase safety and save air;

6. Install condensate separators and drains at branch ends to eliminate need for operators blowing lines to clear out water; and,

7. Use good quality air hose to eliminate breaks.

The cost of a small leak in terms of dollars wasted over a period of time is considerable as the following table shows. Leakage is assumed to be as from a sharp-edged orifice continuously at 100 psiG with air at 7 cents/1000 cu ft.

Diameter of Opening-Inches	Cu Ft Wasted per Month	Cost of Waste per Month
$\frac{1}{32}$	45,400	$3.18
$\frac{1}{16}$	182,000	$12.75
$\frac{1}{8}$	729,000	$51.00
$\frac{1}{4}$	2,920,000	$204.00

GOOD   POOR   POOR

Fig. 27-I.   Hose clamps—proper and improper.

Need for More Capacity

To study the need for greater compressor capacity, it is necessary to survey the actual use of air during peak operating periods when, presumably, air pressures fall below proper values at times. This entails using the following procedure.

1. Record, during several peak hours, the time each compressor runs at full load and each degree of part load (a recording (curve-drawing) wattmeter or ammeter is of great aid at this point because the time at each condition will be clearly shown); and,

2. Keep a record of air pressure during these periods, and from these data and the compressor full load ratings (actual delivery, not piston displacement), calculate air used during peak demand periods (those of low air pressure).

2000-cfm Compressor
With 5 Step Clearance Control

Load Point	Time—Min.	Cu Ft Air Supplied
Full load	32	64,000
¾ load	15	22,500
½ load	13	13,000
Total	60 min.	99,500

Average peak usage (cubic feet per minute) -1658 cfm

The average consumption is not, of course, the absolute peak demand and some judgment is required to determine the actual maximum. A careful comparison of compressor output or loading during the lowest pressure periods will clarify this problem. The amount of additional capacity required will depend not only upon the results of a test, such as the above, but upon possible future expansion of air usage. It is wise to consult the compressor manufacturer at this point.

It should be noted that a similar test, performed when no air is being used, will provide a measure of the total system leakage.

Why Moisture in Compressed Air

Air entering the first stage of any air compressor carries with it a certain amount of native moisture. This is unavoidable, although the quantity carried will vary widely with the ambient temperature and relative humidity. (For a definition of relative humidity see page 2-8). For the purpose of this discussion, relative humidity is assumed to be the same as degree of saturation (see page 3-7). A maximum error of less than 2 percent is involved.

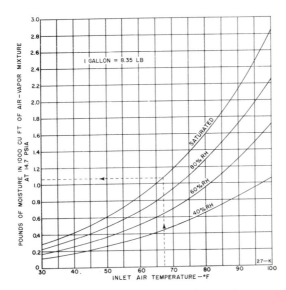

Fig. 27-J. Weight of water vapor entering an air compressor per 1000 cubic feet of total atmospheric inlet volume.

Fig. 27-J shows the effect of ambient temperature and relative humidity on the quantity of moisture in atmospheric air entering a compressor at 14.7 psiA. Under any given condition, the amount of water vapor entering the compressor per 1000 cu ft of mixture may be approximated from these curves.

In any air-vapor mixture, each component has its own partial pressure (see page 3-6) and the air and the vapor are each indifferent to the existence of the other. It follows that the conditions of either component may be studied without reference to the other. In a certain volume of mixture, each component fills the full volume at its own partial pressure. The water vapor may saturate this space (be at its saturation pressure and temperature) or it may be superheated (above saturation temperature for its partial pressure).

As this vapor is compressed, its volume is reduced while at the same time the temperature automatically increases, the vapor becoming superheated. More pounds of vapor are now contained in one cu ft than when originally entering the compressor.

Under the laws of vapors, the maximum quantity of a particular vapor a given space can contain is dependent solely upon the vapor temperature.

As the compressed water vapor is cooled it will eventually reach the temperature at which the space becomes saturated, now containing the maximum it can hold. Any further cooling will force part of the vapor to condense into the liquid form.

The curves of Fig. 27-K shows what happens over a wide range of pressures and temperatures. However, these are saturated vapor curves based on starting with 1000 cu ft of *saturated* air. If the air is not saturated at the compressor inlet (and it usually is not) use Fig. 27-J to ob-

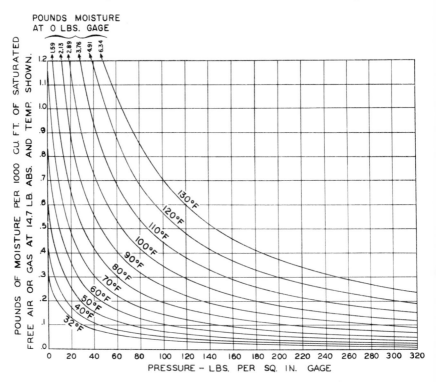

Fig. 27-K. Moisture remaining in saturated air or gas when compressed isothermally to the pressures shown.

tain the initial water vapor weight entering the system per 1000 cu ft. By reading left on Fig. 27-K from the juncture of the final pressure and final temperature, obtain the maximum weight of vapor which this same 1000 cu ft can hold after compression and cooling to saturation. If the latter is less than the former, the difference will be condensed. If the latter is higher, there will be no condensation. It is clearly evident that the lower the temperature and the greater the pressure of compressed air, the greater will be the amount of vapor condensed.

Problems Caused by Water in Compressed Air

Few plant operators need to be told of the problems caused by water in compressed air. They are most apparent to those who operate pneumatic tools, rock drills, automatic pneumatic powered machinery, paint and other sprays, sandblasting equipment, and pneumatic controls. However, almost all applications, particularly of 100-psiG power, could benefit from the elimination of water carry-over. The principal problems might be summarized as:

1. Washing away of required lubrication;
2. Increase in wear and maintenance;
3. Sluggish and inconsistent operation of automatic valves and cylinders;
4. Malfunctioning and high maintenance of control instruments;
5. Spoilage of product by spotting in paint and other types of spraying;
6. Rusting of parts that have been sandblasted;
7. Freezing in exposed lines during cold weather; and,
8. Further condensation and possible freezing of moisture in the exhaust of those more efficient tools which expand the air considerably.

In connection with the last item, in some rock drills there is a 70° drop in temperature from inlet to exhaust. Most portable pneumatic tools have a considerably lower temperature drop, but the above problem sometimes exists.

The increased use of control systems (see Chapter 25) and automatic machinery has made these problems more serious and has spurred activity toward their reduction.

It has been pointed out earlier that the amount of moisture entering the compressor is widely variable, depending upon ambient temperature and relative humidity. In this connection, the data on atmospheric conditions at various points in the United States and Puerto Rico starting on page 34-130 may be of assistance. The problems are usually the worst when both temperature and humidity are high and such data should be used when evaluating any remedies. Pipeline freezing problems are, of course, prevalent only in the winter months.

A fact to remember is that water vapor *as vapor* does no harm in a pneumatic system. It is only when the vapor condenses and remains in the system as liquid that problems exist. The goal, therefore, is to condense *and remove* as much of the vapor as is economically desirable, considering the applications involved.

Two major approaches toward a solution are presented here, each well proven. Comments on additional equipment for rather special cases are appended.

The Conventional System

Two-stage units will always include an intercooler between stages. On air-cooled units for 100- to 250-psiG service, the air between stages is not cooled sufficiently to cause substantial liquid drop out and provision is not usually made for its removal.

Water-cooled intercoolers used on larger units will usually cool sufficiently to condense considerable moisture at cooler pressure. Drainage facilities must always be provided and used. Automatic traps are the best method.

The air compressor plant should *always* include a water-cooled after-cooler followed by a receiver. There are few exceptions to this rule, all due to local conditions or a special use of the air.

Aftercoolers alone, or aftercoolers following intercoolers, will under normal summer conditions condense at 100 psiG up to 70 percent or more of the vapor entering the system. This is a substantial portion, some often being collected in the receiver. Therefore, both cooler and receiver must be kept drained. Inevitably, more water will condense in the distribution lines if the air cools further. This must also be removed if the problems outlined above are to be reduced. To remove this water:

1. Take all feeders off the top of mains and branches;

2. Slope mains and branches toward a dead end;

3. Drain all low points and dead ends through a water leg using automatic traps to insure drainage; and,

4. Incorporate strainers and lubricators in the piping to all tools.

Fig. 27-D illustrates the system.

Temperature of compressed air leaving an aftercooler and receiver will largely depend upon the temperature and quantity of the water used in the cooler. Unfortunately, when atmospheric temperature and humidity are highest and condensation in the cooler is most needed, the water temperature is usually also high. Results are not always all that could be desired.

This is the system used most generally throughout industry and, if applied and operated with understanding and care, will give reasonable results. However, since the air-vapor mixture leaving the receiver is at, or very near, the saturation point, and since the mixture usually cools further in the system, condensation in lines must be expected and its elimination provided for.

The Dried Air System

This system involves processing the compressed air *beyond* the after-cooler and receiver to further reduce moisture content. This requires special equipment, a higher first cost and a higher operating cost. These costs must be balanced against the gains obtained. They may show up as less wear and maintenance of tools and air-operated devices, greater reliability of devices and controls, and greater production through fewer outages for repairs. In many cases reduction or elimination of product spoilage or a better product quality may result. Many automobile plants are drying air with the high priority objective of improving car finish by better paint spraying.

The degree of drying desired will vary with the pneumatic equipment and application involved. The aim is to eliminate further condensation in the line and tool. Prevailing atmospheric conditions also have an influence.

In many 100-psiG installations, a dew point at line pressure of from 50°F to 35°F is felt to be adequate. Occasional equipment may find lower dew points of value even down to minus 50°F. In such cases this may be obtained, at higher cost, of course.

Terminology involves drier outlet dew point at the *line* pressure. This is the saturation temperature of the remaining moisture. If the compressed air temperature is never reduced below this dew point at any point beyond the drying equipment, there will be no further condensation.

Another value sometimes involved when the air pressure is reduced before it is used is the dew point at that lower pressure condition. A major example is the use of 100-psiG (or higher) air reduced to 15 psiG for use in pneumatic instruments and controls. This dew point will be lower because the volume involved increases as the pressure is lowered.

The dew point at atmospheric pressure is often used as a reference point for measurement of drying effect. This is of little interest when handling *compressed* air.

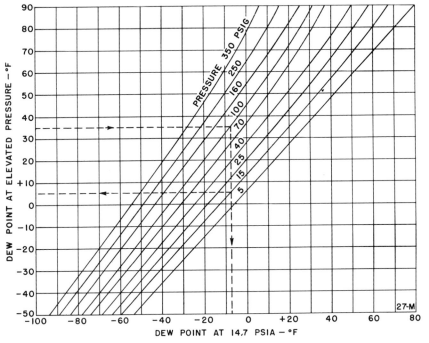

Fig. 27-L. Dew point conversion chart.

Fig. 27-L enables one to determine dew point at the reduced pressure easily. The left scale shows the dew point at the elevated pressure; in the illustrated case the air-vapor mixture has been cooled to 35°F. Drop from the intersection of this value and the elevated pressure line to the reduced pressure line and then back to the left and read the dew point at the reduced pressure. (In the example, 5°F). If the dew point at atmospheric pressure is of interest, drop straight down rather than turning left and read directly (in the example, minus 7°F). Some instrument makers like to have the air supply dried close to minus 10°F dew point at atmospheric pressure. Fig. 27-L is based on the data of pages 34-93 to 34-95. Other data are used by some in the industry who arrive at lower values for the final result in the above example. See notes on page 34-93.

Fig. 27-M shows graphically the amount of moisture remaining in the vapor form when the air-vapor mixture is conditioned to a certain dew point. *Note particularly* that this curve is based on a volume of 1000 cu ft of air-vapor mixture *at its total pressure*. For example, 1000 cu ft at 100 psiG air at 50°F or 1000 cu ft of 15 psiG air at 50°F will hold the same vapor at the dew point. However, 1000 cu ft at 100 psiG and 50°F reduced to 15 psiG will become 3860 cu ft at 50°F, so is capable of holding 3.86 times as much vapor and the dew point will not be reached until the mixture temperature is lowered materially.

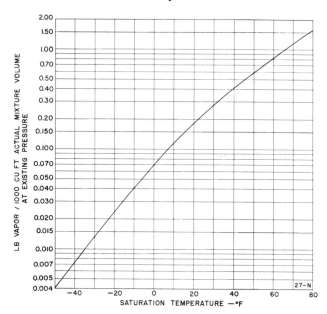

Fig. 27-M. Moisture in air at any pressure per 1000 cubic feet of actual volume at the existing pressure.

General Drying Methods

There are three general methods of drying air — chemical drying, adsorbing, and refrigerating. In all cases, aftercooling and adequate condensate removal must be done ahead of this equipment. The initial and operating costs and the results obtained vary considerably.

These methods are primarily for water vapor removal. Removal of lubricating oil is secondary, although all systems will reduce its carry-over. It must be understood that complete elimination of lubricating oil, particularly in the vapor form, is very difficult and that, when absolutely oil-free air is required, some form of nonlubricated compressor is the best guaranteed method.

Chemical Drying

Chemical driers use materials which combine with or absorb moisture from air when brought into close contact. There are two general types. One, using deliquescent material in the form of pellets or beads, is reputed to obtain a dew point, with 70°F air to the drier, of between 35°F and 50°F depending on material. The material turns into a liquid as the water vapor is absorbed. This liquid must be drained off and the pellets or beads replaced periodically. Entering air above 90°F is not generally recommended.

The second type utilizes an ethylene glycol liquid to absorb the moisture. Standard dew point reduction claimed is 40°F, but greater reductions are said to be possible with special equipment. The glycol is regenerated (dried) in a still using fuel gas or steam as a heating agent. The released moisture is vented to atmosphere. The regenerated glycol is recirculated by a pump, usually driven by compressed air. A water cooled glycol cooler is also required.

Adsorbing

Adsorption is the property of certain extremely porous materials to hold vapors in the pores until the desiccant is either heated or exposed to a drier gas. The material is a solid at all times and operates alternately through drying and reactivation cycles with no change in composition. Adsorbing materials in principal use are activated alumina and silica gel. Molecular sieves are also used. Atmospheric dew points of minus 100°F are readily attained.

Reactivation or regeneration is usually obtained by diverting a portion of the already dried air through a reducing valve or orifice, reducing its pressure to atmospheric, and passing it through the wet desiccant bed. This air, with the moisture it has picked up, is vented to atmosphere. The air diverted may vary from 7 to 17 percent of the main stream flow, depending upon the final dew point desired from the apparatus. Heating the activating air prior to its passing through the bed, or heating the bed itself, is often done. This requires less diverted air since each cu ft will carry much more moisture out of the system. Other modifications are also available to reduce or even eliminate the diverted air quantity.

Refrigeration

Refrigeration for drying compressed air is growing rapidly. It has been applied widely to small installations, sections of larger plants, and even to entire manufacturing plant systems.

Refrigeration has been applied to the air stream both before and after compression. In the *before compression* system, the air must be cooled to a lower temperature for a given *final line pressure dew point*. This takes more refrigeration power for the same end result. Partially offsetting this is a saving in air compressor power per 1000 cfm of *atmospheric* air compressed due to the reduction in volume at compressor inlet caused by the cooling and the removal of moisture. There is also a reduction in discharge temperature on single-stage compressors that may at times have some value. An atmospheric (inlet) dew point of 35°F is claimed. Referred to line pressure (at which condition condensation actually takes place), the above dew point becomes:

Line Pressure psiG	Line Dew Point—°F
25	61
35	67
50	75
70	84
100	94

These systems are usually custom designed.

When air is refrigerated *following compression,* two systems have been used. Flow of air through directly refrigerated coils is used predominately in the smaller- and moderate-sized systems. These are generally standardized for cooling to 35°F which is, of course, the dew point obtained at line pressure. Fig. 27-N diagrams the equipment furnished in a small self-contained direct-refrigeration unit.

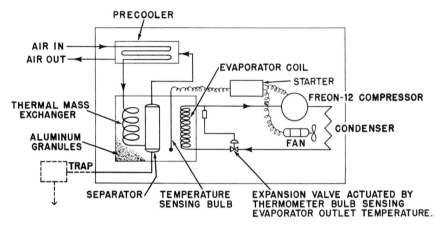

Fig. 27-N.   Diagram of a small refrigeration type compressed-air drier.

The larger systems chill water that is circulated through coils to cool the air. A dew point at line pressure of about 50°F is obtainable by this method. Fig. 27-0 illustrates diagrammatically a typical system of this kind; often known as a *chiller drier.*

The designs shown are regenerative since the incoming air is partially cooled by the outgoing air stream. This reduces the size and first cost of the refrigeration compressor and exchanger. It also reduces power cost and reheats the air returning to the line. Reheating of the air after it is dried has several advantages; (1) the air volume is increased and less *free air* is required to do a job; (2) chance of line condensation is still further reduced; and, (3) sweating of the cold pipe leaving the drier is eliminated. Reheating is done in some cases by electric heaters or by steam coils. Regenerative driers seldom need further reheating.

All refrigeration type driers will remove some oil from the air.

Combination Systems

The use of a combination drier should be investigated when a very low dew point is necessary. Placing a refrigeration system ahead of an adsorbent drier will let the more economical refrigeration system remove most of the vapor, and reduce the load on the desiccant.

Distribution Systems for Dried Air

There may be some who say that the use of dried air eliminates all need for condensate separation devices, drop legs, and drains. See Fig. 27-D, page 27-7. This should not be accepted without thought. Most plants are highly dependent upon their compressed air supply and it should be assured that the air is in at least reasonable condition at all times, even if the drying system is out of use for maintenance or repair. It is possible that the line condensation would be so bad that some air applications would be handicapped or even shut down if there were no protection. Furthermore, a very vital part of all the endeavor to separate water in the conventional system is also the trapping of dirt, pipe scale, etc. This is still necessary with a dried air system. As a minimum, all branch lines should be taken off the top of the main and all feeder lines off the top of the branch.

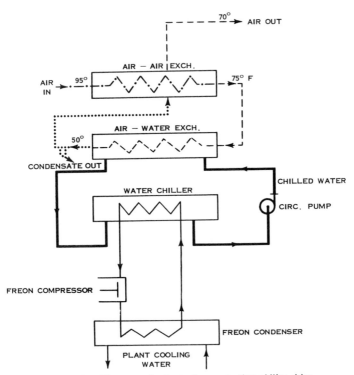

Fig. 27-O. Diagram of a typical regenerative chiller-drier.

Prevention of Line Freezing

Absolute prevention of line freezing can be obtained only when the dew point of the line air is below any temperature to which it may be exposed. Freezing is always possible if there is line condensation when, for example, the line runs outdoors in winter weather or passes through cold storage rooms. This means that the only positive solution to line freezing is air drying.

Relief from freeze-ups can, at times, be obtained by feeding antifreeze into the line ahead of the points where condensate collects. The amounts required are indeterminate except by experience. These antifreeze products must reach and mix with the condensate to prevent freezing. The possible deleterious effects of the vapors on equipment and personnel when carried in the air to the point of use must be considered.

Example of The Effect of Drying Air

As a reasonably typical example of the effect of drying air regardless of the method employed, consider the following:

CFM free air	1000
Hours/day	10
Total inlet cu ft	600,000/10 hrs
Atmosphere	75°F, 76% RH, 14.696 psiA
Weight of vapor	602 lb/10 hrs
Equivalent gallons	72.1/10 hrs (if all condensed)

Substantially the same amount of water vapor would be handled if the atmospheric conditions were either 95°F and 40 percent RH, or 68°F and 96 percent RH.

The following table shows what happens to the vapor content after the above inlet quantity has been compressed to 100 psiG and dried to various dew points. It is assumed that drying as low as 35°F involves, in all cases, cooling the air to that value. Beyond that dew point, drying is by other means and the air temperature remains at 35°F. Not all systems do this, but the example is still relatively accurate.

Dew Point Attained at 100 psiG—°F	Total Moisture Retained		Total Moisture Condensed		
	lb	%	lb	%	Gal
90	166	27.5	436	72.5	52.4
70	86	14.4	516	85.6	61.9
50	42	7.0	560	93.0	67.2
35	23.6	3.9	578	96.1	69.2
20	12.3	2.0	590	98.0	70.7
0	4.7	0.78	597	99.2	71.6
−20	1.6	0.27	600	99.7	71.9
−40	0.5	0.08	601	99.9	72.0

Specialty Equipment

Special devices may be found useful to protect sensitive equipment in certain applications.

Separators

Separators are available from many sources, in many designs, and usually consist of a knock-out chamber and condensate removal trap. Some designs include a removable filter of some type. These, of course, can only remove contaminants condensed to this point and are meant to be placed at the actual point of use. Fig. 27-P shows an effective design of such a separator.

Filters

Filters are special devices, available in many designs and materials and usually are designed for small air quantities. Filters are usually of the replaceable cartridge type. They can be constructed to remove water or oil vapor and do a remarkable cleanup job. Such filters should not be exposed to liquid and operate only on the vapors.

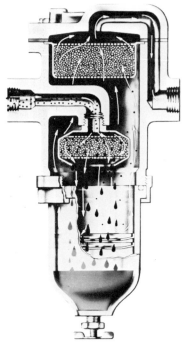

Courtesy of Zeks Industries.

Fig. 27-P.   A typical in-line compressed-air separator to be placed near the point of use.

Sterile Air

A supply of sterile air is occasionally required, as in the manufacture or packaging of medicines.

In the past, it has been considered that compressed air that has reached a temperature of about 350°F will be substantially sterile. Manufacturers of certain chemical driers state that their equipment produces sterile air and certain of the replaceable filter suppliers advise that one or more of their types will remove all bacteria.

Anyone requiring sterile air for any process, should investigate and consider all the above.

Chapter 28

Measurement of Gas Flow

Introduction

An entire book could well be devoted to this broad and complex subject. In these few pages only two areas will be considered — measurement of compressor output (performance) and measurement of air consumption of pneumatic tools and other air-powered devices. Discussion is greatly abridged.

Determination of Compressor Output

Objective

Regardless of compressor type, the first thing to be done is to state the objective. This should include accuracy desired, since this will determine, to a large degree, the test method used. Test methods are available to:

1. Measure within close limits;

2. Approximate the output; and,

3. Determine output relative to some prior standard for comparative purposes.

Methods of Testing

Five methods of measuring gas output or flow are involved within the above three categories:

1. Low pressure nozzle (subcritical flow);
2. High pressure nozzle (critical flow);
3. Sharp-edged orifice plate;
4. Tank pump-up; and,
5. Commercial meter.

General Requirements

In measuring gas the following are important, especially the first three:

1. There must be no leakage into or out of the single compressor system being tested. The system must be isolated.

2. Flow through the measuring devices of methods (1), (2), (3), and (5) above must be steady. Pulsations or resonance cause unpredictable errors. On reciprocating and straight-lobe rotary compressors, large receivers between the compressor and measuring device are necessary.

3. Persons planning and making the test must be fully familiar with use of the equipment involved as well as the objective and accuracy desired. An accurate test is not easy to run and results cannot be relied upon unless *all* details are carefully covered. There must be strict conformity with instructions, established codes, and standards.

4. For methods (1), (2), or (3), the velocity of approach to the measuring device shall be substantially zero. This means that the approach area must be about sixteen times the nozzle or orifice area.

5. Operating conditions should be within only a few percent (for most items 1.0%) of the average during any one test point.

6. Methods of applying and correcting any tests made using a substitute gas or at operating conditions other than those originally specified must be agreed upon in full detail between user and manufacturer prior to making the test.

7. Compressor manufacturer's guarantees apply only "from compressor inlet flange to compressor discharge flange" and any test must take this fact into account. It has been found that on reciprocating compressors particularly, but not solely, the air intake filter and/or intake piping can have considerable influence on capacity and horsepower. These items are not within the scope of the guarantee and manufacturers will insist that all compressors be tested with no intake piping or filter connected. The intake should be open at the compressor inlet flange.

8. Compressors handling gases other than air are more difficult to test, but the codes are rather complete and must be followed. The gas properties must be well-known.

Low-Pressure Nozzle Method

This sub-critical flow method is accepted by the ASME Power Test Code Committee and is endorsed by The Compressed Air and Gas Institute as a method of determining the output of all types of compressors. ASME PTC-9 applies to all displacement compressors, vacuum pumps, and blowers, while PTC-10 applies to all dynamic compressors and exhausters. PTC-19.5 Chapter 4, on Flow Measurement, and other applicable sections should also be referred to. These can be purchased from the American Society Of Mechanical Engineers, 345 East 47th St., New York, N. Y. A fairly complete summary of low pressure nozzle equipment and procedure is given in *Compressed Air and Gas Handbook*, published by Compressed Air and Gas Institute, 122 East 42nd St., New York 10017, N. Y. Only an outline is included here. It is based mainly on PTC-9-1954.

Most tests are made on air and as in Fig. 28-A (arrangements A and B) the discharge or inlet, respectively, is atmospheric. Arrangements C and D (Fig. 28-B) show the layouts for suction and discharge nozzles, respectively, where the gas must be contained within the system and atmospheric inlet or discharge is impossible. Fig. 28-C shows details of baffling and method of locating pressure taps and thermometers.

CAUTION — Arrangements C and D can be applied to closed circuits where the gas being measured is continuously circulated in a loop with an aftercooler following the compressor. This system should not be used with air and certain other gases if there is the *slightest* possibility of oil contamination of the gas with lubricant from any source including bearings, seals, etc. Not to observe this caution is fraught with danger, particularly if the compressor discharge temperature is or *could become* high. Much of the oil getting into the loop remains there, repeated exposure to heat tends to break it down and it could ignite in an atmosphere containing oxygen if the temperature, *even locally*, becomes excessive.

Nozzle Design

The ASME long-radius nozzle proportioned as in Fig. 28-D is the standard for the industry. This table also shows approximate maximum and minimum flow rates for *air* at *flow temperature*. Two columns of the last four cover hydraulic flow through the low-pressure nozzle and the last two cover critical flow for air through high-pressure nozzles as will be discussed later.

The dimensions shown must be closely adhered to, the inside surface must be highly polished, and the throat of the nozzle must be straight and round to very close tolerances if flow coefficients are to be valid.

Fig. 28-E shows a modification useful for small nozzles. This is not ASME approved although results will be reasonably accurate.

Note:—*Fig. 28-A, B, C, F, and G reproduced by permission from material prepared and published by the ASME Power Test Codes Committees. From Test Code for Displacement Compressors, Vacuum Pumps and Blowers (PTC 9-1954).*

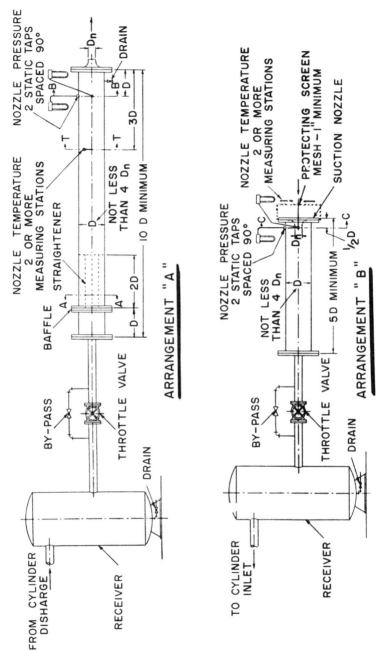

Fig. 28-A. Flow nozzle arrangements for atmospheric inlet or discharge. Arrangement "A" measures compressor discharge quantity; arrangement "B" measures intake quantity.

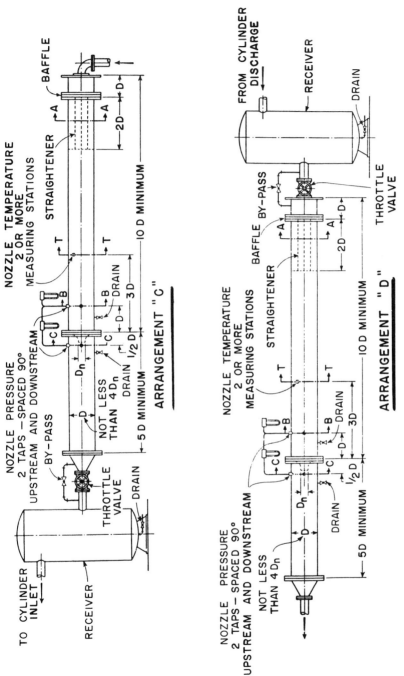

Fig. 28-B. Flow nozzle arrangements when both inlet and discharge are above atmosphere. Arrangement "C" measures compressor inlet quantity; arrangement "D" measures discharge quantity. See text for caution when using these on a recirculating system.

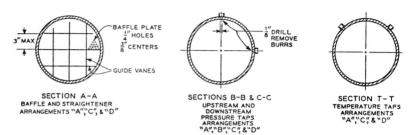

Fig. 28-C.   Nozzle pipe cross sections for Fig. 28-A and 28-B

Flow Coefficients

The coefficient of flow for nozzles depends on the Reynolds number. Reynolds number can be calculated for *air* as follows where

R_e = Reynolds number
W_a = Air flow rate - lb/hr.
μ_e = Absolute viscosity of air - lb/ft sec (see page 26–3)
D_n = Nozzle throat diameter - inches

$$R_e = \frac{W_a}{236\,\mu_e D_n} \tag{28.1}$$

To make the determination of the coefficient a bit easier, Fig. 28-F and 28-G may be used. These apply *only* to nozzles used in accordance with arrangements A and B, Fig. 28-A. For nozzles used in arrangements C and D (Fig. 28-B), the Reynolds number must be used, although a coefficient of 0.990 will be close enough for all practical purposes. If closer values are needed use the following.

Reynolds number	Coefficient
150,000	0.982
200,000	0.987
250,000	0.990
300,000	0.992
350,000	0.993
400,000	0.994
450,000 & higher	0.995

Pulsation Removal

Fig. 28-A shows a receiver on the compressor discharge. This is particularly required when measuring the flow from a reciprocating or straight-lobe compressor where their outflow is intermittent. A receiver may be also necessary on some other displacement units. The combination of receiver volume and throttling will usually dampen the pulsations sufficiently if the receiver has a minimum volume of 40 times the displacement of *one stroke* of the adjacent cylinder of a reciprocating unit. PTC-9 should be referred to for further details on determining the sufficiency of dampening for various types of units.

For dynamic compressors a receiver is not necessary.

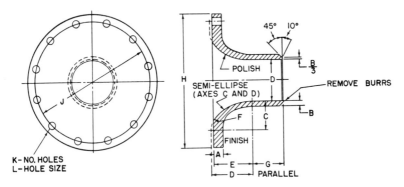

Fig. 28-D-1. Detail dimensions of ASME long-radius flow nozzle and approximate flow rates for both hydraulic- and critical-flow conditions. All dimensions in inches. See chart on next page

Fig. 28-D-1 and 28-D-2 partially reproduced by permission from material prepared and published by ASME Power Test Codes Committees. From Test Code for Displacement Compressors, Vacuum Pumps and Blowers (PTC 9 1954).

General test equipment arrangements, including proportions, are shown in Fig. 28-A. Note the care taken to obtain steady streamline flow.

It is, of course, necessary to eliminate all leakage through pipe joints between the compressor and the nozzle. The compressor must be thoroughly broken in and in good condition throughout.

During the test, the compressor must operate at rated speed and discharge pressure. The latter is maintained by adjusting the amount of throttling to the nozzle tank. The main valve should be fitted with a small bypass for close adjustments. Readings must not be taken until the compressor has been run sufficiently long to bring all temperature and pressure readings to closely steady values for the particular test condition. PTC-9 specifies a one hour minimum test for each point.

The adiabatic flow formula or a modification thereof should be used for calculation. See the *Compressed Air and Gas Handbook* or PTC-9 for these formulas and methods of making the various corrections usually necessary.

The low-pressure nozzle test is the only method normally accepted by manufacturers for checking guarantees.

Critical Flow Method

This test method has reasonable accuracy when carefully run using well-designed and manufactured equipment, although it is generally not considered to be as accurate as the low-pressure nozzle method.

To have critical flow with air, the downstream absolute nozzle pressure has to be less than 50% of the upstream absolute nozzle pressure. See pages 5-10 and 5-15. For this particular nozzle setup, with the nozzle discharging to atmosphere, as shown in Fig. 28-H, (page 28-13) the downstream nozzle pressure is barometric. The upstream nozzle pressure must be 15 psiG or higher.

Dn	A	B	C	E	F	G	H	J	K	L	Head in inches H₂O 150°F 10	Head in inches H₂O 150°F 40	Initial Pressure in psiG 165°F 15	Initial Pressure in psiG 420°F 100
											Hydraulic Flow		Critical Flow	
0.125	0.437	0.250	0.09	0.121	0.01	0.437	7.50	6.00	4	0.750	1	2	6	20
0.1875	0.437	0.250	0.13	0.181	0.01	0.468	7.50	6.00	4	0.750	2	4	14	45
0.250	0.437	0.250	0.17	0.242	0.01	0.500	7.50	6.00	4	0.750	4	8	24	80
0.375	0.625	0.250	0.25	0.363	0.02	0.562	7.50	6.00	4	0.750	9	18	55	180
0.500	0.625	0.250	0.34	0.484	0.03	0.625	7.50	6.00	4	0.750	16	32	99	320
0.750	0.625	0.250	0.50	0.726	0.04	0.750	7.50	6.00	4	0.750	36	71	222	720
1.000	0.9375	0.250	0.67	0.969	0.05	0.875	9.00	7.50	8	0.750	62	127	395	1,280
1.375	1.000	0.250	0.92	1.332	0.07	1.063	11.00	9.50	8	0.875	119	239	747	2,420
2.000	1.000	0.313	1.33	1.938	0.10	1.500	13.50	11.75	8	0.875	253	506	1,580	5,120
2.500	1.000	0.375	1.67	2.422	0.13	1.875	16.00	14.25	12	1.000	397	790	2,470	8,000
3.000	1.000	0.375	2.00	2.906	0.15	2.250	19.00	17.00	12	1.000	565	1,127	3,550	11,500
4.000	1.125	0.438	2.67	3.875	0.20	3.000	23.50	21.25	16	1.125	1,010	2,020	6,300	20,500
5.000	1.188	0.500	3.33	4.844	0.25	3.750	27.50	25.00	20	1.250	1,590	3,160	9,800	32,000
6.000	1.250	0.500	4.00	5.812	0.30	4.500	32.00	29.50	20	1.375	2,260	4,510	14,200	46,000
8.000	1.438	0.625	5.33	7.750	0.40	6.000	46.00	42.75	32	1.625	4,050	8,100	25,000	82,000
10.000	1.688	0.625	6.67	9.688	0.50	7.500	53.00	49.50	36	1.625	6,350	12,600	—	—
12.000	1.875	0.750	8.00	11.625	0.60	9.000	59.50	56.00	44	1.625	9,100	18,200	—	—
18.000	2.375	1.000	12.00	17.438	0.90	13.500	86.50	82.50	60	1.875	20,000	40,000	—	—
24.000	2.750	1.125	16.00	23.250	1.20	18.000	113.25	108.50	68	2.375	36,000	72,000	—	—

*At flow temperature with atmospheric discharge.

Fig. 28-D-2. Dimensions applying to Fig. D-1.

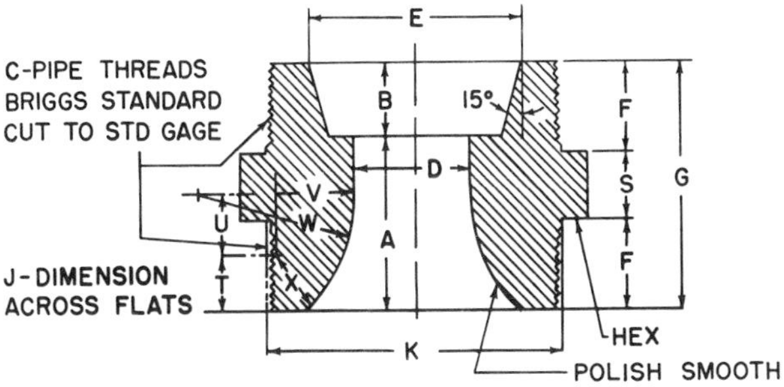

D	1/8	3/16	1/4	3/8	1/2	3/4	1	1 3/8
A	7/32	21/64	7/16	41/64	55/64	1 19/64	1 23/32	2 23/64
B	1 25/32	1 43/64	1 9/16	1 23/64	1 9/64	1 5/64	21/32	57/64
C	1 1/2	1 1/2	1 1/2	1 1/2	1 1/2	2	2	3
E	1 9/16	1 9/16	1 9/16	1 9/16	1 9/16	1 5/8	1 5/8	2 1/2
F	3/4	3/4	3/4	3/4	3/4	15/16	15/16	1 1/4
G	2	2	2	2	2	2 3/8	2 3/8	3 1/4
J	2 1/4	2 1/4	2 1/4	2 1/4	2 1/4	2 1/2	2 1/2	3 3/4
K	1 29/32	1 29/32	1 29/32	1 29/32	1 29/32	2 3/8	2 3/8	3 1/2
S	1/2	1/2	1/2	1/2	1/2	1/2	1/2	3/4
T	1/16	3/32	1/8	11/64	15/64	11/32	15/32	41/64
U	1/16	3/32	1/8	3/16	1/4	3/8	1/2	11/16
V	5/64	1/8	11/64	1/4	11/32	1/2	43/64	59/64
W	11/64	1/4	21/64	1/2	43/64	1	1 21/64	1 53/64
X	1/16	3/32	1/8	3/16	1/4	3/8	1/2	11/16
Max. Cap.* Cu. Ft. per Min.	1.98	4.45	7.91	17.8	31.6	71.2	127	239
Min. Cap* Cu. Ft. per Min.	.988	2.235	3.95	8.89	15.8	35.6	63.2	119

*Free Air - atmospheric discharge.

Fig. 28-E. Details of a small screwed type flow nozzle design. This is generally acceptable but is not ASME approved. All dimensions in inches.

Requirements are:

1. Nozzle diameter, D_n must not exceed 25% of nozzle tank diameter or 0.25D;
2. Any lines leading from receiver other than line to flow nozzle must be blanked off;
3. Line between compressor cylinder and receiver must be short as possible;
4. Receiver must have 40 times volume of dense gas discharged per stroke;
5. Thermometers and gauges must be calibrated; and,
6. Perforated baffle must have a thickness of not less than 1/4″.

To measure capacity by critical-flow nozzles, measurements of upstream nozzle pressure and upstream nozzle temperature must be taken, as shown on Fig. 28-H. The compressor intake pipe and air filter have been removed so the barometric pressure can be considered as the compressor intake pressure. Compressor intake temperature must be measured.

Nozzle design is as in Fig. 28-D. The table indicates the range of flow rates possible between 15 and 100 psiG upstream pressure. The flow coefficient can be assumed at 0.990 with little error or the table using Reynolds number (page 28-6) may be used. The same precautions must be taken as for a low-pressure nozzle test regarding the use of receivers and throttling to limit pulsations ahead of the nozzle. Operating conditions must be steady before the test starts and, for accuracy, the rules of PTC-9 must be followed.

The capacity formula for *air* with critical flow is as follows:

$$Q = \frac{9.285\ CD_n^2 p_1 T_0}{P_0 \sqrt{T_1}} \tag{28.2}$$

where Q = cfm at compressor inlet pressure and temperature conditions
C = discharge coefficient of nozzle
D_n = nozzle diameter in inches
p_1 = upstream nozzle pressure, psiA
T_1 = upstream nozzle temperature, °R
p_0 = compressor inlet pressure, psiA
T_0 = compressor inlet temperature, °R

Variations of this test method are frequently used for approximating the condition of portable compressors to determine their need for repair.

Sharp-Edged Orifice Plate Method

The thin-plate sharp-edged orifice located in a pipeline with sub-critical flow is used widely as a measuring device and is standardized in many applications. These are generally permanent installations, continuously in operation measuring nonpulsating, steady flow in a pipeline. They can give an accuracy close to that of the low-pressure nozzle when the orifice installations, readings, and calculations are made by trained personnel.

With even minor pulsating flow, dirty gas, etc., this device is apt to give results varying substantially from the true value. Laboratory calibration *with the piping used* is recommended in PTC-19.5 Chap. 4. This device is not recommended for general compressor testing.

Pump-Up Test

The pump-up test consists of operating a compressor at a measured speed and discharge pressure and observing the time required to increase the pressure in a tank of measured volume from atmosphere to the rated pressure. From this can be calculated the approximate cfm output of the compressor. The compressor discharge pressure is maintained constant by a manually operated valve between the compressor and receiver. Pulsations are no problem.

The pump-up test is not accurate largely because of the virtual impossibility of determining the average temperature of the air in the tank at the end of the test. Also, the time element involved is usually short. Although it is useful in certain applications, it must be understood that the pump-up test is comparative and qualitative only. Results can not be accepted as authoritative.

Pump-up tests are extremely useful in maintenance work on small units (say up to 25 hp) where comparative results are all that are necessary. Mechanical condition, such as cleanliness of air filter, tightness of piston rings and valves, proper functioning of unloaders, etc., influences the output capacity. If a unit is given a pump-up test when new or in tip-top shape and the time required is noted, any appreciable increase in that time on subsequent tests means that something is wrong. The output has been reduced. Investigation and reconditioning should follow.

In such tests as these, it is best to start with the compressor connected to an empty receiver (no valve between) and let the pressure increase to the maximum of the machine rating. It is important that the tank be completely emptied of condensate, that there be no leaks, and that the upper pressure be the same on all tests.

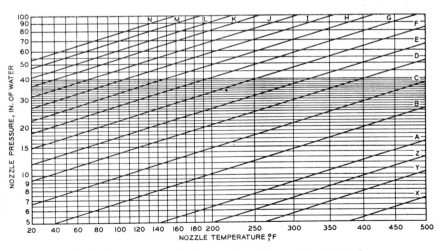

Fig. 28-F. Curve for selecting nozzle coefficient from Fig. 28-G.

Nozzle Diameter, In.

Curve	⅛	3/16	¼	⅜	½	¾	1	1⅜	2	2½	3	4	5	6	8
A	0.938	0.946	0.951	0.957	0.963	0.968	0.973	0.977	0.982	0.984	0.986	0.990	0.993	0.994	0.995
B	0.942	0.948	0.955	0.960	0.965	0.971	0.975	0.979	0.984	0.987	0.989	0.992	0.994	0.995	0.995
C	0.944	0.952	0.959	0.964	0.968	0.974	0.978	0.981	0.986	0.990	0.991	0.994	0.995	0.995	0.995
D	0.947	0.954	0.961	0.966	0.970	0.976	0.980	0.983	0.988	0.991	0.993	0.994	0.995	0.995	0.995
E	0.950	0.957	0.963	0.968	0.972	0.977	0.982	0.985	0.990	0.992	0.994	0.995	0.995	0.995	0.995
F	0.953	0.958	0.964	0.969	0.973	0.978	0.983	0.986	0.991	0.993	0.994	0.995	0.995	0.995	0.995
G	0.956	0.960	0.966	0.970	0.974	0.979	0.984	0.987	0.992	0.994	0.995	0.995	0.995	0.995	0.995
H	0.958	0.962	0.967	0.972	0.976	0.980	0.985	0.988	0.993	0.995	0.995	0.995	0.995	0.995	0.995
I	0.959	0.964	0.968	0.974	0.978	0.982	0.986	0.989	0.994	0.995	0.995	0.995	0.995	0.995	0.995
J	0.960	0.965	0.970	0.975	0.979	0.983	0.987	0.990	0.994	0.995	0.995	0.995	0.995	0.995	0.995
K	0.961	0.966	0.971	0.976	0.980	0.984	0.988	0.991	0.994	0.995	0.995	0.995	0.995	0.995	0.995
L	0.962	0.967	0.972	0.977	0.981	0.985	0.989	0.992	0.995	0.995	0.995	0.995	0.995	0.995	0.995
M	0.963	0.968	0.973	0.978	0.982	0.986	0.990	0.993	0.995	0.995	0.995	0.995	0.995	0.995	0.995
N	0.964	0.969	0.974	0.979	0.983	0.987	0.991	0.994	0.995	0.995	0.995	0.995	0.995	0.995	0.995

Fig. 28-G. Nozzle flow coefficients for air applicable to arrangements "A" and "B", Fig. 28-A, when using ASME flow nozzle. Use Fig. 28-F to select the proper line in the table.

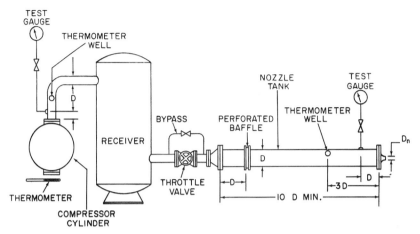

Fig. 28-H. Piping and flow nozzle arrangement for a critical-flow method of measurement.

Pump Up Formula

To *estimate* the time required to pump-up a given receiver or air system, the following formula may be used. The result disregards temperature differences and changes throughout the system. The formula gives, therefore, a somewhat longer time than should actually be required.

$$T = \frac{V\,(p_2 - p_1)}{p_0\,(Acfm)} \qquad (28.3)$$

where T is time required - min.

V is tank (or system) volume-cu ft. (cu ft $=$ gal/7.48)

p_0 is atmospheric pressure - psiA

p_1 is initial tank pressure - psiA (usually atmospheric)

p_2 is final tank pressure - psiA

$Acfm$ is average cfm air delivered by the compressor during the pump-up pressure change

Note that the actual output in cubic feet free air per minute has been used. This is the only basis on which a compressor should be evaluated. The *average* capacity will be greater than *rated* full-pressure capacity by an amount depending on compressor size, type, normal pressure rating, and range of pressure rise. For a two-stage unit, the increase might be two to four percent; for a single-stage unit, ten percent or more. These are highly approximate values.

The average capacity required to pump-up a given volume to a specified pressure may also be determined by this formula. The resultant will be slightly high, but a safe value to use.

Commercial Meters

There are many commercial meters, usually designed for permanent installation. They use a variety of primary devices. Few are suitable for a compressor test, and are not normally so used. One of these, the Tool-o-meter and Drill-o-meter, described a few paragraphs below, has occasionally been used to approximate compressor output. Pulsations must be well-limited and testing personnel must be thoroughly familiar with the meter's operation and limitations. Accuracy with 3 to 5 percent is possible.

Field Tests

Determination of the performance of a compressor for comparison with guarantees, or for other reasons, requires that a test be made to standards which will assure a degree of accuracy acceptable to all parties involved. Manufacturers normally will insist upon a test according to the applicable ASME Power Test Codes. It does not matter whether the test is run in the shop or in the field, provided the Codes are followed in their great detail.

As a practical matter, it is usually much less expensive and quicker to run a shop test. This is also apt to be more accurate. In shop or laboratory testing it is almost always possible to more readily pipe the machine to meet Code standards; auxiliary equipment is more apt to be readily available; a trained staff and calibrated instruments are at hand.

Testing in the field usually lacks some of these uncompromisable necessities. Field piping seldom permits meeting Code standards. Since normal commercial operational instruments are not sufficiently accurate for a test, proper instruments must be obtained, calibrated and installed. A test crew must be trained — one familiar with Code requirements and able to see that they are met.

An ASME test of any kind is a specialist's job. Field tests usually leave much to be desired as to accuracy and completeness. Shop tests are to be preferred. Any test of this nature is expensive.

Measurement of Air Consumption of Tools

The Tool-o-meter and the larger Drill-o-meter are excellent commercial meters for measuring with reasonable accuracy the air consumption of tools and other air operated devices. This sturdy portable in-the-line meter has many uses. Fig. 28-I shows the design. Air enters at the bottom connection and flows through the holes in the perforated cylinder and out the top connection. The pressure drop causing flow is set by the weight of the movable floating piston. This piston and attached parts move up or down as flow quantity increases or decreases.

The flow is read directly on a scale calibrated for the piston position. Readings obtained are correct if the pressure at the meter is 80 psiG at sea level (14.7 psiA barometer) and the flowing air is at 60°F. For other pressures and barometers, corrections may be made from Fig. 28-J. The pressure correction for air varies as the square root of the density. Temperature corrections to 60°F air are given by the formula below. The meter will over-register by approximately 1 percent for each 11°F. All corrections are multipliers.

$$\text{Temp. Correction} = \sqrt{\frac{520}{°F + 460}} \qquad (28.4)$$

Courtesy of New Jersey Meter Company.

Fig. 28-I.   Direct-reading air meter.

There is some pulsation compensation built into these meters in the form of a dash pot, but, for greater accuracy, receivers should be installed between compressor and meter, also between meter and tool. Fig. 28-K shows the perfect arrangement. A thermometer could be placed in a well at the entrance to the inlet (left hand) receiver by using a tee rather than an elbow if such accuracy were warranted.

These meters are used widely for testing pneumatic tools and rock drills to determine their condition relative to standards previously set on new tools. They can also be used to determine the air consumption of a wide range of pneumatic devices and applications in experimental or development work.

Tools should be running under similar conditions for all tests. Riveting hammers can be tested on actual work or striking on a block. Piston and rotary drills, used for drilling, reaming, etc., can be tested accurately with a brake load. For rock drills of the piston type, consumption varies with the nature of the rock, depth and direction of hole, etc., and, to get consistent comparative results, tests should be made under standard condi-

Elevation above Sea Level	Barometer Inches of Mercury	Absolute Pressure of Atmosphere	Gauge Pressure in pounds per square inch at the meter											
			100	90	80	70	60	50	40	30	20	10	5	2
0	29.92	14.7	1.101	1.051	1.000	.946	.888	.827	.760	.687	.605	.511	.456	.420
1000	28.86	14.17	1.138	1.087	1.034	.977	.918	.853	.784	.708	.623	.524	.466	.428
2000	27.82	13.66	1.178	1.125	1.070	1.011	.949	.882	.809	.730	.641	.538	.477	.437
3000	26.81	13.17	1.220	1.165	1.107	1.046	.981	.912	.836	.754	.661	.552	.489	.447
4000	25.83	12.69	1.264	1.206	1.146	1.082	1.015	.943	.864	.778	.681	.567	.501	.456
5000	24.88	12.22	1.309	1.250	1.187	1.121	1.050	.975	.893	.803	.702	.583	.513	.466
6000	23.96	11.77	1.356	1.295	1.230	1.160	1.087	1.009	.923	.829	.723	.599	.526	.476
7000	23.07	11.33	1.406	1.342	1.274	1.202	1.126	1.044	.955	.857	.746	.616	.539	.487
8000	22.21	10.91	1.458	1.391	1.320	1.245	1.166	1.080	.988	.885	.770	.633	.552	.497
9000	21.38	10.50	1.512	1.442	1.368	1.290	1.208	1.119	1.022	.915	.794	.651	.566	.508
10000	20.58	10.11	1.568	1.495	1.418	1.337	1.251	1.159	1.058	.946	.820	.670	.581	.520

Courtesy of New Jersey Meter Company.

Fig. 28-J. Multipliers for converting Tool-o-meter and Drill-o-meter readings. Meters read in cubic feet free air on the basis of 80 psiG inlet pressure, 14.7 psiA atmospheric pressure, and air flow at 60°F. Multipliers correct for atmospheric and inlet pressure variation. See formula 28.4 to correct for inlet temperature.

SUPPLY

TO TOOL

Courtesy of New Jersey Meter Company.

Fig. 28-K. Best arrangement for installing the meter if pulsating flow is possible, as from the compressor or tool.

tions. One common method is to have the drill strike straight down on a steel block or a hardwood block with a steel plate on top, using a short piece of soft steel rod in the drill chuck.

Temperature corrections are not necessary when testing tools. The pressure should be held at some standard value for all tests, however, since tool performance varies considerably with pressure. A reducing valve in the feed line set to hold 95 psiG is suggested. Most tools are designed to operate at 90 psiG and this allows for some pressure drop through the hose and fittings.

It is possible to use these meters for measurement of gases other than air if the readings are specially corrected. The gas specific gravity must be accurately known.

Chapter 29

Pneumatic Tools

Caption Index   **Page**

Introduction

Pneumatic tools, as discussed here, are those air operated devices that are portable and are taken to the work. They are usually hand-held and can be further restricted to tools used principally in production, maintenance, and construction. Those air-powered tools commonly classed as rock drills are discussed in the next chapter.

Pneumatic tools are light, powerful, rugged, and safe. They are built in many sizes and designs and are adaptable to all types of work. Their utility is great and operating cost low. *The cost of the air used plus service life tool cost is less than 5 percent of the total cost of doing a job.* The major part of any job cost is therefore labor. (For cost of air data, see page 27-2). Improved quality, uniformity of production, and greater output per man-hour is attained through the use of properly applied tools. The high ratio of developed power to weight and their compactness give pneumatic tools a decided advantage over other portable tools.

There are two definite types of pneumatic tools; the rotating and the reciprocating or percussion. Rotative machines are essentially air motors coupled to a shaft or spindle to give a rotary motion. Rotary tools predominantly use vane-type motors, although piston-type motors are still used in many tools, particularly hoists. Rotary tools may be further classified as either straight rotary or impact tools. The latter deliver rapid turning impacts or hammer blows when resistance to turning reaches a certain value.

Percussive tools are hammers, one type using a free reciprocating piston to strike repeated blows on a tool held in the end of the barrel. Another type reciprocates a captive piston to pound or ram.

The four types described above are illustrated on the next two pages.

PRODUCTION

Grinder removing excess metal from a motor frame casting.

Torque control rotary impact tool assembling diesel engine flywheel.

PRODUCTION

Controlled power chipping hammer cleaning an iron casting.

Bench rammer for ramming up the
cope of a flask for a small casting.

CONSTRUCTION

Pneumatic holder-on bucking up rivets
being driven by a pneumatic riveter.

Pneumatic hoist lifting material to working
platform during assembly of a large boiler.

CONSTRUCTION

Air powered diaphragm pump dewatering a trench on a construction site.

Bolting a truss member using a torque control impact wrench to assure attainment of proper stress.

Work Classification

In the selection of any tool, it is necessary that the type of work involved be clearly set forth. There are two broad groups here. One is the *dead end* group where the operation comes to a definite halt at intervals. This includes such operations as drilling, nut running, and screw or nail driving. The other group is called *open end* and is continuous, depending upon the operator for termination. Grinding, chipping, and scaling are example. There are also many operations that cannot be specifically classed as either of these.

Speed and power are two factors of vital importance in the selection of tools, but they are not of equal importance on every job. Speed is apt to be more important in dead end operations, while power plays the more important role in open end work. Considering two grinders, for example, as the operator leans on the tool, applying more pressure, the tool with the greater power will better maintain its speed and will remove more metal.

The work to be done can be further classified.

1. Grinding, buffing, sanding;
2. Drilling, reaming, tapping, setting studs;
3. Driving screws, setting nuts;
4. Lifting, dragging;
5. Chipping, riveting, calking, scaling, ramming; and,
6. Specialty operations.

For all these, a wide variety of tools is available. They will differ in weight, speed, power, and type of accessory equipment available, as well as in arrangement of control valve, type of handle, etc.

Selection Factors

The principal factors involved in tool selection are:

1. Tool weight — a light, easily handled tool reduces operator fatigue;
2. Speed — the faster a tool runs under load, the quicker the job is apt to be done;
3. Power — the greater the power (when required), the better the stabilization of speed under load;
4. "Feel" — the operator must be able to use the tool comfortably;
5. Size — it must be such that it can reach the work readily;
6. Quality of finish obtained — this is an important factor in selection;
7. Uniformity — the final effect in such areas as driving screws or running nuts is important;
8. Maintenance — costs are involved; and,
9. Relative efficiency — the output efficiency compared to that of the present tool or method of doing a job.

Once again, the proper pneumatic tool makes it possible for an operator to turn out more and better work; the cost of the tool itself plus the air power required to drive it is usually of little consequence.

Pay-Out Time

In the study of any operation for tool application, it is axiomatic that a new tool must pay for itself. The money to pay for the tool will usually come only from the labor cost reduction. Pay-out time will vary from job to job and cannot be generalized. Actual studies often give pay-out times of from 4 to 24 weeks, but some users allow pay-out times up to one year. It may be found in some operations that, although there is no actual production time saving, the upgrading of product quality should be evaluated.

Keeping Tool Efficiency High

Because of the high proportionate value of the operator's time, every effort should be made at all times to provide him with an efficient tool. This requires attention in several areas.

1. Maintenance of proper air pressure;

2. Preventive maintenance at point of use;

3. Scheduled inspection and repair; and,

4. Replacement when major repairs are required.

Proper Air Pressure

The importance of proper hose selection and the value of proper air pressure has been discussed on pages 27-9 through 27-14 and should be re-read here. The effect of altitude on free air capacity requirement of tools is given on page 34-153.

Industrial tools are designed to perform best at about 90 psiG pressure *at the tool*, but are more often found operating at 85 to 80 psiG or even lower due to distribution system inadequacies. Rather than change large systems, some automotive companies are specifying that new air compressors be designed for 125 psiG discharge, although they may not operate that high immediately. This is primarily intended to restore the tool pressure lost through pipe friction, not to boost it above 90 psiG.

Tools supplied from portable compressors often operate at 100, 110, or even 125 psiG. Their air feed system is simple and, while pressure losses in the line (if any) and the hose may be of consequence, there is usually sufficient reserve in the compressor.

Preventive Maintenance

There are four general causes of premature failure and loss of efficiency in pneumatic tool operation. These are all found at the point of use.

1. Lack of proper piping, separator, trap and drainage facilities to eliminate and prevent carry-over of moisture into the tool — this carry-over destroys lubrication and accelerates wear. The remedy lies in proper attention to the fundamentals of the piping system, and, possibly, to relatively complete air drying. See Chapter 27.

2. Carry-over of dirt, rust, and scale into the tool — this also results from inadequate attention to the requirements of a good air power system and maintenance of its various items. Deterioration of hose linings contributes to this problem. Allied to this is the removal of strainers placed at the inlet of many tools. These should be kept clean — not removed.

PRODUCTION

Screwdriver used in final assembly of platform scales.

Low headroom air powered hoist handling mixing containers in a chemical plant.

PRODUCTION

Impactool being used in assembly of a thread rolling machine.

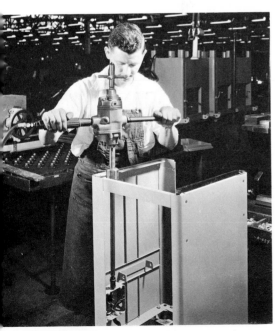

Rotary drill with extension and hole saw attachment cutting holes in meat saw cabinet base.

MAINTENANCE

Digger used in trenching on a maintenance job.

Scaler cleaning a joint on a tank.

MAINTENANCE

Backfilling on a gas line trench with air powered tampers.

Impactool tightening 3½'' bolts on a roll-mill change-over.

PRODUCTION

Surface grinder with cup-type wheel smoothing rough welds on a structural frame.

Small riveter used to drive coated screw nails in the manufacture of pallets.

PRODUCTION

Portable assembly machine tightening bolts on a differential ring gear sub-assembly.

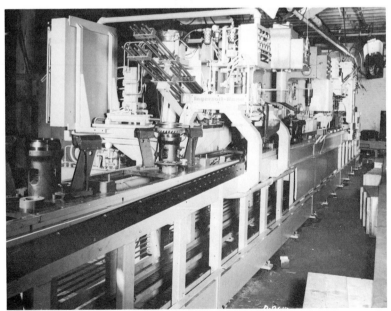

Part of an integrated air powered assembly machine for assembling automobile differentials.

3. Lack of proper lubrication — this accounts for a high percentage of tool failures. Air tools are lubricated with oil carried to it in the air-stream. Oil may be introduced from an oiler placed in the line leading to the tool, or from an oil reservoir within the tool itself, or both. Care must be taken that the lubricant reservoirs are never empty. On most jobs, this means filling once per shift.

4. Physical abuse of tools, dropping, dragging, and throwing — these cannot help but cause deterioration. An operator who is improperly trained in the use of the tool can also damage it severely. Overloading, using a tool on work heavier than it was designed for, will increase repair costs materially.

Regular Inspection and Repair

Scheduled maintenance involves getting the tools back to the repair shop on a regular routine for a checkup. Replacement of worn parts is made before an actual breakdown or a serious loss in efficiency occurs. It is the aim to maintain tool efficiency as close as possible to that of a new tool.

The period between these checkups will vary widely depending upon the use factor involved and the extent of preventive measures. It must be remembered that a reduction of only 10 percent in efficiency will lengthen the time to do a certain amount of work by 10 percent. If an operator gets $5000/year, the increase in cost is $500 which would buy two new average tools.

It has been found that a scheduled maintenance program should include the stocking of surplus tools, to 10 or 20 percent of the tools actually in use. This will materially reduce the number of spare parts required and will permit a more thorough and unrushed overhaul of the worn tool.

A tool tends to deteriorate in a straight line manner based on hours of actual use. Although it is unlikely that *routine* minor overhaul and repair will completely restore the tool to its full output, major manufacturers maintain repair depots where tool overhaul is guaranteed to bring it back to original efficiency. Repair costs tend to rise as the tool gets older.

Replacement

Tool efficiency, however, finally reaches the point where major repairs must be made. This is often considered to be when replacement parts cost equals about 40 percent of the original tool cost. At this time, purchase of a new tool should be considered. Efficiency of the older tool, even if repaired, could not normally equal that of a *new modern* tool, since manufacturers have been successful in increasing tool productive output by 10 to 20 percent per year through improved design.

This situation often leads to a planned annual replacement program, which automatically replaces every year a percentage of the tools of each type being used. The table shows typical use factors and retooling rates for principal tool categories. The maximum tool life is shown in the right column. On this basis, a substantial proportion of all tools are the modern, higher production types and the average output efficiency is kept high. Of course, a plant having different use factors would have different maximum tool life and retooling rates. Replacement rates will also be influenced greatly by the adequacy of the regular maintenance program.

Operation	Average Tool Cost	Retooling Rate	Use Factor	Maximum Tool Life (years)
Grinding......................	$300	25%	50%	4
Backfill tamping and sand ramming.	$330	10%	10%	10
Drilling......................	$275	20%	25%	5
Chipping, Scaling, and Riveting....	$165	50%	50%	2
Screw Driving.................	$200	20%	50%	5
Nut Running (Impact tools).......	$300	33%	50%	3
Nut Running (Angle Wrenches).....	$400	25%	50%	4
Hand Held Rock Drilling, Pavement Breaking, and Digging.......	$440	10%	10%	10
Hoists.......................	$550	5%	10%	20

Table shows maximum tool life for several common air tools. Life is based on average percentage of time tool is in use (use factor). Retooling rate is the percentage of tools that have to be replaced each year so that none will be carried beyond maximum life.

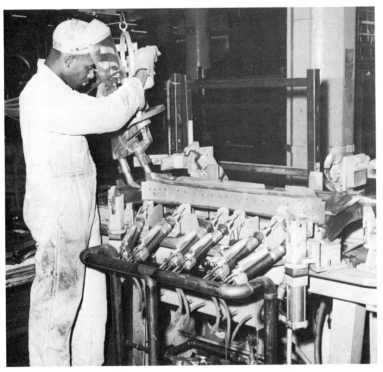

Drilling six holes simultaneously in automobile body back panel with automatic air feed drills.

Chapter 30

Rock Drills

Index   Page

Introduction

The rock drill was probably the first pneumatic tool. Originally designed to be operated by steam, its application for tunneling and mining underground forced the use of compressed air power and did much to speed development of air compressors. The first use of rock drills in tunneling was in 1861 in Europe. The first tunnel was driven with drills in the United States in 1866. Since then, the rock drill has made many things possible that we take for granted. Entire industries, including some of the largest ones, depend upon the excavation of ore or rock for their raw materials. Our transportation systems — railroads, highways, canals, and ship channels — would inevitably follow longer and more circuitous routes had their builders been obliged to attack rock solely with the power of human muscles. Our great dams and hydroelectric plants, our deep-rooted skyscrapers, our water-supply and sewage systems, and numerous other physical works that effect our daily lives and well-being exist largely because of the rock drill.

The first drills used a drilling element that was clamped in the outer end of the piston and reciprocated back and forth, giving a jabbing action to break the rock. This was known as the piston drill. It was not until about 1890 that the first practical percussion, or hammer, drill was perfected. Today, all drills are the hammer type, wherein a piston within the cylinder moves rapidly back and forth, pounding on the end of the drill steel or directly on the bit. This method reproduces the action of the original hand sledge method of drilling where the bit was in contact with the rock at all times and the full effect of each blow could be used for breakage.

Rock Drill Classification

Rock drills may be classified into five general categories:

1. Paving breakers or demolition tools;
2. Jackhamers or sinkers;
   Jackdrills
3. Drifters;
4. Stopers; and,
5. Downhole drills.

Still another grouping covers the method of ejecting the rock cuttings from the hole.

1. *Solid steel* and no means of ejection, used only for demolition and a few maintenance tools.
2. A *dry* drill in which very little air passes through the hollow steel when drilling, but manual means are provided to blow sufficient air through the steel to clear the hole when the drill is stopped.
3. *Blower* which constantly supplies hole cleaning air through the hollow steel and may also have means to blow when the drill is not running.
4. *Wet* drills which have a constant supply of water and air flowing through the drill and hollow steel when the drill is running, most used underground.
5. *Dry* drilling using an *ejector* system which pulls the cuttings through a special bit, hollow steel, and through the drill, and ejects them to a dust collector.

Paving Breakers and Demolition Tools

This group of hand-held tools is designed to accomplish what the name implies. They range in size from 15 to about 150 pounds, use solid steel, and do not have automatic rotation. Fig. 30-A shows the range of sizes.

They are fitted with a wide variety of accessories to best accomplish many specialized jobs, including driving sheathing, driving spikes, digging clay, tamping, etc. Fig. 30-B shows some of these adapters.

Jackhamers or Sinkers

These are used primarily for drilling down holes where the operator holds the tool. These tools use hollow steel and may be either dry or wet drills. They use automatic steel rotation and vary in weight from 15 to 65 pounds. The heavier units are well suited for shaft sinking, excavation, and quarry work. The lighter units are used for general contracting and maintenance.

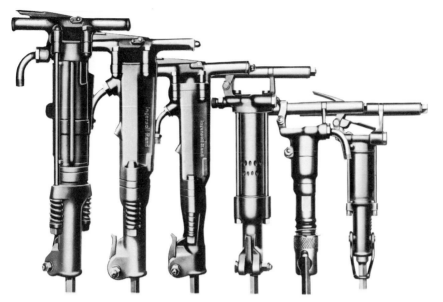

Fig. 30-A.   A typical line of paving breakers.

Jackdrills

Jackdrills are designed for horizontal or nearly horizontal drilling. The jackdrills are connected with a pivotal connection to an air cylinder that keeps the drill advancing as the bit cuts the rock. Many different lengths of feed legs are available and designs consist of single action, telescopic, and retractable. See Fig. 30-C.

Drifters

Drifters were originally used for drilling holes roughly on the horizontal, but are today mounted on rigs that permit their use for drilling down and angle holes. They are self-rotating and use hollow steel for either dry blower or wet drilling. They are heavier tools than those mentioned previously and are usually classified by piston diameter.

Drifters are most often mounted on hydraulic booms, columns, or portable mountings with wheels or crawler chassis. They have various types of mechanical or automatic feed. Fig. 30-G, H, I, J, K, L, M, illustrate some of the mountings and uses of drifters.

Fig. 30-B.   Some of the many accessory tools available for use in paving breakers.

Fig. 30-C.   A Jackdrill with jackleg mounting.

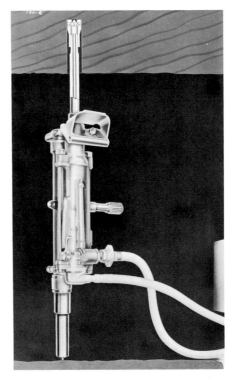

Fig. 30-D.   A typical dry stoper fitted with ejector for cuttings.

Stopers

Stopers are drills especially designed for vertical or nearly vertical overhead drilling. These tools may have hand- or self-rotation and are fitted with an air cylinder feed to keep the drill bit against the rock at all times. Stopers are usually of the wet type but in some applications are fitted with dry dust collecting features. Fig. 30-D illustrates a stoper in use.

The Downhole Drill

This drill is the most efficient of all. The piston strikes directly on the bit and follows the bit down the hole. The bit is an integral part of the drill design. Air is supplied through the hollow drill rod for both power and hole cleaning. Cuttings are ejected to a dust collector on the surface.

These drills are rotated by a separate air-motor at the top of the drill rod. Sizes are available for holes 4-3/4" to 30" diameter. Hole depths to 600 feet are common. These tools are used on truck or crawler mountings in quarries, open pit mines, road construction, and water well drilling.

A typical downhole drill is illustrated in Fig. 30-E.

Fig. 30-E. Section of a downhole drill.   **Fig. 30-F. A typical roller cone bit.**

Rotary Roller Cone Bits

This type of bit (Fig. 30-F) penetrates by cutting, reaming, and crushing. Compressed air is often used for hole cleaning and for rotation power. The roller cone bit is a supplement to the downhole drill and may utilize the same mounting and rotation mechanism.

Mountings

In the past, drifters were often mounted in a cradle or shell clamped to a column, post, or tripod and were either manually or automatically fed forward as drilling progresses. Modern practice is to use hydraulic-powered boom mountings for the feed and drill. Fig. 30-G illustrates an air-powered crawler boom mounting having 180 degree range in drill hole direction between nearly vertical upward and back, beyond vertical, downward.

Fig. 30-H shows such an arrangement of three such boom-supported drifters mounted on a diesel-powered chassis, working underground.

Fig. 30-I illustrates a similar mounting for drilling down and angular holes. This tractor will tow its own portable compressor even up a grade.

For heavier work, larger models are available, some being truck mounted, carrying the necessary compressor to form a self-contained over-the-highway unit. Still larger units for permanent or semi-permanent installation are available in crawler mountings including the necessary compressors. These latter units are used for heavy-duty quarrying and excavating jobs. Fig. 30-J and Fig. 30-K are typical.

Fig. 30-G.   Typical boom mounted drifter on a crawler.

Fig. 30-H. A typical boom mounting used underground.

Fig. 30-I. Trenching with boom mounted drifter. The crawler can tow the compressor.

Fig. 30-J.   A portable truck mounting.

Fig. 30-K. Heavy-duty crawler drill, carrying its own compressor; completely self-contained.

For tunneling and underground work there are special mobile mountings called jumbos that are built to suit the specific requirements of a project. These may be rail, rubber-tired, or tractor mounted for movement to and from the face. Fig. 30-L and Fig. 30-M show two of these. The latter is self-propelled at the working face.

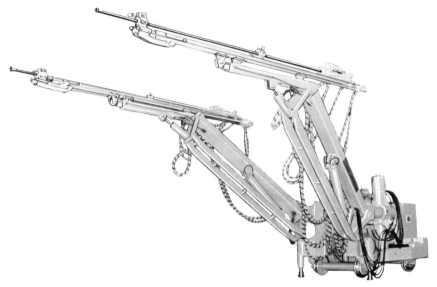

Fig. 30-L   A railcar jumbo used for certain types of tunneling.

Fig. 30-M.   A large rail mounted jumbo as used to drill 2 41-foot bore.   Carries 12 boom mounted drifters.

Underwater drilling to widen or deepen channels also uses rock drills. These are mounted on barges that are completely self-contained. The drill is carried in a ladder mounted on a tower that can be moved along the side of the barge. The barge must be anchored and is usually supported in place by spuds which rest firmly on the bottom. There may be up to three drills per barge. They are of the drifter or the downhole type. Fig. 30-N shows a large barge with three of the latter drills.

Fig. 30-N.   A three-tower drill barge for harbor and river work.

Associated Equipment

Drill Steel Rod

Drill steel rods were, for many years, a single piece with a bit forged on one end and a shank with necessary collar or lugs forged on the other end.

The first improvement was the detachable and replaceable bit screwed on one end of the rod using special threads. This was followed by the use, on certain types of rods, of a special shank piece connected to the rod by a threaded coupling. These changes permitted the choice of the most suitable steel composition and heat treatment for each part, resulting in longer service life and reduced drilling costs.

Rods with integral shanks, but using detachable bits, are used with the lighter drills, while the three-piece construction is prevalent with the drifters and heavy drills.

Drill rods are traditionally round or hexagonal, but a recent heavy-duty rod has a continuous spiral thread for its full length. If a steel should break, only squaring of the end *and chamfering* is required to prepare it for further use. See Fig. 30-O.

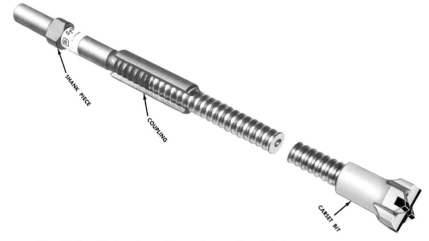

Fig. 30-O. Modern four-piece rod assembly, including shank piece, spiral rolled rod, coupling, and bit.

Drill Bits

Most bits today are of the four point (X) type with tungsten carbide inserts on the cutting faces. These have long service life, but require occasional sharpening.

A newer design, the button type, has multiple imbedded cylinders of tungsten carbide in the face and angular periphery. These inserts crush and fracture the rock. The bit metal wears away to always maintain the inserts beyond the bit face. Although button bits do not require reconditioning as frequently as Carset bits, occasional redressing of the buttons to their original conical shape will significantly extend bit service life. These bits are being used in a wide variety of rocks ranging from limestone to granite with satisfactory results.

Fig. 30-P shows the cutting faces of these two bits. Both are made in sizes and designs suitable for use in the Downhole drill (Fig. 30-E) as well as for attachment to drill rod.

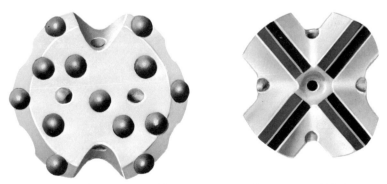

Fig. 30-P. Bit faces-button and four point types with tungsten carbide inserts.

Hoists

Hoists find many uses in connection with rock drill equipment. They are available for either pneumatic or electric operation in most types. One-, two-, or three-cable drums may be provided.

Hoists are used in mines, principally on scraper or slusher service where two or more ropes or cables are required. These machines are so constructed that power may be applied to any drum independently. When one drum is pulling, the others are free to pay out cable. One is referred to as the "pull-rope" drum and the others as "tail-rope drums." See Fig. 30-Q.

Fig. 30-Q.   A double-drum hoist used as a slusher underground.

On mine scraper or slusher service, the double-drum tail rope passes over a sheave located in the heading of the tunnel or stope, and is attached to the back of the scraper, which is usually of the hoe type. The pull rope is attached to the bail or drawbar of the scraper. The sheave is usually anchored somewhat behind and above the material to be moved. The scraper is designed to gather a load as it advances and to release the material when it starts to return. The movement of the scraper is controlled by the alternate action of the hoist at the will of the operator. It may also be automated. See Chapter 25.

Triple-drum slusher hoists operate in the same manner. When one drum pulls, the other drums run free. Triple-drum hoists are used for working a large horizontal area where they eliminate the necessity of frequent relocation of the sheave blocks.

In mining, this method is widely used for scraping material into chutes or mill holes from which it is loaded by gravity into cars on a lower level. Material can also be scraped up a ramp and loaded directly into the cars.

Hoists are usually mounted on a horizontal or vertical flat surface or bar. Turntables are sometimes used where the direction of pull changes frequently. The smallest sizes can be arranged for mounting on a column or crossbar.

Air-driven scraper hoists or slushers are used for safety reasons in many places where electric power lines are not installed, or are regarded as a hazard, or where heat or gas conditions make the exhaust air desirable. They are often recommended for their flexibility, high motor torque, and light weight for the power developed. No harm can result from overloading them, and they can be accurately controlled and operated at any speed up to the maximum that the load will permit.

Maintain the Air Pressure

As with all pneumatic tools, the air supply to rock drills must be maintained at the proper pressure if there is to be maximum production. Most drills are designed for 90 psiG pressure *at the tool.* Use of a needle gauge check when the tool is running is recommended. See the discussion in Chapter 27 regarding the effect of low air pressure and the remedies for it, as well as the importance of proper hose selection. Pressure losses in hose suitable for rock drills will be found on page 34-161.

Air Capacity Required by Rock Drills

The free air consumption of rock drills varies with altitude. Tables presenting approximate correction factors are on page 34-153. When multiple drills are operated from a single-compressor plant, diversity factors may at times be applied in sizing the compressor required. See page 34-152.

Preventive Maintenance

Preventive maintenance with rock drills centers principally in the following areas:

1. Proper lubrication;
2. Protection from water;
3. Keeping dirt out;
4. Chuck maintenance;
5. Use of standard shanks on the steel; and,
6. Keeping side rods tight.

Poor lubrication in a rock drill immediately produces a faster rate of frictional wear. Sliding pressure between unoiled working parts scuffs metal and tears out tiny fragments. The real danger, however, is the heat generated. It creates tiny cracks that speed the destruction of the drill. These small openings lead to progressively larger fractures, metal fatigue sets in, and the part finally breaks.

Of utmost importance is the use of an approved oil introduced by an air line oiler. This cannot be over emphasized.

Moisture is another rock drill enemy and is present in the atmosphere about the drill and often in the air driving it. Rust will form when an oil is used that does not emulsify well with water to provide a uniform coating. An oil that resists the washing action of water is mandatory. Water that enters a wet drill, either because of poor packing or because of excessive water pressure, exposes the tool to rust and corrosion. Corrosion pits all finished surfaces and increases the danger of wear and metal fatigue; each condition accelerates the other. Use of proper air piping and equipment to provide dry air at the drill is an excellent investment.

Abrasives enter a rock drill in three ways; as particles in the air from the compressors, or as pipe scale or flakes of deteriorated rubber from air lines; as dirt picked-up when the drill is dropped in muck or as a result of the tool being left in the blast area; and, as dirt in lubrication oil.

Impurities from the compressor can be reduced by air intake filters. Lines to the drill should always be blown out to keep them clean. Another way to minimize danger to the drill is installing a strainer in the air hose in front of the line oiler. This will catch coarse solids and pipe scale. Some drills have fine wire screen strainers in the goose neck to do the same job but operators occasionally remove them, complaining they impair efficiency. This is only because they aren't serviced regularly. Air strainers and filters are excellent insurance against excessive rock drill wear and should be cleaned at necessary intervals.

Correct alignment of the tool with the steel cannot be maintained with a bad chuck — the component whose job is to hold and correctly align the steel. If a worn chuck is used the steel will present an angle to the blow of the piston or anvil block, and the shank of the steel will not be struck squarely. Broken steels or chipping of the shank will result. The end of the air or water tube may be shorn off or beaten closed. The steel being hit at an angle puts side stresses on the piston and rifle bar, and rotation is impaired. All this means poor drilling efficiency and increased maintenance.

Inspection and prompt repair of drill steel shanks is as important to rock drill performance as replacing worn parts. Out-of-standard shanks cause damage to bits and working parts.

When side rods are loose, excessive play causes wear and misalignment. Strains develop and broken parts result. Loose side or tie rods also allow air leakage between backhead and cylinder or the cylinder and chuck housing, and often causes stripped threads on the rods. Uneven tension on the rods frequently causes the tighter one to break just behind the nut. The misalignment that results from unequal tension harms rotation and can progressively wear the buffer ring until the protective air cushion between piston head and the ring is destroyed.

Chapter 31

Air Lift Pumping

Caption Index   **Page**

Introduction

The air lift was, at one time, a popular method of pumping liquids and mixtures of liquids and solids. Today, many previously favored applications utilize the deep-well (down-the-hole) centrifugal pump. It is more economical than the air lift and, fitted with proper materials, can handle certain corrosive and erosive liquids over a good range of capacities and lifts with reasonable success.

Most present air-lift applications are special, where economy is not a primary factor. Simplicity and absence of moving parts in contact with the liquid are distinct advantages.

This chapter contains data developed from years of experience and extensive testing on an experimental well. However, in applying these data, one must realize that this is not an exact science. Adjustments may be necessary in the final analysis.

Advantages

Following are some favorable features of the air lift, generally in comparison to use of a centrifugal pump.

No moving parts are in the well or in contact with the liquid.

Power is developed on the surface and piped to the bottom. Most deep-well pumps in the United States are driven from an individual surface motor through shafting down the well with well shaft bearings lubricated either by water or from the surface. In Europe, the predominant drive is a direct-coupled under-water motor.

The well diameter in some cases will be less with the air lift.

No stand-by is required for a crucial service. The well piping seldom, if ever, needs replacement. The air compressor may usually be spared by renting portable compressors in an emergency. Deep-well pumps require two wells and two pumps to provide a stand-by.

The compressor is on the surface, always available for proper operating care and maintenance.

A single-compressor plant can service any number of wells, when using proper controls.

The air lift is much more stable in efficiency when water levels change or fluctuate seasonally. Usually no changes need be made, other than possibly to slightly increase the amount of air. In extreme cases, the well pipe length can be altered as necessary at little cost.

The air lift can handle sandy water or gritty liquids for years with little wear and no loss in efficiency.

An air lift installed for most efficient operation, can pump 40 to 50 percent more during peak demands if air is available and the liquid is available for pumping. This cannot be done by a deep-well pump.

Disadvantages

The air lift is less efficient than the deep-well pump. If operation is continuous, this can make quite a difference in power cost. The efficiency of the air lift as a ratio of hydraulic power to compressor brake horsepower will lie generally between 30 and 45 percent.

The air lift usually requires a much deeper and more expensive well than the centrifugal pump. The latter operates with from 2- to 20-foot suction head or submergence regardless of lift, whereas the air lift, for best performance, requires a footpiece submergence below water level of from 50 to 500 feet for lifts from 20 to 750 feet, respectively. Therefore, while a well depth of from 25 to 770 feet will suffice for a centrifugal pump at the above extremes, an air-lift well would, at best efficiency, need to be 70 to 1250 feet deep. Of course, in all cases the well must be deep enough to tap the water bearing stratum. This may nullify this disadvantage if the water stratum is deep. At some loss in efficiency, the air lift will operate at lesser submergence.

How The Air Lift Works

The principle of the air lift is simple; Fig. 31-A illustrates a diagrammatic air lift.

The equipment consists essentially of a "U" tube having unequal legs and a means of supplying compressed air to the bottom of the longer leg. The shorter leg is completely immersed in a reservoir of liquid.

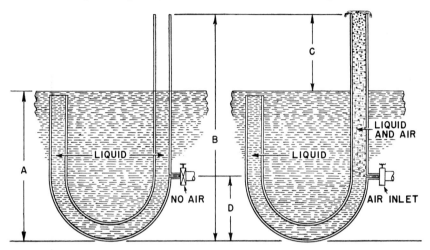

Fig. 31-A.   A diagrammatic air lift.

Dimension A represents the hydrostatic head at the bottom of the tube; B, the distance to the desired point of discharge; C, the actual level of the discharge above the normal hydrostatic level (the lift); and D, the elevation of the air inlet above the bottom of the tube.

Initially, as shown in the left hand sketch, air is closed off and the liquid stands at reservoir level in both legs. In the right hand sketch, air has been admitted through small orifices into the liquid at the foot of the longer straight section of the tube. This forms small bubbles in the liquid and the liquid level at the top of this leg will rise and finally overflow. There is, in our example, no change in reservoir level, but flow has begun.

Flow can occur only when the hydrostatic head of A is greater than that of B. The air lift accomplishes this by aerating and lightening column B. The action is one of a difference in specific gravity, the weight of the left column of solid liquid overbalancing the weight of the right column of aerated liquid sufficiently to overcome friction and cause flow.

When pumping a well, the reservoir is in the ground surrounding the well, the shorter leg is the rock strata through which the water flows to the well, and only the discharge piping from the point of air entry, as installed in the well, is of concern.

Air Lift Systems

There are two main systems used in air-lift practice, the operating principle being indentical. The differences have to do only with the arrangement of the air line and the discharge pipe. There is at the bottom of the well a footpiece designed to provide gentle entry and acceleration of the water, and the proper mixing of the water with small bubbles of air.

Fig. 31-B shows these systems. The outside air line, or VA system, has the air and discharge pipes side by side. This is the more efficient system but takes more room in the well and may limit the discharge pipe size adversely.

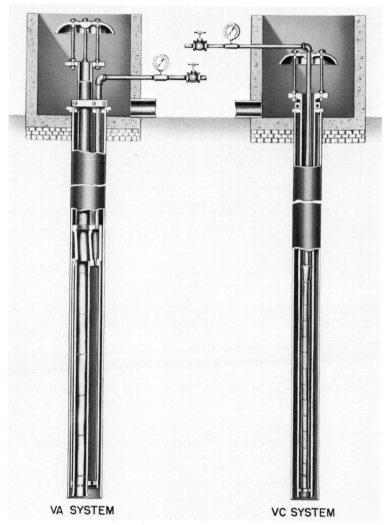

VA SYSTEM　　　　　　　　　VC SYSTEM

Fig. 31-B.　The two principal types of air lift systems.

The second, or inside (VC) system, is shown on the right. The air line is inside the discharge pipe and the full well diameter can be used to install the latter. Although less efficient than the VA type because of increased water friction, it can handle more water for a given well diameter and, if there are variations in water level from time to time, adjustments for efficient operation can be made easily by altering the length of the air line.

Terminology

Terminology of the air lift is illustrated in Fig. 31-C.

DISCHARGE LEVEL is the level of the top outlet of the discharge pipe above the ground.

STATIC WATER LEVEL is the distance from ground level to the water surface in the well when there is no flow and the water level has reached a stable position. This is the reservoir level of Fig. 31-A.

PUMPING WATER LEVEL is the distance from the ground level to the water surface in the well when the air lift is pumping its rated capacity.

AIR INLET LEVEL is, for practical purposes, the distance from the ground level to the top of the footpiece. It will average about six feet above the bottom of the footpiece and should not be less than eight feet above the well bottom.

ELEVATION or LIFT ABOVE GROUND is the distance from the ground level to the top of the discharge pipe. (See Discharge Level above).

DRAW-DOWN is the distance the water level drops from the static position when pumping at rated capacity. It is the head necessary to cause rated flow *into the well bottom* from the subterranean reservoir.

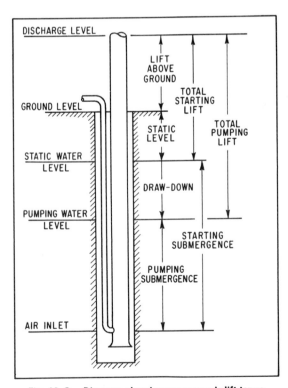

Fig. 31-C.   Diagram showing common air lift terms.

TOTAL STARTING LIFT is the distance from the static water level to the top of the discharge pipe.

TOTAL PUMPING LIFT is the distance from the pumping water level to the top of the discharge pipe.

STARTING SUBMERGENCE is the distance from the static water level to the air inlet. This is the head of water to be overcome by the compressed air to start aeration of the discharge column.

PUMPING SUBMERGENCE is the distance from the pumping water level to the air inlet level. It is the head of water to be overcome by the compressed air during pumping.

Comments on Design

It is seldom that all the data on Fig. 31-C are available immediately after a well is drilled. This is particularly true of the capacity and the draw-down involved in pumping this capacity. The best that can be done is to investigate other wells in the vicinity and to obtain as much information from well drillers as possible. Initial installation of piping should be as simple and as adjustable as possible to permit considerable freedom in testing the well, after which a permanent installation may be made.

Basis of Following Discussion

This presentation uses U.S. gallons as a base. When Imperial gallons are involved, convert to U.S. gallons at the start. One Imperial gallon equals 1.201 U.S. gallons. One liter equals 0.2642 gallons.

Water is the only liquid considered.

Symbols

A set of symbols is presented to aid calculations.

A_1	Net inside area of discharge pipe at top	sq in
A_4	Net inside area of discharge pipe at bottom	sq in
B	Atmospheric pressure	psiA
D	Draw-down	ft
E	Expansion of air volume/ft of discharge pipe	cfm
f	Air line friction loss	psi
L	Total pumping lift	ft
p_P	Pumping air pressure	psiG
p_s	Starting air pressure	psiG
Q_{a1}	Volume of dense air at footpiece	cfm
Q_{a2}	Volume of air at top of discharge pipe	cfm
Q_w	Volume of water flow	cfm
r	Air compression ratio at footpiece	dimensionless
S	Pumping submergence	ft
$\%S$	Percent pumping submergence	%
S_s	Starting submergence	ft
T	Total free air required	cfm
V_a	Quantity of free air required/gallon	cfm/gpm
V_d	Discharge velocity	ft/min
V_e	Entrance velocity	ft/min
W	Water flow	gpm

Fundamental Formulas

$$\% \, S = \frac{100 \, S}{L + S} \tag{31.1}$$

$$T = Q_{a2} = V_a \, W \tag{31.2}$$

$$r = \frac{S}{2.31 \, B} + 1 \tag{31.3}$$

$$Q_w = 0.1337 \, W \tag{31.4}$$

$$Q_{a2} = T \tag{31.5}$$

$$Q_{a1} = \frac{T}{r} \tag{31.6}$$

$$E = \frac{Q_{a2} - Q_{a1}}{L + S} \tag{31.7}$$

$$p_s = \frac{S_s}{2.31} = \frac{S + D}{2.31} \tag{31.8}$$

$$P_p = \frac{S}{2.31} + f \tag{31.9}$$

$$V_d = \frac{144}{A_1} (Q_w + Q_{a2}) \tag{31.10}$$

$$V_e = \frac{144}{A_4} (Q_w + Q_{a1}) \tag{31.11}$$

Air Required

An empirical formula for free air quantity in cubic feet per gallon of water pumped has been developed from many tests. This may be used for preliminary estimating or when the more specific data given later do not cover.

$$V_a = \frac{L}{C \log_{10} \dfrac{S + 34}{34}} \tag{31.12}$$

The constant C may be found for VC and VA systems from Fig. 31-D. This also illustrates the relative economy of the VA system over the VC. The VA is better by 33 percent at 35 percent submergence and by 11 percent at 75 percent submergence.

Submergence

Submergence, as is shown in Fig. 31-C, is the distance from water level to the *top* of the footpiece, which point is to be *not less* than eight feet from well bottom. This allowance consists of six feet for the footpiece and two feet minimum clearance below for free water entry. There are two submergences involved — starting and pumping. Pumping submergence is figured in feet, but converted to percent for some purposes. See formula 31.1.

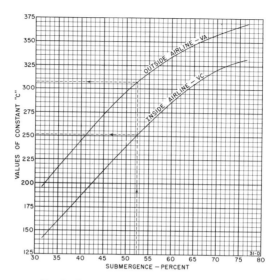

Fig. 31-D.   Constant in formula 31.12 for Vₐ.

Air Pressure

Submergence is the head of water to be overcome to permit air flow into the discharge column. It determines the air pressure required. See formulas 31.8 and 31.9. For starting, most compressor manufacturers allow a 20 percent rise above normal rating on heavy-duty compressors. This should be checked, however, for each case, because modifications may be necessary.

Optimum Values

Submergence influences both air quantity and air pressure. It therefore influences efficiency. Fig. 31-E may be used as a guide for preliminary calculations. These values are generally acceptable for both major systems at the best efficiency point and should be approached as closely as possible.

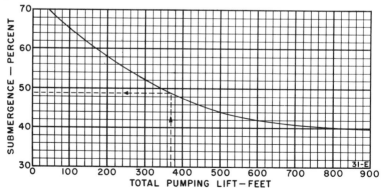

Fig. 31-E.   Approximate percent submergence for optimum efficiency. Use for either system with straight or tapered pipe.

Air Quantity Needed

The air quantity required has been experimentally determined and is shown in Fig. 31-F and Fig. 31-G for the VA and VC systems respectively. These curves shown V_a in free air (at compressor intake conditions). The variables are lift and percent submergence. Note that the higher lifts require lower percent submergence for satisfactory operation. The total air quantity to be supplied by the compressor is the product of W and V_a (31.2).

If the quantity of water pumped is less than 75 gpm, increase V_a from the above curves by about 10 percent. If gpm is over 400, V_a may be decreased slightly. These adjustments are due to relative differences in friction effect.

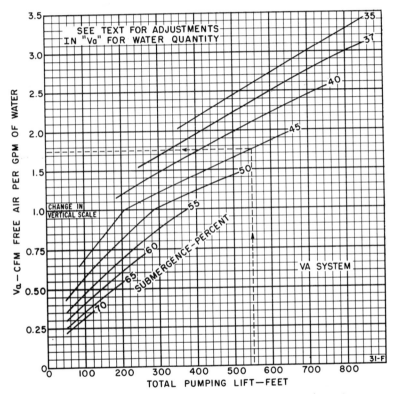

Fig. 31-F.   Cubic feet per gallon for VA (outside air line) air lift.

Low Lift Installations

Test information on very low lift pumping indicates a variation in action from more standard installations. Test data, rationalized somewhat and covering lifts from 6 to 35 ft. shows that the following is more nearly the requirement for V_a and discharge velocity for optimum conditions within this range.

Low Lift Values

Submergence %	Discharge Velocity Ft/min	V_a cu ft/gal
35	1200	0.87
40	1080	0.69
45	970	0.56
50	880	0.46
55	790	0.36
60	700	0.29
65	630	0.23
70	570	0.17
75	510	0.14
80	450	0.11

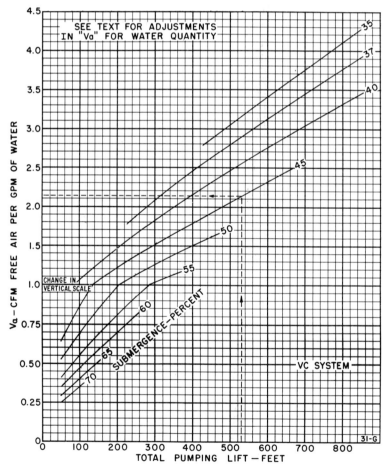

Fig. 31-G.   Cubic feet per gallon for VC (central air line) air lift.

Air Line Sizing

Having estimated the total air requirement and the distance to the footpiece from the surface, the tables of air piping friction losses starting on page 34-77 may be used to size the air line and make a final determination of friction loss. The latter should be kept to 5 psi where possible, although 10 psi is not extreme for the VC system in which the central air line should be kept small to increase water flow area within the discharge line. This also reduces the air pipe surface exposed to water friction.

Discharge Pipe Velocities

Sizing the discharge pipe is probably the most important operation in designing an air lift. Two arrangements are in use. One is a single pipe size from the footpiece to the top of the discharge. This is *straight* piping and may be used in the lower lift applications, but seldom for more than 250 feet.

The second arrangement involves increasing the discharge pipe size at calculated intervals insofar as the well size and commercial pipe sizes will permit. This is known as *tapered* piping and should be used where possible for any air lift when either the submergence or lift exceeds 50 feet.

Velocity of the mixture of air and water in the discharge pipe is of primary importance. There are two chief losses in the pipe; (1) the slippage of the air bubbles through the water, the bubbles moving somewhat faster than the water; and, (2) the normal friction of the mixture on the pipe walls. As flow velocity increases, slippage decreases and friction increases; and, vice versa. There is also an entrance friction loss at the footpiece and a need for acceleration of the water as it enters the pipe.

A constant velocity throughout the pipe length is desirable and would be most efficient, but is unattainable. The air at entry is at its highest pressure and smallest actual bubble volume. As the column ascends, the hydrostatic head is reduced and the bubble expands in proportion to the reduced pressure. At the top of the pipe it theoretically has reached atmospheric pressure.

Since a constant pipe velocity cannot be attained, the air lift is best designed to keep inlet and discharge velocities within a reasonably efficient range.

Straight Pipe

With a straight pipe, good design values are shown in Fig. 31-H and resultant average capacity ranges are shown in Fig. 31-I for the VA and VC systems. These tables are to be considered only as guides and do not preclude the actual checking of velocities.

Tapered Pipe

The average best inlet and discharge velocity ranges are shown by Fig. 31-J. These apply to each section of pipe. Note that the curves are an average of a range extending both above and below the average. These velocities give best performance when used with submergences in accordance with Fig. 31-E.

To act as a guide only, Fig. 31-K show approximate average capacity ranges for various bottom pipe sizes. These will assist in early calculations.

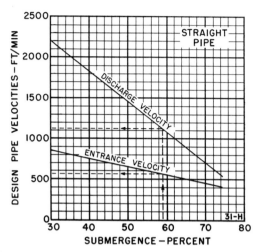

Fig. 31-H. Recommended entrance and discharge velocities with straight pipe (no taper) for lifts of 40 to 250 feet.

Outside Air Line (VA) System

Size Discharge Pipe	Percent Submergence			
	70%	60%	50%	40%
	Gallons of Water Per Minute			
1½	15– 24	13– 20	12– 18	10– 16
2	25– 40	23– 37	20– 35	17– 30
2½	40– 65	37– 60	30– 55	27– 50
3	70–105	65–100	60–100	55– 95
3½	115–150	105–135	100–130	95–120
4	150–190	135–170	130–160	120–150
5	240–350	220–320	200–290	190–275
6	380–560	350–510	320–460	300–440

Central Air Line (VC) System

	70%	60%	50%	40%
2	21– 34	19– 31	17– 29	14– 25
2½	33– 53	30– 49	25– 45	22– 41
3	57– 86	53– 80	49– 65	45– 65
3½	100– 130	91– 117	86– 112	83– 100
4	124– 158	112– 141	108– 133	100– 125
5	206– 300	190– 275	172– 230	164– 235
6	330– 480	300– 440	275– 400	265– 380
8	640– 930	590– 850	530– 775	510– 740
10	1150–1680	1060–1530	960–1400	920–1300

NOTE: The above capacities for lifts of from 20' to 250'.

Fig. 31-I. Approximate water flow for straight pipe—estimating only.

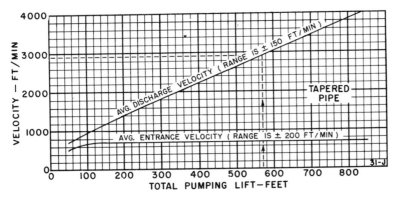

Fig. 31-J. Recommended entrance and discharge velocities with tapered pipe and optimum submergence.

Outside Air Line (VA) System

Size Discharge Pipe at Footpiece Inches	Percent Submergence			
	70%	60%	50%	40%
	Gallons of Water Per Minute			
1½	19– 32	18– 29	16– 26	14– 20
2	34– 57	30– 50	28– 43	26– 39
2½	53– 88	49– 77	44– 66	40– 61
3	97–154	85–135	77–115	69–102
3½	133–222	122–195	110–167	100–153
4	190–305	165–270	150–230	135–210
5	310–520	285–455	260–390	235–355
6	505–840	460–735	420–630	380–580

Central Air Line (VC) System

2	22– 38	16– 31	13– 36	11– 33
2½	33– 57	23– 51	20– 48	16– 42
3	57– 97	40– 88	34– 85	28– 78
3½	80– 140	58– 125	50– 115	40– 105
4	140– 240	100– 210	86– 172	70– 140
5	320– 540	225– 450	190– 380	160– 320
6	460– 780	320– 640	275– 540	239– 460
8	840–1400	585–1175	500–1000	420– 840
10	1400–2350	975–1960	840–1675	700–1400

NOTE: The above capacities for lifts of from 20' to 250'.

Fig. 31-K. Approximate water flow for tapered pipe—estimating only.

Pipe Dimensions

Standard pipe is usually used for both air and discharge lines although various types of tubing may be used if desired. Fig. 31-L provides dimensions of standard weight pipe (schedule 40) required for various air lift calculations and checks. See also 34-64.

The ability to introduce the pipe and footpiece into the well must be checked. On the VA system the sum of the air and discharge pipe coupling outside diameter must be less than the inside diameter of the well. On the VC system the outside diameter of the discharge pipe coupling only need be considered.

	Diameter — inches			Area — sq in		
Nominal Pipe	Inside Pipe	Outside Pipe	Outside Coupling	Inside Pipe	Outside Pipe	Outside Coupling
½	0.622	0.840	1.024	0.304	0.554	0.823
¾	0.824	1.050	1.281	0.533	0.866	1.289
1	1.049	1.315	1.576	0.864	1.358	1.950
1¼	1.380	1.660	1.950	1.495	2.164	2.986
1½	1.610	1.900	2.218	2.036	2.836	3.86
2	2.067	2.375	2.760	3.36	4.43	5.98
2½	2.469	2.875	3.28	4.79	6.49	8.45
3	3.068	3.50	3.95	7.39	9.62	12.25
3½	3.548	4.00	4.59	9.89	12.57	16.55
4	4.026	4.50	5.09	12.73	15.90	20.35
5	5.047	5.56	6.30	20.01	24.31	31.17
6	6.065	6.63	7.36	28.89	34.47	42.54
8	7.981	8.63	9.36	50.03	58.43	68.81
10	10.020	10.75	11.72	78.85	90.76	107.9

See also page 34-64.

Fig. 31-L. Dimensions of standard steel pipe—schedule 40.

Well Down-Flow

When the water stratum is above the footpiece, there must be sufficient area between the well casing and the discharge pipe and footpiece to allow free water flow to the entrance. The water velocity at these down-flow points should approximate 700 ft/min as a maximum.

Chapter 32

Typical Compressed Air Applications

The applications of compressed air are so diverse that any attempt to completely catalog them is impossible. Usage in many cases is dependent only upon the ingenuity of the user in solving his particular problem. The list following, arranged largely by industry, covers many of the more general applications. Some vacuum applications have been included but Chapter 20 should be referred to for more complete coverage. It is hoped that some item may be found useful by the reader in his own area of interest.

Acid Works
Agitating liquids
Pneumatic controls
Transferring liquids
Unloading tank cars
See also Plant Maintenance

Agriculture
Conveying grains
Diggers for harvesting certain products
Fumigating various products
Pruning trees
Spraying insecticides and pesticides
See also Automobile and Truck
      Maintenance
      Food Industries

Amusements
Fun parks
Making artificial snow for skiing

Aircraft Development
Operating wind tunnels
Testing components

Airplane Manufacture
Cleaning machines by jet
Ejecting punchings and stampings
Operating assembly tools
  Drills
  Hammers
  Hoists
  Multiple gang tools
  Reamers
  Riveters
  Screw drivers
Operating clamps
Operating forging hammers
Operating metal-forming stamps
Sandblasting
Spraying paint
See also Plant Maintenance

Airport Operation
Charging landing gear shock absorbers
Motoring jet engines during overhaul
Plane repair and maintenance tools
    (*See* Airplane Manufacture)
Starting jet engines
Testing plane auxiliaries
See also Plant Maintenance

Asphalt Refineries
Agitating and oxidizing
See also Plant Maintenance

Automobile and Truck Maintenance
Agitating cleaning solutions
Changing tires
Cleaning engines and cars
Cleaning parts with soft grit
Cleaning spark plugs
Fender straightening
Inflating tires
Lapping valves
Operating grease guns
Operating jacks, lifts, and hoists
Operating recapping machines
Operating truck road service tools
Operating wrenches, drills and hammers
Spraying metal
Spraying oil, paint, or cleaning solutions

Automobile Manufacture
Cleaning machines by jet
Operating assembly tools
    (*See* Airplane Manufacture)
Operating body hoists
Pneumatic controls
Testing gasoline tanks and radiators
See also Forge shops
    Foundries
    Metalworking Plants
    Plant Maintenance

Bakeries and Confections

Gas ovens
Spraying butter and other coatings
See also Food Industries

Beverage Plants

Bottle washers
Bottling machines
Spraying barrel inside coating
See also Food Industries

Bridge Building

Operating pneumatic tools
  Chipping hammers
  Drills
  Hoists
  Punches
  Reamers
  Riveters
  Wrenches
Operating rivet forges
Operating rock drills for excavating
  foundations, rock sockets and caissons
Sandblasting
Spraying paint

Cement Block Plants

Lifting and racking wet blocks
Operating rammers
Sand sifting

Cement Manufacture

Aeration of bins and silos
Agitation and blending of slurries
Bag cleaning and baling
Blending of raw material
Car dumpers
Cleaning equipment
Clinker cooling
Combustion air
Conveying cement and coal
Filtering slurries
Kiln cleaning
Loading and unloading trucks, cars,
  barges, and ships
Operating hoists and lifts
Pneumatic controls
See also Quarries

Chemical Plants

Aerating and agitating
Air for separation plants
Cleaning equipment
Combustion air
Conveying
Cryogenic uses
Elevating liquids
Filtering-vacuum or pressure
Jet pulverizing
Operating proportioning pumps
Pipe and tube cleaning by drilling and
  blowing
Pneumatic controls
Process air
Transferring liquids
See also Acid Works
         Rubber Factories
         Paint Factories
         Pharmaceutical Manufacture
         Plant Maintenance
         Plastics

Cotton Oil Mills

Cleaning rolls, etc.
Operating formers
Operating hoists and lifts

Clay and Pottery Products

Air-jet cleaning
Conveying materials
Deairing by vacuum
Operating clay presses
Operating hoists and lifts
Sandblasting blemishes from fine
  products
Spraying glazes and colors
Transferring liquids

Concrete Construction

Building forms
Concrete finishing (grinding)
Conveying cement
Spraying concrete
Vibrating concrete

Contracting

Big-hole drilling
See also Bridge building
         Concrete Construction
         Demolition
         Excavating and Foundations
         Highways and Streets
         Pipeline Construction
         Steel Fabrication and Erection
         Well Drilling

Dairy Products

Agitating milk
Bottle cleaning
Transferring milk
See also Food Products

Demolition

Operating tools
  Hoists
  Paving breakers
  Pick hammers
  Rock drills

Electric Power Plants

Blowing pipe for cleaning after erection
Blowing soot
Cleaning boiler and condenser tubes
Cleaning with jets
Conveying pulverized coal
Ejecting sewage
Operating circuit breakers
Pneumatic controls
Pulverizing coal
Repairing boiler walls and baffles
See also Hydroelectric Plants
         Plant Maintenance

Enameling Plants

Sandblasting
Spraying glazes

Excavating and Foundations

Air locks and caissons
Blowing concrete piling forms
Drilling large blast holes
Operating pneumatic tools
  Diggers
  Hoists
  Sludge and sump pumps
  Slusher hoists and scrapers
  Tampers
Operating rock drills
  Big hole drilling
  Drifters
  Downhole drills
  Hand-held drills
  Hole cleaning for straight rotary drills
  Paving breakers
  Pile and sheathing drivers

Food Industries (General Applications)
Agitation of liquids
Air (oxygen) for fermenting tanks
Cleaning equipment with jets
Cleaning containers with jets
Conveying materials
Dehydration of foods
Filtering
Fumigation
Hoisting and lifting
Operating automatic machinery
Pneumatic controls
Sorting nuts, coffee, etc.
Spraying food products
Spreading insecticides and pesticides
Sprinkler systems
Testing containers
Transferring liquids
Vacuum packing
See also Agriculture
       Automobile and Truck
        Maintenance
       Bakeries and Confections
       Beverage Plants
       Dairy Products
       Hospitals and Laboratories
       Meat Packing Plants
       Plant Maintenance

Forge Shops
Blowing scale
Driving keys
Ejection of punchings and stampings
Furnace door air curtains
Hoisting and lifting
Operating bending and straightening
  machines
Operating clutches, brakes, and clamps
Operating forging hammers
Operating oil burners
See also Plant Maintenance

Foundries
Car spotting
Cleaning equipment
Conveying sand
Operating molding machines
Operating pneumatic tools
    Chippers
    Drills
    Grinders
    Hoists and lifts
    Picks
    Rammers
    Wire brushes
Sandblasting
Sand sifting
Spraying cores
See also Plant Maintenance

Furniture Factories
See Woodworking Plants

Gas Transmission and Distribution
Air-LPG gas mixing plants
Boring under roads (earth augers)
Gas engine starting
Line testing
Meter testing
Pneumatic controls
See also Pipeline Construction
      Plant Maintenance

Grain and Flour Handling and Storage
See Food Industries

Glass Plants
Blowing bottles and glassware
Blowing light and electronic tubes
Combustion air
Conveying materials
Etching, frosting, and boring glass
Feeding glass
Operating molds and presses
Operating oil burners
Pneumatic controls
Vacuum plate lifts
See also Plant Maintenance

Government
Air Force
  Starting jet engines
  See also Airplane Manufacture
        Airport Operation
Army
  See Automobile and Truck
     Maintenance
    Demolition
    Ordnance
Muncipal and Public Bodies
  Blowing fire whistles
  Filteration plants
  See also Highways and Streets
Navy
  Charging torpedos
  Starting diesel engines
  Starting jet engines
  See also Marine
       Metal Working Plants
       Ordnance
       Plant Maintenance

Hat Factories
Cleaning by jet
Operating presses
Raising nap by jet

Highways and Streets
Boring under roads (earth augers)
Conveying cement
Driving piles
Operating rock drills
    Blast hole drills
    Drifters
    Hand held drills
    Paving breakers
    Pile and sheathing drivers
Operating pneumatic tools
    Diggers
    Earth augers
    Form pin drivers
    Hoists
    Tampers

Hospitals and Laboratories
Breathing apparatus
Cleaning tubes and catheters
Hyperbeiric oxygenation
Laboratory filtering
Operating centrifuges
Operating laundry machines
Pneumatic controls
Spraying medications
Vacuum for drainage during operations
See also Plant Maintenance

Industrial - Miscellaneous
Air jet pulverizing
Impregnating electrical coils
Ejector type ventilating devices
Operating baling presses

Hydro-electric Plants

Generator braking
Lock maintenance
Navigational horns
Operating governor systems
Operating grease pumps
Operating lock equipment
Operating spillway gates
Pneumatic controls
Prevention of ice damage to dams
Trash screen cleaning
See also Electric Power Plants
        Plant Maintenance

Iron and Steel Mills

Agitating solutions
Air for oxygen separation
Air for blast and open-hearth furnaces
  and Bessemer converters
Car spotting
Drilling open-hearth slag pockets
Dumping ladles
Open hearth flue cleaning
Operating clutches and brakes
Operating furnace doors
Operating loading and handling devices
Operating lubrication systems
Operating pneumatic tools
  Chippers
  Grinders
  Hoists and lifts
Pneumatic controls
Sandblasting
Tapping blast furnaces
Vacuum degassing
See also Plant Maintenance

Laundry and Cleaning Plants

Cleaning furs
Cleaning machines with jets
Cleaning rugs
Filtering solutions
Operating shirt and clothing presses
Spraying cleaning and mothproofing
  solutions

Lumber and Wood Processing

Air dogs on log saw carriages
Bubblers to keep ponds ice-free
Cleaning by jet
Conveying sawdust and chips
Hoisting and lifting
Impregnating wood products
Operating edgers, bumpers, and pickups
Pneumatic controls

Marine

Air breakwaters
Bubble prevention of ice formation
Diving air
Fog horn operation
Marine salvage
Starting and maneuvering ships
Scuba diving air
See also Shipbuilding

Meat Packing Plants

Combustion air
Emptying meat loaf pans
Lard refining
Operating cutting machines and presses
Pneumatic stunner
Stuffing sausages
Testing casings

Metal Working Plants

Agitating solutions
Air gauging of parts
Chip conveying
Cleaning by jet
Operating baling presses
Operating clamps, chucks, clutches,
  and positioners
Operating pneumatic tools
  Caulkers
  Chippers
  Drills
  Grinders
  Hoists and lifts
  Multiple gang tools
  Riveters
  Screwdrivers
  Wrenches
Pneumatic controls
Press and stamp ejection jets
Sandblasting
Shot blasting (hardening)
Spraying lubricant
Spraying metal for repair
Spraying paint
Testing vessels for leaks
See also Enameling plants
        Plant Maintenance

Mining

Air for ventilation
Big hole drilling
Dewatering by air lift
Filtering fines
Operating car spotters
Operating hoists and slushers
Operating pumps
Operating rock drills
  Air feeds
  Drifters
  For primary blast holes
  Hand held tools
  Pile and sheathing drivers
  Stopers
Operating roof-bolting wrenches
See also Plant Maintenance

Monument and Cut Stone Plants

Carving
Drilling
Sandblasting
Surfacing

Office Buildings and Hotels

Ash disposal
Cleaning equipment with jets
Operating elevator doors
Operating laundry machines
Operating sewage ejectors
Operating pneumatic tube systems
Vacuum cleaning
See also Plant Maintenance

Oil Refineries

Combustion air
Emptying and cleaning oil lines
Hoisting and lifting
Operating controls
Recirculating catalyst
Sandblasting
Spraying paint
See also Plant Maintenance

Oil Production
Air pumping of oil
Downhole drilling
Drilling rigs
Hoisting

Ordnance
Hoisting and lifting
Shell-handling equipment
Shell-loading equipment
See also Metalworking Plants
    Plant Maintenance

Ore Processing
Air for smelting
Agitating solutions
Conveying materials
Filtering slurries
Flotation process air
Hoisting
Pelletizing plants
Pneumatic controls
See also Plant Maintenance

Paint Factories
Dressing burr stones
Filling and sealing cans
Hoisting and lifting
Jet pulverizing of colors
Transferring liquids

Paper Mills
Cleaning equipment with jets
Hoisting and lifting
Ice prevention in ponds
Loading squeeze rolls
Molding paper products
Operating clutches
Operating sheet breakers
Passing paper through machine
Pneumatic controls
Pressurizing head box
Removing head box
Removing broke
Vacuum drying
Vacuum for Fourdrinier machine
See also Plant Maintenance

Pharmaceutical Manufacturing
Agitating liquids
Air (oxygen) for antibiotic
    fermentation
Conveying materials
Mixing and blending materials
Operating centrifuges
Pneumatic controls
Pulverizing by jet action
Spray drying
Transferring liquids
Vacuum drying and evaporating
See also Plant Maintenance

Plant Maintenance
Cleaning by air jet
Operating tools
    Chipping and caulking hammers
    Concrete vibrators
    Drills
    Grinders
    Hoists
    Paving breakers
    Riveters
    Scalers
    Tube rollers
    Wrenches
Sandblasting
Spraying metal for repairing
Spraying paint
Sprinkler systems

Pipeline Construction
Operating pneumatic tools
    Caulking hammers
    Diggers
    Earth augers
    Slusher hoists and scrapers
    Tampers
Operating rock drills
    Crawlers
    Drifters
    Hand-held drills
    Pile and sheathing drivers

Plastics Processing
Cleaning equipment by jets
Ejection of molded parts
Inflation of hollow objects in molding
Inflation of tubing during extrusion
Molding by pressure or vacuum
Operating presses
Operating trimmers
Power cylinder operation
Spraying material on forms

Printing Plants
Agitating solutions
Feeding paper to presses
Hoisting and lifting
Jets to separate sheets on presses,
    folders and assembly machines
Operating type-casting machines
Spraying protective coatings

Quarries
Hoisting and moving material
Operating rock drills
    Air feeds
    Blast hole drills
    Channelers
    Drifters
    Hand-held drills
Pumping water
See also Monument and Cut Stone
    Plants

Railroads
Charging train lines
Conveying sand
General applications
    Sandblasting
    Spraying paint
    Transferring liquids
Operating air brakes
Operating car retarders
Operating switch and signal systems
Right-of-way maintenance tools
    Chipping and scaling hammers
    Drills
    Grinders
    Hoists
    Saws
    Spike drivers
    Tie tampers
    Wire brushes
    Wrenches
Rolling stock repair and maintenance
    Chippers and scalers
    Drills
    Grinders
    Hoists and lifts
    Reamers
    Riveters
    Saws
    Tube cleaners and rollers
    Wire brushes
    Wrenches

Rubber Factories

Cleaning molds and machinery
Hoisting and lifting
Mandrel stripping
Opening molds
Operating molds and presses
Pneumatic controls
Spraying
Testing finished product
See also Plant Maintenance

Salt Mining

Air lift for brine solution method of
mining
See also Mining

Service Stations

See Automobile and Truck Maintenance

Shipyards

See Metalworking Plants
Plant Maintenance

Sewage Disposal Plants

Activated sludge aeration
Sewage ejectors
Subaqueous combustion
See also Plant Maintenance

Steam Power Plants

See Electric Power Plants

Steel Fabrication and Erection

Operating pneumatic tools
  Chippers
  Drainage pumps
  Drills
  Grinders
  Hoists
  Punches
  Reamers
  Riveters
  Scalers
  Wrenches
Operating rivet forges
Spraying paint

Sugar Refineries

See Food Industries

Sulphur Mining

Air lift for hot-water-solution mining

Tanneries

Agitating liquids
Hoisting and lifting
Pneumatic controls
Transferring liquid

Textile Mills

Agitating liquids
Cleaning machinery by vacuum and jet
Hoisting and lifting
Humidifying
Operating pressure accumulators
Pneumatic controls
Spraying liquids
Sprinkler systems
Squeeze roll loading
Transferring liquids

Tobacco Processing

Tobacco conditioning
Machine cleaning
Pneumatic controls

Water Works

Aeration with air and carbon dioxide
Air lift for pumping water
Earth augers
See also Plant Maintenance

Well Drilling

Air for testing well flow
Hoists for handling drilling equipment
and pipe
Operation of rock and rotary drills

Woodworking Plants

Cleaning by jet
Conveying saw dust and chips
Hoisting and lifting
Impregnating wood
Operating bending and straightening
presses
Operating **clamps and chucks**
Operating pneumatic tools
  Carving tools
  Drills
  Nail drivers
  Polishers
  Routers
  Sanders
  Screwdrivers
Sandblasting
Spraying paint
Sprinkler systems
See also Plant Maintenance

The Agitation of Liquids in Tanks

Use of compressed air for the agitation of liquids and slurries in tanks
has advantages in many applications. Agitation of milk and slurries are
examples. One of the principal advantages is the simplicity of the installation in the tank containing the liquid.

Unfortunately, there is no exact knowledge as to how much air is required to develop a desired degree of agitation. Experimental work on the
part of the customer is required because of differences in the gravity and
consistency of materials being agitated, the degree of agitation required,
the tank depth, and the area to be covered.

Two general methods may be used. The first is to install a very low
lift inductor either in the center or at one end of the tank. This lifts the
liquid and any contained solids from the bottom to the top and keeps them

in constant circulation. The inductor has been widely used in the cyanide treatment of gold ore. Tanks in this case are large, about 30 ft in diameter and 50 ft deep.

The second method is to install a pattern of piping in the bottom with drilled holes through which the air escapes, agitating the liquid above.

The Inductor

This is an air lift operation (see Chapter 31) with submergence well over 90 percent, much higher than normal. It is improbable that the actual lift or top of the discharge pipe will be more than a foot above the liquid level in the tank. Therefore column aeration is required primarily to provide acceleration energy and to overcome eduction pipe friction.

Accurate information is lacking on this type of operation but, based on air lift tests at relatively low lifts, *order-of-magnitude* values are obtainable. The quantity of free air required to circulate one gallon of water under these conditions should not exceed 0.05. At these conditions the velocity in the eductor pipe should be kept between 200 and 300 feet per minute for best efficiency. This is the velocity based on the combined volume of free air and water (exit velocity). More air *may* be required if the liquid viscosity is greater than that of water.

The rate of circulation must be based on the users estimate of turnover requirements. If an installation should circulate faster than necessary, the air supply can be reduced. If insufficient circulation is obtained, the air supply may be increased bearing in mind that this will also increase the pressure required.

Based on a velocity of 250 ft/min and 0.05 cfm free air/gal, each sq in of *net* inside eductor pipe area should carry about 9.5 gpm of liquid. This value may be used in rough sizing of the pipe.

The air should come into the bottom of the eductor pipe through the bottom of the tank or down into the vat and up through a U. A good footpiece can be made by puncturing a sheet of copper with a number of nail holes, forming the sheet into a tube and fastening it to the air line, capping the top so the air will have to flow through the nail holes. The rough edges of the nail holes should be on the *outside* of the tube footpiece.

To calculate total orifice area required, see the method outlined later in this discussion.

Drilled Piping on Tank Bottom

A much more frequent type of installation is perforated pipe in a suitable pattern in the bottom of the tank. Sufficient pressure is applied inside this piping to force air out through the orifices against the static head of the liquid, thus creating a complex movement of the liquid from the bottom to the top of the tank. The piping layout pattern may be varied in a great many ways and must be left up to the user. Much will depend upon the area to be agitated, the consistency of the material and, once again, the degree of agitation required. Layouts may be a spider pattern radiating from a central point; some include a line along each side of the tank which causes a type of rolling agitation, the liquid flowing downward at the center of the tank; other layouts may include a number of parallel lines across the tank.

The air pressure is usually low. There is a static pressure corresponding to the liquid head on the outside of the orifice and there is a pressure drop through the orifice dependent upon the size of the orifice and the quantity of air flowing.

The usual procedure is to figure the quantity of air required for a given degree of agitation, based upon the square footage crosssectional area in the tank. The following table represents the best consistent information available.

Orifice Submergence Feet	Cubic Feet Per Minute Free Air Per Square Foot of Liquid		
	Moderate Agitation	Complete Agitation	Violent Agitation
1	2.60	5.20	12.40
2	1.69	3.39	7.95
3	1.30	2.60	6.20
4	1.08	2.17	5.15
5	.94	1.88	4.47
6	.84	1.67	4.00
8	.70	1.40	3.32
10	.60	1.21	2.90
12	.54	1.08	2.60
14	.49	.98	2.35
18	.42	.84	2.00
22	.37	.74	1.80
25	.34	.68	1.65

Comparison of actual installations indicates that the above table is safe, and that usually the air requirements will be slightly lower than this. However, it is better to figure a little safe knowing that the air quantity can readily be cut, but cannot usually be increased.

Required Orifice Area - Either Method

From information given previously the total cfm free air required is approximated. The downstream orifice pressure is known from the greatest hydrostatic pressure on the opening. It is suggested that the orifices be designed for not over 2 psi pressure drop. Therefore, the upstream pressure is 2 psi above the downstream. On this basis, the subcritical flow formula may be used.

Q cfm free air at 14.7 psiA and 70°F

p_1 upstream pressure - psiA

A total orifice area - sq in

C flow coefficient

T_1 upstream orifice temperature - °F abs

p_2 hydrostatic pressure - psiA

p_1 initial pressure equals (p_2 + 2 psi) psiA

$$Q = \frac{1640 p_1\, AC}{\sqrt{T_1}} \sqrt{\left(\frac{p_2}{p_1}\right)^{1.43} - \left(\frac{p_2}{p_1}\right)^{1.71}}$$

Since this will always be highly approximate, assume that T_1 is 70°F (530 °R), C is 1.0 and A is 1.0 sq in. The flow then becomes approximately as follows (when the liquid is water).

Orifice Submergence Feet of Water	Cu Ft Free Air/Minute for A of one sq in
5	211
10	230
15	244
20	258
25	271
30	283

This is based on 100 percent flow coefficient (C) and the above will have to be corrected. For holes drilled in a pipe, assume C is 0.65. For hole punched by a nail in flat sheet metal (rolled so there is a slightly rounded entrance) assume C is 0.80. Applying this correction gives one the approximate cfm free air flow through one sq in and permits ready calculation of the gross orifice *throat* area required.

Knowing the total area it is possible to divide this up into a sufficient number of holes to distribute the air over the pipe length in a uniform pattern without getting the holes too close together or too far apart. It would depend upon the size and shape of the tank just what limit should be set but in general the holes should not be less than 3″ apart nor more than 12″ apart. This, of course, is a matter of judgment. If it should turn out that reasonable size holes, say 1/8″ or larger, cannot be used, then the pressure drop should probably be decreased to obtain a greater area and thus keep the holes a reasonable size so that they will not clog.

Where the air feed to the agitation system is at one end of a rather long tank, it is frequently necessary to make the holes near the entrance smaller than at the far end to compensate for the difference in pressure due to pressure drop in the pipe itself.

A good way to control the amount of air after a satisfactorily operating system has been set up is to insert an orifice between two flanges or in a union to restrict the flow to the quantity which has been experimentally determined as necessary. The operator need then pay no attention to the pressure he puts on the system. He just opens the main supply valve wide and the orifice takes care of the necessary pressure reduction. In figuring the *maximum* pressure the compressor must develop, some allowance must be made for loss in the piping from the compressor to the tank.

In the inductor, make the footpiece length 10 to 15 percent of the tank depth and distribute the holes over the total length. The footpiece may have to be larger in diameter than the air line feeding it.

Before purchasing a compressor solely for agitation service, the user should develop and install a system satisfactory to him when operated from a high pressure line or a portable compressor (rented if necessary), making necessary volume and pressure determinations.

THIS INFORMATION IS PRESENTED SOLELY AS A GUIDE. NO PERFORMANCE GUARANTEES ARE MADE OR IMPLIED.

Chapter 33

Sound and Its Measurement

Introduction

Sound, to the average person, is what he can hear. Sound, however, exists in many ranges. Dogs and bats, for example, can hear or react to sound waves pitched far above those that humans can discern. Sounds may be roughly classified as

1. Speech;

2. Music; and,

3. Noise.

Speech is usually pleasant to the ear. Music may or may not be agreeable, depending upon the opinion of the hearer and his musical appreciation: Noise is disagreeable or unwanted sound. This discussion concerns noise as transmitted in atmospheric air.

Everything that moves makes noise, including mosquitoes and compressors. Vibrations (small, large, low frequency, or high frequency) all have their own characteristic effect on the total noise produced. In a compressor installation, many noise generating sources may be present. Operation of valves, ports opening or closing, air pulsation, the driver gears, piping design, room size, wall materials, and proximity to other equipment will all contribute to the resultant noise level.

Each compressor under existing surroundings will have a characteristic *normal* sound. Operators quickly learn to recognize a change. This is the signal for an immediate check and possible stoppage for repair. Noise production, also, is usually an individual matter; two "identical" units may not have identical noise patterns.

The sources of noise generation may generally be determined. However, there often is no practical method of eliminating them. Opening and closing of valves and interruption of steady air flow by port edges and blades are inherent in the design of many compressor types. Manufacturers are usually in a position to recommend auxiliary equipment to reduce to satisfactory limits the more troublesome noises.

Public concern about noise, and noise-induced problems, is growing. Legislation now governs sound levels in many industries. Businessmen specify permissable noise levels in purchased equipment. Communities are putting noise restrictions in zoning laws. Wanting it or not, many acoustically untrained engineers and managers find themselves face-to-face with acoustical problems.

Noise is a complex subject. Acoustics, as practiced today, is as much an art as it is a science. Although it helps to have a basic understanding of what noise is, how it is measured, and what levels are considered permissable, it is best to retain a competent acoustical consultant when faced with noise difficulties.

What Sound Is

Sound, when air-borne, is a variation in air pressure. It is a wave of longitudinal form; that is, the movement of individual particles is back and forth in the direction of wave movement. Energy is required to set up these waves. With noise this is wasted energy; in many cases, the loss is unavoidable and minor.

Sound can be visualized as originating in a point source and radiating from the point in all directions (if there is no interference). The sphere of the wave motion is increased as the wave moves outward, but the *total* energy of the wave over the surface of the sphere is unchanged. Over any small area on the sphere, the energy diminishes rapidly as the sphere grows in size. Thus, the greater the distance from the originating source, the less the intensity of the sound as heard. This varies inversely as the square of the distance from the point source. There is also a slight reduction due to friction of one air particle upon another as the wave progresses.

Note that in these wave motions, the particles do not change their normal positions, one with the other. They merely move back and forth, pushing each other. The effect is to build areas of pressure above atmosphere and adjacent areas of pressure below atmosphere. These variations are tiny but sufficient for discernment by the ear and instruments.

Sound waves can be reflected with a changed direction or can be bounced back. Two or more waves from different sources will combine in a complex form, depending on their individual frequency and amplitude.

Frequency and Amplitude

Frequency is the number of complete cycles of rise and fall in pressure in a given time. It is usually expressed as cycles per second (cps).

Amplitude is the maximum displacement value from the equilibrium point or half the low to high pressure value difference.

Frequency is important in all sound measurements. The audible spectrum, called the audio-frequency range, extends from about 20 cps to 20,000 cps.

Some sounds are pleasant, others grate and are less popular. The difference is in the combination of sounds. Most sounds are made up of a number of components of different frequencies — they are not simple pure tones. Generally speaking what the ear hears as pitch is the lowest audible frequency component in a complex wave.

In music, the higher frequency components are usually integral multiples of the lowest audible frequency. These are called harmonics. The third harmonic of 1000 cps has a frequency of 3000 cps. (For orientation, middle "C" has 256 cps; "A" has 440 cps; high "C" on the piano has 4186 cps.) It is the presence of harmonics that determines tonal quality or timbre. Steady-state notes of the same pitch played on different musical instruments have the same basic frequency; they differ only in harmonic content, or overtones. There are cases in music where dissonances are deliberately introduced, but these may be taken as exceptions.

Noise also is complex in structure. Harmonics may be present, as in musical notes, but in addition there are many more sounds of unrelated frequency. For an understanding of sound problems in industry, not only must the magnitude of the sound be measured, but also the frequencies.

Measures of Sound

Sound power and sound pressure (the power of the wave and the pressure change within it) are not measured directly but by comparison with a reference point (as a ratio). Because the range of values involved is so large (in power, the range is about one billion to one), a logarithmic value is used for both measurements. This involves the decibel (db). There is no method at present, of measuring sound power directly. It is determined from sound pressure through the use of relations between the two.

Sound Power Level

Sound power level *(PWL)* is the acoustic power level in decibels as obtained by the following formula.

$$PWL = 10 \, log_{10} \frac{W}{W_R} \tag{33.1}$$

where W and W_R are the powers of two sounds in watts. The reference level *(W_R)* is usually 10^{-13} watts in the United States, although 10^{-12} watts is becoming more general throughout the world. This formula is basically from electrical engineering, adapted to sound analysis.

Sound Pressure Level

Sound pressure level also is expressed in decibels. It carries a derivation through electrical engineering from the power formula and also has a somewhat arbitrary base. In electrical engineering, power in a fixed system varies as the square of the applied voltage. Voltage is pressure. Therefore 33.1 could be written

$$db = 10 \, log_{10} \left(\frac{P}{P_R}\right)^2, \, or$$

$$db = 20 \, log_{10} \frac{P}{P_R} \tag{33.2}$$

P_R has been set as that of the weakest sound that can be heard by a person with very good hearing in a quiet location. It represents a pressure variation of two ten-thousandths of microbar (one microbar is approximately one millionth of an atmosphere). This is zero decibels.

$$\text{Therefore, } P_R = 0.0002 \text{ microbar} \tag{33.3}$$

A microbar is abbreviated "μ bar". Sound pressure level *(SPL)* becomes

$$SPL = 20 \, log_{10} \frac{P}{0.0002} \, db \, (referred \, to \, 0.0002 \, microbar) \tag{33.4}$$

Pressures here are root-mean-square values (RMS) of the pressure variation. RMS means the square root of the average of squares of actual pressure **differences.**

In both power and pressure ratings, *it must be remembered* that these are

1. A logarithm of a . . . . .
2. Ratio of a . . . . .
3. Power or pressure . . . . .
4. To a *stated* base.

Typical Sound Pressure Levels

Following are wide band sound-pressure levels for a variety of sounds:

Structural Damage	=	140 db
Pain Threshold	=	130 db
Jet Engine	=	130 db
Large Centrifugal Compressor at Open Inlet	=	120 db
Riveter (35 feet)	=	110 db
Train Passing Subway Station	=	100 db
Noisy Factory	=	90 db
Printing Press	=	80 db
Loud Radio	=	78 db
Noisy Office	=	70 db
Typical Office	=	60 db
Residential Kitchen	=	55 db
Quiet Office	=	40 db
Average Threshold of Hearing	=	16 db

For comparison, calculations will show that 1 psiA is equivalent to 170 db, while 1 atmosphere or 14.7 psiA is 194 db.

Velocity of Sound

The speed with which sound travels in air is dependent to some degree on temperature. A value of 1135 ft/sec at 75°F is frequently used. Fig. 6-BC (page 6-49) illustrates the variation. Formulas 5.25 through 5.28 (page 5-15) also apply.

Reference Distance and Surroundings

From what has been said, it is evident that any sound has different values for different distances from the source. A low flying airplane is noiser than one at 10,000 feet. For this reason, a reference to the distance between source and measuring device is required.

Surroundings have a great effect on noise level felt or recorded. Some amplify or increase it due to sympathetic vibration or reflection; some dampen it because portions of the sound are absorbed. Surroundings must be noted as an integral part of any study of sound.

Adding Two Sounds

Suppose one had a factory with a specific sound level in decibels at a specific point. Into this is to be placed a machine, say a compressor. This has a known *SPL* of greater value. What will be the resultant noise level? Will it require treatment of the room to maintain a reasonable noise level?

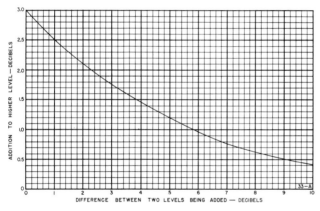

Courtesy of General Radio Company

Fig. 33-A. In the addition of two sounds, correct the higher level sound by the amount shown above.

Say this typical space has a present level of 75 db; the compressor, 85 db (this is an example only). Decibels cannot be added arithmetically; they are logarithms. Each must be converted to relative powers, combined, then converted back to decibels. However, Fig. 33-A does all this. Take the difference between the two db values, enter it in the bottom of the curve and read at the left the increase (correction) to be applied to the *greater* of the two. In the example, the noise pressure level would increase to 85.4 db, which would rate the plant as quite noisy, but not dangerously so.

When the added sound is 10 db or more *below* the other, its contribution to total sound is negligible. *When two sounds of the same decibel level combine, the increase cannot be more than 3 db.*

The Sound Level Meter

A sound level meter is essentially a microphone, an amplifier, and a meter. Variations in pressures are converted to a varying electrical signal. The variations in the electrical signal can then be used to indicate, by means of an appropriately calibrated meter and scale, any arbitrarily selected range of values within the response limits of the microphone.

The average microphone found on sound level meters has a frequency response that is limited to accurate sound-to- electrical signals in the range from 20 to 10,000 cps. The audible spectrum of the human ear goes as high as 20,000 cps. Unless a special condenser microphone is used to extend the range to 20,000 cps, the sound level meter will not be accurate for frequencies above 8000 - 10,000 cps.

Loudness

Sounds at certain frequencies seem louder to the human ear than sounds at other frequencies, even though they have the same decibel level or intensity. A noise of 40 db at 1000 cps *sounds* as loud as a 60 db noise at 100 cps. The average human ear has been found more sensitive to sounds in the 1000- to 2000-cps range than it is at lower frequencies. This subjective effect is more pronounced at lower pressure or intensity levels; above 85 decibels, sounds of equal pressure level, but of different frequencies, sound equally as loud to the human ear.

Curves of this subjective response have been plotted. They are known as "equal loudness contours", and are often used in acoustical studies.

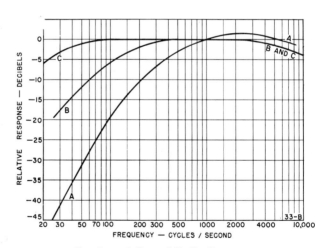

Courtesy of General Radio Company

Fig. 33-B.　Typical acoustical and electrical response curves for a sound meter.

To compensate for this human response, sound level meters usually have three different response networks built into them. The so-called "A" network is used for intensities below 55 db; the "B" for intensities between 55 and 85 db; and the "C" or "flat response" network, for levels above 85 db. Fig. 33-B shows the acoustical and electrical response curves for a typical sound level meter.

Sound Must Be Analyzed

A sound level meter by itself reads the over-all air disturbance — the net result of air vibrations at many wave lengths. This is not enough for a complete understanding of most problems. It gives no indication of the distribution of noise as a function of frequency. The shape of a noise spectrum, that is, the plot of sound pressure level versus frequency, can be extremely important, particularly in problems involving noise control. It is much more costly to reduce low frequency noise than high-frequency noise.

Analyzers determine the frequency *spectrum*, filtering out all wave lengths except those for which the analyzer is designed and set. There are several types.

An octave band analyzer measures the sound pressure level in eight octaves; 25-75; 75-150; 150-300; 300-600; 600-1200; 1200-2400; 2400-4800, and, 4800-10,000. The first and last bands are not true octaves, since an octave band covers a range of frequencies in the ratio of two to one.

A "one-third" octave band analyzer separates the spectrum into bands where the ratio is 1.26 to 1. A 2 percent band width analyzer measures the sound pressure level in a band whose width is always 2 percent of the frequency to which it is tuned. Other percentage band width analyzers are also available.

Constant band width analyzers always operate on a fixed band width — for example, 2 cycles wide.

The narrower the band width, the more accurately frequencies can be identified. This is valuable in locating the source of certain components. Narrow band analyzers are more difficult to operate and take more time to use.

Speech Interference Level

For most problems concerning possible hearing damage, annoyance, and speech interference, the octave band analyzer is very useful. Speech interference level, called S.I.L., is defined as the arithmetic average of the sound pressure levels in the three octave bands 600-1200, 1200-2400, and 2400 4800 cps. Difficulties and misunderstandings in speech communications may be expected if the S.I.L. exceeds certain levels. For example if the S.I.L. exceeds 59 db, conversation will be difficult at two feet distance with normal voice level. With raised voice level, conversation will be difficult if the S.I.L. exceeds 65 db. The recommended S.I.L. depends upon the particular conditions of the location, and how important speech communication may be.

Noise Criteria

A curve of the allowable sound pressure levels over various bands is often set up for a specific case under study and compared to what exists. This is a guide in determining in what bands remedial changes are necessary. Allowable levels are determined by experience. Noise criteria are given an NC reference number equal to the approximate numerical average of the decibels in the three octave bands between 600 and 4800 cps. This number is purely a reference to the possible speech interference level. Below, such curves are expressed in tabular form.

Criteria No.	Octave Band Sound Pressure Levels							
	20 75	75 150	150 300	300 600	600 1200	1200 2400	2400 4800	4800 10,000
NC-30 NC-65	60 82	51 76	43 72	36 68	32 66	30 64	28 63	27 62

Noise Problems

Noise problems are usually associated with their reaction on humans. No adequate measures of the annoyance levels of noises have yet been devised. The extent of our annoyance depends greatly on what we are trying to do at the moment, on our previous conditioning, and on the character of the noise.

The annoyance level of a noise is sometimes assumed to be related directly to the loudness of the noise. Although not completely justifiable, this assumption is sometimes helpful because a loud sound is usually more annoying than one of similar character that is not so loud. High-frequency sounds (above about 2000 cps) are usually more annoying than are lower-frequency sounds of the same sound pressure level. People also differ, and age is a factor. Hearing deteriorates with age, particularly in the higher frequencies.

Noise can influence work output. There is the obvious interference with communication, the deterioration in quality of work output than can occur when the background noise level is high, and the occasional opposite situation where noise is a positive and helpful factor by masking distracting conversation.

The effects of noise on work output depend greatly upon the nature of the work; a long-term job requiring constant vigilance is especially susceptible. Noise is more likely to cause a higher rate of errors and accidents than an actual reduction in total output. This and other results lead to the interpretation that attention wanders from the work at hand more often as the noise level increases.

From the standpoint of noise reduction, two findings are worth noting. First, noise is more likely to lead to increased errors in susceptible tasks if it is above 90 db. Second, high-frequency audible noise seems more harmful in this respect than does low-frequency noise.

Exposure to intense noise may produce hearing damage. Some of the hearing loss may be temporary, with partial or complete recovery after a time. Some damage may be permanent. The risk of permanent damage is a function of the sound pressure level and the time of exposure to that level. The amount of both depends upon the individual. Some people may tolerate louder noises for longer periods than others without risk of damage.

Most authorities agree that the risk of damage to hearing is slight when the wide-band sound pressure level in any octave does not exceed 85 db. The permissible time at higher sound pressure levels decreases rapidly as the level increases. For example, 85 db may be tolerated for an entire eight-hour day without ear protectors. If the sound pressure level is 95 db, the time drops to 48 minutes. At 105 db, the exposure time should not exceed five minutes. Ear protectors are recommended for continuous exposure to sound pressure levels above 85 db.

Noise Control

Many factors must be considered in noise control investigations. Usually each must be handled as an individual problem. Sources of noise must be determined. Sound levels and their component frequencies must be measured. Air- and structure-borne paths usually enter into the problem.

The general approach to noise reduction can be divided into two major parts:

1. Reduction of noise at its source; and,
2. Reduction of noise level at the listener's ear by changes in the path from the source.

When reduction at the source is attempted, a decrease in the radiating power is the most important change that can be made. This usually means a reduction in vibration amplitudes and reduction of the radiation of the sound produced. Decrease in the energy available for producing vibration, changing the coupling between the energy and the acoustical radiating system, and modifying the radiating structure to radiate less are all approaches to this problem.

All are usually quite difficult when considering compressors themselves. Steps should be taken to be sure all bearings are properly fitted and that lubrication is correct. Intake and discharge silencers may be needed and are definitely recommended on certain types of compressors. Vibration isolation mounts may help reduce certain frequencies.

Control of the sound path often is a more practical method of reducing noise level at bothersome points. There are three methods.

1. Change the relative position of the source and listener;
2. Change the acoustical environment; and,
3. Introduce attenuating structures between the source and listener.

Changes in position may involve moving the source and listener further apart. When a noise has a definite direction, as some do, rotation of the source may help.

For relatively long distance improvement, the room may be acoustically treated, but this is of little value when distances are, say, two or three feet. Acoustical materials are chiefly useful in the room where the sound originates. There are many of these materials, but their use is not a cure-all.

Walls, barriers, and total enclosures are types of attenuating structures. Here, also, they are not always effective because they themselves vibrate and become a source.

Certain noise reduction measures are more effective in reducing high-frequency components than they are in reducing those of low-frequency. Other steps must be taken when low-frequency components are predominant.

There is no magic solution applicable to all noise control problems. Each must be considered separately and referred to an expert if a remedy is desired.

Chapter 34

Tables and Charts

INDEX

For your convenience, this index includes the principal tables and charts in this book, whether located in this chapter or elsewhere.

Compressors - Reciprocating

Drivers

Gases

Air - Water Vapor Mixtures

Steam & Water Vapor

Piping

Tools

Vacuum

Miscellaneous

Gas Properties

Fundamental to the design of any compressor is a knowledge of the properties of the gas being handled.

The tables on the next two pages and the charts starting on page 34-8 were prepared after an extensive search of literature and a critical evaluation of sources where differences were encountered.

It is felt that these data represent the most accurate to be found at the time each was studied.

References

1. Selected Values of Physical and Thermodynamic Properties of Hydrocarbons and Related Compounds — API Research Project 44 — Carnegie Press — 1953

2. Tables of Thermal Properties of Gases — National Bureau of Standards Circular 564 — 1955

3. Physical Constants of Hydrocarbons Boiling Below 350°F — American Society for Testing Materials — Special Technical Publication No. 109 — 1950

4. Engineering Data Book — Natural Gasoline Supply Men's Association — 7th Edition — 1957

5. Tables of Thermodynamic Properties of Ammonia — National Bureau of Standards Circular No. 142 — 1945

6. Data Book on Hydrocarbons — Maxwell — Second Printing — 1951

7. Handbook of Chemistry and Physics — Hodgman — 37th Edition

8. American Institute of Physics Handbook — 1957

9. The Merck Index — 7th Edition — 1960

10. Thermodynamic Properties of The Lighter Paraffin Hydrocarbons and Nitrogen — Sage and Lacey — API Project 37 — 1950

11. E. I. DuPont Bulletins on The Freons

12. Thermodynamic Functions of Gases — Vol. 1 and 2 — Din (British)

13. Specific Heats of Certain Gases over Wide Ranges of Pressures and Temperatures — Cornell University Engineering Experiment Station Bulletin No. 30 — 1942

14. Many Handbooks, Magazine Articles and Manufacturer's Data Books have also been used in obtaining and checking various gas properties.

PROPERTIES OF HYDROCARBON AND SPECIAL REFRIGERANT VAPORS

Gas	Chemical Formula	Alternate Designation	Molecular Weight	Boiling Point °F at 14.696 PSIA	Specific Gravity (Air=1.00)	Density lbs/cu ft	Specific Volume cu ft/lb	Specific Heat at Constant Pressure at 14.696 PSIA Btu/lb/°F Minus 40°F	60°F	150°F	300°F	Ratio of Specific Heats K=Cp/Cv Minus 40°F	60°F	150°F	300°F	Molar Heat Capacity at 150°F and 14.696 PSIA Btu/°F/Mole	Critical Temperature °Rankine	Critical Pressure PSIA
					Values at 14.696 PSIA & 60°F			(See Notes)				(See Notes)						
Methane	CH₄	C₁	16.04	-259	0.555	.0424	23.61	.506	.527	.558	.624	1.33	1.31	1.29	1.25	8.95	344	673
Acetylene	C₂H₂		26.04	-119	0.899p	.0686p	14.58p	.353	.397	.427	.469	1.31	1.26	1.24	1.21	11.12	557	905
Ethylene	C₂H₄	Ethene C₂	28.05	-155	0.969p	.0739p	13.53p	.312	.362	.406	.478	1.29	1.24	1.21	1.17	11.39	510	742
Ethane	C₂H₆		30.07	-128	1.047	.0799	12.52	.365	.410	.458	.543	1.22	1.19	1.17	1.14	13.77	550	708
Propylene	C₃H₆	Propene C₃	42.08	-54	1.453p	.1109p	9.021p	.303	.354	.399	.473	1.18	1.15	1.14	1.11	16.79	657	667
Propane	C₃H₈		44.09	-44	1.547	.1180	8.471	.333	.389	.443	.534	1.16	1.13	1.11	1.09	19.53	666	617
Butadiene 1, 2	C₄H₆		54.09	+51	1.867p	.1425p	7.018p		.346	.387	.451		1.12	1.11	1.09	20.93	799	653
Butadiene 1, 3	C₄H₆		54.09	+24	1.867p	.1425p	7.018p		.341	.392	.468		1.12	1.10	1.09	21.26	766	628
Isobutylene	C₄H₈		56.10	+20	1.937p	.1478p	6.766p		.370	.419	.493		1.11	1.09	1.08	23.51	753	580
Butylene	C₄H₈	1-Butene	56.10	+21	1.937p	.1478p	6.766p		.355	.406	.484		1.11	1.10	1.08	22.78	756	583
Isobutane	C₄H₁₀	i-C₄	58.12	+11	2.068	.1578	6.339		.387	.443	.535		1.10	1.10	1.08	25.75	735	529
n-Butane	C₄H₁₀	n-C₄	58.12	+31	2.071	.1581	6.327		.391	.444	.532		1.10	1.10	1.07	25.81	766	551
Isopentane	C₅H₁₂	i-C₅	72.15	+82	2.491p	.190p	5.262p		.401b	.439	.529		1.07b	1.07	1.06	31.67	830	483
n-Pentane	C₅H₁₂	n-C₅	72.15	+97	2.491p	.190p	5.262p		.410b	.441	.528		1.07b	1.07	1.06	31.82	846	489
Benzene	C₆H₆		78.11	+176	2.697p	.206p	4.860p		.301b		.360		1.09b		1.08	23.51	1012	714
n-Hexane	C₆H₁₄	n-C₆	86.17	+156	2.975p	.227p	4.406p		.443b		.526		1.06b		1.05	38.17	915	440
n-Heptane	C₇H₁₆	n-C₇	100.20	+209	3.459p	.264p	3.789p		.474b		.525	1.17	1.04b		1.04	47.49	973	397
n-Octane	C₈H₁₈	n-C₈	114.22	+258	3.943p	.301p	3.324p	.133	.449b		.524		1.04b		1.03	57.00	1025	362
Refrigerant 11 ***	CCl₃F		137.38	+75	4.78b	.365b	2.739b		.134b	.141	.156		1.14b	1.13	1.10	19.37	848	635
Refrigerant 12 ***	CCl₂F₂		120.92	-22	4.27	.326	3.067		.145g				1.14g			17.53g	694	597
Refrigerant 13 ***	CClF₃		104.47	-115	3.62	.276	3.624		.150	.164	.183		1.15	1.13	1.12	17.13	544	561
Refrigerant 21 ***	CHCl₂F		102.93	+48	3.63	.277	3.608		.136	.148	.169		1.18	1.16	1.13	15.23	813	750
Refrigerant 22 ***	CHClF₂		86.48	-41	3.05	.233	4.099		.149	.161	.182		1.20	1.17	1.14	13.92	665	716
Refrigerant 113 ***	C₂Cl₃F₃		187.39	+118	6.04b	.461b	2.169b		.159b	.162	.179		1.08b	1.08b	1.07	30.36	877	495
Refrigerant 114 ***	C₂Cl₂F₄		170.93	+38	6.08	.464	2.155		.157	.168	.188		1.09	1.08	1.07	28.72	754	474

Gas	Chemical Formula	Alternate Designation	Molecular Weight	Boiling Point °F at 14.696 PSIA	Specific Gravity (Air = 1.00) Values at 14.696 & 60°F	Density lbs/cu ft at 14.696	Specific Volume cu ft/lb	Specific Heat at Constant Pressure at 14.696 PSIA Btu/lb °F Minus 40°F	60°F	150°F	300°F	Ratio of Specific Heats K = Cp/Cv at 14.696 PSIA Minus 40°F	60°F	150°F	300°F	Molar Heat Capacity at 150°F and 14.696 PSIA Btu/°F/Mole	Critical Temperature °Rankine	Critical Pressure PSIA
Air (dry) **			28.97	-318	1.000	.0763	13.106	.240	.240	.241	.243	1.40	1.40	1.40	1.39	6.98	239	547
Ammonia	NH_3		17.03	-28	0.594	.0454	22.05		.506	.525	.556		1.30	1.30	1.27	8.94	730	1639
Argon	A		39.94	-303	1.380	.1053	9.497	.125	.125	.125	.124	1.67	1.67	1.67	1.67	4.99	272	705
Carbon Dioxide	CO_2		44.01	-109	1.528	.1166	8.576	.189	.201	.213	.254	1.34	1.30	1.28	1.25	9.37	548	1073
Carbon Monoxide	CO		28.01	-312	0.967	.0738	13.55	.249	.248	.249	.252	1.40	1.40	1.40	1.40	6.97	242	507
Chlorine	Cl_2		70.91	-30	2.48	.1886	5.30		.115				1.35			8.15d	751	1119
Ethylene Oxide	H_2C_2O		44.05	+51	1.52	.116	8.62	225h	.264h	.302h	.355h	1.25h	1.21h	1.19h	1.15h	14.10	844	1043
Helium	He		4.003	-451	0.138	.01054	94.91			1.248a				1.66a		5.00	*24	*151
Hydrogen	H_2		2.016	-423	0.0696	.00531	188.32	3.324	3.409	3.442	3.462	1.42	1.41	1.40	1.40	6.94	*83	*327
Hydrogen Chloride	HCl		36.47	-121	1.271	.0970	10.31		.194				1.41			7.08d	585	1200
Hydrogen Sulphide	H_2S		34.08	-79	1.175	.0897	11.15	.233	.238	.243	.251	1.34	1.33	1.32	1.30	8.28	673	1306
Methyl Chloride	CH_3Cl		50.49	-11	1.777	.1356	7.372		.199f				1.29f			10.05f	749	969
Neon	Ne		20.19	-411	0.697	.0532	18.81	.246	.246	.246		1.66	1.66	1.66		4.97	80	385
Nitric Oxide	NO		30.01	-240	1.038	.0792	12.62	.239	.238	.238	.239	1.38	1.39	1.39	1.38	7.14	323	956
Nitrogen	N_2		28.02	-320	0.967	.0738	13.55	.249	.249	.249	.250	1.40	1.40	1.40	1.40	6.98	227	492
Nitrous Oxide	N_2O		44.02	-127	1.531	.1168	8.56		.21				1.30			9.24d	558	1054
Oxygen	O_2		32.00	-297	1.105	.0843	11.86	.218	.219	.221	.226	1.40	1.40	1.39	1.38	7.07	278	732
Phosgene	$COCl_2$		98.92	+46	3.41	.262	3.82	.123	.136	.146	.158	1.19	1.17	1.16	1.14	14.44	820	823
Sulphur Dioxide	SO_2		64.06	+14	2.254	.1720	5.814		.147				1.25			9.42d	775	1142
Toluene	$CH_3C_6H_5$		92.13	+231	3.181p	.243p	4.121p		.346b		.379		1.07b		1.06	31.87	1069	611
Water Vapor	H_2O	Steam	18.02	+212	0.632b	.0373b	26.80b		.496b		.55c		1.32b		1.31c	8.94	1165	3187

NOTES TO TABLES

a - An average for 0°F to 300°F.

b - At the boiling point.

c - Approximate average for 212°F to 600°F and 14.7 psiA to 200 psiA.

d - At 60°F.

f - At 77°F.

g - At 86°F.

h - Within plus or minus 5 percent.

p - As a perfect gas.

* These are Effective Values to be used only for Generalized Compressibility Charts and gas mixtures. See pages 34 - 50. Actual values are

	T_c	P_c
Helium	9.7°R	33.2 psiA
Hydrogen	59.7°R	188 psiA

** Normal Atmospheric Air contains some moisture. For convenience it is common to consider that, at 68°F and 14.696 psiA, the air is at 36 percent relative humidity, weighs 0.075 lb/cu ft, and has a k value of 1.395. (Based on ASME Test Code for Displacement Compressors).

*** This group of refrigerants is known by trade names such as Freon, Genetron, etc-

Compressibility and Temperature-Entropy Charts

This section contains compressibility and temperature-entropy charts for a number of gases or mixtures of gases frequently compressed. These have been prepared from the latest and best data available. In some cases several sources have been combined to obtain the range desired. It is believed these charts present the characteristics as accurately as existing knowledge permits.

Compressibility is shown as a multiplying factor to be applied to perfect gas volume at a specific condition in order to obtain actual volume.

Temperature-entropy diagrams are included to permit determination of the gas temperature at the completion of adiabatic (isentropic) compression for any compression stage. Note that entering the chart at a specific inlet temperature and pressure and moving horizontally to the discharge pressure, one reads discharge temperature. This frequently varies from values obtained by using perfect gas laws.

This discharge temperature is needed to determine compressibility from the other chart at *discharge* conditions, a factor which enters into many compressor calculations.

For some gases, more than one compressibility chart is presented, to cover the range more adequately.

Gas	Z Chart	T-S Chart
N-Butane (C_4H_{10})	34-9, 10	34-11
Air	34-12	34-13
Ammonia (NH_3)	34-14	34-15
Carbon Dioxide (CO_2)	34-16, 17	34-18
Ethane (C_2H_6)	34-19, 20	34-21
Chlorine (Cl_2)	34-22	34-23
Ethylene (C_2H_4)	34-24, 25	34-26
Isobutane (C_4H_{10})	34-27, 28	34-29
Helium (He)	34-30	34-31
Hydrogen (H_2)	34-32	34-33
Methane (CH_4)	34-34	34-35
Nitrogen (N_2)	34-36	34-37
Propylene (C_3H_6)	34-38	34-39
Propane (C_3H_8)	34-40, 41	34-42
5 Component Synthetic Ammonia Feed Gas	34-43, 44	34-45
76/24 Synthetic Ammonia Mixture	34-46, 47	34-48, 49
Generalized Curves	34-50 thru 55	
Natural Gas	34-56 thru 63	

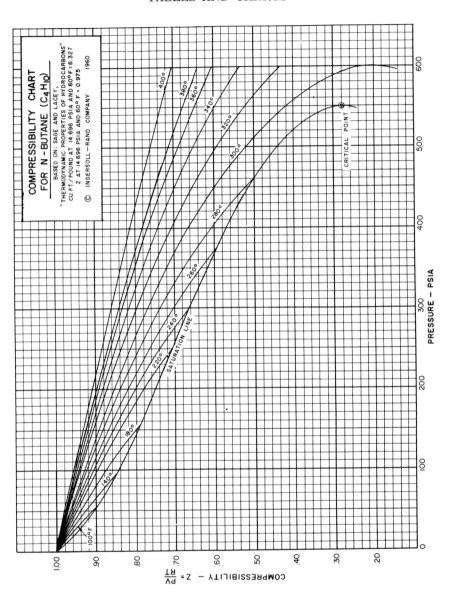

COMPRESSIBILITY CHART
FOR N-BUTANE (C₄H₁₀)

BASED ON: SAGE AND LACEY,
"THERMODYNAMIC PROPERTIES OF HYDROCARBONS"
CU.FT./POUND AT 14.696 PSIA AND 60°F = 6.327
Z AT 14.696 PSIA AND 60°F = 0.975
© INGERSOLL—RAND COMPANY   1960

PRESSURE — PSIA

COMPRESSIBILITY — Z = $\frac{PV}{RT}$

CRITICAL POINT

SATURATION LINE

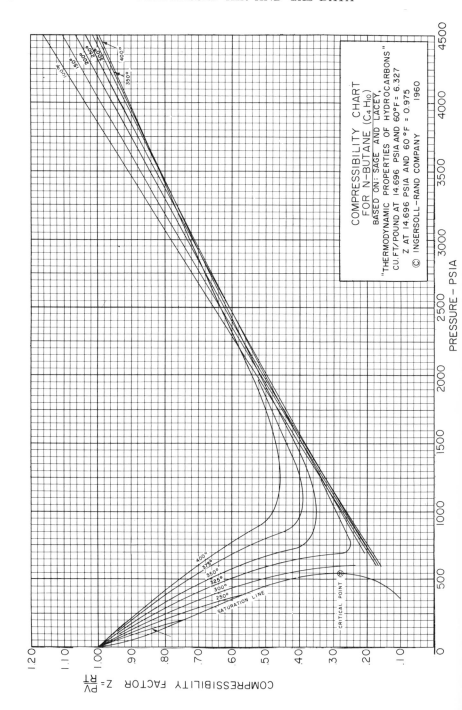

COMPRESSIBILITY CHART
FOR N-BUTANE (C₄H₁₀)
BASED ON: SAGE AND LACEY,
"THERMODYNAMIC PROPERTIES OF HYDROCARBONS"
CU. FT/POUND AT 14.696 PSIA AND 60°F = 6.327
Z AT 14.696 PSIA AND 60 °F = 0.975
© INGERSOLL–RAND COMPANY   1960

PRESSURE – PSIA

COMPRESSIBILITY FACTOR $Z = \dfrac{PV}{RT}$

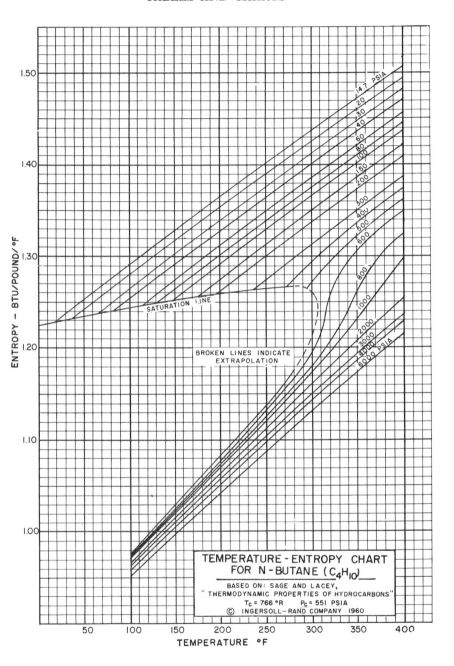

TEMPERATURE - ENTROPY CHART
FOR N-BUTANE (C_4H_{10})

BASED ON: SAGE AND LACEY,
" THERMODYNAMIC PROPERTIES OF HYDROCARBONS"
T_c = 766 °R P_c = 551 PSIA
© INGERSOLL-RAND COMPANY 1960

BROKEN LINES INDICATE
EXTRAPOLATION

SATURATION LINE

ENTROPY — BTU/POUND/°F

TEMPERATURE °F

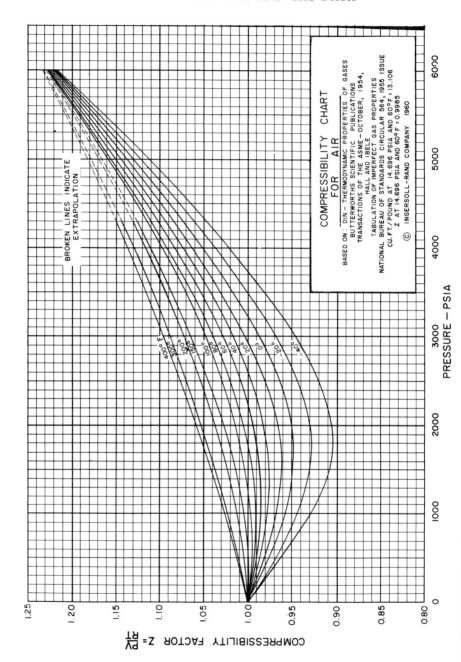

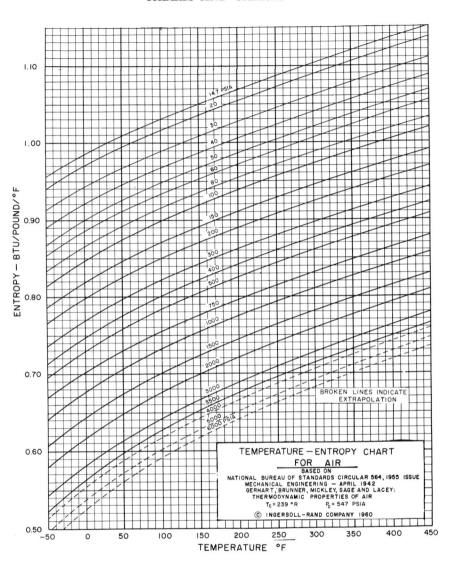

ENTROPY – BTU/POUND/°F

1.10

1.00

0.90

0.80

0.70

0.60

0.50

147 PSIA
20
30
40
50
60
80
100
150
200
300
400
500
750
1000
1500
2000
3000
3500
4000
5000
6000 PSIA

BROKEN LINES INDICATE
EXTRAPOLATION

TEMPERATURE – ENTROPY CHART
FOR AIR
BASED ON
NATIONAL BUREAU OF STANDARDS CIRCULAR 564, 1955 ISSUE
MECHANICAL ENGINEERING – APRIL 1942
GERHART, BRUNNER, MICKLEY, SAGE AND LACEY:
THERMODYNAMIC PROPERTIES OF AIR
T_c = 239 °R P_c = 547 PSIA
© INGERSOLL – RAND COMPANY 1960

-50   0   50   100   150   200   250   300   350   400   450

TEMPERATURE   °F

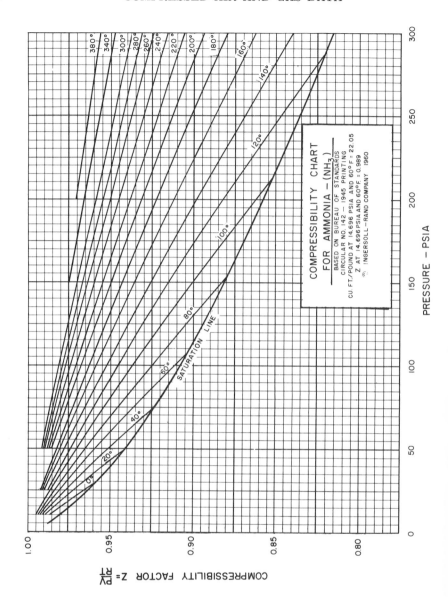

COMPRESSIBILITY CHART
FOR AMMONIA – (NH₃)
BASED ON BUREAU OF STANDARDS
CIRCULAR NO. 142 – 1945 PRINTING
CU FT./POUND AT 14.696 PSIA AND 60°F = 22.05
Z AT 14.696 PSIA AND 60°F = 0.989
© INGERSOLL–RAND COMPANY 1960

PRESSURE – PSIA

COMPRESSIBILITY FACTOR $Z = \dfrac{PV}{RT}$

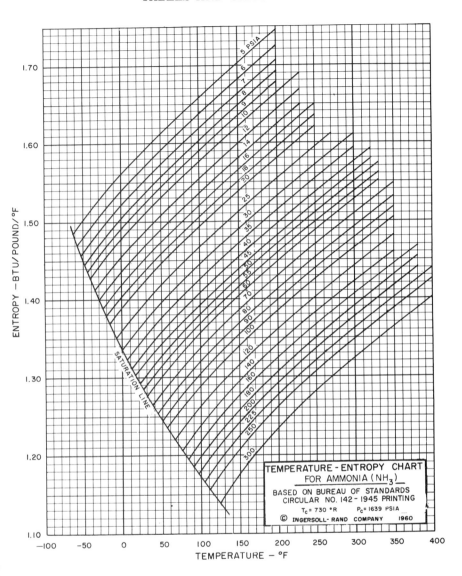

TEMPERATURE - ENTROPY CHART
FOR AMMONIA (NH₃)

BASED ON BUREAU OF STANDARDS
CIRCULAR NO. 142 - 1945 PRINTING

T_c = 730 °R P_c = 1639 PSIA

© INGERSOLL-RAND COMPANY   1960

ENTROPY — BTU/ POUND/ °F

TEMPERATURE — °F

SATURATION LINE

5 PSIA

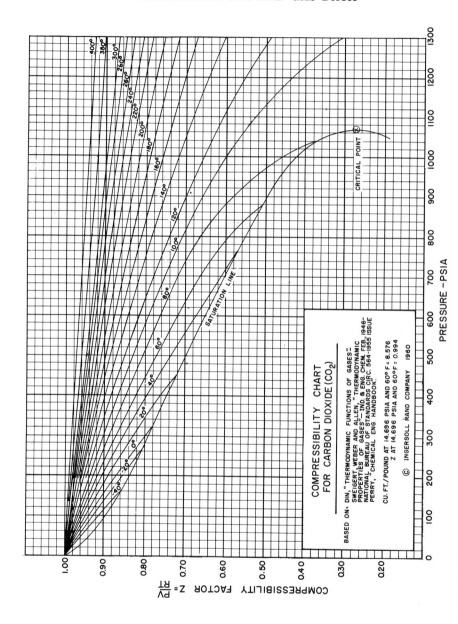

COMPRESSIBILITY CHART
FOR CARBON DIOXIDE (CO₂)

BASED ON: DIN, "THERMODYNAMIC FUNCTIONS OF GASES".
SWEIGERT, WEBER AND ALLEN, "THERMODYNAMIC
PROPERTIES OF GASES". IND. & ENG. CHEM. FEB. 1946-
NATIONAL BUREAU OF STANDARDS CIRC. 564-1955 ISSUE
PERRY, "CHEMICAL ENG HANDBOOK".

CU. FT./POUND AT 14.696 PSIA AND 60° F = 8.576
Z AT 14.696 PSIA AND 60°F = 0.994

© INGERSOLL RAND COMPANY 1960

PRESSURE – PSIA

COMPRESSIBILITY FACTOR $Z = \frac{PV}{RT}$

CRITICAL POINT

SATURATION LINE

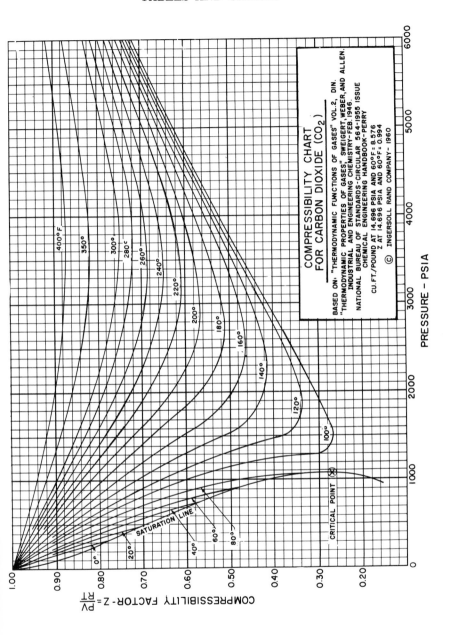

COMPRESSIBILITY CHART
FOR CARBON DIOXIDE (CO_2)

BASED ON: "THERMODYNAMIC FUNCTIONS OF GASES" VOL. 2, DIN.
"THERMODYNAMIC PROPERTIES OF GASES" SWEIGERT, WEBER, AND ALLEN.
INDUSTRIAL AND ENGINEERING CHEMISTRY-FEB.1946.
NATIONAL BUREAU OF STANDARDS-CIRCULAR 564-1955 ISSUE
CHEMICAL ENGINEERING HANDBOOK-PERRY
CU. FT./POUND AT 14,696 PSIA AND 60°F = 8.576
Z AT 14,696 PSIA AND 60°F = 0.994
© INGERSOLL RAND COMPANY-1960

PRESSURE – PSIA

COMPRESSIBILITY FACTOR- $Z = \dfrac{PV}{RT}$

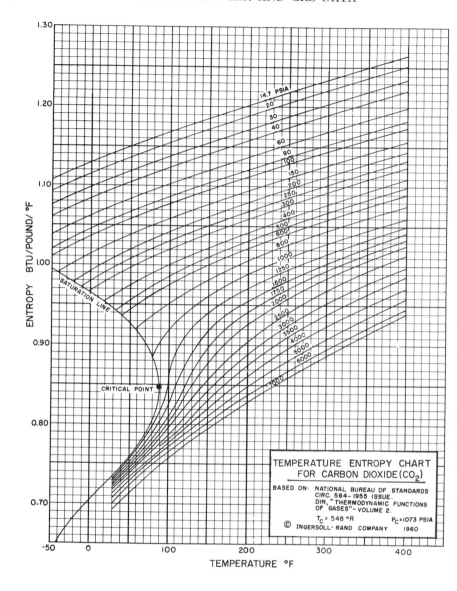

TEMPERATURE ENTROPY CHART
FOR CARBON DIOXIDE(CO_2)

BASED ON: NATIONAL BUREAU OF STANDARDS
CIRC. 564- 1955 ISSUE.
DIN, " THERMODYNAMIC FUNCTIONS
OF 'GASES"- VOLUME 2.

T_c = 548 °R P_c =1073 PSIA
© INGERSOLL- RAND COMPANY   1960

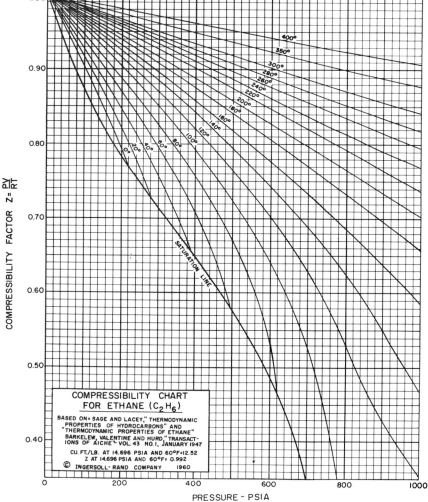

COMPRESSIBILITY FACTOR $Z = \frac{PV}{RT}$

PRESSURE - PSIA

COMPRESSIBILITY CHART
FOR ETHANE (C_2H_6)

BASED ON: SAGE AND LACEY," THERMODYNAMIC
PROPERTIES OF HYDROCARBONS" AND
"THERMODYNAMIC PROPERTIES OF ETHANE"
BARKELEW, VALENTINE AND HURD," TRANSACT-
IONS OF AICHE"- VOL. 43 NO.1, JANUARY 1947

CU. FT./LB. AT 14.696 PSIA AND 60°F=12.52
Z AT 14.696 PSIA AND 60°F= 0.992

© INGERSOLL-RAND COMPANY   1960

SATURATION LINE

400°
350°
300°
280°
260°
240°
220°
200°
180°
140°
120°
100°
80°
60°
40°
20°
0°

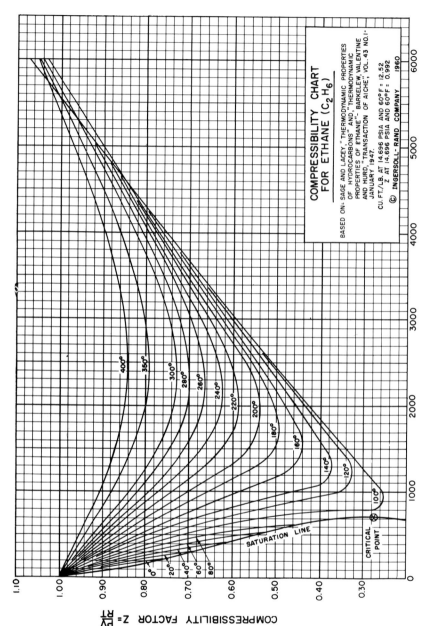

COMPRESSIBILITY CHART
FOR ETHANE (C₂H₆)

BASED ON: SAGE AND LACEY "THERMODYNAMIC PROPERTIES
OF HYDROCARBONS" AND, "THERMODYNAMIC
PROPERTIES OF ETHANE"- BARKELEW, VALENTINE
AND HURD, "TRANSACTION OF AICHE," VOL. 43 NO.1-
JANUARY 1947.

CU. FT./LB. AT 14.696 PSIA AND 60°F = 12.52
Z AT 14.696 PSIA AND 60°F = 0.992
© INGERSOLL-RAND COMPANY 1960

PRESSURE - PSIA

COMPRESSIBILITY FACTOR $Z = \frac{PV}{RT}$

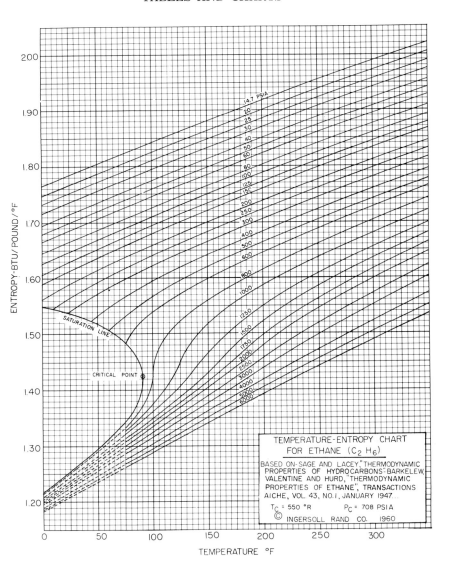

ENTROPY-BTU/POUND/°F

TEMPERATURE °F

TEMPERATURE-ENTROPY CHART
FOR ETHANE $(C_2 H_6)$

BASED ON-SAGE AND LACEY,"THERMODYNAMIC
PROPERTIES OF HYDROCARBONS"-BARKELEW,
VALENTINE AND HURD,"THERMODYNAMIC
PROPERTIES OF ETHANE", TRANSACTIONS
AICHE, VOL. 43, NO.1, JANUARY 1947...

$T_C = 550$ °R $P_C = 708$ PSIA
© INGERSOLL RAND CO. 1960

SATURATION LINE

CRITICAL POINT

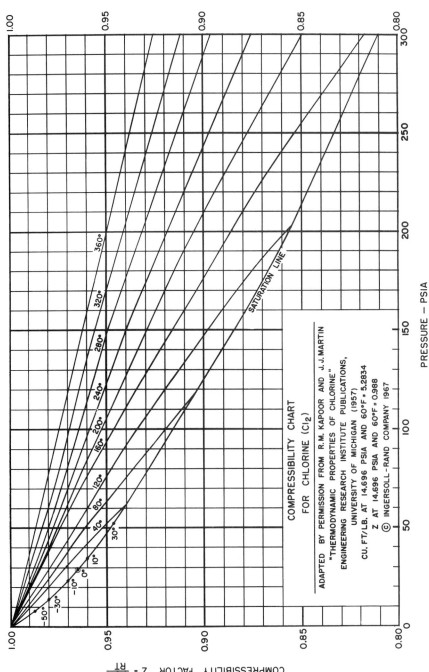

COMPRESSIBILITY CHART
FOR CHLORINE (Cl₂)

ADAPTED BY PERMISSION FROM R.M. KAPOOR AND J.J.MARTIN
"THERMODYNAMIC PROPERTIES OF CHLORINE"
ENGINEERING RESEARCH INSTITUTE PUBLICATIONS,
UNIVERSITY OF MICHIGAN (1957)
CU. FT/LB. AT 14.696 PSIA AND 60°F = 5.2834
Z AT 14.696 PSIA AND 60°F = 0.988
© INGERSOLL-RAND COMPANY 1967

PRESSURE – PSIA

COMPRESSIBILITY FACTOR Z = $\frac{PV}{RT}$

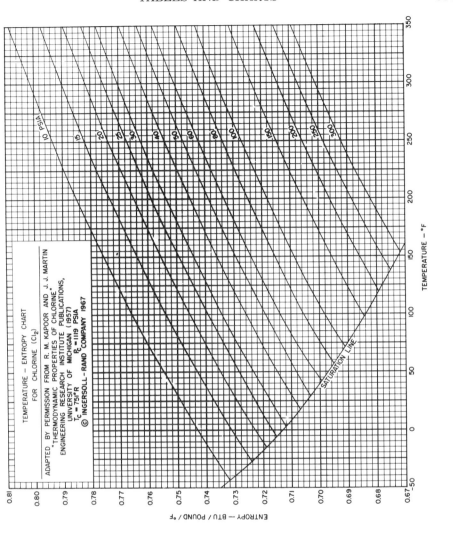

TEMPERATURE – ENTROPY CHART
FOR CHLORINE (Cl₂)

ADAPTED BY PERMISSION FROM R. M. KAPOOR AND J. J. MARTIN
"THERMODYNAMIC PROPERTIES OF CHLORINE"
ENGINEERING RESEARCH INSTITUTE PUBLICATIONS,
UNIVERSITY OF MICHIGAN (1957)
$T_c = 751°R$ $P_c = 1119$ PSIA
© INGERSOLL – RAND COMPANY 1967

TEMPERATURE – °F

ENTROPY – BTU / POUND / °F

10 PSIA   15   20   25   30   40   50   60   80   100   150   200   250   300

SATURATION LINE

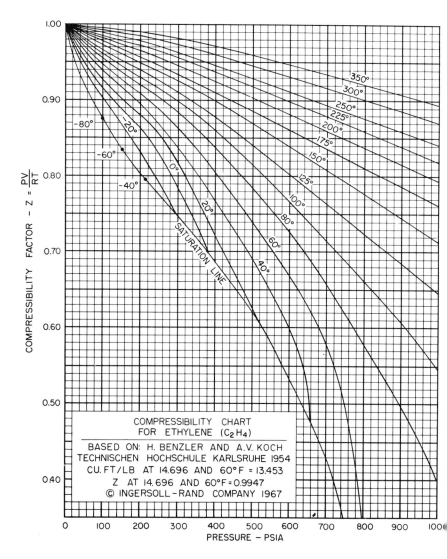

COMPRESSIBILITY FACTOR – Z = $\frac{PV}{RT}$

PRESSURE – PSIA

COMPRESSIBILITY CHART
FOR ETHYLENE (C$_2$H$_4$)

BASED ON: H. BENZLER AND A.V. KOCH
TECHNISCHEN HOCHSCHULE KARLSRUHE 1954
CU. FT/LB AT 14.696 AND 60°F = 13.453
Z AT 14.696 AND 60°F = 0.9947
© INGERSOLL–RAND COMPANY 1967

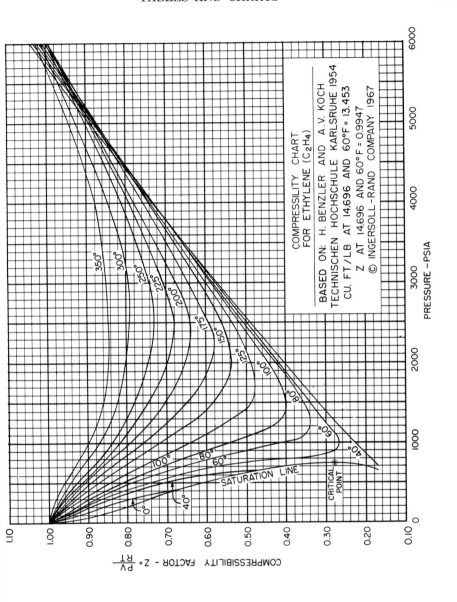

COMPRESSILITY CHART
FOR ETHYLENE (C₂H₄)

BASED ON: H. BENZLER AND A. V. KOCH
TECHNISCHEN HOCHSCHULE KARLSRUHE 1954
CU. FT/LB AT 14.696 AND 60°F = 13.453
Z AT 14.696 AND 60°F = 0.9947
© INGERSOLL-RAND COMPANY 1967

PRESSURE — PSIA

COMPRESSIBILITY FACTOR — $Z = \frac{PV}{RT}$

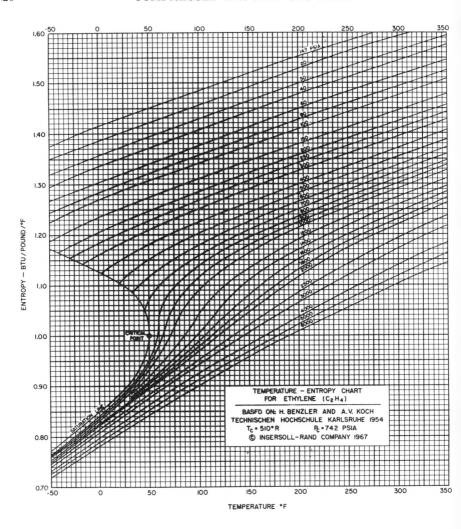

TEMPERATURE – ENTROPY CHART
FOR ETHYLENE (C₂H₄)

BASED ON: H. BENZLER AND A.V. KOCH
TECHNISCHEN HOCHSCHULE KARLSRUHE 1954
T_C = 510°R　　　P_C = 742 PSIA
© INGERSOLL-RAND COMPANY 1967

ENTROPY – BTU / POUND /°F

TEMPERATURE °F

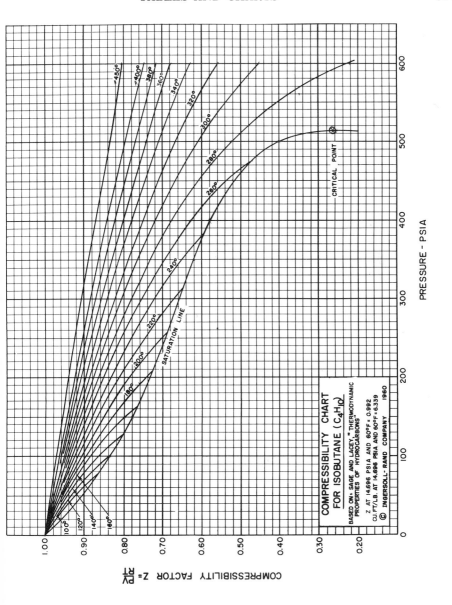

COMPRESSIBILITY CHART
FOR ISOBUTANE (C₄H₁₀)

BASED ON: SAGE AND LACEY'S "THERMODYNAMIC
PROPERTIES OF HYDROCARBONS"

Z AT 14.696 PSIA AND 60°F = 0.992
CU.FT/LB. AT 14.696 PSIA AND 60°F = 6.339

© INGERSOLL-RAND COMPANY 1960

PRESSURE - PSIA

COMPRESSIBILITY FACTOR $Z = \frac{PV}{RT}$

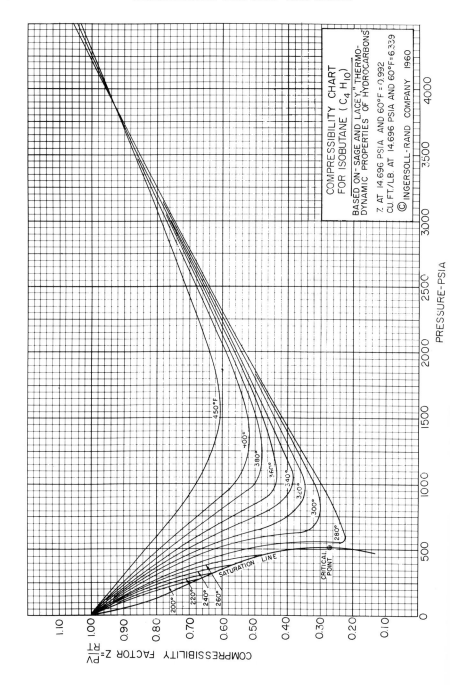

COMPRESSIBILITY CHART
FOR ISOBUTANE (C₄ H₁₀)

BASED ON "SAGE AND LACEY," THERMO-
DYNAMIC PROPERTIES OF HYDROCARBONS

Z AT 14.696 PSIA AND 60°F = 0.992
CU. FT./LB. AT 14.696 PSIA AND 60°F = 6.339
© INGERSOLL-RAND COMPANY 1960

PRESSURE-PSIA

COMPRESSIBILITY FACTOR Z = $\frac{PV}{RT}$

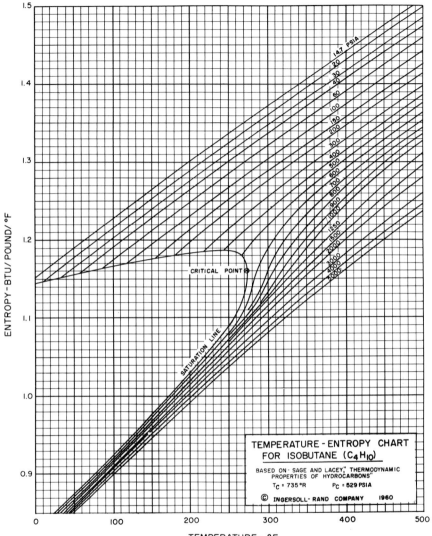

TEMPERATURE - ENTROPY CHART
FOR ISOBUTANE (C4H10)

BASED ON - SAGE AND LACEY, "THERMODYNAMIC
PROPERTIES OF HYDROCARBONS"

T_C = 735 °R P_C = 529 PSIA

© INGERSOLL- RAND COMPANY   1960

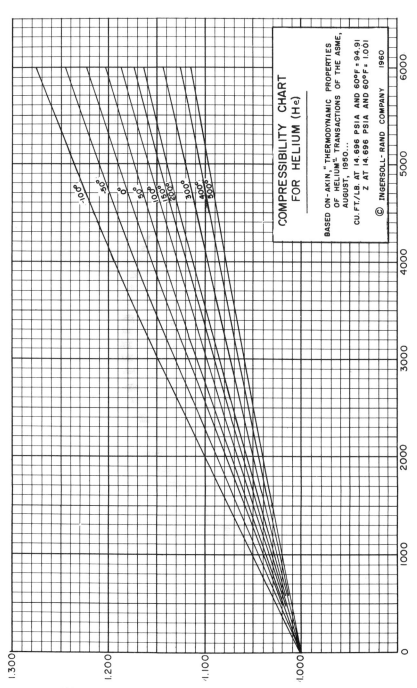

COMPRESSIBILITY CHART
FOR HELIUM (He)

BASED ON-AKIN, "THERMODYNAMIC PROPERTIES
OF HELIUM". TRANSACTIONS OF THE ASME,
AUGUST, 1950....

CU. FT./LB. AT 14.696 PSIA AND 60°F = 94.91
Z AT 14.696 PSIA AND 60°F = 1.001

© INGERSOLL-RAND COMPANY 1960

PRESSURE - PSIA

COMPRESSIBILITY FACTOR $Z = \dfrac{PV}{RT}$

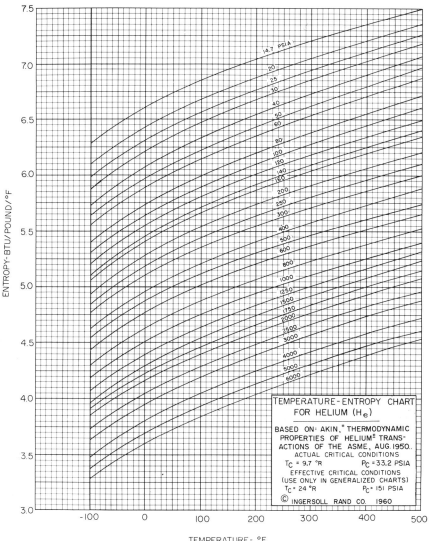

TEMPERATURE-ENTROPY CHART
FOR HELIUM (H$_e$)

BASED ON: AKIN," THERMODYNAMIC
PROPERTIES OF HELIUM" TRANS-
ACTIONS OF THE ASME, AUG. 1950..
ACTUAL CRITICAL CONDITIONS
T$_C$ = 9.7 °R   P$_C$ = 33.2 PSIA
EFFECTIVE CRITICAL CONDITIONS
(USE ONLY IN GENERALIZED CHARTS)
T$_C$ = 24 °R   P$_C$ = 151 PSIA
© INGERSOLL RAND CO. 1960

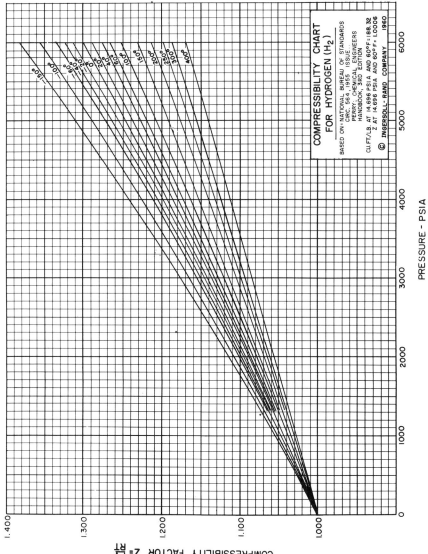

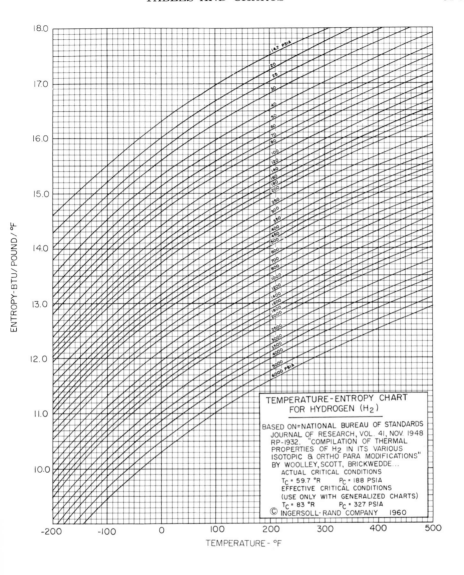

ENTROPY-BTU/POUND/°F

TEMPERATURE-ENTROPY CHART
FOR HYDROGEN (H$_2$)

BASED ON=NATIONAL BUREAU OF STANDARDS
JOURNAL OF RESEARCH, VOL. 41, NOV. 1948
RP-1932. "COMPILATION OF THERMAL
PROPERTIES OF H$_2$ IN ITS VARIOUS
ISOTOPIC & ORTHO PARA MODIFICATIONS"
BY WOOLLEY, SCOTT, BRICKWEDDE...
ACTUAL CRITICAL CONDITIONS
T$_C$ = 59.7 °R   P$_C$ = 188 PSIA
EFFECTIVE CRITICAL CONDITIONS
(USE ONLY WITH GENERALIZED CHARTS)
T$_C$ = 83 °R   P$_C$ = 327 PSIA
© INGERSOLL-RAND COMPANY   1960

TEMPERATURE - °F

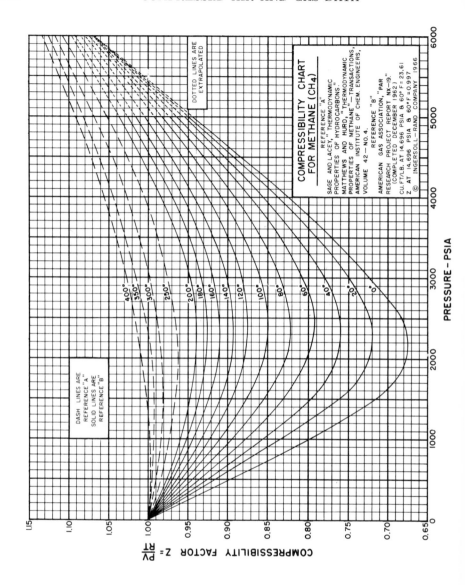

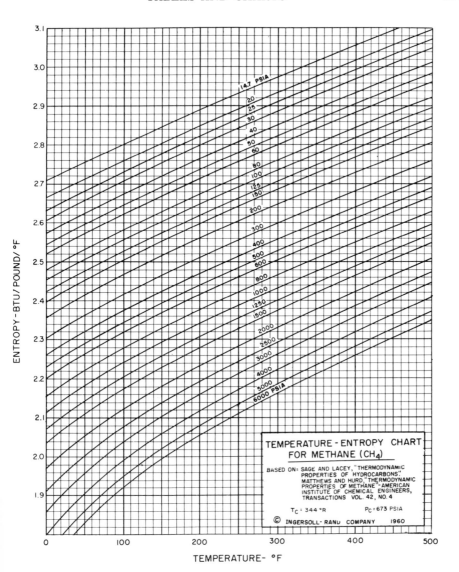

TEMPERATURE - ENTROPY CHART
FOR METHANE (CH₄)

BASED ON: SAGE AND LACEY, "THERMODYNAMIC
PROPERTIES OF HYDROCARBONS."
MATTHEWS AND HURD, "THERMODYNAMIC
PROPERTIES OF METHANE "—AMERICAN
INSTITUTE OF CHEMICAL ENGINEERS,
TRANSACTIONS VOL. 42, NO. 4

$T_C = 344\ °R$ $P_C = 673\ PSIA$

© INGERSOLL- RAND COMPANY   1960

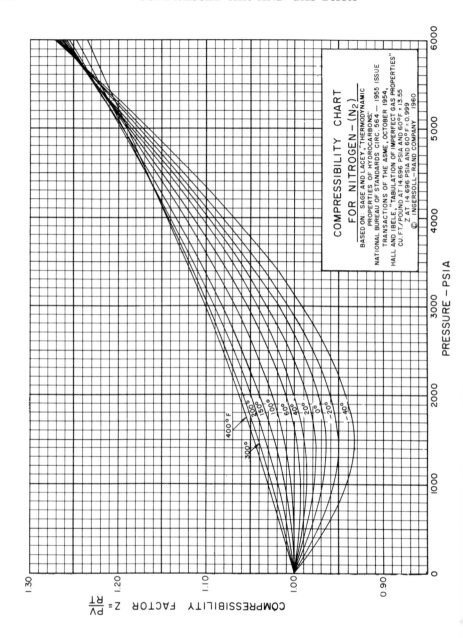

COMPRESSIBILITY CHART
FOR NITROGEN – (N₂)

BASED ON: SAGE AND LACEY, "THERMODYNAMIC
PROPERTIES OF HYDROCARBONS,"
NATIONAL BUREAU OF STANDARDS CIRC. 564 — 1955 ISSUE
TRANSACTIONS OF THE ASME, OCTOBER 1954,
HALL AND IBELE, "TABULATION OF IMPERFECT GAS PROPERTIES"
CU.FT./POUND AT 14.696 PSIA AND 60°F = 13.55
Z AT 14.696 PSIA AND 60°F = 0.999
© INGERSOLL—RAND COMPANY 1960

PRESSURE – PSIA

COMPRESSIBILITY FACTOR $Z = \dfrac{PV}{RT}$

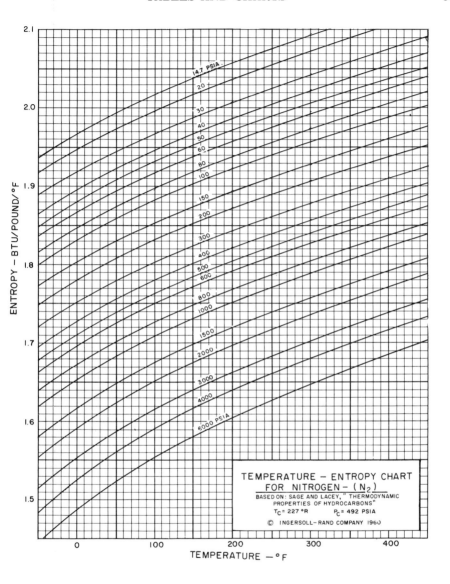

ENTROPY – BTU/POUND/°F

TEMPERATURE – °F

14.7 PSIA
20
30
40
50
60
80
100
150
200
300
400
500
600
800
1000
1500
2000
3000
4000
6000 PSIA

TEMPERATURE – ENTROPY CHART
FOR NITROGEN – (N_2)
BASED ON: SAGE AND LACEY, "THERMODYNAMIC
PROPERTIES OF HYDROCARBONS"
T_C = 227 °R P_C = 492 PSIA
© INGERSOLL–RAND COMPANY 1960

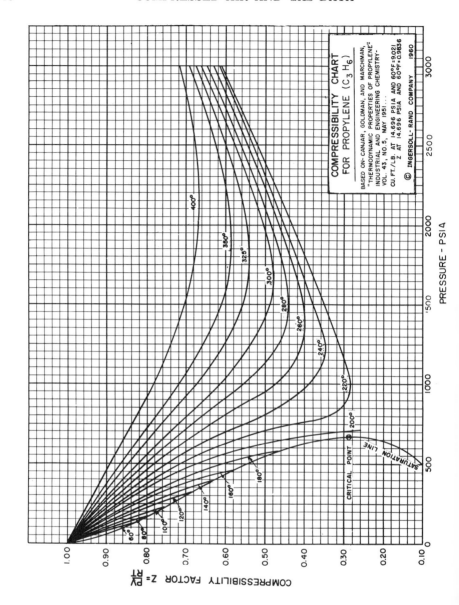

COMPRESSIBILITY CHART
FOR PROPYLENE (C_3H_6)

BASED ON- CANJAR, GOLDMAN, AND MARCHMAN,
"THERMODYNAMIC PROPERTIES OF PROPYLENE"
INDUSTRIAL AND ENGINEERING CHEMISTRY-
VOL. 43, NO. 5, MAY 1951....

CU. FT./LB. AT 14.696 PSIA AND 60°F =9.021
Z AT 14.696 PSIA AND 60°F =0.9836

© INGERSOLL-RAND COMPANY 1960

PRESSURE - PSIA

COMPRESSIBILITY FACTOR $Z = \dfrac{PV}{RT}$

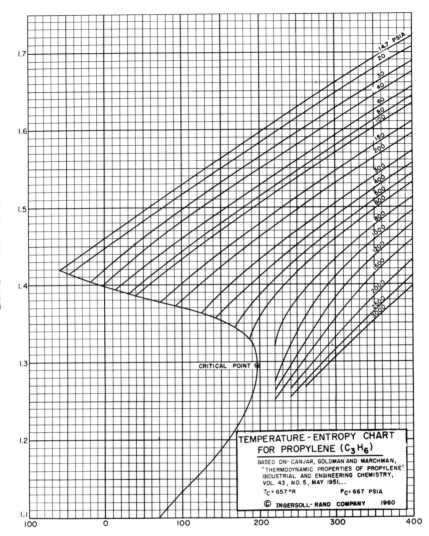

ENTROPY-BTU/POUND/°F

TEMPERATURE- °F

TEMPERATURE - ENTROPY CHART
FOR PROPYLENE (C_3H_6)

BASED ON- CANJAR, GOLDMAN AND MARCHMAN,
"THERMODYNAMIC PROPERTIES OF PROPYLENE"
INDUSTRIAL AND ENGINEERING CHEMISTRY,
VOL. 43, NO. 5, MAY 1951...

$T_C = 657$ °R $P_C = 667$ PSIA

© INGERSOLL- RAND COMPANY   1960

CRITICAL POINT

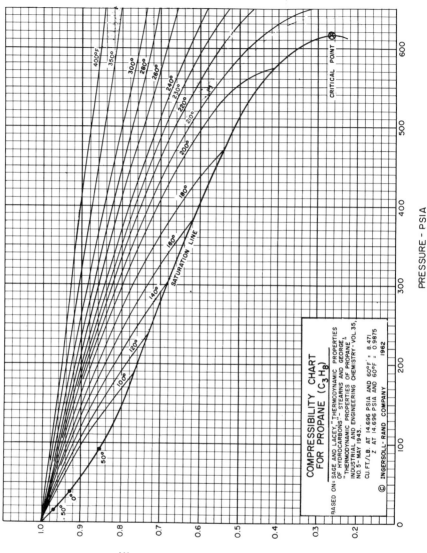

COMPRESSIBILITY CHART
FOR PROPANE (C_3H_8)

BASED ON: SAGE AND LACEY, "THERMODYNAMIC PROPERTIES
OF HYDROCARBONS."-- STEARNS AND GEORGE,
"THERMODYNAMIC PROPERTIES OF PROPANE."
INDUSTRIAL AND ENGINEERING CHEMISTRY-VOL.35,
NO.5-MAY 1943.

CU.FT./LB. AT 14.696 PSIA AND 60°F = 8.471
Z AT 14.696 PSIA AND 60°F = 0.9875

© INGERSOLL- RAND COMPANY　1962

CRITICAL POINT

SATURATION LINE

PRESSURE - PSIA

COMPRESSIBILITY FACTOR Z= $\frac{PV}{RT}$

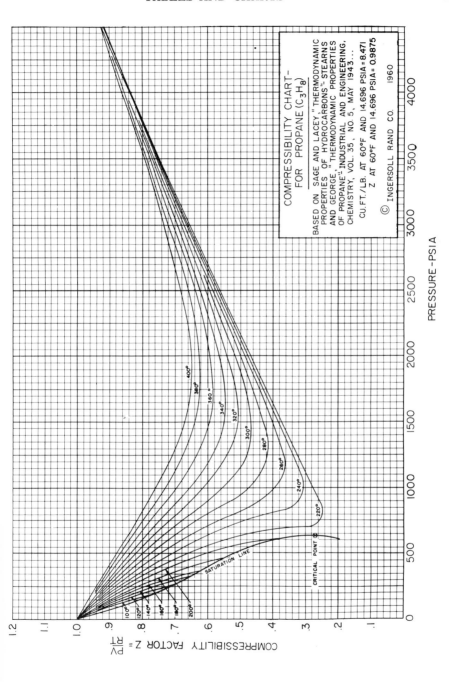

COMPRESSIBILITY CHART - FOR PROPANE (C_3H_8)

BASED ON SAGE AND LACEY, "THERMODYNAMIC PROPERTIES OF HYDROCARBONS"-STEARNS AND GEORGE, "THERMODYNAMIC PROPERTIES OF PROPANE" INDUSTRIAL AND ENGINEERING, CHEMISTRY, VOL. 35, NO. 5, MAY 1943...

CU.FT./LB. AT 60°F AND 14.696 PSIA = 8.471
Z AT 60°F AND 14.696 PSIA = 0.9875

© INGERSOLL RAND CO.   1960

PRESSURE -PSIA

COMPRESSIBILITY FACTOR $Z = \dfrac{PV}{RT}$

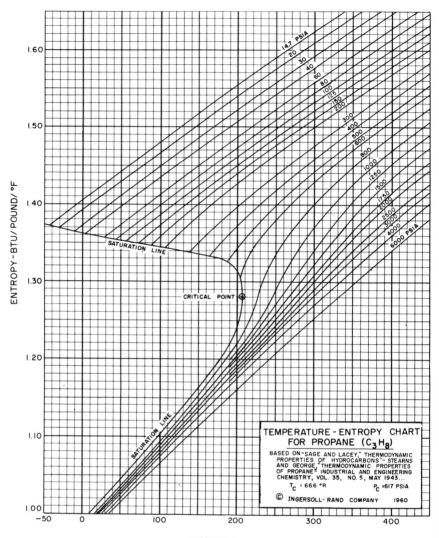

ENTROPY - BTU/ POUND/ °F

TEMPERATURE- °F

TEMPERATURE - ENTROPY CHART
FOR PROPANE (C$_3$H$_8$)

BASED ON "SAGE AND LACEY," THERMODYNAMIC
PROPERTIES OF HYDROCARBONS"- STEARNS
AND GEORGE,"THERMODYNAMIC PROPERTIES
OF PROPANE" INDUSTRIAL AND ENGINEERING
CHEMISTRY, VOL. 35, NO. 5, MAY 1943...

T_C = 666 °R P_C = 617 PSIA

© INGERSOLL- RAND COMPANY   1960

SATURATION LINE

CRITICAL POINT

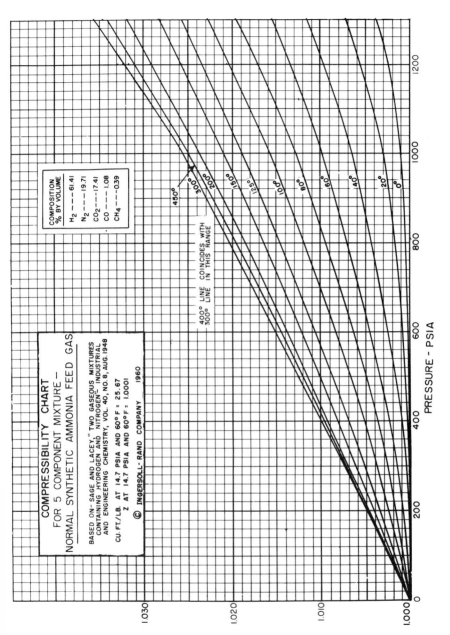

COMPRESSIBILITY CHART
FOR 5 COMPONENT MIXTURE —
NORMAL SYNTHETIC AMMONIA FEED GAS

BASED ON "SAGE AND LACEY" TWO GASEOUS MIXTURES
CONTAINING HYDROGEN AND NITROGEN INDUSTRIAL
AND ENGINEERING CHEMISTRY, VOL. 40, NO. 8, AUG. 1948

CU. FT./LB. AT 14.7 PSIA AND 60° F = 25.67
Z AT 14.7 PSIA AND 60° F = 1.0001

© INGERSOLL-RAND COMPANY 1960

COMPOSITION
% BY VOLUME
H_2 – – – 61.41
N_2 – – – 19.71
CO_2 – – – 17.41
CO – – – 1.08
CH_4 – – – 0.39

400° LINE COINCIDES WITH
300° LINE IN THIS RANGE

450°
300°
200°
150°
125°
100°
80°
60°
40°
20°
0°

PRESSURE - PSIA

COMPRESSIBILITY FACTOR $Z = \dfrac{PV}{RT}$

1.030
1.020
1.010
1.000

0   200   400   600   800   1000   1200

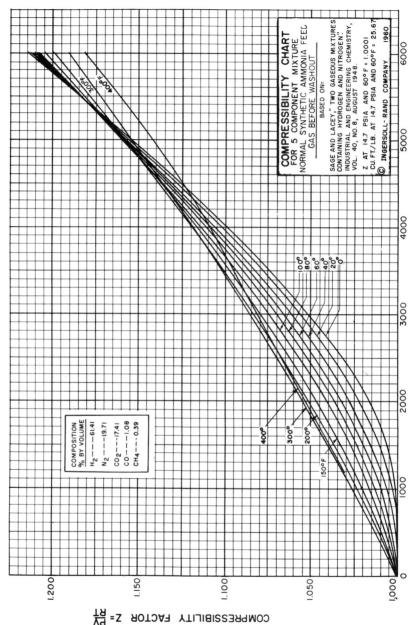

COMPRESSIBILITY CHART
FOR 5 COMPONENT MIXTURE
NORMAL SYNTHETIC AMMONIA FEED
GAS BEFORE WASHOUT

BASED ON:

SAGE AND LACEY," TWO GASEOUS MIXTURES
CONTAINING HYDROGEN AND NITROGEN".
INDUSTRIAL AND ENGINEERING CHEMISTRY,
VOL. 40, NO. 8, AUGUST 1948.

Z AT 14.7 PSIA AND 60°F = 1.0001
CU.FT./LB. AT 14.7 PSIA AND 60°F = 25.67

© INGERSOLL-RAND COMPANY 1960

COMPOSITION
% BY VOLUME
H_2 — — 61.41
N_2 — — 19.71
CO_2 — — 17.41
CO — — 1.08
CH_4 — — 0.39

PRESSURE - PSIA

COMPRESSIBILITY FACTOR $Z = \dfrac{PV}{RT}$

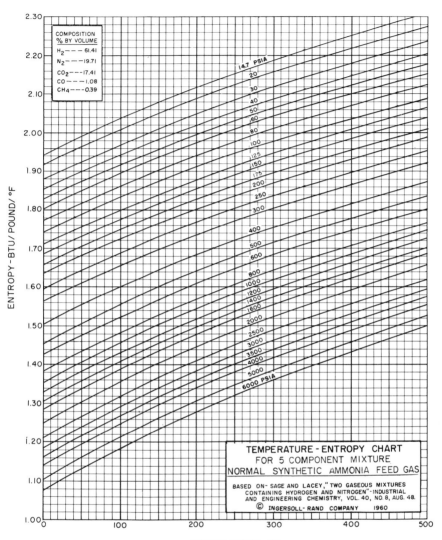

COMPOSITION
% BY VOLUME
H_2 — — 61.41
N_2 — — 19.71
CO_2 — — 17.41
CO — — 1.08
CH_4 — — 0.39

14.7 PSIA
20
30
40
50
60
80
100
125
150
175
200
250
300
400
500
600
800
1000
1200
1400
1600
2000
2500
3000
3500
4000
5000
6000 PSIA

TEMPERATURE - ENTROPY CHART
FOR 5 COMPONENT MIXTURE
NORMAL SYNTHETIC AMMONIA FEED GAS

BASED ON - SAGE AND LACEY," TWO GASEOUS MIXTURES
CONTAINING HYDROGEN AND NITROGEN" - INDUSTRIAL
AND ENGINEERING CHEMISTRY, VOL. 40, NO. 8, AUG. 48.
© INGERSOLL - RAND COMPANY   1960

ENTROPY - BTU/ POUND/ °F

TEMPERATURE - °F

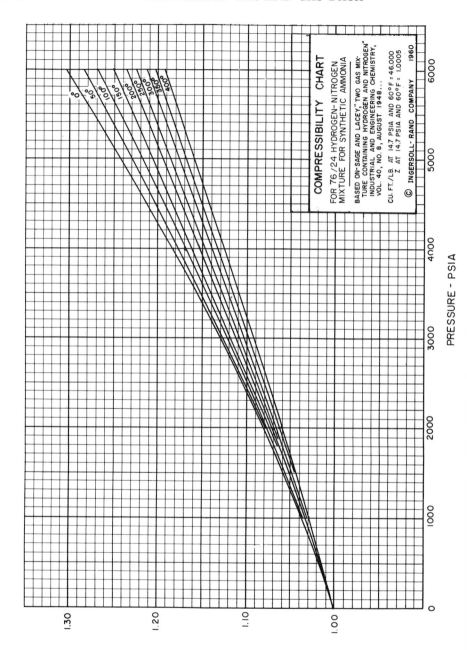

COMPRESSIBILITY CHART

FOR 76/24 HYDROGEN-NITROGEN
MIXTURE FOR SYNTHETIC AMMONIA

BASED ON SAGE AND LACEY, "TWO GAS MIX-
TURE CONTAINING HYDROGEN AND NITROGEN"
INDUSTRIAL AND ENGINEERING CHEMISTRY,
VOL. 40, NO. 8, AUGUST 1948....

CU. FT./LB. AT 14.7 PSIA AND 60°F = 46.000
Z AT 14.7 PSIA AND 60°F = 1.0005

© INGERSOLL-RAND COMPANY 1960

PRESSURE - PSIA

COMPRESSIBILITY FACTOR $Z = \dfrac{PV}{RT}$

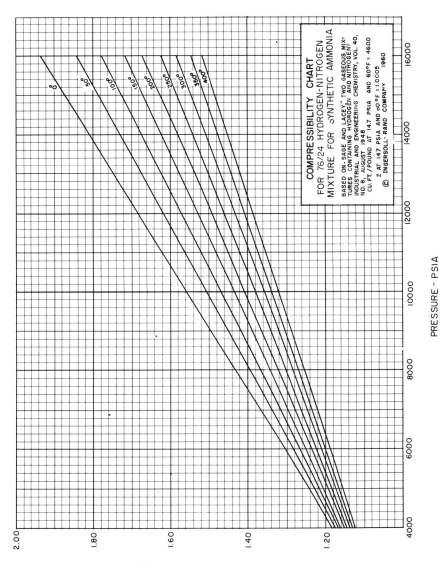

COMPRESSIBILITY CHART
FOR 76/24 HYDROGEN-NITROGEN
MIXTURE FOR SYNTHETIC AMMONIA

BASED ON-SAGE AND LACEY" TWO GASEOUS MIX-
TURES CONTAINING HYDROGEN AND NITROGEN:
INDUSTRIAL AND ENGINEERING CHEMISTRY, VOL. 40,
NO. 8, AUGUST 1948
CU. FT./POUND AT 14.7 PSIA AND 60°F = 46.00
Z AT 14.7 PSIA AND 60°F = 1.0005
© INGERSOLL-RAND COMPANY 1960

PRESSURE - PSIA

COMPRESSIBILITY FACTOR $Z = \frac{PV}{RT}$

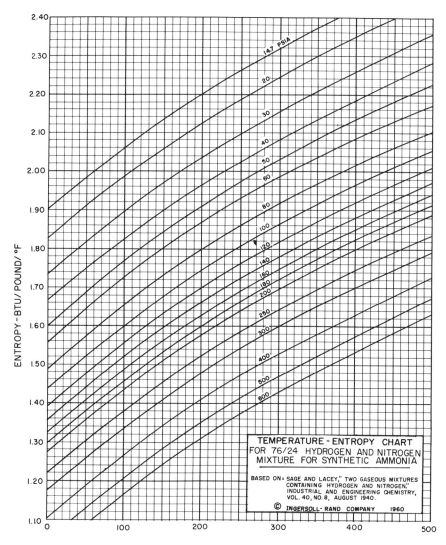

TEMPERATURE - ENTROPY CHART
FOR 76/24 HYDROGEN AND NITROGEN
MIXTURE FOR SYNTHETIC AMMONIA

BASED ON= SAGE AND LACEY," TWO GASEOUS MIXTURES
CONTAINING HYDROGEN AND NITROGEN,"
INDUSTRIAL AND ENGINEERING CHEMISTRY,
VOL. 40, NO. 8, AUGUST 1940.

© INGERSOLL- RAND COMPANY 1960

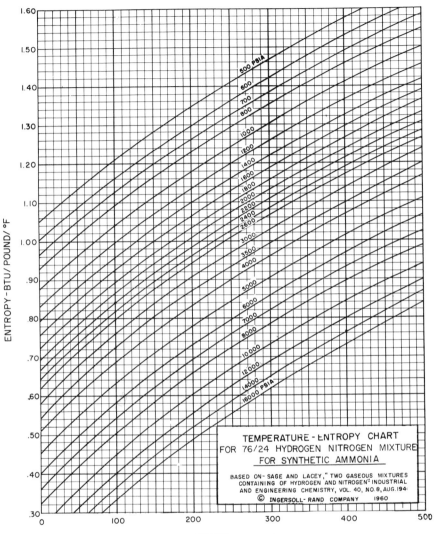

TEMPERATURE - ENTROPY CHART
FOR 76/24 HYDROGEN NITROGEN MIXTURE
FOR SYNTHETIC AMMONIA

BASED ON SAGE AND LACEY," TWO GASEOUS MIXTURES
CONTAINING OF HYDROGEN AND NITROGEN" INDUSTRIAL
AND ENGINEERING CHEMISTRY, VOL. 40, NO. 8, AUG. 1948
© INGERSOLL-RAND COMPANY   1960

Generalized Charts

The generalized charts given here are redrawn by permission from those developed by Mr. L. C. Nelson and Prof. E. F. Obert and presented at the 1953 Annual ASME meeting. They were published in Chemical Engineering in July 1954, from which article these curves have been re-plotted.

Four charts, based on a study of experimental data on 30 gases, have been prepared to cover a wide range of values.

Although steam (H_2O) and ammonia (NH_3) were considered, they do not coordinate well and since excellent tables and charts of their properties are available, their specific rather than generalized data should be used at all times.

Hydrogen and helium also cannot be correlated well with these charts, particularly below $T_r = 2.5$, unless *effective* or pseudo critical conditions are used in place of the *actual* critical conditions. Effective conditions are given below — for use *only* with generalized charts. These are as developed in 1960 by Dr. John M. Lenior, University of Southern California, Los Angeles, Cal. in the case of hydrogen and by Prof. Obert in his 1953 paper in the case of helium.

Note, however that three of these non-comformist gases have been included among the more specific gas compressibility curves and one should always use the latter when suitable.

The four generalized charts cover the following ranges of reduced pressure and reduced temperature. The maximum indicated deviation from experimental data is also shown.

Chart No.	Range pr	Range Tr	Max. Error
1	0 to 0.65	0.7 to 5.0	1.0%
2	0 to 6.5	1.0 to 15.0	2.5%
3	6 to 12.5	1.0 to 15.0	2.5%
4	10 to 42.5	1.0 to 15.0	5%

Effective Critical Conditions

Hydrogen	$T_c = 24°R$	$p_c = 151$ psiA
Helium	$T_c = 83°R$	$p_c = 327$ psiA

Outline of Procedure

1. Calculate pseudo-critical temperature and pseudo-critical pressure for a given gas mixture using the method outlined on page 12. If working with a pure gas rather than a mixture (but do not have a specific compressibility curve for that gas) look up the critical temperature and pressure on page 18 or 19.

2. If interested in compressibility at discharge conditions, estimate the discharge temperature (T_2) from the following formula for adiabatic compression.

$$T_2 = T_1 \times r^{\frac{k-1}{k}}$$

3. Calculate the reduced temperature and pressure for the conditions in question using equations (19) and (20) on page 10.

4. Read the compressibility factor, Z from the applicable generalized chart on following pages.

5. Use this compressibility factor in proper formula to determine volume or horsepower.

Example

Find the compressibility factors at inlet and discharge conditions for the following gas mixture when compressed from 315 psiA and 100°F to 965 psiA.

Gas Component	H_2	N_2	CO_2	CO
Mol Percent	61.4	19.7	17.5	1.4

Step 1. See page 12

      Pseudo — critical Temperature = 195°R

      Pseudo — critical Pressure = 493 psiA

Step. 2 Calculate theoretical discharge temperature

      $r = 965/315 = 3.06$

      $k = 1.37$ (See page 12)

      Theor. disch. temp. $T_2 = 758°R$ (298°F)

Step. 3.

	Inlet	Discharge
Pressure — psiA	315	965
Temperature — °R	560	758
Reduced Temperature	0.64	1.96
Reduced Pressure	2.87	3.88
Compressibility (from chart No. 2)	1.002	1.025

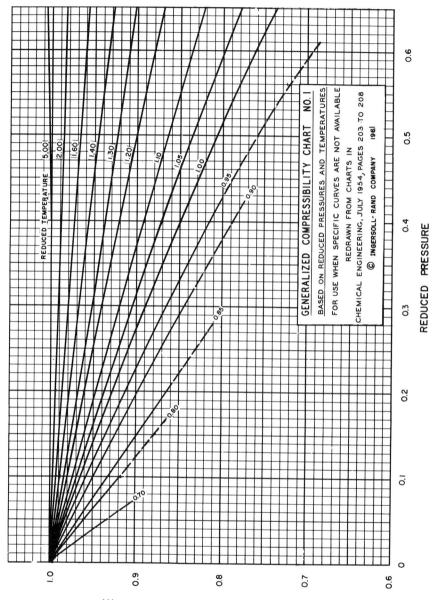

GENERALIZED COMPRESSIBILITY CHART NO. 1

BASED ON REDUCED PRESSURES AND TEMPERATURES

FOR USE WHEN SPECIFIC CURVES ARE NOT AVAILABLE

REDRAWN FROM CHARTS IN

CHEMICAL ENGINEERING, JULY 1954, PAGES 203 TO 208

© INGERSOLL-RAND COMPANY 1961

REDUCED PRESSURE

COMPRESSIBILITY FACTOR $Z = \dfrac{PV}{RT}$

REDUCED TEMPERATURE

5.00
2.00
1.60
1.40
1.30
1.20
1.10
1.05
1.00
0.95
0.90
0.85
0.80
0.70

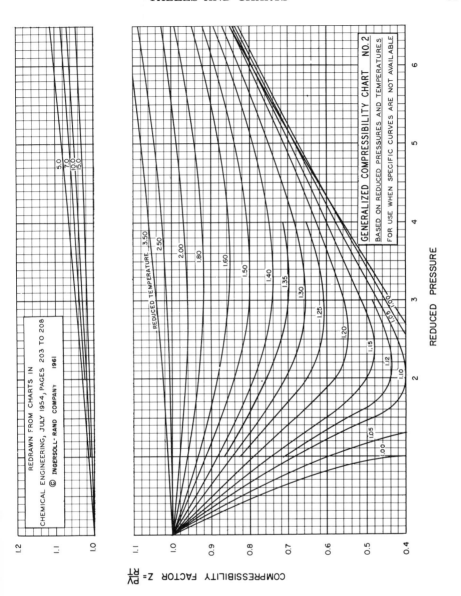

REDUCED PRESSURE

COMPRESSIBILITY FACTOR $Z = \dfrac{PV}{RT}$

GENERALIZED COMPRESSIBILITY CHART NO. 2

BASED ON REDUCED PRESSURES AND TEMPERATURES

FOR USE WHEN SPECIFIC CURVES ARE NOT AVAILABLE

REDRAWN FROM CHARTS IN

CHEMICAL ENGINEERING, JULY 1954, PAGES 203 TO 208

© INGERSOLL-RAND COMPANY 1961

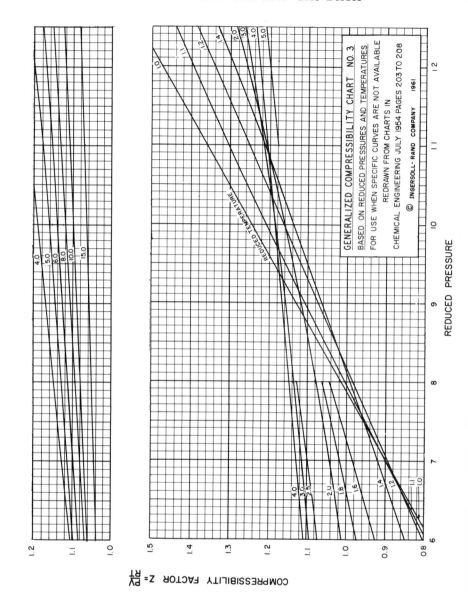

GENERALIZED COMPRESSIBILITY CHART NO. 3

BASED ON REDUCED PRESSURES AND TEMPERATURES

FOR USE WHEN SPECIFIC CURVES ARE NOT AVAILABLE

REDRAWN FROM CHARTS IN

CHEMICAL ENGINEERNG JULY 1954 PAGES 203 TO 208

© INGERSOLL-RAND COMPANY 1961

REDUCED PRESSURE

COMPRESSIBILITY FACTOR Z= $\frac{PV}{RT}$

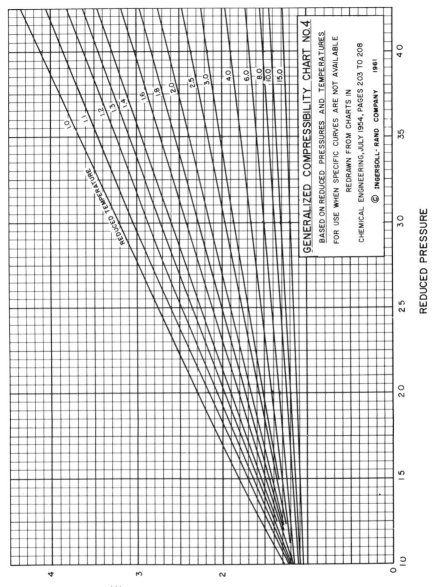

GENERALIZED COMPRESSIBILITY CHART NO.4

BASED ON REDUCED PRESSURES AND TEMPERATURES

FOR USE WHEN SPECIFIC CURVES ARE NOT AVAILABLE

REDRAWN FROM CHARTS IN

CHEMICAL ENGINEERING, JULY 1954, PAGES 203 TO 208

© INGERSOLL-RAND COMPANY 1961

REDUCED PRESSURE

COMPRESSIBILITY FACTOR $Z = \dfrac{PV}{RT}$

Compressibility Factors for Natural Gas

Knowledge of the compressibility of natural gas is vital in the design of natural gas compressors and gas metering. For many years a great deal of study has been given to determination of compressibility of the many and widely varying natural gas mixtures. One approach, available when exact analyses are known, is through Generalized Charts and the use of pseudo-critical ratios. However, exact analyses are not always available or may vary. Since specific gravity is a commonly specified characteristic, attempts have, therefore, been made to relate compressibility to this. It is on such a basis that the following charts are plotted.

Two sources have been used. The basic source is the *American Gas Association Manual For The Determination Of Supercompressibility Factors For Natural Gas — PAR Research Project NX-19*. This was completed December, 1962 and has been used through the range of 0.554 to 0.750 specific gravity, 0 to 500 psiG, and 0 to 200°F (in some cases, higher). The 0.554 specific gravity curves will be found as Methane in the earlier group of charts (page 34-30).

AGA presents data in the form most easily used in correcting meter readings. It is called *supercompressibility,* with the symbol F_{PV}. This is one of several terms called *supercompressibility.* See *Compressibility (Z)* under Definitions in Chapter 2.

$$\text{In AGA tables } F_{pv} = \sqrt{\frac{RT}{pV}}$$

$$\text{while } Z = \frac{pV}{RT}$$

$$\text{therefore, } Z = \frac{1}{F_{pv}^2}$$

The second source, used for higher pressures, is the series of curves developed by Carl Gatlin of the University of Tulsa and presented in *The Pipeline Engineer* during August, September and December, 1957. These have been used to extend the AGA tables. These data are presented for *condensate* gas and also for *miscellaneous casinghead* gas, The latter are lower and are to be used when the gas source and analysis is unknown. Values for miscellaneous gases have been used here. Agreement with AGA at 5000 psiG was within less than two percent. Each chart carries a notation as to the range over which each source was used.

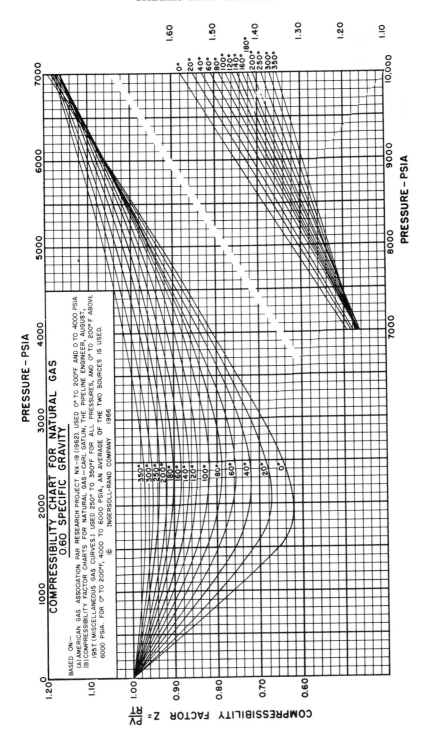

COMPRESSIBILITY CHART FOR NATURAL GAS
0.60 SPECIFIC GRAVITY

PRESSURE – PSIA

PRESSURE – PSIA

COMPRESSIBILITY FACTOR Z = $\frac{PV}{RT}$

BASED ON—
(A) AMERICAN GAS ASSOCIATION PAR RESEARCH PROJECT NX-19 (1962). USED 0° TO 200°F AND 0 TO 4000 PSIA.
(B) COMPRESSIBILITY FACTOR CHARTS FOR NATURAL GAS—CARL GATLIN, THE PIPELINE ENGINEER, AUGUST, 1957 (MISCELLANEOUS GAS CURVES.) USED 250° TO 350°F FOR ALL PRESSURES, AND 0° TO 200°F ABOVE 6000 PSIA. FOR 0° TO 200°F, 4000 TO 6000 PSIA, AN AVERAGE OF THE TWO SOURCES IS USED.
© INGERSOLL–RAND COMPANY 1966

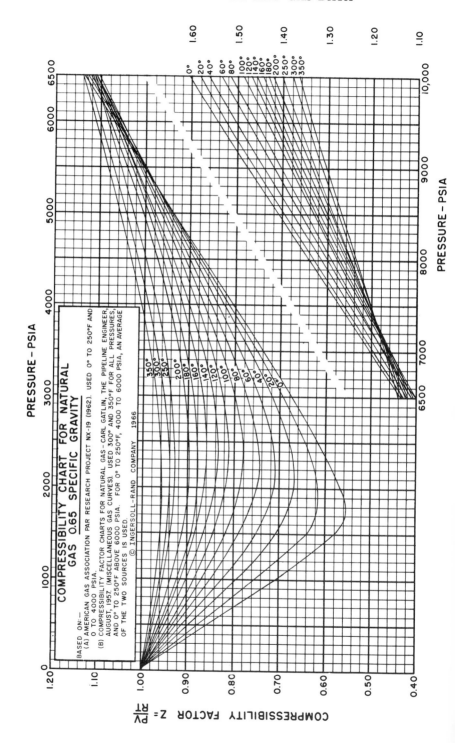

COMPRESSIBILITY CHART FOR NATURAL
GAS 0.65 SPECIFIC GRAVITY

BASED ON:—
(A) AMERICAN GAS ASSOCIATION PAR RESEARCH PROJECT NX-19 (1962). USED 0° TO 250°F AND
    0 TO 4000 PSIA.
(B) COMPRESSIBILITY FACTOR CHARTS FOR NATURAL GAS — CARL GATLIN, THE PIPELINE ENGINEER,
    AUGUST, 1957. (MISCELLANEOUS GAS CURVES). USED 300° AND 350°F FOR ALL PRESSURES,
    AND 0° TO 250°F ABOVE 6000 PSIA. FOR 0° TO 250°F, 4000 TO 6000 PSIA, AN AVERAGE
    OF THE TWO SOURCES IS USED.
    © INGERSOLL-RAND COMPANY, 1966

PRESSURE - PSIA

PRESSURE - PSIA

COMPRESSIBILITY FACTOR $Z = \dfrac{PV}{RT}$

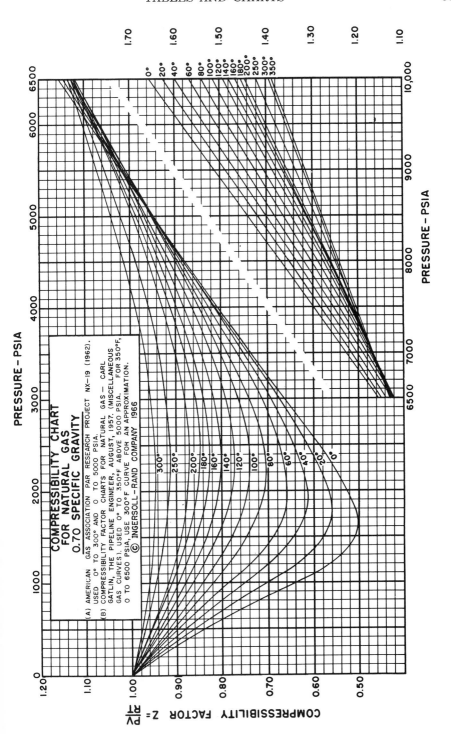

COMPRESSIBILITY CHART
FOR NATURAL GAS
0.70 SPECIFIC GRAVITY

(A) AMERICAN GAS ASSOCIATION PAR RESEARCH PROJECT NX-19 (1962).
USED 0° TO 300° AND 0 TO 5000 PSIA.
(B) COMPRESSIBILITY FACTOR CHARTS FOR NATURAL GAS — CARL
GATLIN, THE PIPELINE ENGINEER, AUGUST, 1957. (MISCELLANEOUS
GAS CURVES). USED 0° TO 350°F ABOVE 5000 PSIA. FOR 350°F,
0 TO 6500 PSIA, USE 300° F CURVE FOR AN APPROXIMATION.
© INGERSOLL – RAND COMPANY 1966

PRESSURE – PSIA

COMPRESSIBILITY FACTOR Z = $\frac{PV}{RT}$

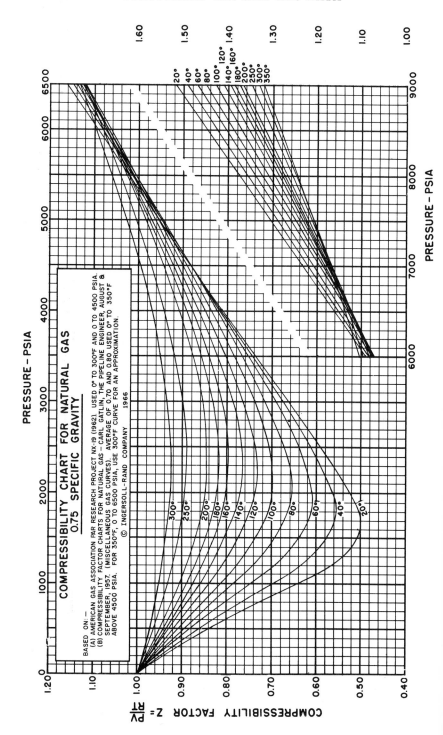

COMPRESSIBILITY CHART FOR NATURAL GAS
0.75 SPECIFIC GRAVITY

BASED ON:—
(A) AMERICAN GAS ASSOCIATION PAR RESEARCH PROJECT NX-19 (1962). USED 0° TO 300°F AND 0 TO 4500 PSIA.
(B) COMPRESSIBILITY FACTOR CHARTS FOR NATURAL GAS — CARL GATLIN, THE PIPELINE ENGINEER, AUGUST &
SEPTEMBER, 1957. (MISCELLANEOUS GAS CURVES). AVERAGE OF 0.70 AND 0.80 USED 0° TO 350°F
ABOVE 4500 PSIA. FOR 350°F, 0 TO 6500 PSIA, USE 300°F CURVE FOR AN APPROXIMATION.

© INGERSOLL-RAND COMPANY 1966

PRESSURE – PSIA

PRESSURE – PSIA

COMPRESSIBILITY FACTOR $Z = \dfrac{PV}{RT}$

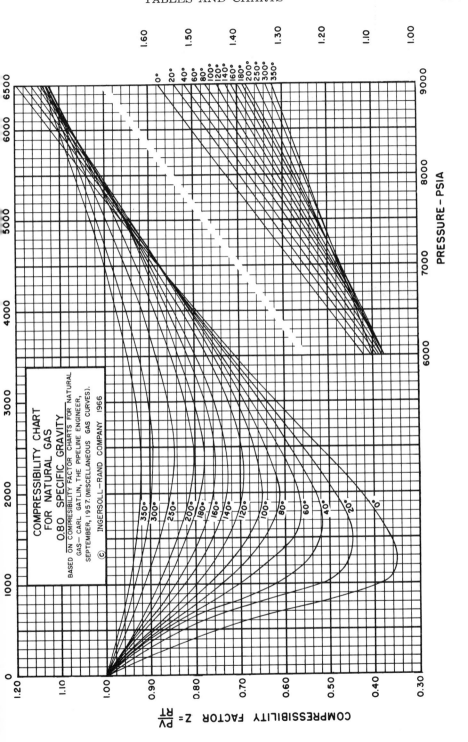

COMPRESSIBILITY CHART
FOR NATURAL GAS
0.80 SPECIFIC GRAVITY
BASED ON COMPRESSIBILITY FACTOR CHARTS FOR NATURAL
GAS— CARL GATLIN, THE PIPELINE ENGINEER,
SEPTEMBER, 1957. (MISCELLANEOUS GAS CURVES).
© INGERSOLL—RAND COMPANY 1966

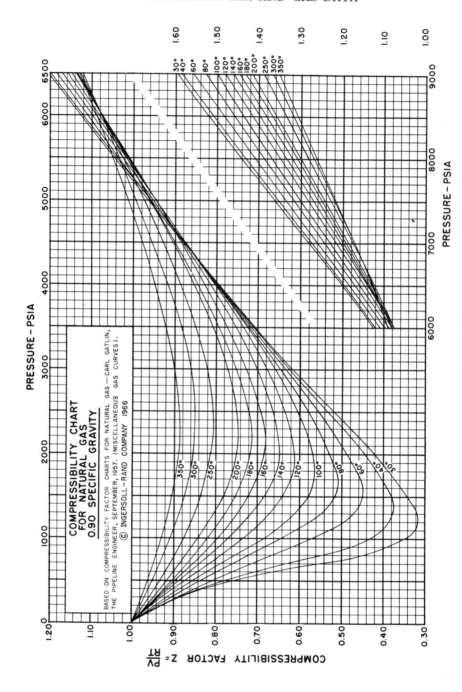

COMPRESSIBILITY CHART
FOR NATURAL GAS
0.90 SPECIFIC GRAVITY

BASED ON COMPRESSIBILITY FACTOR CHARTS FOR NATURAL GAS — CARL GATLIN,
THE PIPELINE ENGINEER, SEPTEMBER, 1957. (MISCELLANEOUS GAS CURVES).
© INGERSOLL-RAND COMPANY 1966

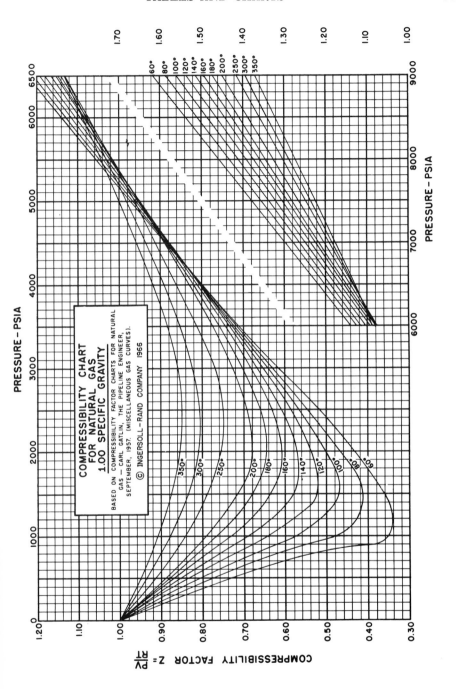

COMPRESSIBILITY CHART
FOR NATURAL GAS
1.00 SPECIFIC GRAVITY

BASED ON COMPRESSIBILITY FACTOR CHARTS FOR NATURAL
GAS — CARL GATLIN, THE PIPELINE ENGINEER,
SEPTEMBER, 1957. (MISCELLANEOUS GAS CURVES).

© INGERSOLL–RAND COMPANY 1966

PRESSURE–PSIA

COMPRESSIBILITY FACTOR Z = $\frac{PV}{RT}$

COMPRESSED AIR AND GAS DATA

STANDARD SEAMLESS CARBON STEEL PIPE FOR INDUSTRIAL GAS AND AIR BASIS ASA B31.10 (1955) SECTION 2 MATERIAL ASTM A-106-B

Nominal Pipe Size	Schedule Number	Dimensions			Cross-section Area			Surface Area		Weight per Foot		Allowable Working Pressure at 450°F
		Outside Diameter	Inside Diameter	Wall Thickness	External	Internal	Metal	Outside	Inside	Bare Pipe	Water in Pipe	
Inches		Inches	Inches	Inches	Sq. In.	Sq. In.	Sq. In.	Sq. Ft./Ft.	Sq. Ft./Ft.	Lbs.	Lbs.	PSIG
⅛	40	.405	.269	.068	.1288	.0568	.0720	.106	.0705	.244	.025	—
¼	40	.540	.364	.088	.2290	.1041	.1249	.141	.0955	.424	.045	—
⅜	40	.675	.493	.091	.3578	.1909	.1669	.177	.130	.567	.083	—
½	40	.840	.622	.109	.5542	.3039	.2503	.220	.164	.850	.132	2055
¾	40	1.050	.824	.113	.8665	.5333	.3332	.275	.217	1.130	.230	1760
1	40	1.315	1.049	.113	1.358	.8640	.4939	.344	.274	1.68	.374	1915
1¼	40	1.660	1.380	.140	2.164	1.495	.6685	.434	.362	2.27	.647	1647
1½	40	1.900	1.610	.145	2.836	2.036	.8001	.497	.421	2.72	.882	1522
2	40	2.375	2.067	.154	4.430	3.355	1.075	.622	.540	3.65	1.45	1338
2½	40	2.875	2.469	.203	6.492	4.788	1.704	.753	.646	5.79	2.07	1676
3	40	3.500	3.068	.216	9.621	7.393	2.228	.916	.802	7.58	3.20	1492
3½	40	4.000	3.548	.226	12.57	9.889	2.680	1.05	.929	9.11	4.28	1385
4	40	4.500	4.026	.237	15.90	12.73	3.174	1.18	1.06	10.79	5.51	1310
5	40	5.563	5.047	.258	24.31	20.01	4.300	1.46	1.32	14.62	8.66	1179
6	40	6.625	6.065	.280	34.47	28.89	5.58	1.73	1.59	18.97	12.5	1097
8	40	8.625	7.981	.322	58.43	50.03	8.40	2.26	2.09	28.55	21.6	999
10	40	10.750	10.020	.365	90.76	78.85	11.91	2.81	2.62	40.48	34.1	930
12	—	12.750	12.000	.375	127.7	113.1	14.58	3.34	3.14	49.6	48.9	808
12	40	12.750	11.938	.406	127.7	111.9	15.75	3.34	3.13	53.6	48.5	888
14	30	14.000	13.250	.375	153.9	137.8	16.05	3.67	3.47	54.6	59.7	735
16	30	16.000	15.250	.375	201.1	182.7	18.40	4.19	4.00	63	79.1	642
18	—	18.000	17.250	.375	254.5	233.7	20.76	4.71	4.51	71	101.2	570
18	30	18.000	17.124	.438	254.5	229.5	24.95	4.71	4.48	82	99.5	684
20	20	20.000	19.250	.375	314.2	291.1	23.12	5.24	5.04	79	126	511
22	20	22.000	21.250	.375	380.2	354.7	25.48	5.76	5.56	87	154	465
24	20	24.000	23.250	.375	452.4	424.6	27.83	6.28	6.09	95	184	426
26	—	26.000	25.250	.375	530.9	500.8	30.19	6.81	6.61	103	217	393
28	—	28.000	27.250	.375	615.8	583.2	32.55	7.33	7.13	111	253	351
30	—	30.000	29.250	.375	706.9	672.0	34.90	7.85	7.66	119	291	339

Courtesy of Crane Co.

EXTRA STRONG SEAMLESS CARBON STEEL PIPE FOR INDUSTRIAL GAS AND AIR
BASIS ASA B31.10 (1955) SECTION 2 MATERIAL ASTM A-106-B

Nominal Pipe Size (Inches)	Schedule Number	Dimensions Outside Diameter (Inches)	Dimensions Inside Diameter (Inches)	Dimensions Wall Thickness (Inches)	Cross-section Area External (Sq. In.)	Cross-section Area Internal (Sq. In.)	Cross-section Area Metal (Sq. In.)	Surface Area Outside (Sq. Ft./Ft.)	Surface Area Inside (Sq. Ft./Ft.)	Weight per Foot Bare Pipe (Lbs.)	Weight per Foot Water in Pipe (Lbs.)	Allowable Working Pressure at 450°F PSIG
⅛	80	.405	.215	.095	.1288	.0364	.0924	.106	.0563	.314	.016	—
¼	80	.540	.302	.119	.2290	.0716	.1574	.141	.0794	.535	.031	—
⅜	80	.675	.423	.126	.3578	.1405	.2173	.177	.111	.738	.061	—
½	80	.840	.546	.147	.5542	.2341	.3201	.220	.143	1.087	.101	3684
¾	80	1.050	.742	.154	.8665	.4330	.4335	.275	.195	1.473	.187	3141
1	80	1.315	.957	.179	1.358	.7193	.6388	.344	.252	2.17	.311	3156
1¼	80	1.660	1.278	.191	2.164	1.283	.8815	.434	.336	3.00	.555	2723
1½	80	1.900	1.500	.200	2.836	1.767	1.069	.497	.393	3.63	.765	2528
2	80	2.375	1.939	.218	4.430	2.953	1.477	.622	.507	5.02	1.28	2264
2½	80	2.875	2.323	.276	6.492	4.238	2.254	.753	.610	7.66	1.83	2561
3	80	3.500	2.900	.300	9.621	6.605	3.016	.916	.761	10.25	2.86	2322
3½	80	4.000	3.364	.318	12.57	8.888	3.678	1.05	.880	12.51	3.85	2177
4	80	4.500	3.826	.337	15.90	11.50	4.407	1.18	1.002	14.98	4.98	2071
5	80	5.563	4.813	.375	24.31	18.19	6.11	1.46	1.260	20.78	7.87	1896
6	80	6.625	5.761	.432	34.47	26.07	8.40	1.73	1.51	28.57	11.3	1876
8	80	8.625	7.625	.500	58.43	45.67	12.76	2.26	2.01	43.39	19.8	1696
10	60	10.750	9.750	.500	90.76	74.66	16.10	2.81	2.55	54.74	32.2	1350
12		12.750	11.750	.500	127.7	108.4	19.25	3.34	3.08	65.4	46.9	1134
12	60	12.750	11.626	.562	127.7	106.2	21.52	3.34	3.04	73	46.0	1298
14		14.000	13.000	.500	153.9	132.7	21.21	3.67	3.40	72	57.4	1030
14	60	14.000	12.812	.594	153.9	128.9	25.02	3.67	3.35	85	55.8	1252
16	40	16.000	15.000	.500	201.1	176.7	24.35	4.19	3.93	83	76.5	899
18		18.000	17.000	.500	254.5	227.0	27.49	4.71	4.45	93	98.2	797
18	40	18.000	16.876	.562	254.5	223.5	31.00	4.71	4.42	105	97.2	912
20	30	20.000	19.000	.500	314.2	283.5	30.65	5.24	4.97	104	123	717
22	30	22.000	21.000	.500	380.4	346.4	33.77	5.76	5.50	115	150	646
24		24.000	23.000	.500	452.4	415.5	36.90	6.28	6.02	125	180	595
24	30	24.000	22.876	.562	452.4	411.0	41.40	6.28	5.99	141	178	681
26	20	26.000	25.000	.500	530.9	490.9	40.05	6.81	6.54	136	213	547
28	20	28.000	27.000	.500	615.8	572.6	43.20	7.33	7.07	147	248	507
30	20	30.000	29.000	.500	706.9	660.5	46.35	7.85	7.59	158	286	475

Courtesy of Crane Co.

Dimensions of Cast-Iron Flanges and Bolts—Class 125 (ASA B-16.1-1960)

Nominal Pipe Size	Diameter of Flange	Thickness of Flange (Min.)	Diameter of Bolt Circle	Number of Bolts	Diameter of Bolts	Diameter of Bolt Holes	Length of Bolts
1	4¼	7/16	3⅛	4	½	⅝	1¾
1¼	4⅝	½	3½	4	½	⅝	2
1½	5	9/16	3⅞	4	½	⅝	2
2	6	⅝	4¾	4	⅝	¾	2¼
2½	7	11/16	5½	4	⅝	¾	2½
3	7½	¾	6	4	⅝	¾	2½
3½	8½	13/16	7	8	⅝	¾	2¾
4	9	15/16	7½	8	⅝	¾	3
5	10	15/16	8½	8	¾	⅞	3
6	11	1	9½	8	¾	⅞	3¼
8	13½	1⅛	11¾	8	¾	⅞	3½
10	16	1 3/16	14¼	12	⅞	1	3¾
12	19	1¼	17	12	⅞	1	3¾
14	21	1⅜	18¾	12	1	1⅛	4¼
16	23½	1 7/16	21¼	16	1	1⅛	4½
18	25	1 9/16	22¾	16	1⅛	1¼	4¾
20	27½	1 11/16	25	20	1⅛	1¼	5
24	32	1⅞	29½	20	1¼	1⅜	5½
30	38¾	2⅛	36	28	1¼	1⅜	6¼
36	46	2⅜	42¾	32	1½	1⅝	7
42	53	2⅝	49½	36	1½	1⅝	7½
48	59½	2¾	56	44	1½	1⅝	7¾

Flanges are rated as follows:

(a) For maximum saturated steam service pressures of 125 psi (Gage) sizes 1 to 12 in., incl. 100 psi (Gage) sizes 14 to 24 in., incl. 50 psi (Gage) size 30 to 48 in., incl.

(b) For maximum liquid and gas service pressures, at 150°F, of 175 psi (Gage) sizes 1 to 12 in., incl. 150 psi (Gage) sizes 14 to 48 in., incl.

(c) For ratings other than specified in (a) and (b) refer to ASA B-16.1 - 1960.

Dimensions of Cast-Iron Flanges, Drilling and Bolts—Class 250 (ASA-B-16.2-1960)

Nominal Pipe Size	Diameter of Flange	Thickness of Flange (Min.)	Diameter of Raised Face	Diameter of Bolt Circle	Diameter of Bolt Holes	Number of Bolts	Size of Bolts	Length of Bolts
1	4 7/8	11/16	2 11/16	3 1/2	3/4	4	5/8	2 1/2
1 1/4	5 1/4	3/4	3 1/16	3 7/8	3/4	4	5/8	2 1/2
1 1/2	6 1/8	13/16	3 9/16	4 1/2	7/8	4	3/4	2 3/4
2	6 1/2	7/8	4 3/16	5	3/4	8	5/8	2 3/4
2 1/2	7 1/2	1	4 15/16	5 7/8	7/8	8	3/4	3 1/4
3	8 1/4	1 1/8	5 11/16	6 5/8	7/8	8	3/4	3 1/2
3 1/2	9	1 3/16	6 5/16	7 1/4	7/8	8	3/4	3 1/2
4	10	1 1/4	6 15/16	7 7/8	7/8	8	3/4	3 3/4
5	11	1 3/8	8 5/16	9 1/4	7/8	8	3/4	4
6	12 1/2	1 7/16	9 11/16	10 5/8	7/8	12	3/4	4
8	15	1 5/8	11 15/16	13	1	12	7/8	4 1/2
10	17 1/2	1 7/8	14 1/16	15 1/4	1 1/8	16	1	5 1/4
12	20 1/2	2	16 7/16	17 3/4	1 1/4	16	1 1/8	5 1/2
14	23	2 1/8	18 15/16	20 1/4	1 1/4	20	1 1/8	6
16	25 1/2	2 1/4	21 1/16	22 1/2	1 3/8	20	1 1/4	6 1/4
18	28	2 3/8	23 5/16	24 3/4	1 3/8	24	1 1/4	6 1/2
20	30 1/2	2 1/2	25 9/16	27	1 3/8	24	1 1/4	6 3/4
24	36	2 3/4	30 1/4	32	1 5/8	24	1 1/2	7 3/4
30	43	3	37 3/16	39 1/4	2	28	1 3/4	8 1/2

Flanges are rated as follows:

(a) For maximum saturated steam service pressures of
250 psi (gage) sizes 1 to 12 in., incl.
200 psi (gage) sizes 14 to 24 in., incl.
100 psi (gage) all size

(b) For maximum liquid and gas service pressures, at 150°F, of
400 psi (gage) sizes 1 to 12 in., incl.
300 psi (gage) sizes 14 to 30 in., incl.

(c) For ratings other than specified in (a) and (b) refer to ASA B-16.2 - 1960.

TYPES OF FORGED STEEL FLANGES

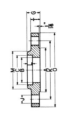

SOCKET WELD

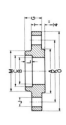

WELDING NECK

SLIP-ON

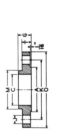

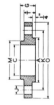

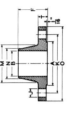

ASA 150 LB FORGED STEEL FLANGE DIMENSIONS

ASA 300 LB FORGED STEEL FLANGE DIMENSIONS

ASA 400 TO 2500 LB FORGED STEEL FLANGE DIMENSIONS

SCREWED

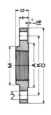

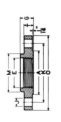

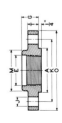

DIMENSIONS ABOVE REFER TO COLUMNS IN TABLE ON APPROPRIATE PAGE.

FORGED STEEL FLANGE PRESSURE-TEMPERATURE RATINGS
ASA STANDARD B16.5

Unlike pipe and welding fittings, forged flange pressure ratings do not vary from industry to industry, a single set of ratings having been established by the American Standards Association.

The maximum allowable non-shock pressures shown herein are those prescribed by ASA Standard B16.5.

Users are reminded that:

(a) PRESSURES may be interpolated for intermediate temperatures.

(b) TEMPERATURES used in determining the ratings are the temperatures on the inside of the pressure-retaining structure.

(c) GASKETS shall conform to Paragraph 2.4 of B16.5.

(d) FLANGES used within the jurisdiction of any specific code will, of course, be subject to the temperature limitations imposed by the code on the particular material involved.

Service Temp. (°F)	PRIMARY SERVICE PRESSURE RATING (lb.) ➤		150	300	400	600	900	1500	2500
	HYDROSTATIC SHELL TEST PRESSURE (PSIG) ➤		425	1100	1450	2175	3250	5400	9000
	Material	Service Temp. (°F)	Maximum, Non-Shock Service Pressure Rating (PSIG)						
-20	Carbon Steel, Carbon Moly, Chrome Moly, and Stainless Steel conforming to the following ASTM Specifications: A-181, Grade I or II; A-105, Grade I or II; A-350, Grade LF1; A-182, Grades F1, F5a, F9, F11, F12, F22, F310, F316, F321 and F347; A-335, *Grades P2, P5b, and P21.	-20 to 100	275	720	960	1440	2160	3600	6000
		150	255	710	945	1420	2130	3550	5915
		200	240	700	930	1400	2100	3500	5830
		250	225	690	920	1380	2070	3450	5750
		300	210	680	910	1365	2050	3415	5690
		350	195	675	900	1350	2025	3375	5625
		400	180	665	890	1330	2000	3330	5550
		450	165	650	870	1305	1955	3255	5430
		500	150	625	835	1250	1875	3125	5210
		550	140	590	790	1180	1775	2955	4925
		600	130	555	740	1110	1660	2770	4620
		650	120	515	690	1030	1550	2580	4300
to	PRIMARY SERVICE PRESSURE RATING (lb.) ➤		150	300	400	600	900	1500	2500
	HYDROSTATIC SHELL TEST PRESSURE (PSIG) ➤		425	925	1250	1875	2775	4650	7725
650	Material	Service Temp. (°F)	Maximum, Non-Shock Service Pressure Rating (PSIG)						
	ASTM Specification A-182, Grade F304.	-20 to 100	275	615	825	1235	1850	3085	5145
		150	255	585	775	1165	1750	2915	4855
		200	240	550	730	1095	1645	2740	4565
		250	225	520	695	1040	1565	2605	4340
		300	210	495	660	985	1480	2470	4115
		350	195	470	630	945	1415	2360	3930
		400	180	450	600	900	1350	2245	3745
		450	165	430	575	860	1290	2150	3585
		500	150	410	550	825	1235	2055	3430
		550	140	395	530	795	1190	1985	3305
		600	130	380	510	765	1145	1910	3180
		650	120	370	490	735	1105	1845	3070

*No flange specification has been written for the grades shown. Flanges made to these grades shall conform in chemistry to the requirements of pipe specification ASTM A-335 and in all other respects to the nearest grade of ASTM A-182.

Courtesy of Crane Co.

ASA 150 LB FORGED STEEL FLANGES

Nominal Pipe Size	Flange Outside Diam. O	Flange Thkn. T	Raised Face Diam. A	Bore Welding Neck, and Socket Wldg. Face B	Bore Slip-On, and Socket Welding Back C	Length thru Hub Welding Neck F	Length thru Hub Slip-On, Screwed, and Socket Welding G	Drilling No. of Holes	Drilling Diam. of Holes J	Drilling Diam. of Bolt Circle K	Depth of Socket L	Diam. of Hub At Base M	Diam. of Hub At Chamfer N
½	3½	7/16	1⅜	0.62	0.88	1⅞	⅝	4	⅝	2⅜	⅜	1 3/16	0.84
¾	3⅞	½	1 11/16	0.82	1.09	2 1/16	⅝	4	⅝	2¾	7/16	1½	1.05
1	4¼	9/16	2	1.05	1.36	2 3/16	11/16	4	⅝	3⅛	½	1 15/16	1.32
1¼	4⅝	⅝	2½	1.38	1.70	2¼	13/16	4	⅝	3½	9/16	2 5/16	1.66
1½	5	11/16	2⅞	1.61	1.95	2 7/16	⅞	4	⅝	3⅞	⅝	2 9/16	1.90
2	6	¾	3⅝	2.07	2.44	2½	1	4	¾	4¾	11/16	3 1/16	2.38
2½	7	⅞	4⅛	2.47	2.94	2¾	1⅛	4	¾	5½	¾	3 9/16	2.88
3	7½	15/16	5	3.07	3.57	2¾	1 3/16	4	¾	6	13/16	4¼	3.50
3½	8½	15/16	5½	3.55	4.07	2 13/16	1¼	8	¾	7	⅞	4 13/16	4.00
4	9	15/16	6 3/16	4.03	4.57	3	1 5/16	8	¾	7½	15/16	5 5/16	4.50
5	10	15/16	7 5/16	5.05	5.66	3½	1 7/16	8	⅞	8½	15/16	6 7/16	5.56
6	11	1	8½	6.07	6.72	3½	1 9/16	8	⅞	9½	1 1/16	7 9/16	6.63
8	13½	1⅛	10⅝	7.98	8.72	4	1¾	8	⅞	11¾	1¼	9 11/16	8.63
10	16	1 3/16	12¾	10.02	10.88	4	1 15/16	12	1	14¼	1 5/16	12	10.75
12	19	1¼	15	12.00	12.88	4½	2 3/16	12	1	17	1 9/16	14⅜	12.75
14	21	1⅜	16¼	13.25	14.14	5	2¼	12	1⅛	18¾	1⅝	15¾	14.00
16	23½	1 7/16	18½	15.25	16.16	5	2½	16	1⅛	21¼	1¾	18	16.00
18	25	1 9/16	21	17.25	18.18	5½	2 11/16	16	1¼	22¾	1 15/16	19⅞	18.00
20	27½	1 11/16	23	19.25	20.20	5 11/16	2⅞	20	1¼	25	2⅛	22	20.00
24	32	1⅞	27¼	23.25	24.25	6	3¼	20	1⅜	29½	2½	26⅛	24.00

DIMENSIONS are shown in inches: see page 34-68.   PRESSURE-TEMPERATURE RATINGS: see page 34-69.

SPECIFICATIONS: Flanges conform to ASTM Specification A-181 and to ASA Standard B16.5, except socket welding flanges 3½" and larger, which are not covered by the ASA Standard.

Courtesy of Crane Co.

ASA 300 LB FORGED STEEL FLANGES

Nom. Pipe Size	Flange Outside Diam.	Flange Thkn.	Raised Face Diam.	Bore: Welding Neck, and Socket Wldg. Face	Bore: Slip-On, and Socket Welding Back	Bore: Screwed	Length thru Hub: Welding Neck	Length thru Hub: Slip-On, Screwed, and Socket Welding	Drilling: No. of Holes	Drilling: Diam. of Holes	Drilling: Diam. of Bolt Circle	Depth of Socket	Diam. of Hub: At Base	Diam. of Hub: At Chamfer
	O	T	A	B	C	E	F	G		J	K	L	M	N
1/2	3 3/4	9/16	1 3/8	0.62	0.88	0.93	2 1/16	7/8	4	5/8	2 5/8	3/8	1 1/2	0.84
3/4	4 5/8	5/8	1 11/16	0.82	1.09	1.14	2 1/4	1	4	3/4	3 1/4	7/16	1 7/8	1.05
1	4 7/8	11/16	2	1.05	1.36	1.41	2 7/16	1 1/16	4	3/4	3 1/2	1/2	2 1/8	1.32
1 1/4	5 1/4	3/4	2 1/2	1.38	1.70	1.75	2 9/16	1 1/16	4	3/4	3 7/8	9/16	2 1/2	1.66
1 1/2	6 1/8	13/16	2 7/8	1.61	1.95	1.99	2 11/16	1 3/16	4	7/8	4 1/2	5/8	2 3/4	1.90
2	6 1/2	7/8	3 5/8	2.07	2.44	2.50	2 3/4	1 5/16	8	3/4	5	11/16	3 5/16	2.38
2 1/2	7 1/2	1	4 1/8	2.47	2.94	3.00	3	1 1/2	8	7/8	5 7/8	3/4	3 15/16	2.88
3	8 1/4	1 1/8	5	3.07	3.57	3.63	3 1/8	1 11/16	8	7/8	6 5/8	13/16	4 5/8	3.50
3 1/2	9	1 3/16	5 1/2	3.55	4.07	4.13	3 3/16	1 3/4	8	7/8	7 1/4	7/8	5 1/4	4.00
4	10	1 1/4	6 3/16	4.03	4.57	4.63	3 3/8	1 7/8	8	7/8	7 7/8	15/16	5 3/4	4.50
5	11	1 3/8	7 5/16	5.05	5.66	5.69	3 7/8	2	8	7/8	9 1/4	—	7	5.56
6	12 1/2	1 7/16	8 1/2	6.07	6.72	6.75	3 7/8	2 1/16	12	7/8	10 5/8	—	8 1/8	6.63
8	15	1 5/8	10 5/8	7.98	8.72	8.75	4 3/8	2 7/16	12	1	13	—	10 1/4	8.63
10	17 1/2	1 7/8	12 3/4	10.02	10.88	10.88	4 5/8	2 5/8	16	1 1/8	15 1/4	—	12 5/8	10.75
12	20 1/2	2	15	12.00	12.88	12.94	5 1/8	2 7/8	16	1 1/4	17 3/4	—	14 3/4	12.75
14	23	2 1/8	16 1/4	13.25	14.14	14.19	5 5/8	3	20	1 1/4	20 1/4	—	16 3/4	14.00
16	25 1/2	2 1/4	18 1/2	15.25	16.16	16.19	5 3/4	3 1/4	20	1 3/8	22 1/2	—	19	16.00
18	28	2 3/8	21	17.25	18.18	18.19	6 1/4	3 1/2	24	1 3/8	24 3/4	—	21	18.00
20	30 1/2	2 1/2	23	19.25	20.20	20.19	6 3/8	3 3/4	24	1 3/8	27	—	23 1/8	20.00
24	36	2 3/4	27 1/4	23.25	24.25	24.19	6 5/8	4 3/16	24	1 5/8	32	—	27 5/8	24.00

DIMENSIONS are shown in inches: see page 34-68. PRESSURE-TEMPERATURE RATINGS: see page 34-69.
SPECIFICATIONS: Flanges conform to ASTM Specification A-181 and to ASA Standard B16.5 except socket welding flanges 3 1/2" and larger, which are not covered by the ASA Standard.

Courtesy of Crane Co.

ASA 400 LB FORGED STEEL FLANGES

Nom. Pipe Size	Flange Outside Diam.	Flange Thkn.*	Raised Face Diam.	Bore: Welding Neck, and Socket Wldg. Face	Bore: Slip-On, and Socket Welding Back	Bore: Screwed	Length thru Hub*: Welding Neck	Length thru Hub*: Slip-On, Screwed, and Socket Welding	Drilling: No. of Holes	Drilling: Diam. of Holes	Drilling: Diam. of Bolt Circle	Depth of Socket	Diam. of Hub: At Base	Diam. of Hub: At Chamfer
	O	T	A	B	C	E	F	G		J	K	L	M	N
½	3¾	9/16	1⅜	0.55	0.88	0.93	2 1/16	⅞	4	⅝	2⅝	⅜	1½	0.84
¾	4⅝	⅝	1 11/16	0.74	1.09	1.14	2¼	1	4	¾	3¼	7/16	1⅞	1.05
1	4⅞	11/16	2	0.96	1.36	1.41	2 7/16	1 1/16	4	¾	3½	½	2⅛	1.32
1¼	5¼	13/16	2½	1.28	1.70	1.75	2⅝	1⅛	4	¾	3⅞	9/16	2½	1.66
1½	6⅛	⅞	2⅞	1.50	1.95	1.99	2¾	1¼	4	⅞	4½	⅝	2¾	1.90
2	6½	1	3⅝	1.94	2.44	2.50	2⅞	1 7/16	8	¾	5	11/16	3 5/16	2.38
2½	7½	1⅛	4⅛	2.32	2.94	3.00	3⅛	1⅝	8	⅞	5⅞	¾	3 15/16	2.88
3	8¼	1¼	5	2.90	3.57	3.63	3¼	1 13/16	8	⅞	6⅝	13/16	4⅝	3.50
3½	9	1⅜	5½	3.36	4.07	4.13	3⅜	1 15/16	8	1	7¼	⅞	5¼	4.00
4	10	1⅜	6 3/16	3.83	4.57	4.63	3½	2	8	1	7⅞	15/16	5¾	4.50
5	11	1½	7 5/16	4.81	5.66	5.69	4	2⅛	8	1	9¼	—	7	5.56
6	12½	1⅝	8½	5.76	6.72	6.75	4 1/16	2¼	12	1	10⅝	—	8⅛	6.63
8	15	1⅞	10⅝	7.63	8.72	8.75	4⅝	2 11/16	12	1⅛	13	—	10¼	8.63
10	17½	2⅛	12¾	9.75	10.88	10.88	4⅞	2⅞	16	1¼	15¼	—	12⅝	10.75
12	20½	2¼	15	11.75	12.88	12.94	5⅜	3⅛	16	1⅜	17¾	—	14¾	12.75
14	23	2⅜	16¼	13.00	14.14	14.19	5⅞	3 5/16	20	1⅜	20¼	—	16¾	14.00
16	25½	2½	18½	15.00	16.16	16.19	6	3 11/16	20	1½	22½	—	19	16.00
18	28	2⅝	21	17.00	18.18	18.19	6½	3⅞	24	1½	24¾	—	21	18.00
20	30½	2¾	23	19.00	20.20	20.19	6⅝	4	24	1⅝	27	—	23⅛	20.00
24	36	3	27¼	23.00	24.25	24.19	6⅞	4½	24	1⅞	32	—	27⅝	24.00

*Dimensions do not include ¼″ raised face. DIMENSIONS are shown in inches. Sizes ½″ through 3½″ are identical with 600 lb. flanges: see page 34-68.
SPECIFICATIONS: Flanges conform to ASTM Specification A-105 and to ASA Standard B16.5 except socket welding flanges which are not covered by the ASA Standard. PRESSURE-TEMPERATURE RATINGS: see page 34-69.

Courtesy of Crane Co.

ASA 600 LB FORGED STEEL FLANGES

Nom. Pipe Size	Flange Outside Diam.	Flange Thkn.*	Raised Face Diam.	Bore: Welding Neck, and Socket Wldg. Face	Bore: Slip-On, and Socket Welding Back	Bore: Screwed	Length thru Hub*: Welding Neck	Length thru Hub*: Slip-On, Screwed, and Socket Welding	Drilling: No. of Holes	Drilling: Diam. of Holes	Drilling: Diam. of Bolt Circle	Depth of Socket	Diam. of Hub: At Base	Diam. of Hub: At Chamfer
	O	T	A	B	C	E	F	G		J	K	L	M	N
½	3¾	9/16	1⅜	0.55	0.88	0.93	2 1/16	⅞	4	⅝	2⅝	⅜	1½	0.84
¾	4⅝	⅝	1 11/16	0.74	1.09	1.14	2¼	1	4	¾	3¼	7/16	1⅞	1.05
1	4⅞	11/16	2	0.96	1.36	1.41	2 7/16	1 1/16	4	¾	3½	½	2⅛	1.32
1¼	5¼	13/16	2½	1.28	1.70	1.75	2⅝	1⅛	4	¾	3⅞	9/16	2½	1.66
1½	6⅛	⅞	2⅞	1.50	1.95	1.99	2¾	1¼	4	⅞	4½	⅝	2¾	1.90
2	6½	1	3⅝	1.94	2.44	2.50	2⅞	1 7/16	8	¾	5	11/16	3 5/16	2.38
2½	7½	1⅛	4⅛	2.32	2.94	3.00	3⅛	1⅝	8	⅞	5⅞	¾	3 15/16	2.88
3	8¼	1¼	5	2.90	3.57	3.63	3¼	1 13/16	8	⅞	6⅝	13/16	4⅝	3.50
3½	9	1⅜	5½	3.36	4.07	4.13	3⅜	1 15/16	8	1	7¼	⅞	5¼	4.00
4	10¾	1½	6 3/16	3.83	4.57	4.63	4	2⅛	8	1	8½	15/16	6	4.50
5	13	1¾	7 5/16	4.81	5.66	5.69	4½	2⅜	8	1⅛	10½	—	7 7/16	5.56
6	14	1⅞	8½	5.76	6.72	6.75	4⅝	2⅝	12	1⅛	11½	—	8¾	6.63
8	16½	2 3/16	10⅝	7.63	8.72	8.75	5¼	3	12	1¼	13¾	—	10¾	8.63
10	20	2½	12¾	9.75	10.88	10.88	6	3⅜	16	1⅜	17	—	13½	10.75
12	22	2⅝	15	11.75	12.88	12.94	6⅛	3⅝	20	1⅜	19¼	—	15¾	12.75
14	23¾	2¾	16¼	13.00	14.14	14.19	6½	3 11/16	20	1½	20¾	—	17	14.00
16	27	3	18½	15.00	16.16	16.19	7	4 3/16	20	1⅝	23¾	—	19½	16.00
18	29¼	3¼	21	17.00	18.18	18.19	7¼	4⅝	20	1¾	25¾	—	21½	18.00
20	32	3½	23	19.00	20.20	20.19	7½	5	24	1¾	28½	—	24	20.00
24	37	4	27¼	23.00	24.25	24.19	8	5½	24	2	33	—	28¼	24.00

*Dimensions do not include ¼″ raised face. DIMENSIONS are shown in inches. Sizes ½″ through 3½″ are identical with 400 lb. flanges: see page 34-68.
SPECIFICATIONS: Flanges conform to ASTM Specification A-105 and to ASA Standard B16.5 except socket welding flanges 3½″ and larger, which are not covered by the ASA Standard. PRESSURE-TEMPERATURE RATINGS: see page 34-69.

Courtesy of Crane Co.

ASA 900 LB FORGED STEEL FLANGES

Nom. Pipe Size	Flange Outside Diam.	Flange Thkn.*	Raised Face Diam.	Bore: Welding Neck, and Socket Wldg. Face	Bore: Slip-On, and Socket Welding Back	Bore: Screwed	Length thru Hub*: Welding Neck	Length thru Hub*: Slip-On, Screwed, and Socket Welding	Drilling: No. of Holes	Drilling: Diam. of Holes	Drilling: Diam. of Bolt Circle	Depth of Socket	Diam. of Hub: At Base	Diam. of Hub: At Chamfer
	O	T	A	B	C	E	F	G		J	K	L	M	N
½	4¾	⅞	1⅜	Must be specified by Purchaser	0.88	0.93	2⅜	1¼	4	⅞	3¼	⅜	1½	0.84
¾	5⅛	1	1^11^/16		1.09	1.14	2¾	1⅜	4	⅞	3½	7/16	1¾	1.05
1	5⅞	1⅛	2		1.36	1.41	2⅞	1⅝	4	1	4	½	2 1/16	1.32
1¼	6¼	1⅛	2½		1.70	1.75	2⅞	1⅝	4	1	4⅜	9/16	2½	1.66
1½	7	1¼	2⅞		1.95	1.99	3¼	1¾	4	1⅛	4⅞	⅝	2¾	1.90
2	8½	1½	3⅝		2.44	2.50	4	2¼	8	1	6½	11/16	4⅛	2.38
2½	9⅝	1⅝	4⅛		2.94	3.00	4⅛	2½	8	1⅛	7½	¾	4⅞	2.88
3	9½	1½	5		3.57	3.63	4	2⅛	8	1	7½	—	5	3.50
4	11½	1¾	6 3/16		4.57	4.63	4½	2¾	8	1¼	9¼	—	6¼	4.50
5	13¾	2	7 5/16		5.66	5.69	5	3⅛	8	1⅜	11	—	7½	5.56
6	15	2 3/16	8½		6.72	6.75	5½	3⅜	12	1¼	12½	—	9¼	6.63
8	18½	2½	10⅝		8.72	8.75	6⅜	4	12	1½	15½	—	11¾	8.63
10	21½	2¾	12¾		10.88	10.88	7¼	4¼	16	1½	18½	—	14½	10.75
12	24	3⅛	15		12.88	12.94	7⅞	4⅝	20	1½	21	—	16½	12.75
14	25¼	3⅜	16¼		14.14	14.19	8⅜	5⅛	20	1⅝	22	—	17¾	14.00
16	27¾	3½	18½		16.16	16.19	8½	5¼	20	1¾	24¼	—	20	16.00
18	31	4	21		18.18	18.19	9	6	20	2	27	—	22¼	18.00
20	33¾	4¼	23		20.20	20.19	9¾	6¼	20	2⅛	29½	—	24½	20.00
24	41	5½	27¼		24.25	24.19	11½	8	20	2⅝	35½	—	29½	24.00

*Dimensions do not include ¼″ raised face. DIMENSIONS are shown in inches. Sizes ½″ through 2½″ are identical with 1500 lb. flanges: see page 34-68

SPECIFICATIONS: Flanges conform to ASTM Specification A-105 and to ASA Standard B16.5 except socket welding flanges which are not covered by the ASA Standard. PRESSURE-TEMPERATURE RATINGS: see page 34-69.

Courtesy of Crane Co.

ASA 1500 LB FORGED STEEL FLANGES

Nom. Pipe Size	Flange Outside Diam.	Flange Thkn.*	Raised Face Diam.	Bore			Length thru Hub*		Drilling			Depth of Socket	Diam. of Hub	
				Welding Neck, and Socket Wldg. Face	Slip-On, and Socket Welding Back	Screwed	Welding Neck	Slip-On, Screwed, and Socket Welding	No. of Holes	Diam. of Holes	Diam. of Bolt Circle		At Base	At Chamfer
	O	T	A	B	C	E	F	G		J	K	L	M	N
½	4¾	⅞	1⅜	Must be specified by Purchaser	0.88	0.93	2⅜	1¼	4	⅞	3¼	⅜	1½	0.84
¾	5⅛	1	1 11/16		1.09	1.14	2¾	1⅜	4	⅞	3½	7/16	1¾	1.05
1	5⅞	1⅛	2		1.36	1.41	2⅞	1⅝	4	1	4	½	2 1/16	1.32
1¼	6¼	1⅛	2½		1.70	1.75	2⅞	1⅝	4	1	4⅜	9/16	2½	1.66
1½	7	1¼	2⅞		1.95	1.99	3¼	1¾	4	1⅛	4⅞	⅝	2¾	1.90
2	8½	1½	3⅝		2.44	2.50	4	2¼	8	1	6½	11/16	4⅛	2.38
2½	9⅝	1⅝	4⅛		2.94	3.00	4⅛	2½	8	1⅛	7½	¾	4⅞	2.88
3	10½	1⅞	5		3.57	3.63	4⅝	2⅞	8	1¼	8	—	5¼	3.50
4	12¼	2⅛	6 3/16		4.57	4.63	4⅞	3 9/16	8	1⅜	9½	—	6⅜	4.50
5	14¾	2⅞	7 5/16		5.66	5.69	6⅛	4⅛	8	1⅝	11½	—	7¾	5.56
6	15½	3¼	8½		6.72	6.75	6¾	4 11/16	12	1½	12½	—	9	6.63
8	19	3⅝	10⅝		8.72	8.75	8⅜	5⅝	12	1¾	15½	—	11½	8.63
10	23	4¼	12¾		10.88	10.88	10	6¼	12	2	19	—	14½	10.75
12	26½	4⅞	15		12.88	12.94	11⅛	7⅛	16	2⅛	22½	—	17¾	12.75
14	29½	5¼	16¼		—	—	11¾	—	16	2⅜	25	—	19½	14.00
16	32½	5¾	18½		—	—	12¼	—	16	2⅝	27¾	—	21¾	16.00
18	36	6⅜	21		—	—	12⅞	—	16	2⅞	30½	—	23½	18.00
20	38¾	7	23		—	—	14	—	16	3⅛	32¾	—	25¼	20.00
24	46	8	27¼		—	—	16	—	16	3⅝	39	—	30	24.00

*Dimensions do not include ¼″ raised face. DIMENSIONS are shown in inches. Sizes ½″ through 2½″ are identical with 900 lb. flanges: see page 34-68.
SPECIFICATIONS: Flanges conform to ASTM Specification A-105 and to ASA Standard B16.5. PRESSURE-TEMPERATURE RATINGS: see page 34-69.

Courtesy of Crane Co.

ASA 2500 LB FORGED STEEL FLANGES

Nom. Pipe Size	Flange Outside Diam.	Flange Thkn.*	Raised Face Diam.	Bore: Welding Neck, and Socket Wldg. Face	Bore: Slip-On, and Socket Welding Back	Bore: Screwed	Length thru Hub*: Welding Neck	Length thru Hub*: Slip-On, Screwed, and Socket Welding	Drilling: No. of Holes	Drilling: Diam. of Holes	Drilling: Diam. of Bolt Circle	Depth of Socket	Diam. of Hub: At Base	Diam. of Hub: At Chamfer
	O	T	A	B	C	E	F	G		J	K	L	M	N
½	5¼	1³⁄₁₆	1⅜	Must be specified by Purchaser	0.88	0.93	2⅞	1⁹⁄₁₆	4	⅞	3½	⅜	1¹¹⁄₁₆	0.84
¾	5½	1¼	1¹¹⁄₁₆		1.09	1.14	3⅛	1¹¹⁄₁₆	4	⅞	3¾	⁷⁄₁₆	2	1.05
1	6¼	1⅜	2		1.36	1.41	3½	1⅞	4	1	4¼	½	2¼	1.32
1¼	7¼	1½	2½		1.70	1.75	3¾	2¹⁄₁₆	4	1⅛	5⅛	⁹⁄₁₆	2⅞	1.66
1½	8	1¾	2⅞		1.95	1.99	4⅜	2⅜	4	1¼	5¾	⅝	3⅛	1.90
2	9¼	2	3⅝		2.44	2.50	5	2¾	8	1⅛	6¾	¹¹⁄₁₆	3¾	2.38
2½	10½	2¼	4⅛		2.94	3.00	5⅝	3⅛	8	1¼	7¾	¾	4½	2.88
3	12	2⅝	5		3.57	3.63	6⅝	3⅝	8	1⅜	9	—	5¼	3.50
4	14	3	6³⁄₁₆		4.57	4.63	7½	4¼	8	1⅝	10¾	—	6½	4.50
5	16½	3⅝	7⁵⁄₁₆		5.66	5.69	9	5⅛	8	1⅞	12¾	—	8	5.56
6	19	4¼	8½		6.72	6.75	10¾	6	8	2⅛	14½	—	9¼	6.63
8	21¾	5	10⅝		8.72	8.75	12½	7	12	2⅛	17¼	—	12	8.63
10	26½	6½	12¾		10.88	10.88	16½	9	12	2⅝	21¼	—	14¾	10.75
12	30	7¼	15		12.88	12.94	18¼	10	12	2⅞	24⅜	—	17⅜	12.75

*Dimensions do not include ¼″ raised face. DIMENSIONS are shown in inches: see page 34-68.
SPECIFICATIONS: Flanges conform to ASTM Specification A-105 and to ASA Standard B16.5 except socket welding and slip-on flanges which are not covered by the ASA Standard. PRESSURE-TEMPERATURE RATINGS: see page 34-69.

Courtesy of Crane Co.

Pressure Losses in Air Piping

Important Notes to Tables on the Following Pages

All pressure drops are approximate. See *Accuracy,* page 26-2.

The data given is based on the flow of air in clean straight standard weight pipe. Flow is turbulent and *non-pulsating.* An absolute roughness of 0.00015 ft has been used.

The tables are calculated for 100 foot lengths of pipe. For longer lines (including equivalent added length for fittings) see page 26-10.

Tabulated pressure losses per 100 ft cover the approximate range from 0.1 psi to 10 percent of initial pressure (psiA). Values are carried one decimal point beyond probable accuracy requirements to bring out differences.

To estimate losses for flows or pressures not tabulated, modify the nearest tabulated flow as follows.

Δp varies inversely as absolute pressure.

Δp varies directly as the flow squared (approximately).

Industrial piping systems often include so many fittings, such as valves, tees, and elbows, that pressure losses in these items may equal or exceed the loss in the straight pipe. The table on page 34-78 provides a method for estimating these losses by relating them to the length of straight pipe having an equivalent pressure loss. These equivalent losses increase dramatically with pipe size.

The equivalent lengths of all fittings is to be added to the length of the straight pipe itself and the pressure loss figured from the total. This must not exceed 10 percent of the line pressure in psiA for use of these data. See page 26-10 *(Lengths Over 100 ft).*

Pressure losses properly estimated using these data should be conservative and allow for some future fouling.

LENGTH OF STRAIGHT PIPE IN FEET HAVING THE SAME PRESSURE LOSS AS THE TABULATED FITTING

Be Sure to Read Notes on Page 34-77

Nominal Pipe Size Inches	Schedule Number	Inside Diameter Inches	Inside Diameter Feet	Globe Valve* L/D = 340	Angle Valve* L/D = 145	Gate Valve* L/D = 13	Swing Check* Valve** L/D = 135	Plug Cock* L/D = 18	45° Std. Elbow L/D = 16	90° Std. Elbow L/D = 30	90° Long Radius Elbow L/D = 20	Standard Tee Run of Tee L/D = 20	Standard Tee Side Outlet L/D = 60	Close Return Bend L/D = 50	90° Welding Elbow Short Radius	90° Welding Elbow Long Radius
½	40	0.622	0.0518	17.6	7.5	.67	7.0	.93	.83	1.55	1.04	1.04	3.11	2.59		
¾	40	0.824	0.0685	23.3	9.9	.89	9.2	1.23	1.10	2.06	1.37	1.37	4.11	3.43		
1	40	1.049	0.0872	29.7	13.6	1.14	11.8	1.57	1.40	2.62	1.74	1.74	5.2	4.36	1.4	1.1
1½	40	1.610	0.134	45.5	19.4	1.74	18.1	2.41	2.14	4.02	2.68	2.68	8.1	6.7	2.1	1.6
2	40	2.067	0.172	59	25.0	2.24	23.2	3.10	2.75	5.2	3.44	3.44	10.3	8.6	2.8	2.1
2½	40	2.469	0.206	70	29.9	2.68	27.8	3.70	3.30	6.2	4.12	4.12	12.4	10.3	3.3	2.5
3	40	3.068	0.256	87	37.1	3.32	34.6	4.60	4.10	7.7	5.1	5.1	15.4	12.8	4.1	3.1
4	40	4.026	0.335	114	48.5	4.35	45.2	6.0	5.4	10.1	6.7	6.7	20.1	16.8	5.4	4.0
5	40	5.047	0.420	143	61	5.5	57	7.6	6.7	12.6	8.4	8.4	25.2	21.0	6.7	5.1
6	40	6.065	0.505	172	73	6.6	68	9.1	8.1	15.1	10.1	10.1	30.3	25.3	8.1	6.1
8	40	7.981	0.665	226	96	8.7	90	12.0	10.7	19.9	13.3	13.3	40.0	33.3	11	8.0
10	40	10.020	0.836	284	121	10.9	113	15.0	13.4	25.1	16.7	16.7	50.2	41.8	13	10
12	40	11.938	0.995			13.0	134	17.9	15.9	29.8	19.9	19.9	60	50	16	12
14	30	13.250	1.104			14.3	149		17.7	33.2	22.1	22.1	66	55	18	13
16	30	15.250	1.270			16.5	171		20.3	38.2	25.4	25.4	76	64	20	15
18	30	17.124	1.430			18.6	193		22.8	43.2	28.6	28.6	86	72	23	17
20	20	19.250	1.600			20.8	216		25.6	48.0	32.0	32.0	96	80	25	19
24	20	23.250	1.940			25.2	262		31.0	58	38:8	38.8	117	97	30	23

*All valves and cocks to be fully open.

**Check valves require 0.50 psi pressure loss to open fully.

Welding elbow data from Midwest Piping Catalog 61 (1961).

L/D values from Crane Co. Technical Paper No. 410 (1957). Both L and D in feet.

PRESSURE LOSS IN POUNDS FOR EACH 100 FEET OF STRAIGHT PIPE

Be Sure to Read Notes on Page 34-77

Line Pressure — PSIG

Nominal Pipe Size	CFM Free Air	10	15	20	30	40	50	75	100	125	150	200	250	300	350
1/2" SCHEDULE 40	10		1.45	1.24	.96	.79	.67	.48	.38	.31	.26	.20	.16	.14	.12
	15			2.68	2.08	1.70	1.43	1.04	.81	.67	.57	.43	.35	.30	.25
	20				3.60	2.94	2.48	1.80	1.41	1.15	.98	.75	.61	.51	.44
	30						5.40	3.90	3.05	2.50	2.12	1.63	1.32	1.11	.96
	40							6.80	5.31	4.37	3.70	2.84	2.30	1.94	1.67
	50								8.20	6.75	5.70	4.37	3.55	2.99	2.58
	60								11.7	9.61	8.16	6.25	5.08	4.27	3.68
	80										14.4	11.0	8.95	7.52	6.50
	100											17.1	13.9	11.7	10.1
3/4" SCHEDULE 40	10	.42	.35	.30	.23	.19	.16	.12							
	20	1.57	1.31	1.12	.87	.71	.60	.43	.34	.28	.24	.18	.15	.12	.11
	35			3.22	2.50	2.04	1.72	1.25	.98	.80	.68	.52	.42	.35	.31
	50				4.95	4.05	3.42	2.47	1.93	1.59	1.35	1.03	.84	.71	.61
	65						5.71	4.12	3.23	2.65	2.25	1.72	1.40	1.18	1.01
	80							6.19	4.74	3.98	3.37	2.58	2.10	1.76	1.52
	100							9.60	7.53	6.40	5.25	4.02	3.26	2.74	2.37
	125								11.7	9.70	8.12	6.22	5.05	4.25	3.67
	150									12.6	11.5	8.85	7.16	6.03	5.20
	200											15.6	12.6	10.6	9.14
	250												19.7	16.6	14.3

PRESSURE LOSS IN POUNDS FOR EACH 100 FEET OF STRAIGHT PIPE
Be Sure to Read Notes on Page 34-77

Nominal Pipe Size	CFM Free Air	Line Pressure — PSIG													
		10	15	20	30	40	50	75	100	125	150	200	250	300	350
1″ SCHEDULE 40	20	.45	.38	.32	.25	.20	.17	.13	.10						
	35	1.29	1.07	.92	.71	.58	.49	.35	.28	.23	.19	.15	.12	.10	
	50			1.81	1.40	1.15	.97	.70	.55	.45	.38	.29	.24	.20	.17
	75				3.10	2.53	2.14	1.54	1.21	.99	.84	.65	.52	.44	.38
	100					4.39	3.70	2.68	2.09	1.72	1.46	1.12	.91	.76	.66
	125						5.70	4.10	3.22	2.64	2.24	1.72	1.39	1.17	1.01
	150							5.88	4.60	3.78	3.20	2.46	1.99	1.68	1.45
	200								8.05	6.61	5.61	4.30	3.49	2.94	2.53
	250									10.3	8.87	6.72	5.45	4.59	3.96
	300										12.6	9.66	7.85	6.60	5.70
	400											17.2	14.0	11.7	10.1
	500												21.8	18.3	15.8
1½″ SCHEDULE 40	50	.31	.25	.22	.17	.14	.12								
	75	.65	.54	.46	.36	.29	.25	.18	.14	.12	.10				
	100	1.13	.94	.80	.62	.51	.43	.31	.24	.20	.17	.13	.11		
	125		1.44	1.24	.96	.78	.66	.48	.37	.31	.26	.20	.16	.14	.12
	150		2.04	1.75	1.35	1.11	.94	.68	.53	.43	.37	.28	.23	.19	.17
	200			3.04	2.36	1.93	1.63	1.18	.92	.76	.64	.49	.40	.34	.29
	250				3.68	3.01	2.54	1.83	1.44	1.18	1.00	.77	.62	.52	.45
	300					4.29	3.62	2.62	2.05	1.74	1.43	1.09	.89	.75	.64
	400						6.35	4.58	3.59	2.94	2.50	1.92	1.55	1.31	1.13
	500							7.12	5.59	4.59	3.89	2.98	2.42	2.03	1.76
	600								8.00	6.55	5.55	4.26	3.46	2.91	2.51
	700								10.8	8.89	7.55	5.78	4.70	3.95	3.40
	800									11.6	9.80	7.50	6.10	5.12	4.42
	1000										15.2	11.7	9.45	7.95	6.86
	1200											16.4	13.3	11.2	9.61
	1400											22.9	18.6	15.6	13.5

PRESSURE LOSS IN POUNDS FOR EACH 100 FEET OF STRAIGHT PIPE
Be Sure to Read Notes on Page 34-77

Line Pressure — PSIG

Nominal Pipe Size	CFM Free Air	10	15	20	30	40	50	75	100	125	150	200	250	300	350
2" SCHEDULE 40	75	.19	.16	.13	.10										
	100	.28	.24	.20	.16	.13	.11								
	150	.69	.57	.49	.38	.31	.26	.19	.15	.12	.10				
	200	1.20	1.00	.85	.66	.54	.46	.33	.26	.21	.18	.14	.11		
	250		1.53	1.31	1.02	.83	.70	.51	.40	.33	.28	.21	.17	.15	.13
	300			1.89	1.47	1.20	1.01	.73	.57	.47	.40	.31	.26	.21	.18
	400				2.50	2.04	1.73	1.25	.98	.80	.68	.52	.42	.36	.31
	500				3.87	3.16	2.67	1.93	1.51	1.24	1.05	.81	.65	.55	.48
	600					4.50	3.81	2.75	2.15	1.77	1.50	1.05	.93	.79	.68
	800							4.87	3.82	3.13	2.66	2.04	1.65	1.39	1.20
	1000							7.55	5.90	4.85	4.12	3.16	2.56	2.16	1.86
	1250								9.12	7.49	6.35	4.87	3.96	3.32	2.87
	1500									10.8	9.17	7.02	5.70	4.80	4.14
	1750										12.5	9.54	7.74	6.50	5.62
	2000										16.3	12.5	10.1	8.50	7.35
	2250											15.8	12.8	10.8	9.30
	2500											19.4	15.8	13.3	11.4
2½" SCHEDULE 40	150	.29	.24	.22	.16	.13	.11								
	200	.50	.42	.36	.28	.23	.19	.14	.11						
	250	.80	.64	.55	.43	.35	.29	.21	.17	.14	.12				
	300	1.08	.90	.77	.60	.49	.41	.30	.23	.19	.16	.13	.10		
	400		1.57	1.34	1.04	.85	.72	.52	.41	.33	.28	.22	.18	.15	.13
	500			2.07	1.60	1.31	1.11	.80	.63	.51	.44	.33	.27	.23	.20
	600			2.95	2.28	1.87	1.58	1.14	.89	.73	.62	.48	.39	.33	.28
	800				4.00	3.27	2.76	2.00	1.56	1.28	1.09	.83	.68	.57	.49
	1000					5.17	4.30	3.10	2.43	1.99	1.69	1.30	1.05	.88	.76
	1250						6.78	4.89	3.83	3.14	2.66	2.04	1.66	1.39	1.20
	1500							6.85	5.36	4.40	3.73	2.87	2.32	1.95	1.68
	2000								9.40	7.82	6.55	5.02	4.07	3.42	2.96
	2500									12.1	10.3	7.86	6.39	5.36	4.62
	3000										14.7	11.3	9.13	7.70	6.62
	3500											15.4	12.5	10.5	9.02
	4000											20.0	16.3	13.7	11.8

PRESSURE LOSS IN POUNDS FOR EACH 100 FEET OF STRAIGHT PIPE
Be Sure to Read Notes on Page 34-77

Line Pressure — PSIG

Nominal Pipe Size	CFM Free Air	10	15	20	30	40	50	75	100	125	150	200	250	300	350
3"	300	.36	.30	.26	.20	.16	.13	.10							
	500	.94	.78	.67	.52	.43	.36	.26	.20	.17	.14	.11			
	750		1.69	1.44	1.12	.92	.78	.56	.44	.36	.30	.23	.19	.16	.14
	1000			2.50	1.94	1.59	1.34	.97	.76	.62	.53	.41	.33	.28	.24
	1500				4.30	3.52	2.98	2.15	1.68	1.38	1.17	.90	.73	.61	.53
	2000						5.29	3.81	2.99	2.47	2.08	1.60	1.30	1.09	.94
	2500							5.96	4.67	3.83	3.26	2.50	2.02	1.70	1.47
SCHEDULE 40	3000							8.58	6.71	5.51	4.68	3.58	2.91	2.45	2.11
	3500								9.15	7.50	6.37	4.89	3.96	3.34	2.88
	4000								11.9	9.80	8.31	6.36	5.16	4.35	3.76
	4500									12.4	10.5	8.06	6.55	5.50	4.75
	5000									15.3	13.0	9.95	8.07	6.80	5.86
	6000											14.3	11.6	9.78	8.45
	7000											19.5	15.9	13.4	11.5
4"	500	.24	.20	.17	.13	.11									
	750	.52	.43	.37	.29	.23	.20	.14	.11						
	1000	.90	.75	.64	.50	.41	.34	.25	.19	.16	.14	.10			
	1500		1.64	1.41	1.09	.89	.75	.54	.43	.35	.30	.23	.18	.16	.13
	2000			2.46	1.91	1.56	1.32	.95	.75	.61	.52	.40	.32	.27	.23
	2500				2.96	2.42	2.04	1.47	1.16	.95	.80	.62	.50	.42	.36
	3000				4.20	3.44	2.91	2.10	1.64	1.35	1.14	.88	.71	.60	.52
	4000						5.15	3.11	2.90	2.38	2.02	1.55	1.26	1.06	.91
SCHEDULE 40	5000							5.75	4.50	3.70	3.14	2.40	1.95	1.64	1.42
	6000							8.22	6.45	5.30	4.50	3.44	2.79	2.35	2.03
	7000								8.77	7.20	6.10	4.68	3.80	3.20	2.76
	8000								11.5	9.40	8.00	6.11	4.95	4.17	3.60
	10,000									14.7	12.5	9.55	7.75	6.52	5.62
	12,000											13.8	11.2	9.40	8.10
	14,000											18.8	15.2	12.8	11.0

PRESSURE LOSS IN POUNDS FOR EACH 100 FEET OF STRAIGHT PIPE
Be Sure to Read Notes on Page 34-77

Line Pressure — PSIG

Nominal Pipe Size	CFM Free Air	10	15	20	25	30	35	40	50	60	80	100	125	150	200
5"	1000	.29	.24	.20	.18	.16	.14	.13	.11						
	1500	.62	.52	.44	.39	.34	.31	.28	.24	.21	.16	.13	.11		
	2000	1.09	.91	.78	.68	.60	.54	.49	.42	.36	.28	.24	.19	.16	.13
	2500		1.39	1.19	1.04	.92	.83	.75	.64	.55	.44	.36	.30	.25	.19
	3000		1.98	1.69	1.48	1.31	1.18	1.07	.91	.79	.62	.51	.42	.36	.27
	4000			2.99	2.61	2.32	2.08	1.89	1.60	1.39	1.09	.90	.74	.63	.48
	5000				4.02	3.68	3.22	2.92	2.47	2.14	1.69	1.40	1.15	.97	.75
	6000						4.60	4.18	3.64	3.07	2.42	2.00	1.64	1.39	1.07
SCHEDULE 40	8000								6.24	5.40	4.26	3.53	2.90	2.46	1.88
	10,000									8.40	6.62	5.47	4.50	3.82	2.92
	12,000										9.50	7.88	6.47	5.50	4.20
	14,000											10.7	8.80	7.46	5.72
	16,000												11.5	9.75	7.47
	18,000												14.5	12.4	9.45
	20,000													15.2	11.7
6"	1500	.25	.20	.18	.15	.14	.12	.11							
	2000	.43	.36	.31	.27	.24	.21	.19	.16	.14	.11				
	2500	.66	.55	.47	.41	.36	.33	.30	.25	.22	.17	.14	.12	.10	
	3000	.94	.78	.67	.58	.52	.47	.42	.36	.31	.24	.20	.17	.14	.11
	4000		1.36	1.16	1.01	.90	.81	.74	.62	.54	.43	.35	.29	.25	.19
	5000			1.80	1.58	1.40	1.26	1.14	.97	.84	.66	.55	.45	.38	.29
	6000			2.58	2.26	2.00	1.80	1.64	1.38	1.20	.95	.78	.64	.55	.42
	8000				3.98	3.54	3.18	2.89	2.44	2.12	1.67	1.38	1.13	.96	.74
SCHEDULE 40	10,000						4.90	4.45	3.77	3.26	2.57	2.13	1.75	1.48	1.14
	12,500								5.85	5.06	4.00	3.30	2.71	2.30	1.76
	15,000									7.30	5.75	4.75	3.90	3.32	2.54
	17,500										7.82	6.47	5.30	4.50	3.46
	20,000											8.45	6.95	5.88	4.51
	25,000												10.8	9.20	7.05
	30,000													13.3	10.2

PRESSURE LOSS IN POUNDS FOR EACH 100 FEET OF STRAIGHT PIPE
Be Sure to Read Notes on Page 34-77

Line Pressure — PSIG

Nominal Pipe Size	CFM Free Air	125	110	100	90	80	70	60	50	40	30	25	20	15	10
8"	3000									.10	.13	.14	.17	.19	.23
	4000					.11	.12	.13	.15	.18	.22	.25	.29	.34	.40
	5000	.10	.11	.12	.13	.15	.17	.19	.22	.26	.31	.35	.41	.47	.57
	7500	.24	.27	.30	.32	.36	.40	.45	.52	.62	.76	.85	.98	1.14	1.37
	10,000	.43	.48	.52	.57	.63	.70	.80	.92	1.08	1.33	1.50	1.71	2.00	
	12,500	.65	.73	.80	.87	.96	1.08	1.22	1.41	1.66	2.04	2.29	2.62		
	15,000	.94	1.06	1.14	1.25	1.38	1.55	1.75	2.02	2.39	2.94	3.30			
	17,500	1.28	1.43	1.56	1.71	1.88	2.10	2.39	2.76	3.26	3.98				
SCHEDULE 40	20,000	1.66	1.85	2.02	2.21	2.44	2.73	3.09	3.56	4.22					
	25,000	2.59	2.90	3.16	3.45	3.81	4.26	4.83	5.58						
	30,000	3.69	4.15	4.50	4.92	5.45	6.08	6.90							
	35,000	5.03	5.64	6.12	6.70	7.40	8.30								
	40,000	6.55	7.35	8.00	8.74	9.66									
	45,000	8.33	9.35	10.2	11.1										
10"	5000										.11	.12	.14	.16	.20
	7500					.11	.13	.14	.16	.19	.24	.27	.31	.36	.43
	10,000	.13	.15	.16	.18	.20	.22	.25	.29	.34	.42	.47	.54	.63	.75
	12,500	.21	.23	.25	.27	.30	.34	.38	.44	.52	.64	.72	.83	.97	1.16
	15,000	.29	.33	.36	.39	.43	.48	.55	.63	.75	.91	1.03	1.18	1.38	
	17,500	.40	.45	.49	.53	.59	.66	.74	.86	1.01	1.24	1.40	1.60	1.87	
	20,000	.50	.58	.63	.69	.76	.85	.96	1.11	1.31	1.60	1.81	2.07		
	25,000	.80	.90	.98	1.07	1.18	1.32	1.50	1.73	2.05	2.50	2.82			
SCHEDULE 40	30,000	1.15	1.28	1.40	1.53	1.69	1.89	2.14	2.47	2.92	3.58				
	35,000	1.56	1.75	1.90	2.08	2.30	2.58	2.92	3.37	3.98					
	40,000	2.04	2.28	2.48	2.72	3.00	3.55	3.80	4.40	5.20					
	50,000	3.16	3.54	3.85	4.20	4.65	5.20	5.90							
	60,000	4.55	5.10	5.55	6.07	6.70	7.50								
	70,000	6.20	6.95	7.55	8.25	9.13									
	80,000	8.10	9.05	9.85	10.8										

PRESSURE LOSS IN POUNDS FOR EACH 100 FEET OF STRAIGHT PIPE

Be Sure to Read Notes on Page 34-77

Line Pressure — PSIG

Nominal Pipe Size	CFM Free Air	10	12.5	15	17.5	20	25	30	40	50	60	70	80	90	100
12"	7,500	.18	.15	.13	.11	.10									
	10,000	.31	.26	.22	.19	.17	.14	.12	.10						
	12,500	.48	.40	.34	.30	.26	.22	.18	.16	.14	.12	.11	.10		
	15,000	.68	.57	.49	.43	.38	.31	.26	.23	.20	.18	.16	.15	.14	.12
SCHEDULE 40	17,500	.92	.77	.66	.58	.51	.42	.35	.31	.27	.24	.22	.20	.18	.16
	20,000	1.20	1.00	.85	.75	.66	.54	.46	.40	.35	.31	.28	.26	.24	.21
	25,000		1.57	1.34	1.17	1.04	.85	.72	.62	.55	.49	.45	.41	.37	.33
	30,000			1.89	1.65	1.47	1.20	1.01	.88	.77	.69	.63	.57	.53	.47
	35,000			2.56	2.24	1.98	1.62	1.37	1.19	1.05	.94	.85	.77	.71	.64
	40,000				2.91	2.59	2.12	1.79	1.55	1.37	1.22	1.11	1.01	.93	.83
	50,000					4.00	3.27	2.78	2.39	2.11	1.89	1.71	1.56	1.44	1.28
	60,000						4.69	3.96	3.43	3.03	2.71	2.45	2.24	2.06	1.84
	80,000								6.10	5.37	4.80	4.35	3.97	3.66	3.26
	100,000									8.40	7.51	6.81	6.21	5.71	5.10
	125,000											10.7	9.70	8.95	7.98
14"	10,000	.18	.16	.15	.14	.13	.11	.10							
SCHEDULE 30	15,000	.40	.36	.33	.30	.28	.25	.22	.18	.15	.13	.12	.10		
	20,000	.69	.63	.58	.53	.49	.43	.38	.31	.26	.23	.20	.18	.16	.15
	25,000	1.06	.97	.89	.82	.76	.66	.59	.48	.41	.35	.31	.28	.25	.23
	30,000	1.53	1.39	1.27	1.17	1.09	.95	.84	.69	.58	.51	.45	.40	.36	.33
	40,000				2.06	1.91	1.67	1.48	1.21	1.02	.89	.78	.70	.64	.58
	50,000					2.96	2.58	2.30	1.88	1.59	1.38	1.21	1.08	.98	.90
	60,000						3.70	3.29	2.69	2.27	1.97	1.73	1.55	1.40	1.28
	80,000								4.76	4.02	3.49	3.08	2.76	2.50	2.28
	100,000									6.29	5.45	4.80	4.30	3.89	3.55
	125,000											7.51	6.73	6.10	5.56
	150,000												9.68	8.86	8.00

PRESSURE LOSS IN POUNDS FOR EACH 100 FEET OF STRAIGHT PIPE
Be Sure to Read Notes on Page 34-77

Line Pressure — PSIG

Nominal Pipe Size	CFM Free Air	10	12.5	15	17.5	20	25	30	40	50	60	70	80	90	100
16" SCHEDULE 30	15,000	.19	.18	.16	.15	.14	.12	.11							
	20,000	.34	.31	.28	.26	.24	.21	.19	.15	.13	.11	.10			
	25,000	.52	.47	.43	.40	.37	.32	.29	.23	.20	.17	.15	.14	.12	.11
	30,000	.74	.67	.62	.57	.53	.46	.41	.33	.28	.25	.22	.19	.17	.16
	40,000	1.30	1.18	1.08	1.00	.93	.81	.72	.59	.50	.43	.38	.34	.31	.28
	50,000			1.69	1.56	1.45	1.27	1.12	.92	.78	.67	.59	.53	.48	.44
	60,000				2.22	2.07	1.81	1.61	1.31	1.11	.96	.85	.76	.69	.63
	80,000						3.19	2.84	2.32	1.96	1.70	1.50	1.34	1.21	1.11
	100,000							4.40	3.60	3.04	2.63	2.32	2.08	1.89	1.72
	125,000									4.73	4.10	3.62	3.24	2.93	2.68
	150,000										5.90	5.20	4.65	4.21	3.85
	175,000											7.10	6.35	5.75	5.25
18" SCHEDULE 30	20,000	.19	.17	.15	.14	.13	.12	.10							
	25,000	.29	.26	.24	.22	.20	.18	.16	.13	.11	.10				
	30,000	.41	.37	.34	.32	.29	.26	.23	.19	.16	.14	.12	.11	.10	
	40,000	.72	.66	.60	.55	.51	.45	.40	.33	.28	.24	.21	.19	.17	.16
	50,000	1.12	1.02	.93	.86	.80	.70	.62	.51	.43	.37	.33	.29	.27	.24
	60,000		1.46	1.33	1.23	1.14	1.00	.89	.73	.61	.53	.47	.42	.38	.35
	80,000				2.17	2.02	1.76	1.56	1.28	1.08	.94	.83	.74	.67	.61
	100,000					3.13	2.74	2.43	1.98	1.68	1.46	1.28	1.15	1.04	.95
	125,000						4.25	3.78	3.09	2.62	2.26	2.00	1.79	1.62	1.48
	150,000								4.40	3.72	3.23	2.85	2.55	2.30	2.10
	175,000										4.40	3.88	3.47	3.14	2.87
	200,000										5.75	5.08	4.55	4.10	3.76

PRESSURE LOSS IN POUNDS FOR EACH 100 FEET OF STRAIGHT PIPE
Be Sure to Read Notes on Page 34-77

Line Pressure — PSIG

Nominal Pipe Size	CFM Free Air	10	12.5	15	17.5	20	25	30	40	50	60	70	80	90	100
20" SCHEDULE 20	25,000	.16	.15	.13	.12	.11	.10								
	30,000	.23	.21	.19	.18	.16	.14	.13	.10						
	40,000	.40	.37	.34	.31	.29	.25	.22	.18	.15	.13	.12	.11	.10	
	50,000	.62	.57	.52	.48	.44	.39	.34	.28	.24	.21	.18	.16	.15	.13
	60,000	.89	.80	.74	.68	.63	.55	.49	.40	.34	.29	.26	.23	.21	.19
	80,000		1.42	1.30	1.20	1.11	.97	.86	.71	.60	.52	.46	.41	.37	.34
	100,000			1.99	1.84	1.71	1.49	1.32	1.08	.91	.79	.70	.63	.57	.52
	125,000					2.65	2.32	2.06	1.68	1.42	1.23	1.09	.97	.88	.80
	150,000						3.33	2.96	2.42	2.04	1.77	1.56	1.40	1.26	1.15
	175,000							4.02	3.28	2.78	2.40	2.12	1.90	1.72	1.57
	200,000								4.29	3.62	3.14	2.77	2.48	2.24	2.05
24" SCHEDULE 20	40,000	.16	.14	.13	.12	.11	.10								
	50,000	.24	.22	.20	.18	.17	.15	.13	.11						
	60,000	.34	.31	.28	.26	.24	.21	.19	.15	.13	.11	.10			
	80,000	.60	.54	.50	.46	.43	.37	.33	.27	.23	.20	.17	.16	.14	.13
	100,000	.92	.84	.77	.71	.66	.58	.51	.42	.35	.31	.27	.24	.22	.20
	125,000	1.44	1.31	1.20	1.10	1.03	.90	.80	.65	.55	.48	.42	.38	.34	.31
	150,000			1.71	1.58	1.46	1.28	1.13	.93	.78	.68	.60	.54	.49	.44
	175,000				2.14	1.99	1.74	1.54	1.26	1.07	.92	.81	.73	.66	.60
	200,000						2.27	2.02	1.65	1.39	1.20	1.06	.95	.86	.79

VALUES OF "X" FOR NORMAL AIR AND PERFECT DIATOMIC GASES

(See page 3-19)

$$X = r^{0.283} - 1$$

See Note at end.

r	0	1	2	3	4	5	6	7	8	9	r	0	1	2	3	4	5	6	7	8	9
1.00	.00 000	028	057	085	113	141	169	198	226	254	1.50	.12 159	180	201	222	243	264	286	307	328	349
1.01	282	310	338	366	394	422	450	478	506	534	1.51	370	391	412	433	454	475	496	517	538	559
1.02	562	590	618	646	673	701	729	757	785	812	1.52	580	601	622	643	664	685	706	726	747	768
1.03	840	868	895	923	951	978	006	034	061	089	1.53	789	810	831	852	872	893	914	935	956	977
1.04	.01 116	144	171	199	226	253	281	308	336	363	1.54	997	018	039	060	080	101	122	142	163	184
1.05	390	418	445	472	500	527	554	581	608	636	1.55	.13 205	225	246	266	287	308	328	349	370	390
1.06	663	690	717	744	771	798	825	852	879	906	1.56	411	431	452	472	493	513	534	554	575	595
1.07	933	960	987	014	041	068	095	122	148	175	1.57	616	636	657	677	698	718	739	759	780	800
1.08	.02 202	229	255	282	309	336	362	389	416	442	1.58	820	841	861	881	902	922	942	963	983	003
1.09	469	495	522	549	575	602	628	655	681	708	1.59	.14 024	044	064	085	105	125	145	165	186	206
1.10	734	760	787	813	840	866	892	919	945	971	1.60	226	246	267	287	307	327	347	367	387	408
1.11	997	024	050	076	102	129	155	181	207	233	1.61	428	448	468	488	508	528	548	568	588	608
1.12	.03 259	285	311	337	363	389	415	441	467	493	1.62	628	648	668	688	708	728	748	768	788	808
1.13	519	545	571	597	623	649	675	700	726	752	1.63	828	848	868	888	908	928	948	968	988	007
1.14	778	804	829	855	881	906	932	958	983	009	1.64	.15 027	047	067	087	107	126	146	166	186	206
1.15	.04 035	060	086	111	137	162	188	213	239	264	1.65	225	245	265	284	304	324	344	363	383	403
1.16	290	315	341	366	391	417	442	467	493	518	1.66	423	442	462	481	501	521	540	560	580	599
1.17	543	569	594	619	644	670	695	720	745	770	1.67	619	638	658	678	697	717	736	756	775	795
1.18	796	821	846	871	896	921	946	971	996	021	1.68	814	834	853	873	892	912	931	951	970	990
1.19	.05 046	071	096	121	146	171	196	221	245	270	1.69	.16 009	028	048	067	087	106	125	145	164	184
1.20	295	320	345	370	394	419	444	469	493	518	1.70	203	222	242	261	280	299	319	338	357	377
1.21	543	567	592	617	641	666	691	715	740	764	1.71	396	415	434	454	473	492	511	531	550	569
1.22	789	813	838	862	887	911	936	960	985	009	1.72	588	607	626	646	665	684	703	722	741	760
1.23	.06 034	058	082	107	131	155	180	204	228	253	1.73	780	799	818	837	856	875	894	913	932	951
1.24	277	301	325	350	374	398	422	446	470	495	1.74	970	989	008	027	046	065	084	103	122	141
1.25	519	543	567	591	615	639	663	687	711	735	1.75	.17 160	179	198	217	236	255	274	292	311	330
1.26	759	783	807	831	855	879	903	927	951	974	1.76	349	368	387	406	425	443	462	481	500	519
1.27	998	022	046	070	094	117	141	165	189	212	1.77	538	556	575	594	613	631	650	669	688	706
1.28	.07 236	260	283	307	331	354	378	402	425	449	1.78	725	744	762	781	800	818	837	856	874	893
1.29	472	496	520	543	567	590	614	637	661	684	1.79	912	930	949	968	986	005	023	042	061	079
1.30	708	731	754	778	801	825	848	871	895	918	1.80	.18 098	116	135	153	172	191	209	228	246	265
1.31	941	965	988	011	035	058	081	104	128	151	1.81	283	302	320	339	357	376	394	412	431	449
1.32	.08 174	197	220	243	267	290	313	336	359	382	1.82	468	486	505	523	541	560	578	596	615	633
1.33	405	428	451	474	497	520	543	566	589	612	1.83	652	670	688	707	725	743	762	780	798	816
1.34	635	658	681	704	727	750	773	795	818	841	1.84	835	853	871	890	908	926	944	962	981	999
1.35	864	887	910	932	955	978	001	023	046	069	1.85	.19 017	035	054	072	090	108	126	144	163	181
1.36	.09 092	115	138	160	182	205	228	250	273	295	1.86	199	217	235	253	271	289	308	326	344	362
1.37	318	341	363	386	408	431	453	476	498	521	1.87	380	398	416	434	452	470	488	506	524	542
1.38	543	566	588	611	633	655	678	700	723	745	1.88	560	578	596	614	632	650	668	686	704	722
1.39	767	790	812	834	857	879	901	923	946	968	1.89	740	758	776	794	811	829	847	865	883	901
1.40	990	012	035	057	079	101	123	145	168	190	1.90	919	937	954	972	990	008	026	044	061	079
1.41	.10 212	234	256	278	300	322	344	366	389	411	1.91	.20 097	115	133	150	168	186	204	221	239	257
1.42	433	455	477	499	521	542	564	586	608	630	1.92	275	292	310	328	345	363	381	399	416	434
1.43	652	674	696	718	740	761	783	805	827	849	1.93	452	469	487	504	522	540	557	575	593	610
1.44	871	892	914	936	958	979	001	023	045	066	1.94	628	645	663	681	698	716	733	751	768	786
1.45	.11 088	110	131	153	175	196	218	239	261	283	1.95	804	821	839	856	874	891	909	926	944	961
1.46	304	326	347	369	390	412	433	455	476	498	1.96	979	996	013	031	048	066	083	101	118	135
1.47	520	541	562	584	605	627	648	669	691	712	1.97	.21 153	170	188	205	222	240	257	275	292	309
1.48	734	755	776	798	819	840	862	883	904	925	1.98	327	344	361	379	396	413	431	448	465	482
1.49	947	968	989	010	032	053	074	095	116	138	1.99	500	517	534	552	569	586	603	620	638	655

VALUES OF "X" FOR NORMAL AIR AND PERFECT DIATOMIC GASES

(See page 3-19)

$$X = r^{0.283} - 1$$

See Note at end.

r	0	1	2	3	4	5	6	7	8	9
2.00	.21 672	689	707	724	741	758	775	792	810	827
2.01	844	861	878	895	913	930	947	964	981	998
2.02	.22 015	032	049	066	084	101	118	135	152	169
2.03	186	203	220	237	254	271	288	305	322	339
2.04	356	373	390	407	424	441	458	474	491	508
2.05	525	542	559	576	593	610	627	644	660	677
2.06	694	711	728	745	762	778	795	812	829	846
2.07	863	879	896	913	930	946	963	980	997	013
2.08	.23 030	047	064	080	097	114	130	147	164	181
2.09	197	214	231	247	264	281	297	314	331	347
2.10	364	380	397	414	430	447	463	480	497	513
2.11	530	546	563	579	596	613	629	646	662	679
2.12	695	712	728	745	761	778	794	811	827	844
2.13	860	877	893	909	926	942	959	975	992	008
2.14	.24 024	041	057	074	090	106	123	139	155	172
2.15	188	204	221	237	253	270	286	302	319	335
2.16	351	368	384	400	416	433	449	465	481	498
2.17	514	530	546	563	579	595	511	627	644	660
2.18	676	692	708	724	741	757	773	789	805	821
2.19	838	854	870	886	902	918	934	950	966	983
2.20	999	015	031	047	063	079	095	111	127	143
2.21	.25 159	175	191	207	223	239	255	271	287	303
2.22	319	335	351	367	383	399	415	431	447	463
2.23	479	495	511	526	542	558	574	590	606	622
2.24	638	654	669	685	701	717	733	749	765	780
2.25	796	812	828	844	859	875	891	907	923	938
2.26	954	970	986	001	017	033	049	064	080	096
2.27	.26 112	127	143	159	175	190	206	222	237	253
2.28	269	284	300	316	331	347	363	378	394	409
2.29	425	441	456	472	488	503	519	534	550	566
2.30	581	597	612	628	643	659	675	690	706	721
2.31	737	752	768	783	799	814	830	845	861	876
2.32	892	907	923	938	954	969	984	000	015	031
2.33	.27 046	062	077	092	108	123	139	154	169	185
2.34	200	216	231	246	262	277	292	308	323	338
2.35	354	369	384	400	415	430	446	461	476	492
2.36	507	522	538	553	568	583	599	614	629	644
2.37	660	675	690	705	721	736	751	766	781	797
2.38	812	827	842	857	873	888	903	918	933	948
2.39	964	979	994	009	024	039	054	070	085	100
2.40	.28 115	130	145	160	175	190	205	220	236	251
2.41	266	281	296	311	326	341	356	371	386	401
2.42	416	431	446	461	476	491	506	521	536	551
2.43	566	581	596	611	626	641	656	671	686	701
2.44	716	730	745	760	775	790	805	820	835	850
2.45	865	879	894	909	924	939	954	969	984	998
2.46	.29 013	028	043	058	073	087	102	117	132	147
2.47	162	176	191	206	221	235	250	265	280	295
2.48	309	324	339	353	368	383	398	412	427	442
2.49	457	471	486	501	515	530	545	559	574	589

r	0	1	2	3	4	5	6	7	8	9
2.50	.29 604	618	633	647	662	677	691	706	721	735
2.51	750	765	779	794	808	823	838	852	867	881
2.52	896	911	925	940	954	969	984	998	013	027
2.53	.30 042	056	071	085	100	114	129	144	158	173
2.54	187	202	216	231	245	260	274	289	303	318
2.55	332	346	361	375	390	404	419	433	448	462
2.56	476	491	505	520	534	548	563	577	592	606
2.57	620	635	649	663	678	692	707	721	735	750
2.58	764	778	793	807	821	836	850	864	879	893
2.59	907	921	936	950	964	979	993	007	021	036
2.60	.31 050	064	079	093	107	121	136	150	164	178
2.61	193	207	221	235	249	264	278	292	306	320
2.62	335	349	363	377	391	405	420	434	448	462
2.63	476	490	505	519	533	547	561	575	589	603
2.64	618	632	646	660	674	688	702	716	730	744
2.65	759	773	787	801	815	829	843	857	871	885
2.66	899	913	927	941	955	969	983	997	011	025
2.67	.32 039	053	067	081	095	109	123	137	151	165
2.68	179	193	207	221	235	249	262	276	290	304
2.69	318	332	346	360	374	388	402	416	429	443
2.70	457	471	485	499	513	527	540	554	568	582
2.71	596	610	624	637	651	665	679	693	707	720
2.72	734	748	762	776	789	803	817	831	845	858
2.73	872	886	900	913	927	941	955	968	982	996
2.74	.33 010	023	037	051	065	078	092	106	119	133
2.75	147	161	174	188	202	215	229	243	256	270
2.76	284	297	311	325	338	352	366	379	393	407
2.77	420	434	448	461	475	488	502	516	529	543
2.78	556	570	584	597	611	624	638	651	665	679
2.79	692	706	719	733	746	760	773	787	801	814
2.80	828	841	855	868	882	895	909	922	936	949
2.81	963	976	990	003	017	030	044	057	070	084
2.82	.34 097	111	124	138	151	165	178	191	205	218
2.83	232	245	259	272	285	299	312	326	339	352
2.84	366	379	393	406	419	433	446	459	473	486
2.85	500	513	526	540	553	566	580	593	606	620
2.86	633	646	660	673	686	700	713	726	739	753
2.87	766	779	793	806	819	832	846	859	872	886
2.88	899	912	925	939	952	965	978	991	005	018
2.89	.35 031	044	058	071	084	097	110	124	137	150
2.90	163	176	190	203	216	229	242	255	269	282
2.91	295	308	321	334	347	361	374	387	400	413
2.92	426	439	452	466	479	492	505	518	531	544
2.93	557	570	584	597	610	623	636	649	662	675
2.94	688	701	714	727	740	753	767	780	793	806
2.95	819	832	845	858	871	884	897	910	923	936
2.96	949	962	975	988	001	014	027	040	053	066
2.97	.36 079	092	105	118	131	144	157	169	182	195
2.98	208	221	234	247	260	273	286	299	312	324
2.99	337	350	363	376	389	402	415	428	440	453

VALUES OF "X" FOR NORMAL AIR AND PERFECT DIATOMIC GASES

(See page 3-19)

$$X = r^{0.283} - 1$$

See Note at end

r	0	1	2	3	4	5	6	7	8	9
3.0	0.3647	0.3659	0.3672	0.3685	0.3698	0.3711	0.3723	0.3736	0.3749	0.3761
3.1	0.3774	0.3786	0.3799	0.3811	0.3824	0.3836	0.3849	0.3861	0.3874	0.3886
3.2	0.3898	0.3911	0.3923	0.3935	0.3947	0.3959	0.3971	0.3984	0.3996	0.4008
3.3	0.4020	0.4032	0.4044	0.4056	0.4068	0.4080	0.4091	0.4103	0.4115	0.4127
3.4	0.4139	0.4150	0.4162	0.4174	0.4186	0.4197	0.4209	0.4220	0.4232	0.4244
3.5	0.4255	0.4267	0.4278	0.4290	0.4301	0.4313	0.4324	0.4335	0.4347	0.4358
3.6	0.4369	0.4380	0.4392	0.4403	0.4414	0.4425	0.4437	0.4448	0.4459	0.4470
3.7	0.4481	0.4492	0.4503	0.4514	0.4525	0.4536	0.4547	0.4558	0.4569	0.4580
3.8	0.4591	0.4602	0.4612	0.4623	0.4634	0.4645	0.4656	0.4666	0.4677	0.4688
3.9	0.4698	0.4709	0.4720	0.4730	0.4741	0.4752	0.4762	0.4773	0.4783	0.4794
4.0	0.4804	0.4815	0.4825	0.4835	0.4846	0.4856	0.4867	0.4877	0.4887	0.4898
4.1	0.4908	0.4918	0.4928	0.4939	0.4949	0.4959	0.4970	0.4980	0.4990	0.5000
4.2	0.5010	0.5020	0.5030	0.5040	0.5050	0.5060	0.5070	0.5080	0.5090	0.5100
4.3	0.5110	0.5120	0.5130	0.5140	0.5150	0.5160	0.5170	0.5179	0.5189	0.5199
4.4	0.5209	0.5219	0.5228	0.5238	0.5248	0.5258	0.5267	0.5277	0.5287	0.5296
4.5	0.5306	0.5316	0.5325	0.5335	0.5344	0.5354	0.5363	0.5373	0.5382	0.5392
4.6	0.5401	0.5411	0.5420	0.5430	0.5439	0.5449	0.5458	0.5467	0.5477	0.5486
4.7	0.5495	0.5505	0.5514	0.5523	0.5533	0.5542	0.5551	0.5560	0.5570	0.5579
4.8	0.5588	0.5597	0.5606	0.5616	0.5625	0.5634	0.5643	0.5652	0.5661	0.5670
4.9	0.5679	0.5688	0.5697	0.5706	0.5715	0.5724	0.5733	0.5742	0.5751	0.5760
5.0	0.5769	0.5778	0.5787	0.5796	0.5805	0.5814	0.5822	0.5831	0.5840	0.5849
5.1	0.5858	0.5867	0.5875	0.5884	0.5893	0.5902	0.5910	0.5919	0.5928	0.5936
5.2	0.5945	0.5954	0.5962	0.5971	0.5980	0.5988	0.5997	0.6006	0.6014	0.6023
5.3	0.6031	0.6040	0.6048	0.6057	0.6065	0.6074	0.6082	0.6091	0.6099	0.6108
5.4	0.6116	0.6125	0.6133	0.6142	0.6150	0.6159	0.6167	0.6175	0.6184	0.6192
5.5	0.6200	0.6209	0.6217	0.6225	0.6234	0.6242	0.6250	0.6258	0.6267	0.6275
5.6	0.6283	0.6291	0.6300	0.6308	0.6316	0.6324	0.6332	0.6340	0.6349	0.6357
5.7	0.6365	0.6373	0.6381	0.6389	0.6397	0.6405	0.6413	0.6421	0.6430	0.6438
5.8	0.6446	0.6454	0.6462	0.6470	0.6478	0.6486	0.6494	0.6502	0.6509	0.6517
5.9	0.6525	0.6533	0.6541	0.6549	0.6557	0.6565	0.6573	0.6581	0.6588	0.6596
6.0	0.6604	0.6612	0.6620	0.6628	0.6635	0.6643	0.6651	0.6659	0.6666	0.6674
6.1	0.6682	0.6690	0.6697	0.6705	0.6713	0.6721	0.6729	0.6736	0.6744	0.6752
6.2	0.6759	0.6767	0.6774	0.6782	0.6789	0.6797	0.6805	0.6812	0.6820	0.6827
6.3	0.6835	0.6843	0.6850	0.6858	0.6865	0.6873	0.6880	0.6888	0.6895	0.6903
6.4	0.6910	0.6918	0.6925	0.6933	0.6940	0.6948	0.6955	0.6963	0.6970	0.6978
6.5	0.6985	0.6992	0.7000	0.7007	0.7014	0.7021	0.7028	0.7036	0.7043	0.7050
6.6	0.7058	0.7065	0.7073	0.7080	0.7087	0.7095	0.7102	0.7110	0.7117	0.7124
6.7	0.7131	0.7138	0.7145	0.7153	0.7160	0.7167	0.7174	0.7181	0.7189	0.7196
6.8	0.7203	0.7210	0.7217	0.7224	0.7232	0.7239	0.7246	0.7253	0.7260	0.7267
6.9	0.7274	0.7281	0.7288	0.7295	0.7302	0.7309	0.7316	0.7323	0.7330	0.7338
7.0	0.7345	0.7352	0.7359	0.7366	0.7373	0.7380	0.7386	0.7393	0.7400	0.7407
7.1	0.7414	0.7421	0.7428	0.7435	0.7442	0.7449	0.7456	0.7463	0.7470	0.7477
7.2	0.7483	0.7490	0.7497	0.7504	0.7511	0.7518	0.7524	0.7531	0.7538	0.7545
7.3	0.7552	0.7559	0.7565	0.7572	0.7579	0.7586	0.7592	0.7599	0.7606	0.7613
7.4	0.7620	0.7626	0.7633	0.7640	0.7646	0.7653	0.7660	0.7666	0.7673	0.7680
7.5	0.7687	0.7693	0.7700	0.7706	0.7713	0.7720	0.7726	0.7733	0.7740	0.7746
7.6	0.7753	0.7760	0.7766	0.7773	0.7779	0.7786	0.7792	0.7799	0.7806	0.7812
7.7	0.7819	0.7825	0.7832	0.7838	0.7845	0.7851	0.7858	0.7864	0.7871	0.7877
7.8	0.7884	0.7890	0.7897	0.7903	0.7910	0.7916	0.7923	0.7929	0.7936	0.7946
7.9	0.7949	0.7955	0.7961	0.7968	0.7974	0.7981	0.7987	0.7993	0.8000	0.8002

VALUES OF "X" FOR NORMAL AIR AND PERFECT DIATOMIC GASES

(See page 3-19)

$$X = r^{0.283} - 1$$

See Note.

r	0	1	2	3	4	5	6	7	8	9
8.0	0.8013	0.8019	0.8025	0.8032	0.8038	0.8044	0.8051	0.8057	0.8063	0.8070
8.1	0.8076	0.8082	0.8089	0.8095	0.8101	0.8108	0.8114	0.8120	0.8126	0.8133
8.2	0.8139	0.8145	0.8151	0.8158	0.8164	0.8170	0.8176	0.8183	0.8189	0.8195
8.3	0.8201	0.8207	0.8214	0.8220	0.8226	0.8232	0.8238	0.8245	0.8251	0.8257
8.4	0.8263	0.8269	0.8275	0.8281	0.8228	0.8294	0.8300	0.8306	0.8312	0.8318
8.5	0.8324	0.8330	0.8336	0.8343	0.8349	0.8355	0.8361	0.8367	0.8373	0.8379
8.6	0.8385	0.8391	0.8397	0.8403	0.8409	0.8415	0.8421	0.8427	0.8433	0.8439
8.7	0.8445	0.8451	0.8457	0.8463	0.8469	0.8475	0.8481	0.8487	0.8493	0.8499
8.8	0.8505	0.8511	0.8517	0.8523	0.8529	0.8535	0.8541	0.8547	0.8552	0.8558
8.9	0.8564	0.8570	0.8576	0.8582	0.8588	0.8594	0.8600	0.8605	0.8611	0.8617
9.0	0.8623	0.8629	0.8635	0.8641	0.8646	0.8652	0.8658	0.8664	0.8670	0.8676
9.1	0.8681	0.8687	0.8693	0.8699	0.8705	0.8710	0.8716	0.8722	0.8728	0.8734
9.2	0.8739	0.8745	0.8751	0.8757	0.8762	0.8768	0.8774	0.8779	0.8785	0.8791
9.3	0.8797	0.8802	0.8808	0.8814	0.8819	0.8825	0.8831	0.8837	0.8842	0.8848
9.4	0.8854	0.8859	0.8865	0.8871	0.8876	0.8882	0.8888	0.8893	0.8899	0.8905
9.5	0.8910	0.8916	0.8921	0.8927	0.8933	0.8938	0.8944	0.8949	0.8955	0.8961
9.6	0.8966	0.8972	0.8977	0.8983	0.8989	0.8994	0.9000	0.9005	0.9011	0.9016
9.7	0.9022	0.9028	0.9033	0.9039	0.9044	0.9050	0.9055	0.9061	0.9066	0.9072
9.8	0.9077	0.9083	0.9088	0.9094	0.9099	0.9105	0.9110	0.9116	0.9121	0.9127
9.9	0.9132	0.9138	0.9143	0.9149	0.9154	0.9159	0.9165	0.9170	0.9176	0.9181
10.0	0.9187	0.9192	0.9198	0.9203	0.9208	0.9214	0.9219	0.9225	0.9230	0.9235
10.1	0.9241	0.9246	0.9252	0.9257	0.9262	0.9268	0.9273	0.9278	0.9284	0.9289
10.2	0.9295	0.9300	0.9305	0.9311	0.9316	0.9321	0.9327	0.9332	0.9337	0.9343
10.3	0.9348	0.9353	0.9358	0.9364	0.9369	0.9374	0.9380	0.9385	0.9390	0.9396
10.4	0.9401	0.9406	0.9411	0.9417	0.9422	0.9427	0.9342	0.9438	0.9443	0.9448
10.5	0.9453	0.9459	0.9464	0.9469	0.9474	0.9480	0.9485	0.9490	0.9495	0.9500
10.6	0.9506	0.9511	0.9516	0.9521	0.9526	0.9532	0.9537	0.9542	0.9547	0.9552
10.7	0.9558	0.9563	0.9568	0.9573	0.9578	0.9583	0.9589	0.9594	0.9599	0.9604
10.8	0.9609	0.9614	0.9619	0.9625	0.9630	0.9635	0.9640	0.9645	0.9650	0.9655
10.9	0.9660	0.9665	0.9671	0.9676	0.9681	0.9686	0.9691	0.9696	0.9701	0.9706
11.0	0.9711	0.9716	0.9721	0.9726	0.9732	0.9737	0.9742	0.9747	0.9752	0.9757
11.1	0.9762	0.9767	0.9772	0.9777	0.9782	0.9787	0.9792	0.9797	0.9802	0.9807
11.2	0.9812	0.9817	0.9822	0.9827	0.9832	0.9837	0.9842	0.9847	0.9852	0.9857
11.3	0.9862	0.9867	0.9872	0.9877	0.9882	0.9887	0.9892	0.9897	0.9902	0.9907
11.4	0.9912	0.9916	0.9921	0.9926	0.9931	0.9936	0.9941	0.9946	0.9951	0.9956
11.5	0.9961	0.9966	0.9971	0.9975	0.9980	0.9985	0.9990	0.9995	1.0000	1.0005
11.6	1.0010	1.0015	1.0019	1.0024	1.0029	1.0034	1.0039	1.0044	1.0049	1.0054
11.7	1.0058	1.0063	1.0068	1.0073	1.0078	1.0083	1.0087	1.0092	1.0097	1.0102
11.8	1.0107	1.0112	1.0116	1.0121	1.0126	1.0131	1.0136	1.0140	1.0145	1.0150
11.9	1.0155	1.0160	1.0164	1.0169	1.0174	1.0179	1.0184	1.0188	1.0193	1.0198
12.0	1.0203	1.0207	1.0212	1.0217	1.0222	1.0226	1.0231	1.0236	1.0241	1.0245

NOTE: Taken from "Engineering Computations for Air and Gases," by Moss and Smith, Transactions A.S.M.E. vol. 52, 1930, paper APM-52-8. For nozzles $r = p_1/p_2$. For compressors $r = p_2/p_1$. For other k values, see correction curve on page 34-92.

r	x	r	x	r	x	r	x	r	x
12.5	1.0428	17.0	1.2295	21.5	1.3828	26.0	1.5144	30.5	1.6306
13.0	1.0666	17.5	1.2479	22.0	1.3983	26.5	1.5280	31.0	1.6434
13.5	1.0887	18.0	1.2659	22.5	1.4136	27.0	1.5414	31.5	1.6547
14.0	1.1103	18.5	1.2835	23.0	1.4287	27.5	1.5546	32.0	1.6666
14.5	1.1314	19.0	1.3008	23.5	1.4435	28.0	1.5678	32.5	1.6783
15.0	1.1520	19.5	1.3189	24.0	1.4581	28.5	1.5794	33.0	1.6899
15.5	1.1720	20.0	1.3345	24.5	1.4725	29.0	1.5933	33.5	1.7014
16.0	1.1916	20.5	1.3509	25.0	1.4867	29.5	1.6059	34.0	1.7127
16.5	1.2108	21.0	1.3669	25.5	1.5006	30.0	1.6183	34.5	1.7240

Values of X from 12.5 to 34.5 calculated by Ingersoll-Rand Company.

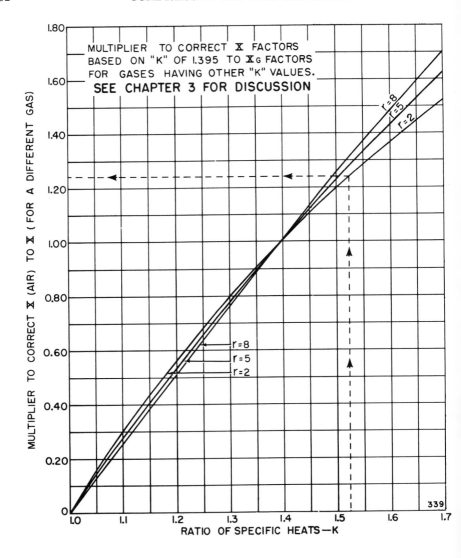

THERMODYNAMIC PROPERTIES OF SATURATED WATER VAPOR

Temp. °F	Absolute Pressure p X 10⁵			Specific Volume Sat. Vapor cu ft/lb X 10⁻⁵	Enthalpy, Btu per lb		
	In Hg	mm Hg	Lb/Sq In		Sat Solid	Evap.	Sat. Vapor
−160	0.01008	0.256	0.004949	36070.	−222.05	1212.43	990.38
−155	0.01840	0.467	0.009040	20080.	−220.44	1213.02	992.58
−150	0.03298	0.836	0.01620	11390.	−218.82	1213.62	994.80
−145	0.05803	1.476	0.02850	6577.	−217.17	1214.17	997.00
−140	0.1003	2.55	0.04928	3864.	−215.49	1214.70	999.21
−135	0.1706	4.33	0.08380	2308.	−213.80	1215.22	1001.42
−130	0.2856	7.25	0.1403	1400.	−212.08	1215.71	1003.63
−125	0.4708	11.98	0.2312	862.2	−210.34	1216.18	1005.84
−120	0.7649	19.4	0.3757	538.6	−208.58	1216.63	1008.05
−115	1.226	31.1	0.6019	341.1	−206.79	1217.05	1010.26
−110	1.938	49.1	0.9517	218.9	−204.98	1217.45	1012.47
−105	3.025	76.8	1.486	142.2	−203.14	1217.82	1014.68
−100	4.664	118.6	2.291	93.52	−201.28	1218.17	1016.89
−95	7.108	180.7	3.491	62.23	−199.40	1218.50	1019.10
−90	10.71	272.	5.260	41.86	−197.49	1218.80	1021.31
−85	15.96	405.	7.841	28.46	−195.56	1219.08	1023.52
−80	23.55	597.	11.57	19.55	−193.60	1219.33	1025.73
−75	34.39	872.	16.89	13.56	−191.62	1219.56	1027.94
−70	49.74	1263.	24.43	9.501	−189.61	1219.76	1030.15
−65	71.28	1810.	35.01	6.715	−187.58	1219.94	1032.36
−60	101.2	2570.	49.72	4.788	−185.52	1220.10	1034.58
−55	142.6	3620.	70.01	3.443	−183.44	1220.23	1036.79
−50	199.0	5050.	97.76	2.496	−181.34	1220.34	1039.00
−48	227.0	5760.	111.5	2.200	−180.49	1220.37	1039.88
−46	258.5	6560.	127.0	1.941	−179.64	1220.40	1040.76
−44	294.0	7460.	144.4	1.715	−178.78	1220.43	1041.65
−42	334.0	8470.	164.1	1.516	−177.92	1220.45	1042.53
−40	379.0	9610.	186.1	1.343	−177.06	1220.48	1043.42
−38	429.5	10910.	211.0	1.191	−176.19	1220.49	1044.30
−36	486.2	12380.	238.8	1.057	−175.32	1220.51	1045.19
−34	549.7	13970.	270.0	0.9391	−174.45	1220.52	1046.07
−32	620.8	15800.	304.9	0.8355	−173.57	1220.52	1046.95

Extracted by permission from ASHRAE Guide and Data Book 1965.

Compiled by John A. Goff and S. Gratch.

NOTE: The tables on pages 34-93 through 34-95 are based on the properties of water vapor over a solid (ice). Other researchers advise that it is possible to calculate the water vapor properties over *super-cooled water* from these data. Such data are used by some in the gas drying industry and result in dew points lower and vapor pressures higher than in the tables shown. This editor, however, believes that the use of the super-cooled water basis is unrealistic and that the tables shown represent more realistic, (at least, more conservative) data. Properties over ice are used by the U. S. Air Force and other government agencies.

THERMODYNAMIC PROPERTIES OF SATURATED WATER VAPOR

Temp. °F	Absolute Pressure p × 10²			Specific Volume Sat. Vapor cu ft/lb × 10⁻⁴	Enthalpy, Btu per lb		
	In Hg	mm Hg	Lb/Sq In		Sat. Solid	Evap.	Sat. Vapor
−30	0.7003	17.80	0.3440	7.441	−172.68	1220.52	1047.84
−28	0.7891	20.03	0.3876	6.634	−171.80	1220.52	1048.72
−26	0.8882	22.55	0.4363	5.921	−170.91	1220.51	1049.60
−24	0.9987	25.38	0.4905	5.290	−170.01	1220.50	1050.49
−22	1.122	27.53	0.5509	4.732	−169.12	1220.49	1051.36
−20	1.259	31.97	0.6181	4.237	−168.21	1220.47	1052.26
−19	1.333	33.84	0.6545	4.011	−167.76	1220.46	1052.70
−18	1.410	35.8	0.6928	3.797	−167.31	1220.45	1053.14
−17	1.493	37.9	0.7332	3.596	−166.85	1220.43	1053.58
−16	1.579	40.0	0.7757	3.407	−166.40	1220.42	1054.02
−15	1.670	42.4	0.8204	3.228	−165.94	1220.41	1054.47
−14	1.766	44.8	0.8676	3.060	−165.48	1220.39	1054.91
−13	1.867	47.4	0.9172	2.901	−165.03	1220.38	1055.35
−12	1.974	50.1	0.9694	2.750	−164.57	1220.36	1055.79
−11	2.086	53.0	1.024	2.609	−164.11	1220.34	1056.23
−10	2.203	55.9	1.082	2.475	−163.65	1220.32	1056.67
−9	2.327	59.1	1.143	2.349	−163.18	1220.30	1057.12
−8	2.457	62.4	1.207	2.229	−162.72	1220.28	1057.56
−7	2.594	65.8	1.274	2.116	−162.26	1220.26	1058.00
−6	2.737	69.5	1.344	2.010	−161.79	1220.23	1058.44
−5	2.888	73.4	1.419	1.909	−161.33	1220.21	1058.88
−4	3.047	77.4	1.496	1.814	−160.86	1220.18	1059.32
−3	3.213	81.5	1.578	1.723	−160.39	1220.15	1059.76
−2	3.388	86.0	1.664	1.638	−159.92	1220.13	1060.21
−1	3.572	90.6	1.754	1.557	−159.45	1220.10	1060.65
0	3.764	95.6	1.849	1.481	−158.98	1220.07	1061.09
1	3.966	100.8	1.948	1.408	−158.51	1220.04	1061.53
2	4.178	106.0	2.052	1.340	−158.04	1220.01	1061.97
3	4.400	111.8	2.161	1.257	−157.56	1219.97	1062.41
4	4.633	117.6	2.276	1.214	−157.09	1219.94	1062.85
5	4.878	124.0	2.396	1.155	−156.61	1219.90	1063.29
6	5.134	130.3	2.521	1.100	−156.14	1219.88	1063.74

Extracted by permission from ASHRAE Guide and Data Book 1965.
Compiled by John A. Goff and S. Gratch.

See notes on page 34-93.

THERMODYNAMIC PROPERTIES OF SATURATED WATER VAPOR

Temp. °F	Absolute Pressure			Specific Volume Sat. Vapor cu ft/lb	Enthalpy, Btu per lb		
	In Hg	mm Hg	Lb/Sq In		Sat. Solid	Evap.	Sat. Vapor
7	0.05402	1.372	0.02653	10480.	−155.66	1219.84	1064.18
8	0.05683	1.441	0.02791	9979.	−155.18	1219.80	1064.62
9	0.05977	1.518	0.02936	9507.	−154.70	1219.76	1065.06
10	0.06286	1.596	0.03087	9060.	−154.22	1219.72	1065.50
11	0.06608	1.680	0.03246	8636.	−153.74	1219.68	1065.94
12	0.06946	1.761	0.03412	8234.	−153.26	1219.64	1066.38
13	0.07300	1.854	0.03585	7851.	−152.77	1219.59	1066.82
14	0.07669	1.950	0.03767	7489.	−152.29	1219.55	1067.26
15	0.08056	2.05	0.03957	7144.	−151.80	1219.50	1067.70
16	0.08461	2.15	0.04156	6817.	−151.32	1219.46	1068.14
17	0.08884	2.26	0.04363	6505.	−150.83	1219.41	1068.58
18	0.09326	2.37	0.04581	6210.	−150.34	1219.36	1069.02
19	0.09789	2.48	0.04808	5929.	−149.85	1219.31	1069.46
20	0.1027	2.60	0.05045	5662.	−149.36	1219.26	1069.90
21	0.1078	2.74	0.05293	5408.	−148.87	1219.21	1070.34
22	0.1130	2.87	0.05552	5166.	−148.38	1219.16	1070.78
23	0.1186	3.01	0.05823	4936.	−147.88	1219.10	1071.22
24	0.1243	3.16	0.06105	4717.	−147.39	1219.05	1071.66
25	0.1303	3.31	0.06400	4509.	−146.89	1218.98	1072.09
26	0.1366	3.46	0.06708	4311.	−146.40	1218.93	1072.53
27	0.1431	3.64	0.07030	4122.	−145.90	1218.87	1072.97
28	0.1500	3.81	0.07365	3943.	−145.40	1218.81	1073.41
29	0.1571	3.98	0.07715	3771.	−144.90	1218.75	1073.85
30	0.1645	4.17	0.08080	3608.	−144.40	1218.69	1074.29
31	0.1723	4.38	0.08461	3453.	−143.90	1218.63	1074.73
32	0.1803	4.58	0.08858	3305.	−143.40	1218.56	1075.16

Extracted by permission from ASHRAE Guide and Data Book 1965.

Compiled by John A. Goff and S. Gratch.

See notes on page 34-93.

PROPERTIES OF SATURATED STEAM—TEMPERATURE TABLE
32° to 212°F

Temp °F	Absolute Pressure			Vacuum In Hg Ref to 29.921'' Bar at 32°F	Specific volume sat vap ft³/lb	Total Heat or Enthalpy Btu per lb		
	In Hg	mm Hg	Lb/ Sq In			Sat Liquid	Evap	Sat Vapor
32	0.1803	4.579	0.08854	29.741	3306.	0.00	1075.8	1075.8
33	0.188	4.77	0.0922	29.733	3180.	1.01	1075.2	1076.2
34	0.196	4.97	0.0960	29.725	3061.	2.02	1074.7	1076.7
35	0.204	5.17	0.1000	29.717	2947.	3.02	1074.1	1077.1
36	0.212	5.38	0.1040	29.709	2837.	4.03	1073.6	1077.6
37	0.220	5.60	0.1082	29.701	2732.	5.04	1073.0	1078.0
38	0.229	5.82	0.1126	29.692	2632.	6.04	1072.4	1078.4
39	0.238	6.05	0.1171	29.683	2536.	7.04	1071.9	1078.9
40	0.248	6.29	0.1217	29.673	2444.	8.05	1071.3	1079.3
41	0.258	6.54	0.1265	29.663	2356.	9.05	1070.7	1079.7
42	0.268	6.80	0.1315	29.653	2271.	10.05	1070.1	1080.2
43	0.278	7.07	0.1367	29.643	2190.	11.06	1069.5	1080.6
44	0.289	7.34	0.1420	29.632	2112.	12.06	1068.9	1081.0
45	0.300	7.63	0.1475	29.621	2036.4	13.06	1068.4	1081.5
46	0.312	7.93	0.1532	29.609	1964.3	14.06	1067.8	1081.9
47	0.324	8.23	0.1591	29.597	1895.1	15.07	1067.3	1082.4
48	0.336	8.55	0.1653	29.585	1828.6	16.07	1066.7	1082.8
49	0.349	8.87	0.1716	29.572	1764.7	17.07	1066.1	1083.2
50	0.363	9.21	0.1781	29.558	1703.2	18.07	1065.6	1083.7
51	0.376	9.56	0.1849	29.545	1644.2	19.07	1065.0	1084.1
52	0.391	9.92	0.1918	29.530	1587.6	20.07	1064.4	1084.5
53	0.405	10.29	0.1990	29.516	1533.3	21.07	1063.9	1085.0
54	0.420	10.68	0.2064	29.501	1481.0	22.07	1063.3	1085.4
55	0.436	11.07	0.2141	29.485	1430.7	23.07	1062.7	1085.8
56	0.452	11.48	0.2220	29.469	1382.4	24.06	1062.2	1086.3
57	0.469	11.90	0.2302	29.452	1335.9	25.06	1061.6	1086.7
58	0.486	12.34	0.2386	29.435	1291.1	26.06	1061.0	1087.1
59	0.504	12.79	0.2473	29.417	1248.1	27.06	1060.5	1087.6
60	0.522	13.25	0.2563	29.399	1206.7	28.06	1059.9	1088.0
61	0.541	13.73	0.2655	29.380	1166.8	29.06	1059.3	1088.4
62	0.560	14.23	0.2751	29.361	1128.4	30.05	1058.8	1088.9
63	0.580	14.74	0.2850	29.341	1091.4	31.05	1058.2	1089.3
64	0.601	15.26	0.2951	29.320	1055.7	32.05	1057.6	1089.7
65	0.622	15.80	0.3056	29.299	1021.4	33.05	1057.1	1090.2
66	0.644	16.36	0.3164	29.277	988.4	34.05	1056.5	1090.6
67	0.667	16.94	0.3276	29.254	956.6	35.05	1056.0	1091.0
68	0.690	17.53	0.3390	29.231	925.9	36.04	1055.5	1091.5
69	0.714	18.15	0.3509	29.207	896.3	37.04	1054.9	1091.9
70	0.739	18.78	0.3631	29.182	867.9	38.04	1054.3	1092.3
71	0.765	19.43	0.3756	29.156	840.4	39.04	1053.8	1092.8
72	0.791	20.10	0.3886	29.130	813.9	40.04	1053.2	1093.2
73	0.818	20.79	0.4019	29.103	788.4	41.03	1052.6	1093.6
74	0.846	21.49	0.4156	29.075	763.8	42.03	1052.1	1094.1
75	0.875	22.23	0.4298	29.046	740.0	43.03	1051.5	1094.5
76	0.905	22.98	0.4443	29.016	717.1	44.03	1050.9	1094.9
77	0.935	23.75	0.4593	28.986	694.9	45.02	1050.4	1095.4
78	0.967	24.55	0.4747	28.954	673.6	46.02	1049.8	1095.8
79	0.999	25.37	0.4906	28.922	653.0	47.02	1049.2	1096.2
80	1.032	26.22	0.5069	28.889	633.1	48.02	1048.6	1096.6
81	1.066	27.09	0.5237	28.855	613.9	49.02	1048.1	1097.1
82	1.102	27.98	0.5410	28.819	595.3	50.01	1047.5	1097.5
83	1.138	28.90	0.5588	28.783	577.4	51.01	1046.9	1097.9
84	1.175	29.85	0.5771	28.746	560.2	52.01	1046.4	1098.4

PROPERTIES OF SATURATED STEAM—TEMPERATURE TABLE

32° to 212°F (Continued)

Temp °F	Absolute Pressure			Vacuum In Hg Ref to 29.921'' Bar at 32°F	Specific volume sat vap ft³/lb	Total Heat or Enthalpy Btu per lb		
	In Hg	mm Hg	Lb/ Sq In			Sat Liquid	Evap	Sat Vapor
85	1.213	30.82	0.5959	28.708	543.5	53.00	1045.8	1098.8
86	1.253	31.82	0.6152	28.668	527.3	54.00	1045.2	1099.2
87	1.293	32.85	0.6351	28.628	511.7	55.00	1044.7	1099.7
88	1.335	33.90	0.6556	28.586	496.7	56.00	1044.1	1100.1
89	1.378	34.99	0.6766	28.543	482.1	56.99	1043.5	1100.5
90	1.422	36.11	0.6982	28.499	468.0	57.99	1042.9	1100.9
91	1.467	37.25	0.7204	28.454	454.4	58.99	1042.4	1101.4
92	1.513	38.43	0.7432	28.408	441.3	59.99	1041.8	1101.8
93	1.561	39.64	0.7666	28.360	428.5	60.98	1041.2	1102.2
94	1.610	40.89	0.7906	28.311	416.2	61.98	1040.7	1102.6
95	1.660	42.16	0.8153	28.261	404.3	62.98	1040.1	1103.1
96	1.712	43.48	0.8407	28.209	392.8	63.98	1039.5	1103.5
97	1.765	44.82	0.8668	28.156	381.7	64.97	1038.9	1103.9
98	1.819	46.21	0.8935	28.102	370.9	65.97	1038.4	1104.4
99	1.875	47.63	0.9210	28.046	360.5	66.97	1037.8	1104.8
100	1.933	49.09	0.9492	27.988	350.4	67.97	1037.2	1105.2
101	1.992	50.58	0.9781	27.929	340.6	68.96	1036.6	1105.6
102	2.052	52.12	1.0078	27.869	331.1	69.96	1036.1	1106.1
103	2.114	53.69	1.0382	27.807	321.9	70.96	1035.5	1106.5
104	2.178	55.31	1.0695	27.743	313.1	71.96	1034.9	1106.9
105	2.243	56.97	1.1016	27.678	304.5	72.95	1034.3	1107.3
106	2.310	58.67	1.1345	27.611	296.2	73.95	1033.8	1107.8
107	2.379	60.42	1.1683	27.542	288.1	74.95	1033.3	1108.2
108	2.449	62.21	1.2029	27.472	280.3	75.95	1032.7	1108.6
109	2.521	64.04	1.2384	27.400	272.7	76.94	1032.1	1109.0
110	2.596	65.93	1.2748	27.325	265.4	77.94	1031.6	1109.5
111	2.672	67.86	1.3121	27.249	258.3	78.94	1031.0	1109.9
112	2.749	69.84	1.3504	27.172	251.4	79.94	1030.4	1110.3
113	2.829	71.86	1.3896	27.092	244.7	80.94	1029.8	1110.7
114	2.911	73.94	1.4298	27.010	238.2	81.93	1029.2	1111.1
115	2.995	76.07	1.4709	26.926	231.9	82.93	1028.7	1111.6
116	3.081	78.25	1.5130	26.840	225.8	83.93	1028.1	1112.0
117	3.169	80.49	1.5563	26.752	219.9	84.93	1027.5	1112.4
118	3.259	82.78	1.6006	26.662	214.2	85.92	1026.9	1112.8
119	3.351	85.12	1.6459	26.570	208.7	86.92	1026.3	1113.2
120	3.466	87.52	1.6924	26.475	203.27	87.92	1025.8	1113.7
121	3.543	89.99	1.7400	26.378	198.03	88.92	1025.2	1114.1
122	3.642	92.51	1.7888	26.279	192.95	89.92	1024.6	1114.5
123	3.744	95.09	1.8387	26.177	188.02	90.91	1024.0	1114.9
124	3.848	97.73	1.8897	26.073	183.25	91.91	1023.4	1115.3
125	3.954	100.43	1.9420	25.967	178.61	92.91	1022.9	1115.8
126	4.063	103.20	1.9955	25.858	174.10	93.91	1022.3	1116.2
127	4.175	106.32	2.0503	25.746	169.72	94.91	1021.7	1116.6
128	4.289	108.94	2.1064	25.632	165.47	95.91	1021.1	1117.0
129	4.406	111.90	2.1638	25.515	161.35	96.90	1020.5	1117.4
130	4.525	114.94	2.2225	25.396	157.34	97.90	1020.0	1117.9
131	4.647	118.04	2.2826	25.274	153.44	98.90	1019.4	1118.3
132	4.773	121.22	2.3440	25.148	149.66	99.90	1018.8	1118.7
133	4.901	124.47	2.4069	25.020	145.99	100.90	1018.2	1119.1
134	5.031	127.80	2.4712	24.890	142.42	101.90	1017.6	1119.5
135	5.165	131.20	2.5370	24.756	138.95	102.90	1017.0	1119.9
136	5.302	134.68	2.6042	24.619	135.58	103.90	1016.4	1120.3
137	5.442	138.23	2.6729	24.479	132.30	104.89	1015.9	1120.8

PROPERTIES OF SATURATED STEAM—TEMPERATURE TABLE

32° to 212°F (Continued)

Temp °F	Absolute Pressure			Vacuum In Hg Ref to 29.921" Bar at 32°F	Specific volume sat vap ft³/lb	Total Heat or Enthalpy Btu per lb		
	In Hg	mm Hg	Lb/ Sq In			Sat Liquid	Evap	Sat Vapor
138	5.585	141.86	2.743	24.336	129.12	105.89	1015.3	1121.2
139	5.732	145.58	2.815	24.189	126.02	106.89	1014.7	1121.6
140	5.881	149.38	2.889	24.040	123.01	107.89	1014.1	1122.0
141	6.034	153.27	2.964	23.887	120.08	108.89	1013.5	1122.4
142	6.190	157.23	3.040	23.731	117.23	109.89	1012.9	1122.8
143	6.350	161.29	3.119	23.571	114.46	110.89	1012.3	1123.2
144	6.513	165.44	3.199	23.408	111.77	111.89	1011.7	1123.6
145	6.680	169.67	3.281	23.24	109.15	112.89	1011.2	1124.1
146	6.850	173.99	3.365	23.07	106.60	113.89	1010.6	1124.5
147	7.024	178.41	3.450	22.90	104.12	114.89	1010.0	1124.9
148	7.202	182.93	3.537	22.72	101.71	115.89	1009.4	1125.3
149	7.384	187.55	3.627	22.53	99.36	116.89	1008.8	1125.7
150	7.569	192.25	3.718	22.35	97.07	117.89	1008.2	1126.1
151	7.759	197.08	3.811	22.16	94.85	118.89	1007.6	1126.5
152	7.952	201.98	3.906	21.97	92.68	119.89	1007.0	1126.9
153	8.150	207.01	4.003	21.77	90.57	120.89	1006.4	1127.3
154	8.351	212.12	4.102	21.57	88.52	121.89	1005.8	1127.7
155	8.557	217.35	4.203	21.36	86.52	122.89	1005.2	1128.1
156	8.767	222.68	4.306	21.15	84.58	123.89	1004.7	1128.6
157	8.981	228.12	4.411	20.94	82.69	124.89	1004.1	1129.0
158	9.200	233.68	4.519	20.72	80.84	125.89	1003.5	1129.4
159	9.424	239.37	4.629	20.50	79.04	126.89	1002.9	1129.8
160	9.652	245.16	4.741	20.27	77.29	127.89	1002.3	1130.2
161	9.885	251.08	4.855	20.03	75.58	128.89	1001.7	1130.6
162	10.122	257.10	4.971	19.80	73.92	129.89	1001.1	1131.0
163	10.364	263.25	5.090	19.55	72.30	130.89	1000.5	1131.4
164	10.611	269.52	5.212	19.31	70.73	131.89	999.9	1131.8
165	10.863	275.92	5.335	19.06	69.19	132.89	999.3	1132.2
166	11.120	282.45	5.461	18.80	67.69	133.89	998.7	1132.6
167	11.382	289.10	5.590	18.54	66.23	134.89	998.1	1133.0
168	11.649	295.89	5.721	18.27	64.80	135.90	997.5	1133.4
169	11.921	302.79	5.855	18.00	63.41	136.90	996.9	1133.8
170	12.199	309.86	5.992	17.72	62.06	137.90	996.3	1134.2
171	12.483	317.07	6.131	17.44	60.74	138.90	995.7	1134.6
172	12.772	324.41	6.273	17.15	59.45	139.90	995.1	1135.0
173	13.066	331.88	6.417	16.86	58.20	140.90	994.5	1135.4
174	13.366	339.50	6.565	16.56	56.97	141.90	993.9	1135.8
175	13.671	347.24	6.715	16.25	55.78	142.91	993.3	1136.2
176	13.983	355.17	6.868	15.94	54.61	143.91	992.7	1136.6
177	14.301	363.25	7.024	15.62	53.48	144.91	992.1	1137.0
178	14.625	371.48	7.183	15.30	52.37	145.91	991.5	1137.4
179	14.955	379.86	7.345	14.97	51.29	146.92	990.8	1137.7
180	15.291	388.39	7.510	14.63	50.23	147.92	990.2	1138.1
181	15.633	397.08	7.678	14.29	49.20	148.92	989.6	1138.5
182	15.982	405.94	7.850	13.94	48.19	149.92	989.0	1138.9
183	16.337	414.96	8.024	13.58	47.21	150.93	988.4	1139.3
184	16.699	424.16	8.202	13.22	46.25	151.93	987.8	1139.7
185	17.068	433.53	8.383	12.85	45.31	152.93	987.2	1140.1
186	17.443	443.05	8.567	12.48	44.40	153.94	986.6	1140.5
187	17.825	452.76	8.755	12.10	43.51	154.94	986.0	1140.9
188	18.214	462.64	8.946	11.71	42.64	155.94	985.4	1141.3
189	18.611	472.72	9.141	11.31	41.79	156.95	984.8	1141.7

PROPERTIES OF SATURATED STEAM—TEMPERATURE TABLE

32° to 212°F (Continued)

Temp °F	Absolute Pressure			Vacuum In Hg Ref to 29.921'' Bar at 32°F	Specific volume sat vap ft³/lb	Total Heat or Enthalpy Btu per lb		
	In Hg	mm Hg	Lb/ Sq In			Sat Liquid	Evap	Sat Vapor
190	19.014	482.96	9.339	10.91	40.96	157.95	984.1	1142.0
191	19.425	493.40	9.541	10.50	40.15	158.95	983.4	1142.4
192	19.843	504.01	9.746	10.08	39.36	159.96	982.8	1142.8
193	20.269	514.83	9.955	9.65	38.58	160.96	982.2	1143.2
194	20.703	525.86	10.168	9.22	37.83	161.97	981.6	1143.6
195	21.144	537.06	10.385	8.78	37.09	162.97	981.0	1144.0
196	21.593	548.46	10.605	8.33	36.37	163.97	980.4	1144.4
197	22.050	560.07	10.830	7.87	35.66	164.98	979.7	1144.7
198	22.515	571.88	11.058	7.41	34.97	165.98	979.1	1145.1
199	22.987	583.87	11.290	6.93	34.30	166.99	978.5	1145.5
200	23.467	596.06	11.526	6.45	33.64	167.99	977.9	1145.9
201	23.957	608.51	11.767	5.96	32.99	169.00	977.2	1146.3
202	24.455	621.16	12.011	5.47	32.37	170.00	976.6	1146.6
203	24.960	633.98	12.259	4.96	31.75	171.01	976.0	1147.0
204	25.475	647.07	12.512	4.44	31.15	172.02	975.4	1147.4
205	25.998	660.35	12.769	3.92	30.56	173.02	974.8	1147.8
206	26.531	673.89	13.031	3.39	29.99	174.03	974.2	1148.2
207	27.074	687.68	13.297	2.85	29.43	175.03	973.5	1148.5
208	27.625	701.68	13.568	2.30	28.88	176.04	972.9	1148.9
209	28.185	715.90	13.844	1.74	28.34	177.04	972.2	1149.3
210	28.755	730.38	14.123	1.16	27.82	178.05	971.6	1149.7
211	29.334	745.08	14.406	0.59	27.31	179.06	970.9	1150.0
212	29.921	760.00	14.696	0.00	26.80	180.07	970.3	1150.4

Tables on pages 34-96 through 34-99 reproduced by permission of the authors and publishers from "Thermodynamic Properties of Steam" by Keenan and Keyes (1936) except absolute pressures in mm Hg and lb per sq in and vacuum in in. Hg which were calculated by Ingersoll-Rand.

PROPERTIES OF SATURATED STEAM—PRESSURE TABLE

Abs press in. Hg.	Temp °F	Specific Volume cu ft per lb		Enthalpy (Total Heat) Btu per lb		Entropy Btu/°F/lb	
		Sat Liquid	Sat Vapor	Sat Liquid	Sat Vapor	Sat Liquid	Sat Vapor
0.25	40.23	0.01602	2423.7	8.28	1079.4	0.0166	2.1589
0.50	58.80	0.01604	1256.4	26.86	1087.5	0.0532	2.0985
0.75	70.43	0.01606	856.1	38.47	1092.5	0.0754	2.0635
1.00	79.03	0.01608	652.3	47.05	1096.3	0.0914	2.0387
1.5	91.72	0.01611	444.9	59.71	1101.7	0.1147	2.0041
2.0	101.14	0.01614	339.2	69.10	1105.7	0.1316	1.9797
2.5	108.71	0.01616	274.9	76.65	1108.9	0.1449	1.9609
3.0	115.06	0.01618	231.6	82.99	1111.6	0.1560	1.9456
4.0	125.43	0.01622	176.7	93.34	1116.0	0.1738	1.9214
5	133.76	0.01626	143.25	101.66	1119.4	0.1879	1.9028
6	140.78	0.01630	120.72	108.67	1122.3	0.1996	1.8877
7	146.86	0.01633	104.46	114.75	1124.8	0.2097	1.8750
8	152.24	0.01635	92.16	120.13	1127.0	0.2186	1.8640
9	157.09	0.01638	82.52	124.97	1129.0	0.2264	1.8543
10	161.49	0.01640	74.76	129.38	1130.8	0.2335	1.8456
11	165.54	0.01642	68.38	133.43	1132.4	0.2400	1.8378
12	169.28	0.01644	63.03	137.18	1133.9	0.2460	1.8307
13	172.78	0.01646	58.47	140.68	1135.3	0.2516	1.8241
14	176.05	0.01648	54.55	143.96	1136.6	0.2568	1.8181
15	179.14	0.01650	51.14	147.06	1137.8	0.2616	1.8125
16	182.05	0.01652	48.14	149.98	1138.9	0.2662	1.8072
17	184.82	0.01654	45.48	152.75	1140.0	0.2705	1.8023
18	187.45	0.01655	43.11	155.39	1141.1	0.2746	1.7977
19	189.96	0.01657	40.99	157.91	1142.1	0.2784	1.7933
20	192.37	0.01658	39.07	160.33	1143.0	0.2822	1.7891
21	194.68	0.01660	37.32	162.65	1143.9	0.2857	1.7851
22	196.90	0.01661	35.73	164.87	1144.7	0.2891	1.7814
23	199.03	0.01663	34.28	167.02	1145.5	0.2923	1.7779
24	201.09	0.01664	32.94	169.09	1146.3	0.2955	1.7744
25	203.08	0.01666	31.70	171.09	1147.0	0.2985	1.7711
26	205.00	0.01667	30.56	173.02	1147.8	0.3014	1.7679
27	206.87	0.01668	29.50	174.90	1148.5	0.3042	1.7649
28	208.67	0.01669	28.52	176.72	1149.2	0.3069	1.7619
29	210.43	0.01671	27.60	178.48	1149.9	0.3096	1.7591
30	212.13	0.01672	26.74	180.19	1150.5	0.3122	1.7564
lb/in²							
0.20	53.14	0.01603	1526.0	21.21	1085.0	0.0422	2.1163
0.25	59.30	0.01604	1235.3	27.36	1087.7	0.0542	2.0970
0.30	64.47	0.01605	1039.5	32.52	1090.0	0.0641	2.0812
0.35	68.93	0.01605	898.5	36.97	1091.9	0.0725	2.0678
0.40	72.86	0.01606	791.9	40.89	1093.6	0.0799	2.0563
0.45	76.38	0.01607	708.5	44.41	1095.1	0.0865	2.0462
0.50	79.58	0.01608	641.4	47.60	1096.4	0.0924	2.0372
0.60	85.21	0.01609	540.0	53.21	1098.9	0.1028	2.0216
0.70	90.08	0.01610	466.9	58.07	1101.0	0.1117	2.0085
0.80	94.38	0.01612	411.7	62.36	1102.8	0.1194	1.9971
0.90	98.24	0.01613	368.4	66.21	1104.5	0.1263	1.9871
1.0	101.74	0.01614	333.6	69.70	1106.0	0.1326	1.9782
1.2	107.92	0.01616	280.9	75.87	1108.6	0.1435	1.9628

PROPERTIES OF SATURATED STEAM—PRESSURE TABLE

(Continued)

Abs press lb/in²	Temp °F	Specific Volume cu ft per lb		Enthalpy (Total Heat) Btu per lb		Entropy Btu/°F/lb	
		Sat Liquid	Sat Vapor	Sat Liquid	Sat Vapor	Sat Liquid	Sat Vapor
1.4	113.26	0.01618	243.0	81.20	1110.8	0.1528	1.9498
1.6	117.99	0.01620	214.3	85.91	1112.8	0.1610	1.9386
1.8	122.23	0.01621	191.8	90.14	1114.6	0.1683	1.9288
2.0	126.08	0.01623	173.73	93.99	1116.2	0.1749	1.9200
2.2	129.62	0.01624	158.85	97.52	1117.7	0.1809	1.9120
2.4	132.89	0.01626	146.38	100.79	1119.1	0.1864	1.9047
2.6	135.94	0.01627	135.78	103.78	1120.3	0.1916	1.8981
2.8	138.79	0.01629	126.65	106.68	1121.5	0.1963	1.8920
3.0	141.48	0.01630	118.71	109.37	1122.6	0.2008	1.8863
3.5	147.57	0.01633	102.72	115.46	1125.1	0.2109	1.8735
4.0	152.97	0.01636	90.63	120.86	1127.3	0.2198	1.8625
4.5	157.83	0.01638	81.16	125.71	1129.3	0.2276	1.8528
5.0	162.24	0.01640	73.52	130.13	1131.1	0.2347	1.8441
5.5	166.30	0.01643	67.24	134.19	1132.7	0.2411	1.8363
6.0	170.06	0.01645	61.98	137.96	1134.2	0.2472	1.8292
6.5	173.56	0.01647	57.50	141.47	1135.6	0.2528	1.8227
7.0	176.85	0.01649	53.64	144.76	1136.9	0.2581	1.8167
7.5	179.94	0.01651	50.29	147.86	1138.1	0.2629	1.8110
8.0	182.86	0.01653	47.34	150.79	1139.3	0.2674	1.8057
8.5	185.64	0.01654	44.73	153.57	1140.4	0.2718	1.8008
9.0	188.28	0.01656	42.40	156.22	1141.4	0.2759	1.7962
9.5	190.80	0.01658	40.31	158.75	1142.3	0.2798	1.7918
10	193.21	0.01659	38.42	161.17	1143.3	0.2835	1.7876
11	197.75	0.01662	35.14	165.73	1145.0	0.2903	1.7800
12	201.96	0.01665	32.40	169.96	1146.6	0.2967	1.7730
13	205.88	0.01667	30.06	173.91	1148.1	0.3027	1.7665
14	209.56	0.01670	28.04	177.61	1149.5	0.3083	1.7605
14.696	212.00	.01672	26.80	180.07	1150.4	.3120	1.7566
15	213.03	.01672	26.29	181.11	1150.8	.3135	1.7549
20	227.96	.01683	20.089	196.16	1156.3	.3356	1.7319
25	240.07	.01692	16.303	208.42	1160.6	.3533	1.7139
30	250.33	.01701	13.746	218.82	1164.1	.3680	1.6993
35	259.28	.01708	11.898	227.91	1167.1	.3807	1.6870
40	267.25	.01715	10.498	236.03	1169.7	.3919	1.6763
45	274.44	.01721	9.401	243.36	1172.0	.4019	1.6669
50	281.01	.01727	8.515	250.09	1174.1	.4110	1.6585
55	287.07	.01732	7.787	256.30	1175.9	.4193	1.6509
60	292.71	.01738	7.175	262.09	1177.6	.4270	1.6438
65	297.97	.01743	6.655	267.50	1179.1	.4342	1.6374
70	302.92	.01748	6.206	272.61	1180.6	.4409	1.6315
75	307.60	.01753	5.816	277.43	1181.9	.4472	1.6259
80	312.03	.01757	5.472	282.02	1183.1	.4531	1.6207
85	316.25	.01761	5.168	286.39	1184.2	.4587	1.6158
90	320.27	.01766	4.896	290.56	1185.3	.4641	1.6112
95	324.12	.01770	4.652	294.56	1186.2	.4692	1.6068
100	327.81	.01774	4.432	298.40	1187.2	.4740	1.6026
105	331.36	.01778	4.232	302.10	1188.1	.4787	1.5986
110	334.77	.01782	4.049	305.66	1188.9	.4832	1.5948

PROPERTIES OF SATURATED STEAM—PRESSURE TABLE

(Continued)

Abs press lb/in²	Temp °F	Specific Volume cu ft per lb		Enthalpy (Total Heat) Btu per lb		Entropy Btu/°F/lb	
		Sat Liquid	Sat Vapor	Sat Liquid	Sat Vapor	Sat Liquid	Sat Vapor
115	338.07	.01785	3.882	309.11	1189.7	.4875	1.5912
120	341.25	.01789	3.728	312.44	1190.4	.4916	1.5878
125	344.33	.01792	3.587	315.68	1191.1	.4956	1.5844
130	347.32	.01796	3.455	318.81	1191.7	.4995	1.5812
135	350.21	.01800	3.333	321.85	1192.4	.5032	1.5781
140	353.02	.01802	3.220	324.82	1193.0	.5069	1.5751
145	355.76	.01806	3.114	327.70	1193.5	.5104	1.5722
150	358.42	.01809	3.015	330.51	1194.1	.5138	1.5694
155	361.01	.01812	2.922	333.24	1194.6	.5172	1.5666
160	363.53	.01815	2.834	335.93	1195.1	.5204	1.5640
165	366.00	.01818	2.752	338.54	1195.6	.5235	1.5615
170	368.41	.01822	2.675	341.09	1196.0	.5266	1.5590
175	370.76	.01825	2.601	343.59	1196.5	.5296	1.5566
180	373.06	.01827	2.532	346.03	1196.9	.5325	1.5542
185	375.31	.01831	2.466	348.94	1197.3	.5354	1.5518
190	377.57	.01833	2.404	350.79	1197.6	.5381	1.5497
195	379.67	.01836	2.344	353.10	1198.0	.5409	1.5474
200	381.79	.01839	2.288	355.36	1198.4	.5435	1.5453
205	383.86	.01842	2.234	357.58	1198.7	.5461	1.5432
210	385.90	.01844	2.183	359.77	1199.0	.5487	1.5412
215	387.89	.01847	2.134	361.91	1199.3	.5512	1.5392
220	389.86	.01850	2.087	364.02	1199.6	.5537	1.5372
225	391.79	.01852	2.042	366.09	1199.9	.5561	1.5353
230	393.68	.01854	1.999	368.13	1200.1	.5585	1.5334
235	395.54	.01857	1.9579	370.14	1200.4	.5608	1.5316
240	397.37	.01860	1.9183	372.12	1200.6	.5631	1.5298
245	399.18	.01863	1.8803	374.08	1200.9	.5653	1.5280
250	400.95	.01865	1.8438	376.00	1201.1	.5675	1.5263
260	404.42	.01870	1.7748	379.76	1201.5	.5719	1.5229
270	407.78	.01875	1.7107	383.42	1201.9	.5760	1.5196
280	411.05	.01880	1.6511	386.98	1202.3	.5801	1.5164
290	414.23	.01885	1.5954	390.46	1202.6	.5841	1.5133
300	417.33	.01890	1.5433	393.84	1202.8	.5879	1.5104
320	423.29	.01899	1.4485	400.39	1203.4	.5952	1.5046
340	428.97	.01908	1.3645	406.66	1203.7	.6022	1.4992
360	434.40	.01917	1.2895	412.67	1204.1	.6090	1.4941
380	439.60	.01925	1.2222	418.45	1204.3	.6153	1.4891
400	444.59	.0193	1.1613	424.0	1204.5	.6214	1.4844
420	449.39	.0194	1.1061	429.4	1204.6	.6272	1.4799
440	454.02	.0195	1.0556	434.6	1204.6	.6329	1.4755
460	458.50	.0196	1.0094	439.7	1204.6	.6383	1.4713
480	462.82	.0197	.9670	444.6	1204.5	.6436	1.4673
500	467.01	.0197	.9278	449.4	1204.4	.6487	1.4634
550	476.93	.0199	.8422	460.8	1203.9	.6608	1.4542
600	486.21	.0201	.7698	471.6	1203.2	.6720	1.4454
650	494.89	.0203	.7084	481.8	1202.3	.6826	1.4373
700	503.10	.0205	.6554	491.5	1201.2	.6925	1.4296
750	510.85	.0207	.6093	500.8	1199.1	.7019	1.4223

PROPERTIES OF SATURATED STEAM—PRESSURE TABLE

(Continued)

Abs press lb/in²	Temp °F	Specific Volume cu ft per lb		Enthalpy (Total Heat) Btu per lb		Entropy Btu/°F/lb	
		Sat Liquid	Sat Vapor	Sat Liquid	Sat Vapor	Sat Liquid	Sat Vapor
800	518.23	.0209	.5687	509.7	1198.6	.7108	1.4153
850	525.26	.0210	.5328	518.3	1197.1	.7194	1.4085
900	531.98	.0212	.5006	526.6	1195.4	.7275	1.4020
950	538.42	.0214	.4717	534.6	1193.6	.7355	1.3957
1000	544.61	.0216	.4456	542.4	1191.8	.7430	1.3897
1050	550.57	.0218	.4218	550.0	1189.9	.7504	1.3838
1100	556.31	.0220	.4001	557.4	1187.8	.7575	1.3780
1150	561.86	.0221	.3802	564.6	1185.6	.7644	1.3723
1200	567.22	.0223	.3619	571.7	1183.4	.7711	1.3667
1250	572.42	.0225	.3450	578.6	1181.0	.7776	1.3612
1300	577.46	.0227	.3293	585.4	1178.6	.7840	1.3559
1400	587.10	.0231	.3012	598.7	1173.4	.7963	1.3454
1500	596.23	.0235	.2765	611.6	1167.9	.8082	1.3351
1600	604.90	.0239	.2548	624.1	1162.1	.8196	1.3249
1700	613.15	.0243	.2354	636.3	1155.9	.8306	1.3149
1800	621.03	.0247	.2179	648.3	1149.4	.8412	1.3049
2000	635.82	.0257	.1878	671.7	1135.1	.8619	1.2849
2500	668.13	.0287	.1307	730.6	1091.1	.9126	1.2322
3000	695.36	.0346	.0858	802.5	1020.3	.9731	1.1615
3206.2	705.40	.0503	.0503	902.7	902.7	1.0580	1.0580

PROPERTIES OF SUPERHEATED STEAM

Abs Press Lb/In² (Sat temp)		* Sat Water	Sat Vapor	Temperature—Degrees Fahrenheit						
				300°	400°	500°	600°	700°	800°	900°
1 (101.74)	v	.02	333.6	452.3	512.0	571.6	631.2	690.8	750.4	809.9
	h	69.7	1106.0	1195.8	1241.7	1288.3	1335.7	1383.8	1432.8	1482.7
	s	.1362	1.9782	2.1153	2.1720	2.2233	2.2702	2.3137	2.3542	2.3923
5 (162.24)	v	.02	73.52	90.25	102.26	114.22	126.16	138.10	150.03	161.95
	h	130.1	1131.1	1195.0	1241.2	1288.0	1335.4	1383.6	1432.7	1482.6
	s	.2347	1.8441	1.9370	1.9942	2.0456	2.0927	2.1361	2.1767	2.2148
10 (193.21)	v	.02	38.42	45.00	51.04	57.05	63.03	69.01	74.98	80.95
	h	161.2	1143.3	1193.9	1240.6	1287.5	1335.1	1383.4	1432.5	1482.4
	s	.2835	1.7876	1.8595	1.9172	1.9689	2.0160	2.0596	2.1002	2.1383
14.696 (212.00)	v	.02	26.80	30.53	34.68	38.78	42.86	46.94	51.00	55.07
	h	180.1	1150.4	1192.8	1239.9	1287.1	1334.8	1383.2	1432.3	1482.3
	s	.3120	1.7566	1.8160	1.8743	1.9261	1.9734	2.1070	2.0576	2.0958
20 (227.96)	v	.02	20.09	22.36	25.43	28.46	31.47	34.47	37.46	40.45
	h	196.2	1156.3	1191.6	1239.2	1286.6	1334.4	1382.9	1432.1	1482.1
	s	.3356	1.7319	1.7808	1.8396	1.8918	1.9392	1.9829	2.0235	2.0618
40 (267.25)	v	.017	10.498	11.040	12.628	14.168	15.688	17.198	18.702	20.20
	h	236.0	1169.7	1186.8	1236.5	1284.8	1333.1	1381.9	1431.3	1481.4
	s	.3919	1.6763	1.6994	1.7608	1.8140	1.8619	1.9058	1.9467	1.9850
60 (292.71)	v	.017	7.175	7.259	8.357	9.403	10.427	11.441	12.449	13.452
	h	262.1	1177.6	1181.6	1233.6	1283.0	1331.8	1380.9	1430.5	1480.8
	s	.4270	1.6438	1.6492	1.7135	1.7678	1.8162	1.8605	1.9015	1.9400
80 (312.03)	v	.018	5.472		6.220	7.020	7.797	8.562	9.322	10.077
	h	282.0	1183.1		1230.7	1281.1	1330.5	1379.9	1429.7	1480.1
	s	.4531	1.6207		1.6791	1.7346	1.7836	1.8281	1.8694	1.9079
100 (327.81)	v	.018	4.432		4.937	5.589	6.218	6.835	7.446	8.052
	h	298.4	1187.2		1227.6	1279.1	1329.1	1378.9	1428.9	1479.5
	s	.4740	1.6062		1.6518	1.7085	1.7581	1.8029	1.8443	1.8829
120 (341.25)	v	.018	3.728		4.081	4.636	5.165	5.683	6.195	6.702
	h	312.4	1190.4		1224.4	1277.2	1327.7	1377.8	1428.1	1478.8
	s	.4916	1.5878		1.6287	1.6869	1.7370	1.7822	1.8237	1.8625
140 (353.02)	v	.018	3.220		3.468	3.954	4.413	4.861	5.301	5.738
	h	324.8	1193.0		1221.1	1275.2	1326.4	1376.8	1427.3	1478.2
	s	.5069	1.5751		1.6087	1.6683	1.7190	1.7645	1.8063	1.8451
160 (363.53)	v	.018	2.834		3.008	3.443	3.849	4.244	4.631	5.015
	h	335.9	1195.1		1217.6	1273.1	1325.0	1375.7	1426.4	1477.5
	s	.5204	1.5640		1.5908	1.6519	1.7033	1.7491	1.7911	1.8301
180 (373.06)	v	.018	2.532		2.649	3.044	3.411	3.764	4.110	4.452
	h	346.0	1196.9		1214.0	1271.0	1323.5	1374.7	1425.6	1476.8
	s	.5325	1.5542		1.5745	1.6373	1.6894	1.7355	1.7776	1.8167
200 (381.79)	v	.018	2.288		2.361	2.726	3.060	3.380	3.693	4.002
	h	355.4	1198.4		1210.3	1268.9	1322.1	1373.6	1224.8	1476.2
	s	.5435	1.5453		1.5594	1.6240	1.6767	1.7232	1.7655	1.8048
220 (389.86)	v	.019	2.087		2.125	2.465	2.772	3.066	3.352	3.634
	h	364.0	1199.6		1206.5	1266.7	1320.7	1372.6	1424.0	1475.5
	s	.5537	1.5372		1.5435	1.6117	1.6652	1.7120	1.7545	1.7939
240 (397.37)	v	.0186	1.9183		1.9276	2.247	2.533	2.804	3.068	3.327
	h	372.1	1200.6		1202.5	1264.5	1319.2	1371.5	1323.2	1474.8
	s	.5631	1.5298		1.5319	1.6003	1.6546	1.7017	1.7444	1.7839

PROPERTIES OF SUPERHEATED STEAM—(Continued)

Abs Press Lb/In² (Sat temp)		* Sat Water	Sat Vapor	Temperature—Degrees Fahrenheit						
				600°	700°	800°	900°	1000°	1200°	1400°
260 (404.42)	v	.0187	1.7748	2.330	2.582	2.827	3.067	3.305	3.776	4.242
	h	379.8	1201.5	1317.7	1370.4	1422.3	1474.2	1526.3	1632.5	1741.7
	s	.5719	1.5229	1.6447	1.6922	1.7352	1.7748	1.8118	1.8799	1.9420
280 (411.05)	v	.0188	1.6511	2.156	2.392	2.621	2.845	3.066	3.504	3.938
	h	387.0	1202.3	1316.2	1369.4	1421.5	1473.5	1525.8	1632.1	1741.4
	s	.5801	1.5164	1.6354	1.6834	1.7265	1.7662	1.8033	1.8716	1.9337
300 (417.33)	v	.0189	1.5433	2.005	2.227	2.442	2.652	2.859	3.269	3.674
	h	393.8	1202.8	1314.7	1368.3	1420.6	1472.8	1525.2	1631.7	1741.0
	s	.5879	1.5104	1.6268	1.6751	1.7184	1.7582	1.7954	1.8638	1.9260
350 (431.72)	v	.0191	1.3260	1.7036	1.8980	2.084	2.266	2.445	2.798	3.147
	h	409.7	1203.9	1310.9	1365.5	1418.5	1471.1	1523.8	1630.7	1740.3
	s	.6056	1.4966	1.6070	1.6563	1.7002	1.7403	1.7777	1.8463	1.908
400 (444.59)	v	.0193	1.1613	1.4770	1.6508	1.8161	1.9767	2.134	2.445	2.751
	h	424.0	1204.5	1306.9	1362.7	1416.4	1469.4	1522.4	1629.6	1739.5
	s	.6214	1.4844	1.5894	1.6398	1.6842	1.7247	1.7623	1.8311	1.8936
500 (467.01)	v	.0197	.9278	1.1591	1.3044	1.4405	1.5715	1.6996	1.9504	2.197
	h	449.4	1204.4	1298.6	1357.0	1412.1	1466.0	1519.6	1627.6	1737.9
	s	.6487	1.4634	1.5588	1.6115	1.6571	1.6982	1.7363	1.8056	1.8683
600 (486.21)	v	.0201	.7698	.9463	1.0732	1.1899	1.3013	1.4096	1.6208	1.8279
	h	471.6	1203.2	1289.9	1351.1	1407.7	1462.5	1516.7	1625.5	1736.3
	s	.6720	1.4454	1.5323	1.5875	1.6343	1.6752	1.7147	1.7846	1.8476
700 (503.10)	v	.0205	.6554	.7934	.9077	1.0108	1.1082	1.2024	1.3853	1.5641
	h	491.5	1201.2	1280.6	1345.0	1403.2	1459.0	1513.9	1623.5	1734.8
	s	.6925	1.4296	1.5084	1.5665	1.6147	1.6573	1.6963	1.7666	1.8299
800 (518.23)	v	.0209	.5687	.6779	.7833	.8763	.9633	1.0470	1.2088	1.3662
	h	509.7	1198.6	1270.7	1338.6	1398.6	1455.4	1511.0	1621.4	1733.2
	s	.7108	1.4153	1.4863	1.5476	1.5972	1.6407	1.6801	1.7510	1.8146
1000 (544.61)	v	.0216	.4456	.5140	.6084	.6878	.7604	.8294	.9615	1.0893
	h	542.4	1191.8	1248.8	1325.3	1389.2	1448.2	1505.1	1617.3	1730.0
	s	.7430	1.3897	1.4450	1.5141	1.5670	1.6121	1.6525	1.7245	1.7886
1200 (567.22)	v	.0223	.3619	.4016	.4909	.5617	.6250	.6843	.7967	.9046
	h	571.7	1183.4	1223.5	1311.0	1379.3	1440.7	1499.2	1613.1	1726.9
	s	.7711	1.3667	1.4052	1.4843	1.5409	1.5879	1.6293	1.7025	1.7672
1400 (587.10)	v	.0231	.3012	.3174	.4062	.4714	.5281	.5805	.6789	.7727
	h	598.7	1173.4	1193.0	1295.5	1369.1	1433.1	1493.2	1608.9	1723.7
	s	.7963	1.3454	1.3639	1.4567	1.5177	1.5666	1.6093	1.6836	1.7489
1600 (604.9)	v	.0239	.2548		.3417	.4034	.4553	.5027	.5906	.6738
	h	624.1	1162.1		1278.7	1358.4	1425.3	1487.0	1604.6	1720.5
	s	.8196	1.3249		1.4303	1.4964	1.5476	1.5914	1.6669	1.7328
1800 (621.03)	v	.0247	.2179		.2907	.3502	.3986	.4421	.5218	.5968
	h	648.3	1149.4		1260.3	1347.2	1417.4	1480.8	1600.4	1717.3
	s	.8412	1.3049		1.4044	1.4765	1.5301	1.5752	1.6520	1.7185
2000 (635.82)	v	.0257	.1878		.2489	.3074	.3532	.3935	.4668	.5352
	h	671.7	1135.1		1240.0	1335.5	1409.2	1474.5	1596.1	1714.1
	s	.8619	1.2849		1.3783	1.4576	1.5139	1.5603	1.6384	1.7055

Reproduced by permission of the authors and publisher from "Thermodynamic Properties of Steam" by Keenan and Keyes, (1936).

*v—Specific volume in cu ft/lb   h—Total heat in Btu/lb   s—Enthropy in Btu/°F/lb

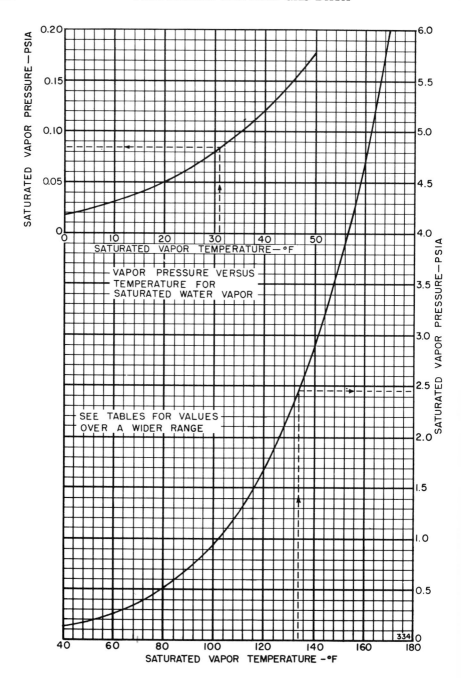

VAPOR PRESSURE VERSUS
TEMPERATURE FOR
SATURATED WATER VAPOR

SEE TABLES FOR VALUES
OVER A WIDER RANGE

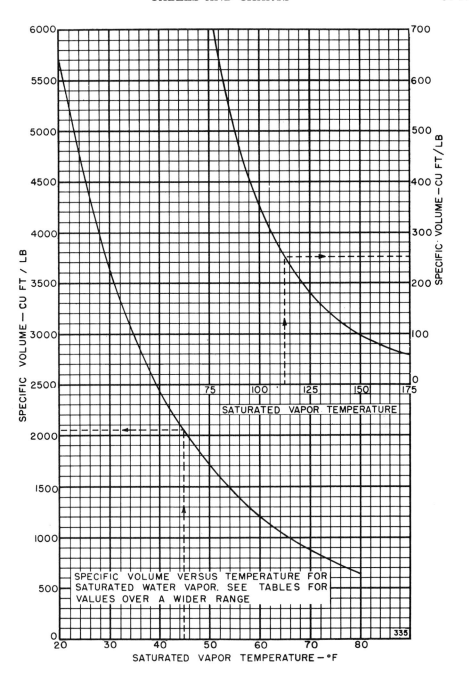

SPECIFIC VOLUME VERSUS TEMPERATURE FOR SATURATED WATER VAPOR. SEE TABLES FOR VALUES OVER A WIDER RANGE

335

THEORETICAL WATER RATE IN POUNDS PER BHP-HOUR

100 Psi Gage Initial Pressure (Saturation Temperatures 338°F)

Exhaust Pressure	Initial Temperature—°F					
	Saturated	400	450	500	550	600
	Initial Superheat—°F					
Inches Hg Abs.	0	62	112	162	212	262
1.0	7.60	7.34	7.13	6.91	6.70	6.50
2.0	8.44	8.13	7.88	7.63	7.40	7.16
3.0	9.04	8.70	8.43	8.16	7.89	7.63
4.0	9.54	9.18	8.89	8.60	8.31	8.02
PSI Gage						
0	16.9	16.2	15.6	14.9	14.3	13.6
5	19.4	18.6	17.8	17.0	16.2	15.3
10	22.0	21.0	20.1	19.1	18.1	17.2
15	24.7	23.6	22.4	21.3	20.1	19.1
20	27.7	26.3	25.1	23.7	22.4	21.2
25	31.0	29.4	27.9	26.2	24.8	23.6
30	34.6	32.8	30.9	29.1	27.6	26.2
35	38.7	36.7	34.4	32.4	30.6	29.1
40	43.4	41.1	38.5	36.3	34.4	32.7
45	48.9	46.2	43.2	40.6	38.5	36.6
50	——	52.3	48.9	46.1	43.5	41.3

150 Psi Gage Initial Pressure (Saturation Temperature 366°F)

Inches Hg Abs.	Initial Superheat—°F					
	0	34	84	134	184	234
1.0	7.14	6.99	6.78	6.58	6.38	6.19
2.0	7.84	7.67	7.44	7.22	6.99	6.77
3.0	8.35	8.17	7.92	7.66	7.42	7.18
4.0	8.77	8.57	8.30	8.04	7.78	7.52
PSI Gage						
0	14.4	14.1	13.6	13.1	12.5	12.0
5	16.2	15.8	15.2	14.5	13.9	13.3
10	17.9	17.4	16.7	16.0	15.3	14.5
15	19.6	19.1	18.3	17.5	16.6	15.8
20	21.3	20.8	19.9	19.0	18.0	17.1
25	23.2	22.6	21.6	20.5	19.5	18.4
30	25.0	24.5	23.3	22.1	21.0	19.8
40	29.3	28.5	27.1	25.6	24.2	23.0
50	34.3	33.3	31.6	29.7	28.0	26.5
60	40.2	39.1	36.8	34.6	32.6	30.9
70	47.3	45.8	43.2	40.6	38.2	36.2
80	——	——	51.1	48.1	45.3	42.9

Based on Keenan and Keyes Tables, published 1938 by ASME.

Rankine cycle efficiency of driver must be applied to obtain actual water rate. See Chapter 5 for discussion. See Chapter 15 for approximate Rankine cycle efficiencies of engines and turbines for compressor drive.

THEORETICAL WATER RATE IN POUNDS PER BHP-HOUR

200 Psi Gage Initial Pressure (Saturation Temperature 388°F)

Exhaust Pressure	Initial Temperature—°F							
	Saturated	450	500	550	600	650	700	750
Inches Hg Abs.	Initial Superheat—°F							
	0	62	112	162	212	262	312	362
1.0	6.84	6.57	6.37	6.18	5.99	5.81	5.64	5.47
2.0	7.46	7.17	6.95	6.73	6.52	6.32	6.12	5.93
3.0	7.92	7.60	7.36	7.12	6.90	6.67	6.46	6.25
4.0	8.29	7.95	7.69	7.44	7.20	6.96	6.73	6.51
PSI Gage								
0	13.1	12.5	12.0	11.5	11.1	10.6	10.2	9.73
5	14.4	13.7	13.2	12.7	12.1	11.6	11.1	10.6
10	15.7	15.0	14.4	13.8	13.2	12.6	12.0	11.4
20	18.3	17.4	16.6	15.9	15.1	14.4	13.7	13.1
30	20.9	19.9	19.0	18.0	17.1	16.2	15.4	14.7
40	23.8	22.5	21.4	20.3	19.2	18.2	17.3	16.5
50	26.8	25.3	24.1	22.7	21.5	20.4	19.4	18.5
60	30.1	28.6	27.0	25.4	24.1	22.8	21.7	20.7
70	34.0	32.1	30.2	28.4	26.9	25.5	24.3	23.2
80	38.3	36.1	33.9	31.9	30.2	28.6	27.3	26.0
90	43.5	41.0	38.2	35.9	34.0	32.3	30.7	29.3
100	49.6	46.4	43.3	40.7	38.5	36.6	34.8	33.3

250 Psi Gage Initial Pressure (Saturation Temperature 406°F)

Inches Hg Abs.	Initial Superheat—°F							
	0	44	94	144	194	244	294	344
1.0	6.62	6.43	6.22	6.03	5.85	5.67	5.51	5.35
2.0	7.20	6.98	6.76	6.55	6.35	6.15	5.96	5.77
3.0	7.62	7.39	7.15	6.92	6.69	6.49	6.28	6.08
4.0	7.95	7.71	7.45	7.21	6.98	6.75	6.53	6.31
PSI Gage								
0	12.1	11.7	11.3	10.9	10.4	10.0	9.62	9.23
5	13.3	12.9	12.3	11.8	11.4	10.9	10.4	9.99
10	14.4	13.9	13.3	12.8	12.3	11.7	11.2	10.7
20	16.5	15.9	15.2	14.6	13.9	13.3	12.6	12.0
30	18.5	17.9	17.1	16.3	15.5	14.8	14.0	13.4
40	20.7	19.9	19.0	18.1	17.2	16.3	15.5	14.8
50	23.0	22.1	21.0	20.0	18.9	17.9	17.0	16.2
60	25.3	24.4	23.2	21.9	20.7	19.6	18.6	17.8
70	27.9	26.8	25.4	24.0	22.7	21.5	20.4	19.5
80	30.7	29.5	28.0	26.3	24.8	23.6	22.4	21.3
100	37.3	35.9	33.8	31.7	29.8	28.3	26.9	25.6
120	45.7	43.7	41.0	38.5	36.3	34.4	32.7	31.2

Based on Keenan and Keyes Tables, published 1938 by ASME.

Rankine cycle efficiency of driver must be applied to obtain actual water rate. See Chapter 5 for discussion. See Chapter 15 for approximate Rankine cycle efficiencies of engines and turbines for compressor drive.

THEORETICAL WATER RATE IN POUNDS PER BHP-HOUR

300 Psi Gage Initial Pressure (Saturation Temperature 422°F)

Exhaust Pressure	Initial Temperature—°F							
	Saturated	500	550	600	650	700	750	800
Inches Hg Abs.	Initial Superheat—°F							
	0	78	128	178	228	278	328	378
1.0	6.46	6.12	5.92	5.75	5.58	5.41	5.25	5.09
2.0	7.01	6.63	6.42	6.22	6.02	5.84	5.66	5.49
3.0	7.39	6.99	6.76	6.55	6.34	6.14	5.94	5.76
4.0	7.70	7.28	7.04	6.81	6.58	6.37	6.17	5.97
PSI Gage								
0	11.5	10.8	10.4	10.0	9.60	9.22	8.85	8.51
10	13.5	12.6	12.1	11.6	11.1	10.6	10.2	9.47
20	15.3	14.3	13.6	13.1	12.5	11.9	11.3	10.8
30	17.0	15.8	15.1	14.4	13.8	13.1	12.5	11.9
40	18.7	17.4	16.6	15.8	15.0	14.3	13.6	13.0
50	20.5	19.1	18.2	17.3	16.3	15.5	14.8	14.1
60	22.4	20.8	19.7	18.7	17.7	16.8	16.0	15.3
70	24.3	22.6	21.4	20.2	19.1	18.2	17.3	16.5
80	26.5	24.5	23.2	21.8	20.6	19.6	18.7	17.9
100	31.2	28.7	27.0	25.4	24.1	22.8	21.8	20.8
120	36.6	33.5	31.5	29.7	28.1	26.8	25.5	24.4
150	47.6	43.2	40.5	38.1	36.0	34.2	32.7	31.2

400 Psi Gage Initial Pressure (Saturation Temperature 448°F)

Inches Hg Abs.	Initial Superheat—°F							
	0	52	102	152	202	252	302	352
1.0	6.22	5.99	5.78	5.59	5.43	5.26	5.11	4.96
2.0	6.72	6.46	6.23	6.03	5.84	5.69	5.49	5.32
3.0	7.07	6.78	6.55	6.34	6.13	5.93	5.75	5.57
4.0	7.34	7.05	6.81	6.58	6.36	6.15	5.95	5.77
PSI Gage								
0	10.6	10.2	9.77	9.39	9.03	8.68	8.35	8.03
10	12.2	11.7	11.2	10.7	10.3	9.90	9.48	9.09
20	13.7	13.0	12.5	11.9	11.4	10.9	10.5	10.0
30	15.0	14.3	13.7	13.1	12.5	11.9	11.4	10.8
40	16.3	15.6	14.8	14.1	13.5	12.8	12.2	11.7
50	17.6	16.8	16.0	15.2	14.5	13.7	13.1	12.5
60	18.9	18.0	17.2	16.3	15.5	14.7	14.0	13 3
80	21.7	20.6	19.6	18.5	17.5	16.6	15.8	15.1
100	24.7	23.4	22.2	20.9	19.7	18.7	17.8	17.0
120	27.9	26.5	25.0	23.5	22.2	21.0	20.0	19.1
150	33.7	31.8	29.8	28.0	26.4	25.0	23.8	22.7
200	46.6	43.7	40.6	38.1	36.0	34.1	32.4	30.9

Based on Keenan and Keyes Tables, published 1938 by ASME.

Rankine cycle efficiency of driver must be applied to obtain actual water rate. See Chapter 5 for discussion.
See Chapter 15 for approximate Rankine cycle efficiencies of engines and turbines for compressor drive.

THEORETICAL WATER RATE IN POUNDS PER BHP-HOUR

500 Psi Gage Initial Pressure (Saturation Temperature 470°F)

Exhaust Pressure	Initial Temperature—°F							
	550	600	650	700	750	800	850	900
Inches Hg Abs.	Initial Superheat—°F							
	80	130	180	230	280	330	380	430
1.0	5.70	5.51	5.33	5.17	5.01	4.87	4.72	4.59
2.0	6.13	5.92	5.73	5.54	5.37	5.21	5.05	4.90
3.0	6.43	6.19	5.99	5.80	5.61	5.44	5.27	5.11
4.0	6.66	6.43	6.21	6.00	5.81	5.63	5.45	5.28
PSI Gage								
0	9.38	9.00	8.65	8.32	8.01	7.70	7.41	7.13
10	10.7	10.2	9.79	9.39	9.02	8.66	8.30	7.97
20	11.8	11.2	10.8	10.3	9.87	9.45	9.06	8.67
30	12.8	12.2	11.7	11.1	10.7	10.2	9.73	9.31
40	13.8	13.1	12.5	11.9	11.4	10.9	10.4	9.94
60	15.7	14.9	14.2	13.5	12.8	12.2	11.7	11.2
80	17.6	16.7	15.8	15.0	14.3	13.6	13.0	12.4
100	19.6	18.6	17.6	16.6	15.7	15.0	14.3	13.7
120	21.7	20.5	19.3	18.3	17.3	16.5	15.8	15.1
150	25.2	23.6	22.2	21.0	19.9	19.0	18.1	17.4
200	32.1	30.0	28.1	26.6	25.3	24.1	23.0	22.0
250	41.4	38.6	36.2	34.2	32.4	30.9	29.4	28.3

600 Psi Gage Initial Pressure (Saturation Temperature 489°F)

Inches Hg Abs.	Initial Superheat—°F							
	61	111	161	211	261	311	361	411
1.0	——	5.45	5.26	5.10	4.94	4.80	4.65	4.52
2.0	——	5.84	5.64	5.46	5.29	5.12	4.97	4.82
3.0	——	6.11	5.90	5.70	5.52	5.35	5.18	5.02
4.0	——	6.32	6.10	5.90	5.70	5.52	5.35	5.18
PSI Gage								
0	——	8.73	8.38	8.05	7.75	7.46	7.19	6.93
20	——	10.8	10.3	9.88	9.45	9.06	8.68	8.33
40	——	12.4	11.9	11.3	10.8	10.3	9.87	9.44
60	——	14.0	13.3	12.7	12.1	11.5	11.0	10.5
80	——	15.5	14.7	14.0	13.3	12.6	12.0	11.5
100	——	17.1	16.2	15.3	14.5	13.8	13.1	12.6
125	——	19.0	18.0	17.0	16.1	15.3	14.6	14.0
150	——	21.1	19.9	18.7	17.8	16.9	16.1	15.4
175	——	23.4	21.9	20.7	19.6	18.6	17.8	17.0
200	——	25.9	24.2	22.8	21.6	20.6	19.6	18.8
250	——	31.6	29.5	27.8	26.3	25.0	23.9	22.9
300	——	39.1	36.5	34.4	32.5	31.0	29.6	28.2

Based on Keenan and Keyes Tables, published 1938 by ASME.

Rankine cycle efficiency of driver must be applied to obtain actual water rate. See Chapter 5 for discussion. See Chapter 15 for approximate Rankine cycle efficiencies of engines and turbines for compressor drive.

THEORETICAL WATER RATE IN POUNDS PER BHP-HOUR
800 Psi Gage Initial Pressure (Saturation Temperature 520°F)

Exhaust Pressure	Initial Temperature—°F							
	650	700	750	800	850	900	950	1000
Inches Hg Abs.	Initial Superheat—°F							
	130	180	230	280	330	380	430	480
1.0	5.19	5.01	4.85	4.70	4.56	4.43	4.30	4.18
2.0	5.54	5.35	5.17	5.01	4.85	4.71	4.57	4.43
3.0	5.78	5.58	5.39	5.21	5.05	4.89	4.74	4.60
4.0	5.98	5.76	5.56	5.37	5.20	5.04	4.89	4.74
PSI Gage								
0	8.04	7.72	7.42	7.14	6.88	6.63	6.39	6.16
20	9.73	9.30	8.92	8.54	8.19	7.86	7.55	7.25
40	11.1	10.5	10.1	9.62	9.21	8.80	8.43	8.09
60	12.2	11.7	11.1	10.6	10.1	9.64	9.23	8.86
80	13.4	12.7	12.1	11.5	10.9	10.4	10.0	9.59
100	14.5	13.7	13.0	12.4	11.8	11.2	10.8	10.3
150	17.3	16.3	15.4	14.6	13.9	13.3	12.7	12.2
200	20.3	19.0	17.9	17.0	16.2	15.4	14.8	14.2
250	23.6	22.1	20.9	19.7	18.8	17.9	17.1	16.5
300	27.4	25.6	24.2	22.9	21.8	20.8	19.9	19.1
350	31.9	29.9	28.2	26.7	25.3	24.2	23.2	22.2
400	37.5	35.0	33.1	31.3	29.8	28.4	27.2	26.1

1000 Psi Gage Initial Pressure (Saturation Temperature 546°F)

Inches Hg Abs.	Initial Superheat—°F							
	104	154	204	254	304	354	404	454
1.0	——	4.97	4.80	4.65	4.50	4.37	4.24	4.12
2.0	——	5.29	5.10	4.94	4.78	4.63	4.49	4.36
3.0	——	5.51	5.31	5.13	4.97	4.81	4.66	4.52
4.0	——	5.67	5.47	5.29	5.11	4.95	4.80	4.65
PSI Gage								
0	——	7.51	7.21	6.93	6.67	6.43	6.19	5.98
20	——	8.98	8.57	8.22	7.88	7.56	7.26	6.98
40	——	10.1	9.60	9.18	8.77	8.41	8.06	7.72
60	——	11.0	10.5	10.0	9.57	9.15	8.74	8.38
80	——	12.0	11.3	10.8	10.3	9.82	9.39	9.00
100	——	12.8	12.2	11.6	11.0	10.5	10.0	9.59
150	——	15.0	14.1	13.4	12.7	12.1	11.5	11.1
200	——	17.1	16.1	15.2	14.4	13.8	13.1	12.6
250	——	19.5	18.2	17.2	16.3	15.6	14.9	14.3
300	——	21.9	20.5	19.4	18.4	17.5	16.8	16.1
400	——	27.9	26.1	24.7	23.4	22.3	21.3	20.4
500	——	35.9	33.6	31.8	30.1	28.7	27.4	26.3

Based on Keenan and Keyes Tables, published 1938 by ASME.

Rankine cycle efficiency of driver must be applied to obtain actual water rate. See Chapter 5 for discussion.
See Chapter 15 for approximate Rankine cycle efficiencies of engines and turbines for compressor drive.

DISCHARGE OF AIR THROUGH AN ORIFICE

In cubic feet of free air per minute at standard atmospheric pressure of 14.7 lb per sq. in. absolute and 70°F.

Gauge Pressure before Orifice in Pounds per sq. in.	DIAMETER OF ORIFICE										
	1/64"	1/32"	1/16"	1/8"	1/4"	3/8"	1/2"	5/8"	3/4"	7/8"	1"
	Discharge in cubic feet of free air per minute										
1	.028	.112	.450	1.80	7.18	16.2	28.7	45.0	64.7	88.1	115
2	.040	.158	.633	2.53	10.1	22.8	40.5	63.3	91.2	124	162
3	.048	.194	.775	3.10	12.4	27.8	49.5	77.5	111	152	198
4	.056	.223	.892	3.56	14.3	32.1	57.0	89.2	128	175	228
5	.062	.248	.993	3.97	15.9	35.7	63.5	99.3	143	195	254
6	.068	.272	1.09	4.34	17.4	39.1	69.5	109	156	213	278
7	.073	.293	1.17	4.68	18.7	42.2	75.0	117	168	230	300
9	.083	.331	1.32	5.30	21.2	47.7	84.7	132	191	260	339
12	.095	.379	1.52	6.07	24.3	54.6	97.0	152	218	297	388
15	.105	.420	1.68	6.72	26.9	60.5	108	168	242	329	430
20	.123	.491	1.96	7.86	31.4	70.7	126	196	283	385	503
25	.140	.562	2.25	8.98	35.9	80.9	144	225	323	440	575
30	.158	.633	2.53	10.1	40.5	91.1	162	253	365	496	648
35	.176	.703	2.81	11.3	45.0	101	180	281	405	551	720
40	.194	.774	3.10	12.4	49.6	112	198	310	446	607	793
45	.211	.845	3.38	13.5	54.1	122	216	338	487	662	865
50	.229	.916	3.66	14.7	58.6	132	235	366	528	718	938
60	.264	1.06	4.23	16.9	67.6	152	271	423	609	828	1082
70	.300	1.20	4.79	19.2	76.7	173	307	479	690	939	1227
80	.335	1.34	5.36	21.4	85.7	193	343	536	771	1050	1371
90	.370	1.48	5.92	23.7	94.8	213	379	592	853	1161	1516
100	.406	1.62	6.49	26.0	104	234	415	649	934	1272	1661
110	.441	1.76	7.05	28.2	113	254	452	705	1016	1383	1806
120	.476	1.91	7.62	30.5	122	274	488	762	1097	1494	1951
125	.494	1.98	7.90	31.6	126	284	506	790	1138	1549	2023
150	.582	2.37	9.45	37.5	150	338	600	910	1315	1789	2338
200	.761	3.10	12.35	49.0	196	441	784	1225	1764	2401	3136
250	.935	3.80	15.18	60.3	241	542	964	1508	2169	2952	3856
300	.995	4.88	18.08	71.8	287	646	1148	1795	2583	3515	4592
400	1.220	5.98	23.81	94.5	378	851	1512	2360	3402	4630	6048
500	1.519	7.41	29.55	117.3	469	1055	1876	2930	4221	5745	7504
750	2.240	10.98	43.85	174.0	696	1566	2784	4350	6264	8525	11136
1000	2.985	14.60	58.21	231.0	924	2079	3696	5790	8316	11318	14784

Table is based on 100% coefficient of flow. For well rounded entrance multiply values by 0.97. For sharp edged orifices a multiplier of 0.61 may be used for approximate results.

Values for pressures from 1 to 15 lbs gauge calculated by standard adiabatic formula.

Values for pressures above 15 lb gauge calculated by approximate formula proposed by S. A. Moss.

$$W = 0.5303 \frac{ACp_1}{\sqrt{T_1}}$$

Where:
W = discharge in lbs. per sec
A = area of orifice in sq in.
C = Coefficient of flow
p_1 = Upstream total pressure in lbs. per sq. in. absolute
T_1 = Upstream temperature in °F. abs.

Values used in calculating above table were; $C = 1.0$, p_1 = gauge pressure + 14.7 lbs./sq. in. $T_1 = 530°F.$ abs.

Weights (W) were converted to volumes using density factor of 0.07494 lbs./cu. ft. This is correct for dry air at 14.7 lbs. per sq. in. absolute pressure and 70°F.

Formula cannot be used where p_1 is less than two times the downstream pressure.

(See page 5-10 for a discussion of orifice flow).

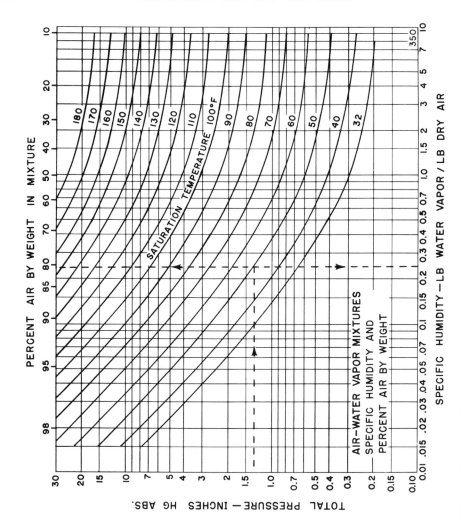

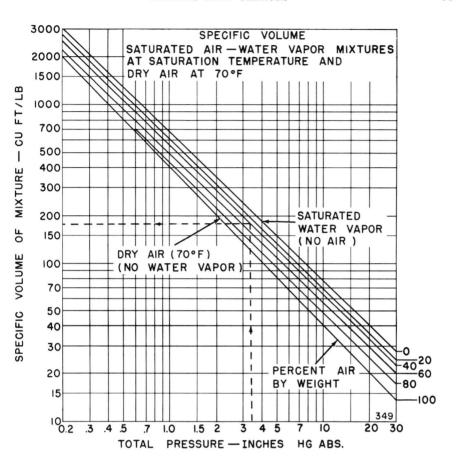

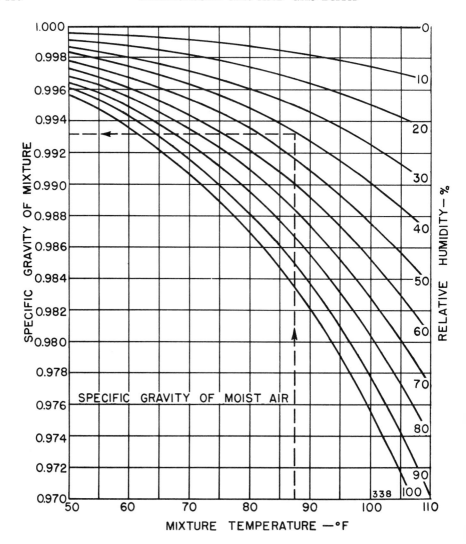

SPECIFIC GRAVITY OF MOIST AIR

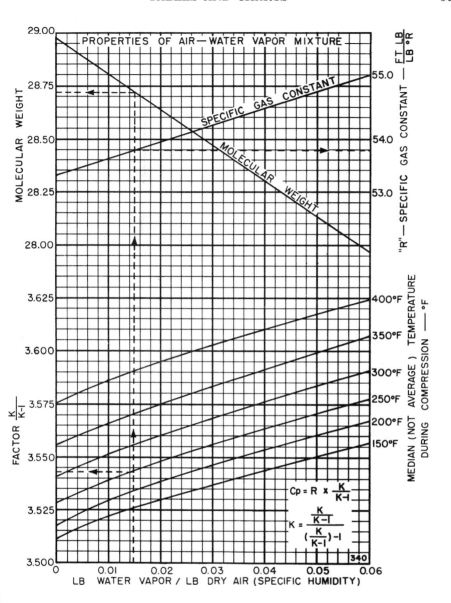

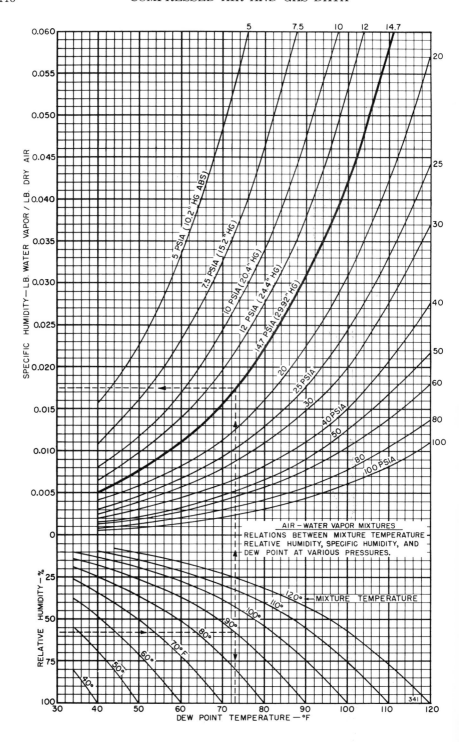

AIR — WATER VAPOR MIXTURES
RELATIONS BETWEEN MIXTURE TEMPERATURE
RELATIVE HUMIDITY, SPECIFIC HUMIDITY, AND
DEW POINT AT VARIOUS PRESSURES.

WEIGHT OF WATER IN A CUBIC FOOT OF AIR AT VARIOUS
TEMPERATURES AND PERCENTAGES OF SATURATION

Based on atmospheric pressure of 14.7 lbs. abs.

Temp. °F.	Percentage of Saturation									
	10	20	30	40	50	60	70	80	90	100
	Grains	Grains	Grains	Grains	Grains	Grains	Grains	Grains	Grains	Grains
−10	.028	.057	.086	.114	.142	.171	.200	.228	.256	.285
0	.048	.096	.144	.192	.240	.289	.337	.385	.433	.481
10	.078	.155	.233	.310	.388	.466	.543	.621	.698	.776
20	.124	.247	.370	.494	.618	.741	.864	.988	1.112	1.235
30	.194	.387	.580	.774	.968	1.161	1.354	1.548	1.742	1.935
32	.211	.422	.634	.845	1.056	1.268	1.479	1.690	1.902	2.113
35	.237	.473	.710	.946	1.183	1.420	1.656	1.893	2.129	2.366
40	.285	.570	.855	1.140	1.424	1.709	1.994	2.279	2.564	2.849
45	.341	.683	1.024	1.366	1.707	2.048	2.390	2.731	3.073	3.414
50	.408	.815	1.223	1.630	2.038	2.446	2.853	3.261	3.668	4.076
55	.485	.970	1.455	1.940	2.424	2.909	3.394	3.879	4.364	4.849
60	.574	1.149	1.724	2.298	2.872	3.447	4.022	4.596	5.170	5.745
62	.614	1.228	1.843	2.457	3.071	3.685	4.299	4.914	5.528	6.142
64	.656	1.313	1.969	2.625	3.282	3.938	4.594	5.250	5.907	6.563
66	.701	1.402	2.103	2.804	3.504	4.205	4.906	5.607	6.308	7.009
68	.748	1.496	2.244	2.992	3.740	4.488	5.236	5.984	6.732	7.480
70	.798	1.596	2.394	3.192	3.990	4.788	5.586	6.384	7.182	7.980
72	.851	1.702	2.552	3.403	4.254	5.105	5.956	6.806	7.657	8.508
74	.907	1.813	2.720	3.626	4.533	5.440	6.346	7.253	8.159	9.066
76	.966	1.931	2.896	3.862	4.828	5.793	6.758	7.724	8.690	9.655
78	1.028	2.055	3.083	4.111	5.138	6.166	7.194	8.222	9.249	10.277
80	1.093	2.187	3.280	4.374	5.467	6.560	7.654	8.747	9.841	10.934
82	1.163	2.325	3.488	4.650	5.813	6.976	8.138	9.301	10.463	11.625
84	1.236	2.471	3.707	4.942	6.178	7.414	8.649	9.885	11.120	12.326
86	1.313	2.625	3.938	5.251	6.564	7.877	9.189	10.502	11.814	13.137
88	1.394	2.787	4.181	5.575	6.968	8.362	9.756	11.150	12.543	13.997
90	1.479	2.958	4.437	5.916	7.395	8.874	10.353	11.832	13.311	14.780
92	1.569	3.138	4.707	6.276	7.844	9.413	10.982	12.551	14.120	15.639
94	1.663	3.327	4.990	6.654	8.317	9.980	11.644	13.307	14.971	16.624
96	1.763	3.525	5.288	7.050	8.813	10.576	12.338	14.101	15.863	17.676
98	1.867	3.734	5.601	7.468	9.336	11.203	13.070	14.937	16.804	18.661
100	1.977	3.953	5.930	7.906	9.883	11.860	13.836	15.813	17.789	19.766

Condensed from a circular of the U. S. Weather Bureau.

NOTE: 1 grain = 1/7000 lb. See page 3-8.

RELATIVE HUMIDITY OF AIR FROM READINGS OF WET AND DRY BULB THERMOMETERS

Temperature of air degrees F.	Difference between wet and dry bulb Thermometer Degrees Fahrenheit																								
	1	2	3	4	5	6	7	8	9	10	11	12	13	14	15	16	17	18	19	20	21	22	23	24	25
−10	46																								
0	67	33																							
10	78	56	34	13																					
20	85	70	55	40	26	12																			
30	89	78	67	56	46	36	26	16	6																
32	89	79	69	59	49	39	30	20	11	2															
35	91	81	72	63	54	45	36	27	19	10	2														
40	92	83	75	68	60	52	45	37	29	22	15	7	0												
45	93	86	78	71	64	57	51	44	38	31	25	18	12	6											
50	93	87	80	74	67	61	55	49	43	38	32	27	21	16	10	5	0								
55	94	88	82	76	70	65	59	54	49	43	38	33	28	23	19	14	9	5	0						
60	94	89	83	78	73	68	63	58	53	48	43	39	34	30	26	21	17	13	9	5	1				
62	94	89	84	79	74	69	64	59	54	50	45	41	36	32	28	24	20	16	12	8	4	1			
64	95	90	84	79	74	70	65	60	56	51	47	43	38	34	30	26	22	18	15	11	7	4	0		
66	95	90	85	80	75	71	66	61	57	53	48	44	40	36	32	29	25	21	17	14	10	7	3	0	
68	95	90	85	80	76	71	67	62	58	54	50	46	42	38	34	31	27	23	20	16	13	10	6	3	
70	95	90	86	81	77	72	68	64	59	55	51	48	44	40	36	33	29	25	22	19	15	12	9	6	3
72	95	91	86	82	77	73	69	65	61	57	53	49	45	42	38	34	31	28	24	21	18	15	12	9	6
74	95	91	86	82	78	74	69	65	61	58	54	50	47	43	39	36	33	29	26	23	20	17	14	11	8
76	96	91	87	82	78	74	70	66	62	59	55	51	48	44	41	38	34	31	28	25	22	19	16	13	11
78	96	91	87	83	79	75	71	67	63	60	56	53	49	46	43	39	36	33	30	27	24	21	18	16	13
80	96	91	87	83	79	75	72	68	64	61	57	54	50	47	44	41	38	35	32	29	26	23	20	18	15
82	96	92	88	84	80	76	72	69	65	61	58	55	51	48	45	42	39	36	33	30	28	25	22	20	17
84	96	92	88	84	80	76	73	69	66	62	59	56	52	49	46	43	40	37	35	32	29	26	24	21	19
86	96	92	88	84	81	77	73	70	66	63	60	57	53	50	47	44	42	39	36	33	31	28	26	23	21
88	96	92	88	85	81	77	74	70	67	64	61	57	54	51	48	46	43	40	37	35	32	30	27	25	22
90	96	92	89	85	81	78	74	71	68	65	61	58	55	52	49	47	44	41	39	36	34	31	29	26	24
92	96	92	89	85	82	78	75	72	68	65	62	59	56	53	50	48	45	42	40	37	35	32	30	28	25
94	96	93	89	85	82	79	75	72	69	66	63	60	57	54	51	49	46	43	41	38	36	33	31	29	27
96	96	93	89	86	82	79	76	73	69	66	63	61	58	55	52	50	47	44	42	39	37	35	32	30	28
98	96	93	89	86	83	79	76	73	70	67	64	61	58	56	53	50	48	45	43	40	38	36	34	32	29
100	96	93	89	86	83	80	77	73	70	68	65	62	59	56	54	51	49	46	44	41	39	37	35	33	30

Condensed from Circular F of the U. S. Weather Bureau.

NOTE: This table is made up for a barometric pressure of 30 inches. For lower barometric pressures the relative humidity for corresponding temperature differences is slightly higher. The error resulting from the use of the above table for lower barometric pressures will increase with the wet-bulb depression and with lower air temperatures. For a difference between the wet- and dry-bulb thermometers of 10° with 80°F. dry-bulb temperature, the percentage of error for 29 inches barometer is 0.5; for 27 inches, 1.0; for 25 inches, 1.5; and for 23 inches, 2.0. For example, at 30 inches barometer the relative humidity, with 80°F. dry-bulb temperature and 10° wet-bulb depression, is 61 per cent; whereas for the same conditions at 2 inches barometer the humidity is 63 per cent.

Relative Humidity is the ratio of the actual vapor pressure to the vapor pressure at saturation. See page 3-6. In the above table, it is expressed as percent.

WEIGHT OF DRY AIR AT VARIOUS PRESSURES AND TEMPERATURES AT SEA LEVEL

Temp. of Air Deg. Fahr.	Gauge Pressure, Pounds — Weight in Pounds per Cubic Foot																					
	0	5	10	20	30	40	50	60	70	80	90	100	110	120	130	140	150	175	200	225	250	300
-20	.0900	.1205	.1515	.2125	.2744	.3360	.3970	.4580	.5190	.5800	.6410	.702	.7635	.825	.886	.948	1.010	1.165	1.318	1.465	1.625	1.930
-10	.0882	.1184	.1485	.2090	.2685	.3283	.3880	.4478	.5076	.5674	.6272	.687	.747	.807	.868	.928	.989	1.139	1.288	1.438	1.588	1.890
0	.0864	.1160	.1455	.2040	.2630	.3215	.3800	.4385	.4970	.5555	.6140	.672	.731	.790	.849	.908	.968	1.114	1.260	1.406	1.553	1.850
10	.0846	.1136	.1425	.1995	.2568	.3145	.3720	.4292	.4863	.5433	.6006	.658	.716	.774	.832	.889	.947	1.090	1.233	1.376	1.520	1.810
20	.0828	.1112	.1395	.1955	.2516	.3071	.3645	.4205	.4770	.5330	.5890	.645	.701	.757	.813	.869	.927	1.067	1.208	1.348	1.489	1.770
30	.0811	.1088	.1366	.1916	.2465	.3015	.3570	.4121	.4672	.5221	.5771	.632	.687	.742	.797	.852	.908	1.046	1.184	1.322	1.460	1.735
40	.0795	.1067	.1338	.1876	.2415	.2954	.3503	.4038	.4576	.5114	.5652	.619	.673	.727	.781	.835	.890	1.025	1.161	1.296	1.431	1.701
50	.0780	.1045	.1310	.1839	.2367	.2905	.3432	.3960	.4487	.5014	.5541	.607	.660	.713	.766	.819	.873	1.006	1.139	1.271	1.403	1.668
60	.0764	.1025	.1283	.1803	.2323	.2840	.3362	.3882	.4402	.4927	.5447	.596	.649	.700	.752	.804	.856	.988	1.116	1.245	1.376	1.636
70	.0750	.1005	.1260	.1770	.2280	.2791	.3302	.3808	.4316	.4824	.5332	.584	.635	.686	.737	.788	.839	.967	1.095	1.223	1.350	1.604
80	.0736	.0988	.1239	.1738	.2237	.2739	.3242	.3738	.4234	.4729	.5224	.572	.622	.673	.723	.774	.824	.949	1.074	1.199	1.325	1.573
90	.0723	.0970	.1218	.1707	.2195	.2688	.3182	.3670	.4154	.4639	.5122	.561	.611	.660	.709	.759	.809	.932	1.054	1.177	1.300	1.544
100	.0710	.0954	.1197	.1676	.2155	.2638	.3122	.3602	.4079	.4555	.5033	.551	.599	.648	.696	.745	.794	.914	1.035	1.155	1.276	1.517
110	.0698	.0937	.1176	.1645	.2115	.2593	.3070	.3542	.4011	.4481	.4950	.542	.589	.637	.685	.732	.780	.899	1.017	1.135	1.254	1.491
120	.0686	.0921	.1155	.1618	.2080	.2549	.3018	.3481	.3944	.4403	.4866	.533	.579	.626	.673	.720	.767	.884	1.001	1.118	1.234	1.465
130	.0674	.0905	.1135	.1590	.2045	.2505	.2966	.3446	.3924	.4296	.4770	.524	.570	.616	.662	.708	.754	.869	.984	1.099	1.214	1.440
140	.0663	.0889	.1115	.1565	.2015	.2465	.2915	.3364	.3813	.4262	.4711	.516	.561	.606	.651	.696	.742	.855	.968	1.081	1.194	1.416
150	.0652	.0874	.1096	.1541	.1985	.2425	.2865	.3308	.3751	.4193	.4636	.508	.552	.596	.640	.685	.730	.841	.953	1.064	1.175	1.392
175	.0626	.0840	.1054	.1482	.1910	.2335	.2755	.3181	.3607	.4033	.4450	.488	.531	.573	.616	.658	.701	.808	.914	1.021	1.128	1.337
200	.0603	.0809	.1014	.1427	.1840	.2248	.2655	.3054	.3473	.3882	.4291	.470	.511	.552	.592	.633	.674	.776	.879	.982	1.084	1.287
225	.0581	.0779	.0976	.1373	.1770	.2163	.2555	.2949	.3344	.3738	.4120	.452	.491	.531	.570	.609	.649	.747	.846	.944	1.043	1.240
250	.0560	.0751	.0941	.1323	.1705	.2085	.2466	.2845	.3223	.3602	.3981	.436	.474	.513	.551	.589	.627	.722	.817	.912	1.007	1.197
275	.0541	.0726	.0910	.1278	.1645	.2011	.2378	.2745	.3111	.3478	.3844	.421	.458	.494	.531	.568	.605	.697	.789	.881	.972	1.155
300	.0523	.0707	.0881	.1237	.1592	.1945	.2300	.2654	.3008	.3362	.3716	.407	.442	.478	.513	.549	.585	.673	.762	.852	.940	1.118
350	.0491	.0658	.0825	.1160	.1495	.1828	.2160	.2492	.2824	.3156	.3488	.382	.415	.449	.482	.516	.549	.632	.715	.799	.883	1.048
400	.0463	.0621	.0779	.1090	.1405	.1720	.2035	.2348	.2661	.2974	.3287	.360	.391	.423	.454	.486	.517	.596	.674	.753	.831	.987
450	.0437	.0586	.0735	.1033	.1330	.1628	.1925	.2220	.2515	.2810	.3105	.340	.369	.399	.429	.458	.488	.562	.637	.711	.786	.934
500	.0414	.0555	.0696	.0978	.1260	.1540	.1820	.2100	.2380	.2660	.2940	.326	.351	.379	.407	.435	.463	.534	.604	.675	.746	.885
550	.0394	.0528	.0661	.0930	.1198	.1464	.1730	.1996	.2262	.2528	.2794	.306	.333	.359	.386	.413	.440	.507	.573	.641	.709	.841
600	.0376	.0504	.0631	.0885	.1140	.1395	.1650	.1904	.2158	.2412	.2668	.292	.317	.343	.368	.393	.419	.483	.547	.611	.675	.801

Based on perfect gas laws and air weight of .08071 lbs. per cu. ft. at 32°F and barometric pressure of 14.696 lbs. per sq. in.

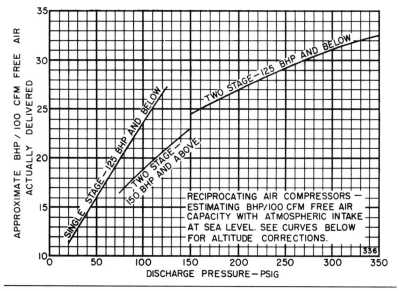

RECIPROCATING AIR COMPRESSORS —
ESTIMATING BHP/100 CFM FREE AIR
CAPACITY WITH ATMOSPHERIC INTAKE
AT SEA LEVEL. SEE CURVES BELOW
FOR ALTITUDE CORRECTIONS.

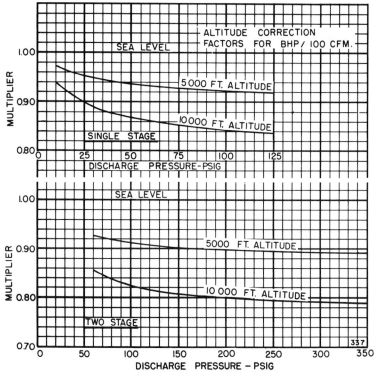

ALTITUDE CORRECTION
FACTORS FOR BHP/100 CFM.

TYPICAL COMPOSITION OF COMMERCIAL FUEL GASES

Constituent	Percent by Volume						
	Blast Furnace Gas	Blue Water Gas From Coke	Carbureted Water Gas	Coke Oven Gas	Natural Gas	Oil Gas	Producer Gas
H_2	2.9	47.3	37.0	52.3	See page 24-2	48.7	14.9
CO	25.3	37.0	33.5	6.0		12.3	27.4
CH_4	0.5	1.3	13.5	30.6		24.8	2.1
CO_2	12.8	5.4	3.4	1.9		4.7	4.5
N_2	58.5	8.3	4.8	4.9		4.8	50.5
O_2	——	0.7	0.5	0.5		0.5	0.3
Illum.	——	——	7.3	3.8		4.2	0.3
Specific Gravity Air = 1.0	1.02	0.57	0.65	0.41	0.55 to 1.00	0.48	0.85
HHV BTU/cu ft.	94	287	525	578	950 to 1150	541	161

Each column is an average of dry gas analyses from several sources.

STANDARD HARDNESS CONVERSION TABLES FOR STEEL

Rockwell			Brinell	Vickers
Diamond Cone Penetrator			10 mm Standard Ball 3000 Kg Load	Diamond Pyramid
C Scale 150 Kg Load	D Scale 100 Kg Load	A Scale 60 Kg Load		
68	76.9	85.6	——	940
67	76.1	85.0	——	900
66	75.4	84.5	——	865
65	74.5	83.9	——	832
64	73.8	83.4	——	800
63	73.0	82.8	——	772
62	72.2	82.3	——	746
61	71.5	81.8	——	720
60	70.7	81.2	——	697
59	69.9	80.7	——	674
58	69.2	80.1	——	653
57	68.5	79.6	——	633
56	67.7	79.0	——	613
55	66.9	78.5	——	595
54	66.1	78.0	——	577
53	65.4	77.4	——	560
52	64.6	76.8	500	544
51	63.8	76.3	487	528
50	63.1	75.9	475	513
49	62.1	75.2	464	498
48	61.4	74.7	451	484
47	60.8	74.1	442	471
46	60.0	73.6	432	458
45	59.2	73.1	421	446
44	58.5	72.5	409	434
43	57.7	72.0	400	423
42	56.9	71.5	390	412
41	56.2	70.9	381	402
40	55.4	70.4	371	392
39	54.6	69.9	362	382
38	53.8	69.4	353	372
37	53.1	68.9	344	363
36	52.3	68.4	336	354
35	51.5	67.9	327	345
34	50.8	67.4	319	336
33	50.0	66.8	311	327
32	49.2	66.3	301	318
31	48.4	65.8	294	310
30	47.7	65.3	286	302
29	47.0	64.7	279	294
28	46.1	64.3	271	286
27	45.2	63.8	264	279
26	44.6	63.3	258	272
25	43.8	62.8	253	266
24	43.1	62.4	247	260
23	42.1	62.0	243	254
22	41.6	61.5	237	248
21	40.9	61.0	231	243
20	40.1	60.5	226	238

Data from ASTM E 140-58.
Conversion of hardness values must be considered as somewhat approximate.

WIRE AND SHEET METAL GAGES

(Diameters and thickness in decimal parts of an inch)

Gage No.	American wire gage, or Brown & Sharpe (for non-ferrous sheet and wire)	Steel wire gage or Washburn & Moen or Roebling (for steel wire)	Birmingham wire gage (B.W.G.) or Stubs iron wire (for steel rods or sheets)	Stubs steel wire gage	British Imperial standard wire gage (S.W.G.)	U.S. standard gage for wrought iron sheet (480 lb per cu ft)	U.S. standard gage for steel and open-hearth iron sheet (489.6 lb per cu ft)	British standard for iron and steel sheets and hoops, 1914 (B.G.)
0000000	....	0.4900	....	....	0.500	0.500	0.4902	0.6666
000000	....	0.4615	....	....	0.464	0.469	0.4596	0.6250
00000	....	0.4305	....	....	0.432	0.438	0.4289	0.5883
0000	0.460	0.3938	0.454	....	0.400	0.406	0.3983	0.5416
000	0.410	0.3625	0.425	....	0.372	0.375	0.3676	0.5000
00	0.365	0.3310	0.380	....	0.348	0.344	0.3370	0.4452
0	0.325	0.3065	0.340	....	0.324	0.312	0.3064	0.3964
1	0.289	0.2830	0.300	0.227	0.300	0.281	0.2757	0.3532
2	0.258	0.2625	0.284	0.219	0.276	0.266	0.2604	0.3147
3	0.229	0.2437	0.259	0.212	0.252	0.250	0.2451	0.2804
4	0.204	0.2253	0.238	0.207	0.232	0.234	0.2298	0.2500
5	0.182	0.2070	0.220	0.204	0.212	0.219	0.2145	0.2225
6	0.162	0.1920	0.203	0.201	0.192	0.203	0.1991	0.1981
7	0.144	0.1770	0.180	0.199	0.176	0.188	0.1838	0.1764
8	0.128	0.1620	0.165	0.197	0.160	0.172	0.1685	0.1570
9	0.114	0.1483	0.148	0.194	0.144	0.156	0.1532	0.1398
10	0.102	0.1350	0.134	0.191	0.128	0.141	0.1379	0.1250
11	0.091	0.1205	0.120	0.188	0.116	0.125	0.1225	0.1113
12	0.081	0.1055	0.109	0.185	0.104	0.109	0.1072	0.0991
13	0.072	0.0915	0.095	0.182	0.092	0.094	0.0919	0.0882
14	0.064	0.0800	0.083	0.180	0.080	0.078	0.0766	0.0785
15	0.057	0.0720	0.072	0.178	0.072	0.070	0.0689	0.0699
16	0.051	0.0625	0.065	0.175	0.064	0.062	0.0613	0.0625
17	0.045	0.0540	0.058	0.172	0.056	0.056	0.0551	0.0556
18	0.040	0.0475	0.049	0.168	0.048	0.050	0.0490	0.0495
19	0.036	0.0410	0.042	0.164	0.040	0.0438	0.0429	0.0440
20	0.032	0.0348	0.035	0.161	0.036	0.0375	0.0368	0.0392
21	0.0285	0.0317	0.032	0.157	0.032	0.0344	0.0337	0.0349
22	0.0253	0.0286	0.028	0.155	0.028	0.0312	0.0306	0.0313
23	0.0226	0.0258	0.025	0.153	0.024	0.0281	0.0276	0.0278
24	0.0201	0.0230	0.022	0.151	0.022	0.0250	0.0245	0.0248
25	0.0179	0.0204	0.020	0.148	0.020	0.0219	0.0214	0.0220
26	0.0159	0.0181	0.018	0.146	0.018	0.0188	0.0184	0.0196
27	0.0142	0.0173	0.016	0.143	0.0164	0.0172	0.0169	0.0175
28	0.0126	0.0162	0.014	0.139	0.0148	0.0156	0.0153	0.0156
29	0.0113	0.0150	0.013	0.134	0.0136	0.0141	0.0138	0.0139
30	0.0100	0.0140	0.012	0.127	0.0124	0.0125	0.0123	0.0123
31	0.0089	0.0132	0.010	0.120	0.0116	0.0109	0.0107	0.0110
32	0.0080	0.0128	0.009	0.115	0.0108	0.0102	0.0100	0.0098
33	0.0071	0.0118	0.008	0.112	0.0100	0.0094	0.0092	0.0087
34	0.0063	0.0104	0.007	0.110	0.0092	0.0086	0.0084	0.0077
35	0.0056	0.0095	0.005	0.108	0.0084	0.0078	0.0077	0.0069
36	0.0050	0.0090	0.004	0.106	0.0076	0.0070	0.0069	0.0061
37	0.0045	0.0085	....	0.103	0.0068	0.0066	0.0065	0.0054
38	0.0040	0.0080	....	0.101	0.0060	0.0062	0.0061	0.0048
39	0.0035	0.0075	....	0.099	0.0052	0.0059	0.0057	0.0043
40	0.0031	0.0070	....	0.097	0.0048	0.0055	0.0054	0.0039
41	....	0.0066	....	0.095	0.0044	0.0053	0.0052	0.0034
42	....	0.0062	....	0.092	0.0040	0.0051	0.0050	0.0031
43	....	0.0060	....	0.088	0.0036	0.0049	0.0048	0.0027
44	....	0.0058	....	0.085	0.0032	0.0047	0.0046	0.0024
45	....	0.0055	....	0.081	0.0028	....	....	0.0022
46	....	0.0052	....	0.079	0.0024	....	....	0.0019
47	....	0.0050	....	0.077	0.0020	....	....	0.0017
48	....	0.0048	....	0.075	0.0016	....	....	0.0015
49	....	0.0046	....	0.072	0.0012	....	....	0.0014
50	....	0.0044	....	0.069	0.0010	....	....	0.0012

DECIMAL EQUIVALENTS

Inches		Millimeter Equivalents of Fractions of an Inch	Inches		Millimeter Equivalents of Fractions of an Inch
Fraction	Decimal Equivalent		Fraction	Decimal Equivalent	
4ths and 8ths			**64ths**		
1/8	.125	3.175	1/64	.015625	.397
1/4	.250	6.350	3/64	.046875	1.191
3/8	.375	9.525	5/64	.078125	1.984
1/2	.500	12.700	7/64	.109375	2.778
5/8	.625	15.875	9/64	.140625	3.572
3/4	.750	19.050	11/64	.171875	4.366
7/8	.875	22.225	13/64	.203125	5.159
16ths			15/64	.234375	5.953
			17/64	.265625	6.747
1/16	.0625	1.588	19/64	.296875	7.541
3/16	.1875	4.763	21/64	.328125	8.334
5/16	.3125	7.938	23/64	.359375	9.128
7/16	.4375	11.113	25/64	.390625	9.922
9/16	.5625	14.288	27/64	.421875	10.716
11/16	.6875	17.463	29/64	.453125	11.509
13/16	.8125	20.638	31/64	.484375	12.303
15/16	.9375	23.813	33/64	.515625	13.097
			35/64	.546875	13.891
32nds			37/64	.578125	14.684
			39/64	.609375	15.478
			41/64	.640625	16.272
1/32	.03125	.794	43/64	.671875	17.066
3/32	.09375	2.381	45/64	.703125	17.859
5/32	.15625	3.969	47/64	.734375	18.653
7/32	.21875	5.556	49/64	.765625	19.447
9/32	.28125	7.144	51/64	.796875	20.241
11/32	.34375	8.731	53/64	.828125	21.034
13/32	.40625	10.319	55/64	.859375	21.828
15/32	.46875	11.906	57/64	.890625	22.622
17/32	.53125	13.494	59/64	.921875	23.416
19/32	.59375	15.081	61/64	.953125	24.209
21/32	.65625	16.669	63/64	.984375	25.003
23/32	.71875	18.256			
25/32	.78125	19.844			
27/32	.84375	21.431			
29/32	.90625	23.019			
31/32	.96875	24.606			

CONVERSION FACTORS

Units of Length	Multiply units in left column by proper factor below							
	in.	ft.	yd.	mile	mm.	cm.	m.	km.
1 inch	1	0.0833	0.0278	——	25.40	2.540	0.0254	——
1 foot	12	1	0.3333	——	304.8	30.48	0.3048	——
1 yard	36	3	1	——	914.4	91.44	0.9144	——
1 mile	——	5280	1760	1	——	——	1609.3	1.609
1 millimeter	0.0394	0.0033	——	——	1	0.100	0.001	——
1 centimeter	0.3937	0.0328	0.0109	——	10	1	0.01	——
1 meter	39.37	3.281	1.904	——	1000	100	1	0.001
1 kilometer	——	3281	1094	0.6214	——	——	1000	1

(1 micron = 0.001 millimeter)

Units of Area	Multiply units in left column by proper factor below						
	sq. in.	sq. ft.	acre	sq. mile	sq. cm.	sq. m.	hectare
1 sq. inch	1	0.0069	——	——	6.452	——	——
1 sq. foot	144	1	——	——	929.0	0.0929	——
1 acre	——	43,560	1	0.0016	——	4047	0.4047
1 sq. mile	——	——	640	1	——	——	259.0
1 sq. centimeter	0.1550	——	——	——	1	0.0001	——
1 sq. meter	1550	10.76	——	——	10,000	1	——
1 hectare	——	——	2.471	——	——	10,000	1

Units of Volume	Multiply units in left column by proper factor below							
	cu. in.	cu. ft.	cu yd.	cu. cm.	cu. meter	liter	U.S. gal.	Imp. gal.
1 cu. inch	1	——	——	16.387	——	0.0164	——	——
1 cu. foot	1728	1	0.0370	28.317	0.0283	28.32	7.481	6.229
1 cu. yard	46,656	27	1	——	0.7646	764.5	202.0	168.2
1 cu. centimetr	0.0610	——	——	1	——	0.0010	——	——
1 cu. meter	61,023	35.31	1.308	1,000,000	1	999.97	264.2	220.0
1 liter	61.025	0.0353	——	1000.028	0.0010	1	0.2642	0.2200
1 U.S. gallon	231	0.1337	——	3785.4	——	3.785	1	0.8327
1 Imperial gallon	277.4	0.1605	——	4546.1	——	4.546	1.201	1

CONVERSION FACTORS

Units of Weight	Multiply units in left column by proper factor below						
	grain	oz.	lb.	ton	gram	kg.	metric ton
1 grain	1	——	——	——	0.0648	——	——
1 ounce	437.5	1	0.0625	——	28.35	0.0283	——
1 pound	7000	16	1	0.0005	453.6	0.4536	——
1 ton	——	32,000	2000	1	——	907.2	0.9072
1 gram	15.43	0.0353	——	——	1	0.001	——
1 kilogram	——	35.27	2.205	——	1000	1	0.001
1 metric ton	——	35,274	2205	1.1023	——	1000	1

Units of Density	Multiply units in left column by proper factor below				
	lb/cu. in.	lb/cu. ft.	lb/gal.	g/cu. cm.	g/liter
1 pound/cu. in.	1	1728	231.0	27.68	27,680
1 pound/cu. ft.	——	1	0.1337	0.0160	16.019
1 pound/gal.	0.00433	7.481	1	0.1198	119.83
1 gram/cu. cm.	0.0361	62.43	8.345	1	1000.0
1 gram/liter	——	0.0624	0.00835	0.001	1

Units of Pressure	Multiply units in left column by proper factor below						
	lb/sq. in.	lb/sq. ft.	int. ata.	kg/cm²	mm Hg at 32°F	in. Hg at 32°F	ft. water at 39.2°F
1 pound/sq. in.	1	144	——	0.0703	51.713	2.0359	2.307
1 pound/sq. ft.	0.00694	1	——	——	0.3591	0.01414	0.01602
1 intern. atmosphere	14.696	2116.2	1	1.0333	760	29.921	33.90
1 kilogram/sq. cm.	14.223	2048.1	0.9678	1	735.56	28.958	32.81
1 millimeter-mercury— 1 torr (torricelli)—	0.0193	2.785	——	——	1	0.0394	0.0446
1 inch mercury	0.4912	70.73	0.0334	0.0345	25.400	1	1.133
1 foot water	0.4335	62.42	——	0.0305	22.418	0.8826	1

CONVERSION FACTORS

Units of Energy	Multiply units in left column by proper factor below					
	ft.-lb.	Btu	g. cal.	Joule	kw-hr.	ph-hr.
1 foot-pound	1	0.001285	0.3240	1.3556	——	——
1 Btu	778.2	1	252.16	1054.9	——	——
1 gram calorie	3.0860	0.003966	1	4.1833	——	——
1 int. Joule	0.7377	0.000948	0.2390	1	——	——
1 int. kilowatt-hour	2,655,656	3412.8	860,563	——	1	1.3412
1 horsepower-hour	1,980,000	2544.5	641,617	——	0.7456	1

Units of Specific Energy	Multiply units in left column by proper factor below				
	absolute Joule/g	int. Joule/g	cal/g	int. cal/g	Btu/lb.
1 absolute Joule/gram	1	0.99984	0.23901	0.23885	0.42993
1 int. Joule/gram	1.000165	1	0.23904	0.23892	0.43000
1 calorie/gram	4.1840	4.1833	1	0.99935	1.7988
1 int. calorie/gram	4.1867	4.1860	1.00065	1	1.8000
1 Btu/lb.	2.3260	2.3256	0.55592	0.55556	1

Units of Power (rate of energy use)	Multiply units in left column by proper factor below								
	hp	watt	kw	Btu/min.	Btu/hr.	ft-lb/sec.	ft-lb/min.	g.cal/sec.	metric hp
1 horsepower	1	745.7	0.7475	42.41	2544.5	550	33.000	178.2	1.014
1 watt	——	1	0.001	0.0569	3.413	0.7376	44.25	0.2390	0.00136
1 kilowatt	1.3410	1000	1	56.88	3412.8	737.6	44,254	239.0	1.360
1 Btu per minute	——	——	——	1	60	12.97	778.2	4.203	0.0239
1 metric hp	0.9863	735.5	0.7355	41.83	2509.6	542.5	32.550	175.7	1

Units of Refrigeration	Multiply units in left column by factor below					
	Btu(IT)/min.	Btu(IT)/hr.	kg cal/hr.	ton (U.S.) comm	ton (BRIT.) comm	frigorie/hr.
1 ton (U.S.) comm	200	12,000	3025.9	1	0.8965	3025.9
1 ton (Brit) comm	223.08	13,385	3375.2	1.1154	1	3375.2
1 frigorie/hr.	0.06609	3.9657	1	0.0003305	0.0002963	1

Note:—Btu is International Steam Table Btu(IT).   1 frigorie = 1 kg cal (**Not** IT).

Weather Data for United States of America and Puerto Rico

The following tables are based on U. S. Dept. of Commerce Weather Bureau Local Climatalogical Data for the locations listed. The 1961 Summary has been used. Many stations are at the city airport.

Columns 1 and 2 have been obtained by calculation from the listed altitude of ground level at the weather station. NACA Report No. 538 was used in making the conversion.

Columns 3 and 4 (*normal* yearly average temperature maximum and minimum) are for the period 1921 through 1950. Columns 5 and 6 are means of the maximum and minimum *monthly* averages. Almost without exception the maximum and minimum were in July and January respectively. All extremes (columns 7 and 8) include records through 1961.

Columns 9 and 10 (relative humidity) may be teamed with dry bulb temperatures of columns 3 and 4 without serious error, since the maximum temperature will always occur during the day and the minimum at night. Columns 11, 12, 13 and 14 indicate the variation in the average monthly humidity measurements.

Location	Normal Atmospheric Pressure		Dry Bulb Temperature — °F						Relative Humidity — %					
	Inches of Mercury	PSIA	Normal Ave. Over a Year		Monthly Ave.		Records		Yearly Mean		Monthly Mean Day		Monthly Mean Night	
			Max.	Min.	Max.	Min.	Max.	Min.	Day	Night	Min.	Max.	Min.	Max.
Column	1	2	3	4	5	6	7	8	9	10	11	12	13	14
ALABAMA														
Birmingham	29.27	14.38	74	51	90	37	106	8	59	84	49	71	76	88
Mobile	29.59	14.54	77	58	90	43	104	3	66	87	53	78	82	91
Montgomery	29.71	14.60	77	54	91	40	98	11	64	88	44	75	79	97
ALASKA														
Anchorage	29.82	14.65	43	27	65	4	81	15	66	72	48	76	61	82
Fairbanks	29.46	14.48	36	16	71	-20	93	-30	64	74	42	81	62	91
ARIZONA														
Flagstaff	23.09	11.35	59	30	81	14	94	-66	40	73	24	55	58	80
Tucson	27.23	13.37	82	53	99	36	111	-16	28	48	13	40	24	67
Yuma	29.71	14.60	88	61	106	42	120	16	23	42	12	35	26	56
ARKANSAS														
Fort Smith	29.44	14.46	73	51	93	30	111	28	57	81	49	68	72	88
Little Rock	29.64	14.56	73	52	91	34	107	-9	59	80	51	68	70	86
CALIFORNIA														
Fresno	29.57	14.52	77	49	99	38	111	-5	48	73	21	83	40	94
Los Angeles	29.82	14.64	69	52	76	44	106	21	64	78	48	74	60	89
Red Bluff	29.55	14.51	75	51	97	37	114	36	42	61	17	72	34	81
Sacramento	29.90	14.69	73	49	90	39	112	21	53	78	28	82	60	90
Sandberg	25.35	12.46	64	47	86	34	102	22	44	—	25	59	—	—
San Francisco	29.91	14.70	65	47	73	41	106	3	69	85	63	78	80	90
COLORADO														
Denver	24.63	12.10	64	36	86	18	99	20	43	68	32	59	59	78
Grand Junction	25.07	12.32	64	40	92	16	102	-16	38	54	17	63	29	75
CONNECTICUT														
Hartford	29.74	14.61	61	39	83	20	96	-14	61	80	52	77	72	90
DELAWARE														
Wilmington	29.84	14.65	65	44	86	25	102	-26	63	81	52	74	73	88

Location	Normal Atmospheric Pressure		Dry Bulb Temperature — °F						Relative Humidity — %					
			Normal Ave. Over a Year		Extremes				Yearly Mean		Monthly Mean			
					Monthly Ave.		Records				Day		Night	
	Inches of Mercury	PSIA	Max.	Min.	Max.	Min.	Max.	Min.	Day	Night	Min.	Max.	Min.	Max.
Column	1	2	3	4	5	6	7	8	9	10	11	12	13	14
DISTRICT OF COLUMBIA														
Washington	29.91	14.70	65	48	87	29	103	1	58	76	46	69	67	82
FLORIDA														
Jacksonville	29.90	14.69	79	59	88	46	105	17	64	87	47	79	82	89
Miami	29.91	14.70	85	67	90	58	98	32	67	85	55	79	81	88
Tallahassee	29.85	14.67	79	56	90	43	103	15	64	88	49	78	84	92
Tampa	29.90	14.69	81	63	90	52	98	24	65	87	51	79	84	92
GEORGIA														
Atlanta	28.88	14.18	72	52	88	36	92	10	60	79	42	70	64	88
Savannah	29.87	14.68	77	56	90	43	104	14	64	86	51	80	81	91
Thomasville	29.62	14.54	78	58	91	43	106	13	56	70	50	62	62	78
HAWAII														
Honolulu	29.91	14.70	80	71	83	67	88	57	65	75	55	74	68	80
IDAHO														
Boise	26.98	13.26	62	39	90	23	111	-4	48	64	19	76	31	82
Idaho Falls	25.10	12.34	57	25	89	2	103	-43	—	—	—	—	—	—
ILLINOIS														
Chicago	29.27	14.38	59	41	81	18	104	-15	61	78	51	75	72	83
Moline	29.30	14.39	60	40	87	15	106	-23	62	82	51	77	74	87
Springfield	29.30	14.39	62	43	88	20	112	-15	61	81	50	75	74	89
INDIANA														
Indianapolis	29.08	14.28	63	42	86	21	104	-19	64	83	52	78	76	87
South Bend	29.10	14.29	59	40	85	17	101	-22	66	83	54	80	78	90
IOWA														
Des Moines	28.91	14.20	60	41	87	12	105	-21	62	80	52	73	71	88
Dubuque	28.79	14.14	56	38	84	11	99	-26	64	82	52	77	76	87
Sioux City	28.76	14.13	60	37	87	10	107	-20	55	75	41	66	63	85

Location	Normal Atmospheric Pressure		Dry Bulb Temperature — °F						Relative Humidity — %					
			Normal Ave. Over a Year		Extremes				Yearly Mean		Monthly Mean			
					Monthly Ave.		Records				Day		Night	
	Inches of Mercury	PSIA	Max.	Min.	Max.	Min.	Max.	Min.	Day	Night	Min.	Max.	Min.	Max.
Column	1	2	3	4	5	6	7	8	9	10	11	12	13	14
KANSAS														
Goodland	26.18	12.86	64	35	92	16	111	-26	48	76	38	63	64	84
Wichita	28.52	14.01	68	46	90	23	113	-10	54	77	48	66	67	85
KENTUCKY														
Louisville	29.42	14.45	67	46	88	27	94	-8	65	84	56	74	76	92
LOUISIANA														
Lake Charles	29.91	14.70	78	59	91	43	104	12	66	89	55	76	84	93
New Orleans	29.92	14.70	78	63	90	47	102	17	66	83	59	73	78	85
Shreveport	29.65	14.56	76	57	93	39	106	15	58	82	52	65	73	90
MAINE														
Caribou	29.26	14.37	47	28	76	1	96	-41	68	81	53	83	73	89
Portland	29.85	14.66	55	34	77	14	100	-39	69	83	57	82	75	91
MARYLAND														
Baltimore	29.76	14.62	65	45	87	25	102	-4	61	79	50	72	70	87
MASSACHUSETTS														
Boston	29.90	14.69	59	43	81	21	100	-12	61	73	54	71	67	80
Worcester	28.87	14.18	55	39	80	17	93	-19	62	74	49	75	66	82
MICHIGAN														
Detroit	29.26	14.37	58	41	82	19	105	-16	62	78	51	76	72	83
Muskegon	29.26	14.37	56	38	80	18	97	-14	67	82	56	79	77	87
Sault Ste. Marie	29.15	14.30	49	30	75	7	98	-25	72	86	57	83	80	92
MINNESOTA														
Duluth	28.41	13.96	47	29	75	1	97	-35	67	83	55	79	76	92
Minneapolis—St. Paul	29.04	14.26	55	36	83	5	104	-31	61	78	50	76	68	85
MISSISSIPPI														
Jackson	29.59	14.54	77	54	93	39	100	10	61	85	53	68	77	92

Location	Normal Atmospheric Pressure		Dry Bulb Temperature — °F						Relative Humidity — %					
			Extremes						Yearly Mean		Monthly Mean			
	Inches of Mercury	PSIA	Normal Ave. Over a Year		Monthly Ave.		Records		Day	Night	Day		Night	
			Max.	Min.	Max.	Min.	Max.	Min.			Min.	Max.	Min.	Max.
Column	1	2	3	4	5	6	7	8	9	10	11	12	13	14
MISSOURI														
Kansas City	29.15	14.32	66	46	89	22	113	-13	55	74	48	67	67	79
St. Louis	29.35	14.42	66	47	89	24	99	-5	60	78	53	70	67	88
Springfield	28.58	14.04	66	46	87	25	113	-11	61	82	52	72	74	89
MONTANA														
Billings	26.26	12.91	59	36	87	14	105	-22	44	58	24	56	37	73
Glasgow	27.54	13.53	54	31	87	0	108	-50	53	73	38	76	55	82
Missoula	26.63	13.09	57	31	85	14	105	-15	60	79	26	92	47	91
NEBRASKA														
Lincoln	28.70	14.10	63	42	89	15	105	-10						
Scottsbluff	25.89	12.72	63	34	89	12	107	-27	47	73	38	60	65	82
NEVADA														
Elko	24.83	12.20	62	29	91	10	104	-43	42	64	18	73	35	80
Las Vegas	27.65	13.59	80	53	105	31	113	21	23	37	8	51	14	68
Reno	25.46	12.51	68	31	89	20	104	-16	61	80	18	67	43	82
NEW HAMPSHIRE														
Concord	29.56	14.52	57	32	82	12	100	-37	61	82	48	76	74	90
NEW JERSEY														
Trenton	29.86	14.67	62	45	85	26	106	-14						
NEW MEXICO														
Albuquerque	24.61	12.10	69	44	91	22	101	7	34	53	17	54	30	72
Roswell	26.21	12.88	74	46	92	25	103	-1	37	67	19	66	41	86
NEW YORK														
Albany	29.62	14.55	57	37	82	15	100	-26	63	80	51	74	73	88
Binghamton	29.01	14.25	58	39	82	17	103	-28	67	82	55	77	77	88
Buffalo	29.18	14.33	56	39	78	19	90	-20	70	82	60	79	75	89
New York	29.78	14.63	62	46	85	26	106	-15	60	72	53	67	65	80

Location	Normal Atmospheric Pressure		Dry Bulb Temperature — °F						Relative Humidity — %					
			Normal Ave. Over a Year		Monthly Ave.		Extremes Records		Yearly Mean		Monthly Mean			
											Day		Night	
	Inches of Mercury	PSIA	Max.	Min.	Max.	Min.	Max.	Min.	Day	Night	Min.	Max.	Min.	Max.
Column	1	2	3	4	5	6	7	8	9	10	11	12	13	14
NORTH CAROLINA														
Asheville	27.62	13.57	67	46	84	30	99	−2	60	84	47	74	76	92
Raleigh	29.46	14.47	71	49	88	33	105	7	61	83	47	77	73	91
Wilmington	29.90	14.69	74	53	87	38	104	11	67	87	51	82	81	96
NORTH DAKOTA														
Fargo	28.97	14.23	52	30	82	−4	102	−30	60	79	44	76	66	88
Williston	27.95	13.73	52	30	83	−2	110	−50	56	75	38	71	67	80
OHIO														
Cincinnati	29.11	14.29	65	45	87	24	109	−17	60	79	50	73	70	87
Cleveland	29.09	14.28	60	41	80	21	92	−7	66	79	56	78	68	90
OKLAHOMA														
Oklahoma City	28.57	14.03	71	50	92	28	107	−4	58	80	48	67	71	88
OREGON														
Medford	28.55	14.05	67	41	90	30	115	−3	56	80	26	90	50	93
Pendleton	28.36	13.96	63	42	90	25	113	−22	53	68	23	79	38	83
Portland	28.89	14.69	62	47	79	35	107	3	67	83	46	84	70	91
PENNSYLVANIA														
Harrisburg	29.56	14.52	63	44	85	24	102	−8	58	76	49	68	67	84
Philadelphia	29.92	14.70	64	45	85	26	93	−4	62	78	55	74	69	84
Pittsburgh	28.70	14.10	60	41	85	24	95	−10	63	80	54	71	72	91
PUERTO RICO														
San Juan	29.87	14.68	83	73	86	70	96	62	73	86	60	82	81	89
RHODE ISLAND														
Providence	29.86	14.67	58	41	82	22	97	−9	63	77	53	76	68	85
SOUTH CAROLINA														
Charleston	29.88	14.68	76	55	88	42	103	14	67	88	50	84	82	94
Columbia	29.69	14.58	76	53	91	37	107	4	59	85	45	73	77	91

Location	Normal Atmospheric Pressure		Dry Bulb Temperature — °F						Relative Humidity — %					
			Normal Ave. Over a Year		Extremes				Yearly Mean		Monthly Mean			
					Monthly Ave.		Records				Day		Night	
	Inches of Mercury	PSIA	Max.	Min.	Max.	Min.	Max.	Min.	Day	Night	Min.	Max.	Min.	Max.
Column	1	2	3	4	5	6	7	8	9	10	11	12	13	14
SOUTH DAKOTA														
Huron	28.56	14.04	58	33	86	2	109	-34	61	82	49	77	75	87
Rapid City	26.66	13.10	58	34	85	12	109	-25	50	68	36	66	56	75
TENNESSEE														
Memphis	29.64	14.56	72	52	90	34	106	-11	60	81	50	71	73	87
Nashville	29.31	14.40	71	50	89	31	107	-15	59	82	50	72	70	89
TEXAS														
Abilene	28.07	13.79	76	52	94	33	107	5	47	70	36	55	58	81
Amarillo	26.22	12.89	71	43	90	24	108	-14	45	70	38	53	60	78
Corpus Christi	29.87	14.68	81	63	90	49	104	18	67	88	57	75	82	93
Dallas	29.41	14.45	77	56	95	36	111	2	54	76	44	63	64	85
El Paso	25.92	12.73	76	50	94	33	109	-6	31	48	17	44	29	63
Houston	29.88	14.68	79	61	92	45	105	10	64	88	56	72	81	93
Midland	26.96	13.25	77	51	94	31	109	-1	39	63	29	45	49	73
UTAH														
Milford	24.87	12.22	65	33	92	13	104	-28	38.5	—	17	67	—	—
Salt Lake City	25.63	12.59	64	39	91	20	107	-10	45	65	16	74	36	83
VERMONT														
Burlington	29.57	14.53	55	34	80	10	101	-30	66	80	53	77	72	86
VIRGINIA														
Norfolk	29.90	14.69	68	50	87	34	103	11	61	80	50	78	73	88
Roanoke	28.67	14.08	67	46	88	29	104	3	56	76	44	67	66	87
WASHINGTON														
Seattle	29.50	14.50	59	42	75	32	99	23	70	81	43	83	64	89
Spokane	27.46	13.50	56	38	84	21	108	-6	56	72	20	87	36	88
Yakima	28.79	14.14	65	36	89	20	108	-25	49	74	25	80	52	87

Location	Normal Atmospheric Pressure		Dry Bulb Temperature — °F							Relative Humidity — %					
			Normal Ave. Over a Year		Extremes						Yearly Mean		Monthly Mean			
					Monthly Ave.		Records						Day		Night	
	Inches of Mercury	PSIA	Max.	Min.	Max.	Min.	Max.	Min.	Day	Night	Min.	Max.	Min.	Max.
Column	1	2	3	4	5	6	7	8	9	10	11	12	13	14
WEST VIRGINIA														
Charleston	28.93	14.21	68	44	88	27	102	−6	60	81	48	70	68	92
Parkersburg	29.26	14.38	65	45	86	25	106	−27	62	80	49	76	74	84
WISCONSIN														
Green Bay	29.19	14.34	53	34	81	9	99	−31	66	83	55	77	77	90
La Crosse	29.23	14.36	56	36	83	7	103	−37	62	81	51	73	74	89
Milwaukee	29.21	14.35	55	38	79	14	96	−17	66	81	58	77	74	86
WYOMING														
Cheyenne	23.86	11.73	58	32	82	15	96	−20	54	63	31	58	56	75
Lander	24.38	11.99	55	31	85	6	101	−31	45	61	27	61	44	69
Sheridan	25.90	12.74	58	31	86	8	106	−31	51	72	31	69	56	80

COMPRESSED AIR AND GAS DATA

LOGARITHMS TO BASE 10

Nat. Nos.	0	1	2	3	4	5	6	7	8	9	Proportional Parts								
											1	2	3	4	5	6	7	8	9
10	0000	0043	0086	0128	0170	0212	0253	0294	0334	0374	4	8	12	17	21	25	29	33	37
11	0414	0453	0492	0531	0569	0607	0645	0682	0719	0755	4	8	11	15	19	23	26	30	34
12	0792	0828	0864	0899	0934	0969	1004	1038	1072	1106	3	7	10	14	17	21	24	28	31
13	1139	1173	1206	1239	1271	1303	1335	1367	1399	1430	3	6	10	13	16	19	23	26	29
14	1461	1492	1523	1553	1584	1614	1644	1673	1703	1732	3	6	9	12	15	18	21	24	27
15	1761	1790	1818	1847	1875	1903	1931	1959	1987	2014	3	6	8	11	14	17	20	22	25
16	2041	2068	2095	2122	2148	2175	2201	2227	2253	2279	3	5	8	11	13	16	18	21	24
17	2304	2330	2355	2380	2405	2430	2455	2480	2504	2529	2	5	7	10	12	15	17	20	22
18	2553	2577	2601	2625	2648	2672	2695	2718	2742	2765	2	5	7	9	12	14	16	19	21
19	2788	2810	2833	2856	2878	2900	2923	2945	2967	2989	2	4	7	9	11	13	16	18	20
20	3010	3032	3054	3075	3096	3118	3139	3160	3181	3201	2	4	6	8	11	13	15	17	19
21	3222	3243	3263	3284	3304	3324	3345	3365	3385	3404	2	4	6	8	10	12	14	16	18
22	3424	3444	3464	3483	3502	3522	3541	3560	3579	3598	2	4	6	8	10	12	14	15	17
23	3617	3636	3655	3674	3692	3711	3729	3747	3766	3784	2	4	6	7	9	11	13	15	17
24	3802	3820	3838	3856	3874	3892	3909	3927	3945	3962	2	4	5	7	9	11	12	14	16
25	3979	3997	4014	4031	4048	4065	4082	4099	4116	4133	2	3	5	7	9	10	12	14	15
26	4150	4166	4183	4200	4216	4232	4249	4265	4281	4298	2	3	5	7	8	10	11	13	15
27	4314	4330	4346	4362	4378	4393	4409	4425	4440	4456	2	3	5	6	8	9	11	13	14
28	4472	4487	4502	4518	4533	4548	4564	4579	4594	4609	2	3	5	6	8	9	11	12	14
29	4624	4639	4654	4669	4683	4698	4713	4728	4742	4757	1	2	4	6	7	9	10	12	13
30	4771	4786	4800	4814	4829	4843	4857	4871	4886	4900	1	3	4	6	7	9	10	11	13
31	4914	4928	4942	4955	4969	4983	4997	5011	5024	5038	1	3	4	6	7	8	10	11	12
32	5051	5065	5079	5092	5105	5119	5132	5145	5159	5172	1	3	4	5	7	8	9	11	12
33	5185	5198	5211	5224	5237	5250	5263	5276	5289	5302	1	3	4	5	6	8	9	10	12
34	5315	5328	5340	5353	5366	5378	5391	5403	5416	5428	1	3	4	5	6	8	9	10	11
35	5441	5453	5465	5478	5490	5502	5514	5527	5539	5551	1	2	4	5	6	7	9	10	11
36	5563	5575	5587	5599	5611	5623	5635	5647	5658	5670	1	2	4	5	6	7	8	10	11
37	5682	5694	5705	5717	5729	5740	5752	5763	5775	5786	1	2	3	5	6	7	8	9	10
38	5798	5809	5821	5832	5843	5855	5866	5877	5888	5899	1	2	3	5	6	7	8	9	10
39	5911	5922	5933	5944	5955	5966	5977	5988	5999	6010	1	2	3	4	5	7	8	9	10
40	6021	6031	6042	6053	6064	6075	6085	6096	6107	6117	1	2	3	4	5	6	8	9	10
41	6128	6138	6149	6160	6170	6180	6191	6201	6212	6222	1	2	3	4	5	6	7	8	9
42	6232	6243	6253	6263	6274	6284	6294	6304	6314	6325	1	2	3	4	5	6	7	8	9
43	6335	6345	6355	6365	6375	6385	6395	6405	6415	6425	1	2	3	4	5	6	7	8	9
44	6435	6444	6454	6464	6474	6484	6493	6503	6513	6522	1	2	3	4	5	6	7	8	9
45	6532	6542	6551	6561	6571	6580	6590	6599	6609	6618	1	2	3	4	5	6	7	8	9
46	6628	6637	6646	6656	6665	6675	6684	6693	6702	6712	1	2	3	4	5	6	7	7	8
47	6721	6730	6739	6749	6758	6767	6776	6785	6794	6803	1	2	3	4	5	5	6	7	8
48	6812	6821	6830	6839	6848	6857	6866	6875	6884	6893	1	2	3	4	4	5	6	7	8
49	6902	6911	6920	6928	6937	6946	6955	6964	6972	6981	1	2	3	4	4	5	6	7	8
50	6990	6998	7007	7016	7024	7033	7042	7050	7059	7067	1	2	3	3	4	5	6	7	8
51	7076	7084	7093	7101	7110	7118	7126	7135	7143	7152	1	2	3	3	4	5	6	7	8
52	7160	7168	7177	7185	7193	7202	7210	7218	7226	7235	1	2	2	3	4	5	6	7	7
53	7243	7251	7259	7267	7275	7284	7292	7300	7308	7316	1	2	2	3	4	5	6	6	7
54	7324	7332	7340	7348	7356	7364	7372	7380	7388	7396	1	2	2	3	4	5	6	6	7

Log π = 0.49715.   Log$_e$ = 2.3026 $\times$ Log$_{10}$

LOGARITHMS TO BASE 10

(Continued)

Nat. Nos.	0	1	2	3	4	5	6	7	8	9	Proportional Parts								
											1	2	3	4	5	6	7	8	9
55	7404	7412	7419	7427	7435	7443	7451	7459	7466	7474	1	2	2	3	4	5	5	6	7
56	7482	7490	7497	7505	7513	7520	7528	7536	7543	7551	1	2	2	3	4	5	5	6	7
57	7559	7566	7574	7582	7589	7597	7604	7612	7619	7627	1	2	2	3	4	5	5	6	7
58	7634	7642	7649	7657	7664	7672	7679	7686	7694	7701	1	1	2	3	4	4	5	6	7
59	7709	7716	7723	7731	7738	7745	7752	7760	7767	7774	1	1	2	3	4	4	5	6	7
60	7782	7789	7796	7803	7810	7818	7825	7832	7839	7846	1	1	2	3	4	4	5	6	6
61	7853	7860	7868	7875	7882	7889	7896	7903	7910	7917	1	1	2	3	4	4	5	6	6
62	7924	7931	7938	7945	7952	7959	7966	7973	7980	7987	1	1	2	3	3	4	5	6	6
63	7993	8000	8007	8014	8021	8028	8035	8041	8048	8055	1	1	2	3	3	4	5	5	6
64	8062	8069	8075	8082	8089	8096	8102	8109	8116	8122	1	1	2	3	3	4	5	5	6
65	8129	8136	8142	8149	8156	8162	8169	8176	8182	8189	1	1	2	3	3	4	5	5	6
66	8195	8202	8209	8215	8222	8228	8235	8241	8248	8254	1	1	2	3	3	4	5	5	6
67	8261	8267	8274	8280	8287	8293	8299	8306	8312	8319	1	1	2	3	3	4	5	5	6
68	8325	8331	8338	8344	8351	8357	8363	8370	8376	8382	1	1	2	3	3	4	4	5	6
69	8388	8395	8401	8407	8414	8420	8426	8432	8439	8445	1	1	2	2	3	4	4	5	6
70	8451	8457	8463	8470	8476	8482	8488	8494	8500	8506	1	1	2	2	3	4	4	5	6
71	8513	8519	8525	8531	8537	8543	8549	8555	8561	8567	1	1	2	2	3	4	4	5	5
72	8573	8579	8585	8591	8597	8603	8609	8615	8621	8627	1	1	2	2	3	4	4	5	5
73	8633	8639	8645	8651	8657	8663	8669	8675	8681	8686	1	1	2	2	3	4	4	5	5
74	8692	8698	8704	8710	8716	8722	8727	8733	8739	8745	1	1	2	2	3	4	4	5	5
75	8751	8756	8762	8768	8774	8779	8785	8791	8797	8802	1	1	2	2	3	3	4	5	5
76	8808	8814	8820	8825	8831	8837	8842	8848	8854	8859	1	1	2	2	3	3	4	5	5
77	8865	8871	8876	8882	8887	8893	8899	8904	8910	8915	1	1	2	2	3	3	4	4	5
78	8921	8927	8932	8938	8943	8949	8954	8960	8965	8971	1	1	2	2	3	3	4	4	5
79	8976	8982	8987	8993	8998	9004	9009	9015	9020	9025	1	1	2	2	3	3	4	4	5
80	9031	9036	9042	9047	9053	9058	9063	9069	9074	9079	1	1	2	2	3	3	4	4	5
81	9085	9090	9096	9101	9106	9112	9117	9122	9128	9133	1	1	2	2	3	3	4	4	5
82	9138	9143	9149	9154	9159	9165	9170	9175	9180	9186	1	1	2	2	3	3	4	4	5
83	9191	9196	9201	9206	9212	9217	9222	9227	9232	9238	1	1	2	2	3	3	4	4	5
84	9243	9248	9253	9258	9263	9269	9274	9279	9284	9289	1	1	2	2	3	3	4	4	5
85	9294	9299	9304	9309	9315	9320	9325	9330	9335	9340	1	1	2	2	3	3	4	4	5
86	9345	9350	9355	9360	9365	9370	9375	9380	9385	9390	1	1	2	2	3	3	4	4	5
87	9395	9400	9405	9410	9415	9420	9425	9430	9435	9440	0	1	1	2	2	3	3	4	4
88	9445	9450	9455	9460	9465	9469	9474	9479	9484	9489	0	1	1	2	2	3	3	4	4
89	9494	9499	9504	9509	9513	9518	9523	9528	9533	9538	0	1	1	2	2	3	3	4	4
90	9542	9547	9552	9557	9562	9566	9571	9576	9581	9586	0	1	1	2	2	3	3	4	4
91	9590	9595	9600	9605	9609	9614	9619	9624	9628	9633	0	1	1	2	2	3	3	4	4
92	9638	9643	9647	9652	9657	9661	9666	9671	9675	9680	0	1	1	2	2	3	3	4	4
93	9685	9689	9694	9699	9703	9708	9713	9717	9722	9727	0	1	1	2	2	3	3	4	4
94	9731	9736	9741	9745	9750	9754	9759	9763	9768	9773	0	1	1	2	2	3	3	4	4
95	9777	9782	9786	9791	9795	9800	9805	9809	9814	9818	0	1	1	2	2	3	3	4	4
96	9823	9827	9832	9836	9841	9845	9850	9854	9859	9863	0	1	1	2	2	3	3	4	4
97	9868	9872	9877	9881	9886	9890	9894	9899	9903	9908	0	1	1	2	2	3	3	4	4
98	9912	9917	9921	9926	9930	9934	9939	9943	9948	9952	0	1	1	2	2	3	3	4	4
99	9956	9961	9965	9969	9974	9978	9983	9987	9991	9996	0	1	1	2	2	3	3	3	4

ESTIMATED PERFORMANCE OF CENTRIFUGAL COMPRESSORS
For a first approximation study at the Design Point only.

Basic assumptions:
Straight through flow only. No gas added or removed between stages.
Single casing compressor.
Impeller speed close to design optimum.
Each impeller develops close to 9500 polytropic head.
(See pages 3-22 and 4-30)

Information obtainable:
Approximate brake horsepower;
Probable number of stages.
Probable discharge temperature.
Probable speed.

Items which must be known concerning the Design Point.
Intake pressure-psiA.
Intake temperature-°F.
Intake volume. This must be the actual inhaled cfm at the compressor flange allowing for moisture content. See page 4-2 for intake volume formulas.
Discharge pressure-psiA.
Compressibility, if material. This applies to both intake and discharge conditions. See page 3-9, 3-13 and 3-21 for compressibility discussion. Specific and generalized compressibility charts are included in this chapter.
Ratio of specific heats *(k)*, if gas is not air.
Molecular weight, if gas is not air.

Tabulate from the curves on the next five pages:
Basic horsepower for air at 14.5 psiA intake.
Basic head for air.
Correction for specific heat ratio *(k)*, if gas is not air.
Temperature rise multiplier.
Compressor speed — rpm.

Compressor brake horsepower at shaft

Multiply *Basic horsepower* by *"k" value correction factor,* by *Actual intake pressure,* by *Average of intake and discharge compressibility.* Divide result *by 14.5* and *Intake compressibility* factor. Round out result.

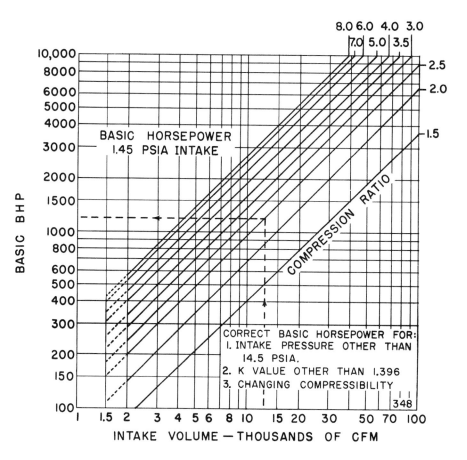

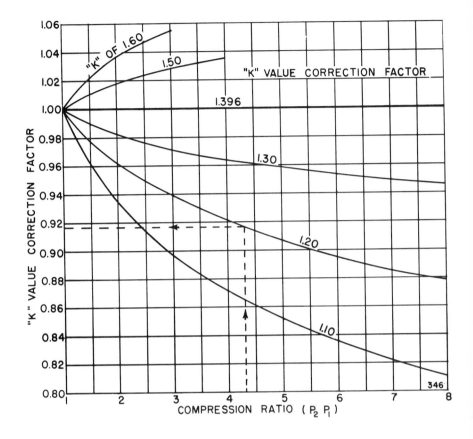

Number of stages

Multiply *Basic head* by *"k" value correction factor,* by *28.95,* by *Average of intake and discharge compressibility.* Divide result by *Molecular weight* and *9500.* Next higher whole number will be probable number of stages.

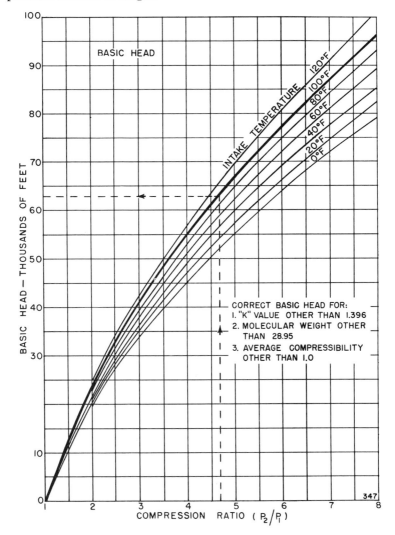

BASIC HEAD

INTAKE TEMPERATURE

120°F
100°F
80°F
60°F
40°F
20°F
0°F

BASIC HEAD — THOUSANDS OF FEET

CORRECT BASIC HEAD FOR:
1. "K" VALUE OTHER THAN 1.396
2. MOLECULAR WEIGHT OTHER THAN 28.95
3. AVERAGE COMPRESSIBILITY OTHER THAN 1.0

347

COMPRESSION RATIO (P_2/P_1)

Discharge temperature

Multiply *Temperature rise multiplier* by *Intake temperature in °Abs (°F + 460)*. This is temperature rise in °F. Add this to Intake temperature °F to obtain Discharge temperature *(°F)*. If this exceeds 450°F, refer to manufacturer.

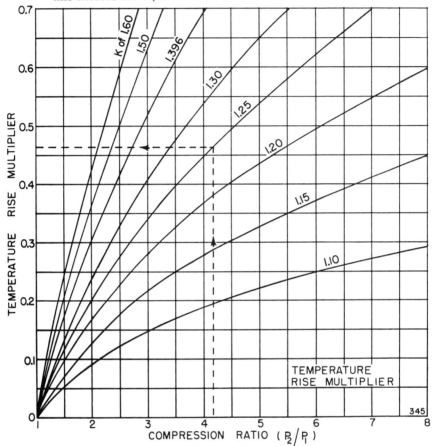

Discharge Volume

Obtain discharge volume by multiplying *Intake volume* by *Intake presssure psiA* and by *Discharge temperature in °Abs (°F + 460)*. Divide result by *Discharge pressure (psiA* and by *Intake temperature (°Abs)*. If result approaches or is less than 500 cfm, refer to manufacturer.

Compressor speed

Read direct to center of shaded area which shows the range usually involved.

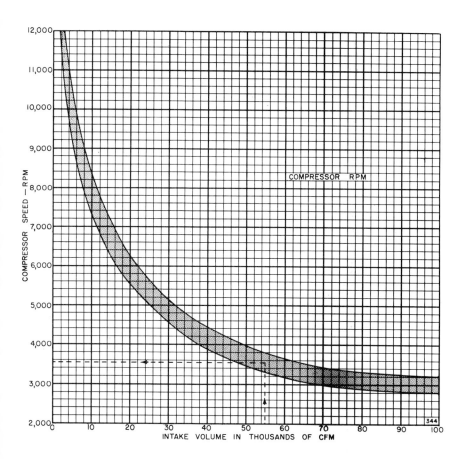

BHP/MILLION CU FT/24 HOURS

For Reciprocating Compresors Only — 200 hp and Above

Curves A, B, and C (next pages) are based on the volume at *14.4 psiA* and intake temperature.

To obtain bhp/100 cfm at intake conditions multiply bhp/million of each stage by its absolute intake pressure and divide by 100.

Figure each stage separately and add to get the total bhp.

These data do *not* apply to natural gas pipeline compressors.

Refer to the manufacturer when compression ratio is below 1.40.

Corrections to be Applied

Compressibility is assumed to be 1.0.

Volumes to be handled in each upper stage must be corrected to the actual temperature and moisture content at inlet to that stage.

Interstage pressure drop must be allowed for when intercoolers are used. For approximate purposes, reduce the theoretical upper stage intake pressures by 3 percent. Theoretical interstage pressures may be obtained as follows:

1. Obtain the overall compression ratio (r_t);
2. Obtain the theoretical ratio per stage (r_s) by taking the s root of r_t, where s is the number of stages; and
3. Multiply r_s by the absolute intake pressure of the stage being considered.

This gives the absolute discharge pressure of this stage and the *theoretical* absolute intake to the next stage. Correct the latter for pressure drop as noted above.

Intake pressure correction is given on Curve D and *gas specific gravity correction on* Curve E. These are multipliers to bhp/million or bhp/100. (See second paragraph above).

See page 3-19 for compressibility corrections.

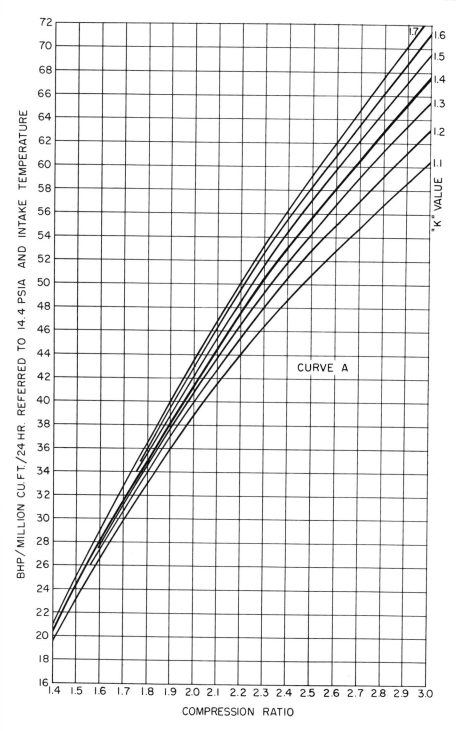

CURVE A

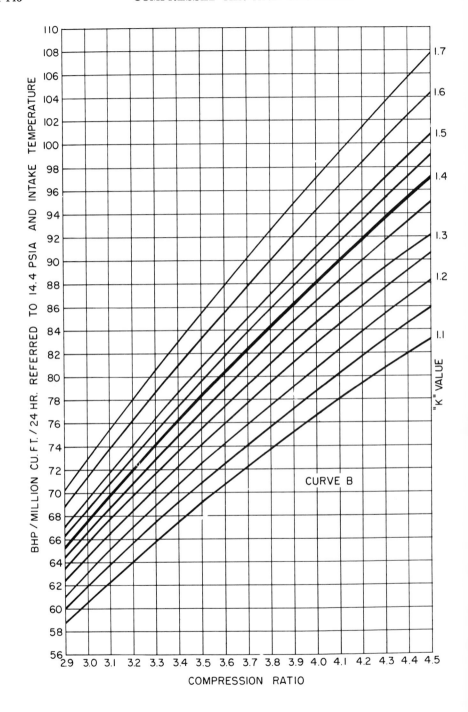

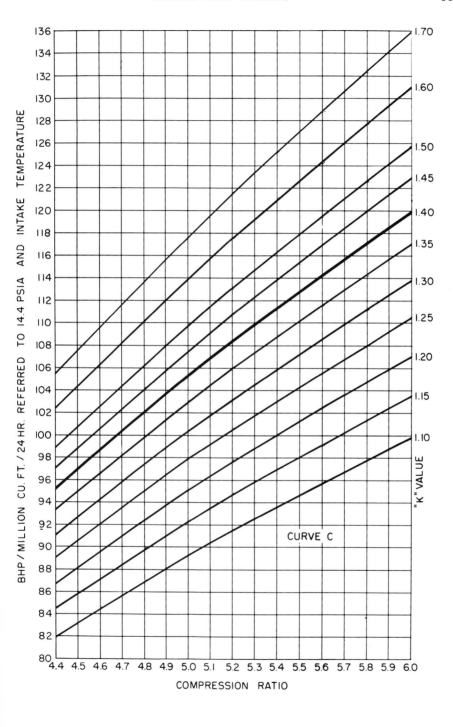

BHP / MILLION CU. FT. / 24 HR. REFERRED TO 14.4 PSIA AND INTAKE TEMPERATURE

COMPRESSION RATIO

"K" VALUE

CURVE C

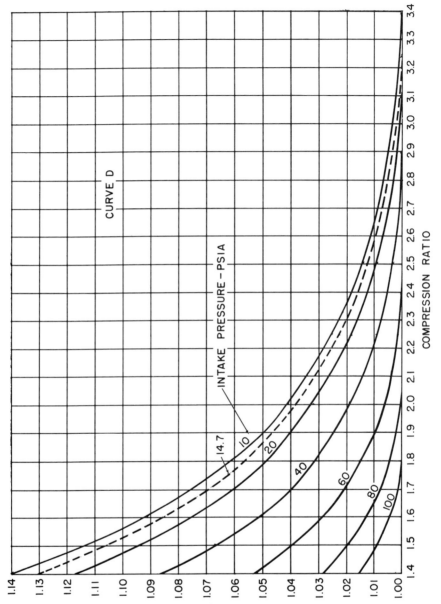

CURVE D

INTAKE PRESSURE – PSIA

COMPRESSION RATIO

MULTIPLIER FOR INTAKE PRESSURE CORRECTION
APPLY TO BHP/MILLION CURVE

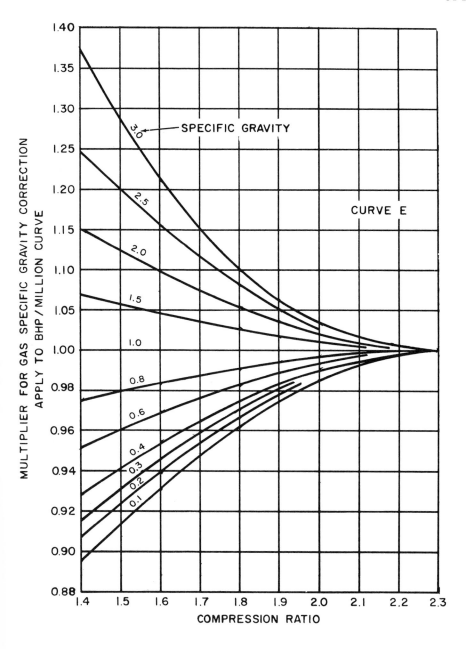

Multipliers for Air Consumption of Rock Drills

Operating in Multiple from One Compressor System

The following table represents the latest thinking with regard to the relative air capacity required to operate a varying number of rock drills from a single compressor system. The factors have been materially increased over those previously in use. This has been done because of marked changes in drills and drilling practices within recent years. Consider the following.

1. Mounted drills now predominate. The relative number of hand-held tools has fallen.

2. Automatic feed is practically universal.

3. Bit improvement permits the use of longer feed changes. The on-throttle time per hour is greater.

4. Multiple drill or jumbo mountings require that all drills operate at the same time. The diversity factor is substantially 1.00.

Number of Drills

1	2	3	4	5	6	7	8	9	10	12	15	20	30	40	50	70
1.0	2.0	3.0	4.0	5.0	6.0	6.8	7.5	8.2	9.0	10.5	12.6	16.0	23.5	31.0	38.0	52.5

These are approximate values and will vary with type of work, type of rock, etc. The factor is usually less than the total number of drills on the line because not all will be operating at once.

Miscellaneous Data

Circumference of circle	x	.3188	=	diameter
Diameter of circle	x	3.1416	=	circumference
Dia. of circle squared	x	.7854	=	area
Dia. of sphere squared	x	3.1416	=	surface
Dia. of sphere cubed	x	.5236	=	volume
Cubic feet (of water)	x	62.425	=	pounds
Cubic foot of ice	x	57.2	=	pounds

Water is at is greatest density at 39.2°F (4°C).

Sea water is 2 to 3 percent heavier than fresh.

Air Consumption Multipliers for Altitude Operation

Rock Drills and Pneumatic Tools

Based on 80 to 100 psiG Air Pressure

An air tool operating at a given speed is, in effect, a meter passing a relatively constant volume of *compressed* air regardless of the pressure at the tool inlet. The volume of *free air* required however, will be dependent not only upon the pressure at the tool inlet, but upon the current atmospheric pressure. The multiplier from compressed air volume to free air volume is inlet pressure (psiA) divided by atmospheric pressure (psiA).

It is obvious that for a given initial pressure this multiplier is greater at an altitude than at sea level. Therefore since manufacturers rate tools at sea level conditions, when a tool is to operate at altitude, the *free air* volume to be supplied must be increased above the normal rating. The following table give multipliers for this calculation. Although drills and tools vary somewhat due to design, use of this multiplier will provide safe values. It should be borne in mind that the *free air* consumption of the tool is required to properly size the required compressor.

This table does not allow for any compressor capacity reduction which might occur due to using a sea level compressor at an altitude. This would be of significance only with a single stage compressor, in which case refer to the manufacturer since the unit may not be satisfactory for altitude operation. See page 34-154.

Altitude

Feet	0	1000	2000	3000	4000	5000	6000	7000	8000	9000	10,000	12,500	15,000
Meters	0	305	610	915	1220	1526	1831	2136	2441	2746	3050	3813	4577
Multiplier	1.00	1.02	1.05	1.08	1.11	1.14	1.18	1.22	1.26	1.30	1.34	1.46	1.58

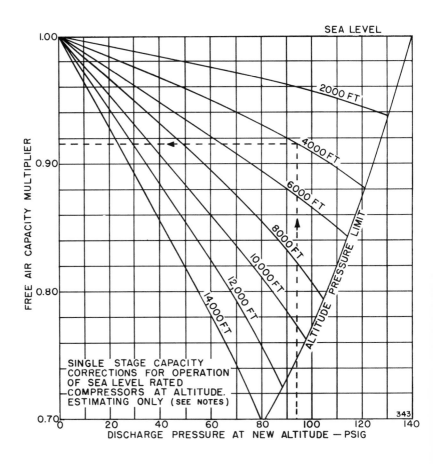

The above chart is for preliminary estimating of capacity only. Obtain specific information on both capacity and bhp altitude ratings from manufacturer before proceeding.

Based on 8 percent clearance.

The altitude discharge pressure must never exceed the lower of normal sea level rating or that indicated by the altitude limit.

Multiply the sea level rated capacity at the operating pressure (based on the above paragraph) by the multiplier to obtain approximate altitude capacity output.

This allows only for change in compressor capacity. Tools require more free air at altitude. See page 34-153.

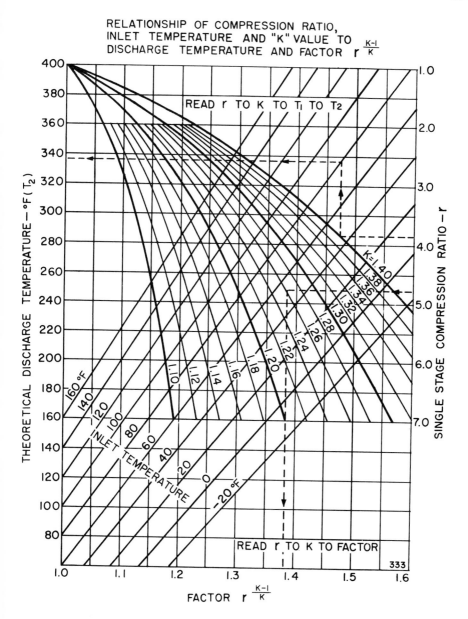

RELATIONSHIP OF COMPRESSION RATIO, INLET TEMPERATURE AND "K" VALUE TO DISCHARGE TEMPERATURE AND FACTOR $r^{\frac{K-1}{K}}$

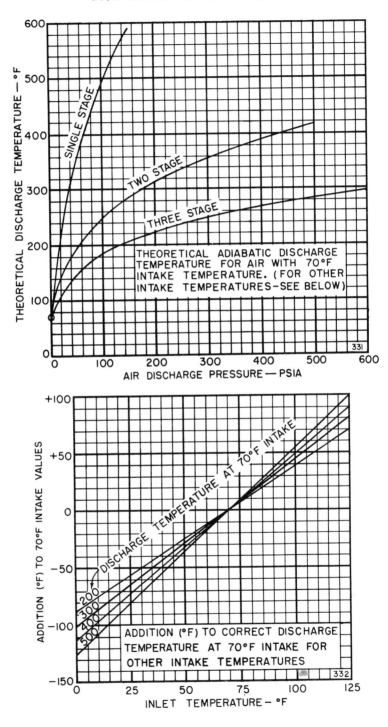

THEORETICAL ADIABATIC DISCHARGE TEMPERATURE FOR AIR WITH 70°F INTAKE TEMPERATURE. (FOR OTHER INTAKE TEMPERATURES-SEE BELOW)

DISCHARGE TEMPERATURE AT 70°F INTAKE

ADDITION (°F) TO CORRECT DISCHARGE TEMPERATURE AT 70°F INTAKE FOR OTHER INTAKE TEMPERATURES

Friction Loss in Hose Serving Rock Drills

These tables are a logical development from such test data as were available. Included were tests run with and without an air-line lubricator ahead of the hose. The oil fog in the air when a lubricator is used causes a considerable increase in pressure loss. Two of tables are therefore presented — one based on clean, dry compressed air, and the other on air containing oil fog. The amount of oil fed by the lubricator is critical. A normal of 0.4 pints per hour per 100 cfm of free air flowing has been assumed. This will satisfactory lubricate most rock drills.

Losses include both hose and couplings. Couplings are by Ingersoll-Rand and Hose Accessories Company of Philadelphia, Pa. Hose is assumed to be smooth. See page 26-15.

Accuracy is probably to plus-or-minus 10 percent.

The tables are based on 70°F flowing air temperature. The following comments assume a constant flow volume of free air at compressor inlet temperature (constant weight flow).

Rock drills do not always operate on 70°F compressed air. Many operate directly from portable compressors, in which case, the air flowing through the hose may be at 130°F or higher. Air may also be heated after compression to temperatures which may reach 400°F (say 350°F at hose inlet). These temperatures will materially influence pressure loss shown in the tables.

The only approach to this problem is theoretical, which indicates that the pressure loss due to friction increases directly as the *absolute* temperature. Multipliers would be as follows:

Flowing Air Temperature °F	Friction Loss Multiplier
70	1.00
130	1.11
200	1.24
250	1.34
300	1.43
350	1.53

These should hold closely for clean, dry air, but would be high for air carrying oil fog due to the difference in the shape of the friction factor curve. The magnitude of the reduction from the above is not known, but 10 to 15 percent could be considered safe.

(See page 27-10 for pressure losses in hoses for small tools).

PRESSURE LOSS IN HOSE

Lubrication Only at Tool - No Line Lubricator (See note on Page 34-161)

Hose Length and Inside Diameter	CFM Free Air	Line Pressure—PSIG						
		60	80	100	120	150	200	300
50 Feet 3/4"	60	3.1	2.4	2.0				
	80	5.3	4.2	3.5	2.9	2.4	1.8	1.2
	100	8.1	6.4	5.2	4.5	3.6	2.8	1.9
	120		9.0	7.4	6.3	5.1	3.9	2.7
	140		12.0	9.9	8.4	6.9	5.3	3.6
	160			12.7	10.8	8.9	6.8	4.6
	180				13.6	11.1	8.5	5.8
	200				16.6	13.5	10.4	7.1
	220					16.2	12.4	8.4
50 Feet 1"	120	2.7	2.1					
	150	4.1	3.2	2.7	2.3			
	180	5.8	4.6	3.8	3.2	2.6	2.0	1.3
	210	7.7	6.1	5.0	4.3	3.5	2.7	1.8
	240		7.9	6.5	5.5	4.5	3.4	2.3
	270		9.8	8.1	6.9	5.6	4.3	2.9
	300		12.0	9.9	8.4	6.9	5.3	3.6
	330			11.8	10.0	8.2	6.3	4.3
	360			13.9	11.9	9.7	7.4	5.0
	390				13.8	11.3	8.7	5.9
	420				15.9	13.0	10.0	6.8
	450					14.8	11.4	7.7
50 Feet 1¼"	200	2.4						
	250	3.7	2.9	2.4	2.0			
	300	5.2	4.1	3.4	2.9	2.3	1.8	1.2
	350	7.0	5.5	4.5	3.8	3.1	2.4	1.6
	400	8.9	7.0	5.8	4.9	4.0	3.1	2.1
	450		8.8	7.3	6.2	5.0	3.9	2.6
	500		10.8	8.9	7.6	6.2	4.7	3.2
	550			10.7	9.1	7.4	5.7	3.9
	600			12.6	10.7	8.7	6.7	4.6
	650			14.6	12.4	10.2	7.8	5.3
	700				14.3	11.7	9.0	6.1
	750					13.3	10.2	6.9
	800					15.0	11.5	7.8
50 Feet 1½"	300	2.1						
	400	3.7	2.9	2.4	2.0			
	500	5.6	4.4	3.7	3.1	2.5	1.9	1.3
	600	8.0	6.3	5.2	4.4	3.6	2.8	1.9
	700		8.5	7.0	5.9	4.9	3.7	2.5
	800		10.9	9.0	7.7	6.3	4.8	3.2
	900			11.2	9.5	7.8	6.0	4.1
	1000			13.6	11.6	9.5	7.3	4.9
	1100				14.0	11.4	8.8	6.0
	1200					13.6	10.4	7.1
	1300					15.8	12.1	8.3

PRESSURE LOSS IN HOSE

Lubrication Only at Tool - No Line Lubricator (See note on Page 34-161)

Hose Length and Inside Diameter	CFM Free Air	Line Pressure—PSIG						
		60	80	100	120	150	200	300
50 Feet	600	1.9						
	800	3.2	2.5	2.1				
	1000	5.0	3.9	3.2	2.7	2.2	1.7	1.1
	1200	7.0	5.5	4.5	3.8	3.1	2.4	1.6
2″	1400	9.3	7.4	6.1	5.2	4.2	3.2	2.2
	1600		9.6	7.9	6.7	5.5	4.2	2.8
	1800		12.1	9.9	8.4	6.9	5.3	3.6
	2000			12.2	10.4	8.5	6.5	4.4
	2200			14.6	12.5	10.2	7.8	5.3
	2400				14.7	12.0	9.2	6.3
	2600					14.1	10.8	7.3
	2800					16.2	12.4	8.5
50 Feet	1000	1.7						
	1500	3.7	2.9	2.4	2.0			
	2000	6.5	5.1	4.2	3.6	2.9	2.2	1.5
	2500	10.0	7.9	6.5	5.5	4.5	3.4	2.3
2½″	3000		11.2	9.3	7.9	6.4	4.9	3.3
	3500			12.4	10.6	8.7	6.6	4.5
	4000				13.7	11.2	8.6	5.8
	4500					14.0	10.7	7.3
50 Feet	2000	2.5	2.0					
	2500	3.9	3.0	2.5	2.1			
	3000	5.5	4.4	3.6	3.1	2.5	1.9	1.3
	3500	7.5	5.9	4.9	4.1	3.4	2.6	1.7
3″	4000	9.8	7.6	6.3	5.3	4.4	3.3	2.3
	4500		9.6	7.9	6.7	5.5	4.2	2.8
	5000		11.7	9.6	8.2	6.7	5.1	3.5
	5500			11.5	9.8	8.0	6.1	4.2
	6000			13.6	11.5	9.4	7.2	4.9
	6500				13.5	11.0	8.4	5.7
	7000				15.6	12.7	9.8	6.6
	7500					14.5	11.1	7.6
25 Feet	5000	1.9						
	6000	2.7	2.1	1.7			1.2	
	7000	3.6	2.8	2.3	2.0		1.2	
	8000	4.7	3.7	3.0	2.6	2.1	1.6	
4″	9000	5.9	4.6	3.8	3.2	2.6	2.0	
	10000	7.2	5.7	4.7	4.0	3.2	2.5	
	11000	8.7	6.8	5.6	4.8	3.9	3.0	
	12000		8.1	6.7	5.7	4.6	3.5	
	13000		9.4	7.8	6.6	5.4	4.1	
	14000			9.0	7.6	6.2	4.8	
	15000				8.7	7.1	5.4	
	16000				9.8	8.0	6.2	
	17000					9.1	6.9	

PRESSURE LOSS IN HOSE

With Airline Lubricator - Oil Fog in Air (See note on page 34-161)

Hose Length and Inside Diameter	CFM Free Air	Line Pressure—PSIG						
		60	80	100	120	150	200	300
50 Feet	50	2.7	2.1					
	60	4.1	3.2	2.6	2.2			
	70	5.9	4.7	3.8	3.3	2.7	2.0	1.4
	80	8.2	6.4	5.3	4.5	3.7	2.8	1.9
¾″	90		8.6	7.1	6.0	4.9	3.8	2.6
	100		11.2	9.2	7.8	6.4	4.9	3.3
	110			11.7	9.9	8.1	6.2	4.2
	120			14.5	12.3	10.1	7.7	5.2
	130				15.1	12.3	9.4	6.4
	140					14.8	11.4	7.7
50 Feet	80	1.7						
	100	2.9	2.3	1.9				
	120	4.5	3.5	2.9	2.5	2.0	1.5	1.0
	140	6.6	5.2	4.3	3.6	3.0	2.3	1.5
1″	160	9.2	7.3	6.0	5.1	4.2	3.2	2.1
	180		9.8	8.1	6.9	5.6	4.3	2.9
	200		12.6	10.6	9.0	7.3	5.6	3.8
	220			13.4	11.4	9.3	7.1	4.9
	240				14.2	11.6	8.9	6.1
	260					14.3	10.9	7.4
50 Feet	150	2.3						
	180	3.6	2.9	2.4	2.0			
	210	5.4	4.2	3.5	3.0	2.4	1.8	1.2
	240	7.5	5.9	4.9	4.2	3.4	2.6	1.7
1¼″	270		8.0	6.6	5.6	4.6	3.5	2.4
	300		10.4	8.6	7.3	6.0	4.6	3.1
	330			11.0	9.3	7.6	5.8	4.0
	360			13.7	11.7	9.6	7.3	5.0
	390				14.4	11.8	9.0	6.1
	420					14.3	10.9	7.5
50 Feet	220	2.2						
	260	3.4	2.6	2.2				
	300	4.8	3.8	3.1	2.7	2.2	1.7	1.1
	340	6.6	5.2	4.3	3.7	3.0	2.3	1.5
1½″	380	8.8	7.0	5.7	4.9	4.0	3.0	2.1
	420		9.0	7.4	6.3	5.1	3.9	2.7
	460		11.4	9.4	8.0	6.5	5.0	3.4
	500			11.7	9.9	8.1	6.2	4.2
	540			14.2	12.1	9.9	7.6	5.2
	580				14.6	11.9	9.1	6.2
	620					14.1	10.8	7.4

PRESSURE LOSS IN HOSE

With Airline Lubricator - Oil Fog in Air (See note on page 34-161)

Hose Length and Inside Diameter	CFM Free Air	Line Pressure—PSIG						
		60	80	100	120	150	200	300
50 Feet **2″**	400	2.0						
	480	3.2	2.5	2.0				
	560	4.7	3.7	3.1	2.6	2.1	1.6	1.1
	640	6.7	5.3	4.3	3.7	3.0	2.3	1.6
	720	9.1	7.2	5.9	5.0	4.1	3.1	2.1
	800		9.4	7.8	6.6	5.4	4.1	2.8
	880			10.0	8.5	6.9	5.3	3.6
	960			12.6	10.7	8.7	6.7	4.5
	1040				13.2	10.8	8.3	5.6
	1120					13.2	10.1	6.9
50 Feet **2½″**	700	2.4						
	800	3.5	2.7	2.2				
	900	4.7	3.7	3.0	2.6	2.1	1.6	1.1
	1000	6.2	4.9	4.0	3.4	2.8	2.1	1.4
	1100	7.9	6.2	5.1	4.4	3.6	2.7	1.8
	1200		7.8	6.5	5.5	4.5	3.4	2.3
	1300		9.7	8.0	6.8	5.6	4.3	2.9
	1400		11.8	9.8	8.3	6.8	5.2	3.5
	1500			11.7	10.0	8.2	6.2	4.2
	1600			14.0	11.9	9.7	7.4	5.1
	1700				14.0	11.4	8.8	6.0
	1800					13.3	10.2	6.9
50 Feet **3″**	1000	2.2						
	1200	3.5	2.8	2.3				
	1400	5.3	4.2	3.4	2.9	2.4	1.8	1.2
	1600	7.5	5.9	4.9	4.2	3.4	2.6	1.8
	1800	10.5	8.2	6.7	5.7	4.7	3.6	2.4
	2000		10.8	8.9	7.6	6.2	4.8	3.2
	2200			11.5	9.8	8.0	6.1	4.1
	2400			14.4	12.3	10.0	7.7	5.2
	2600				15.2	12.4	9.5	6.5
	2800					15.1	11.6	7.9
25 Feet **4″**	2400	2.2						
	2800	3.3	2.6	2.1				
	3200	4.7	3.7	3.0	2.6	2.1	1.6	1.1
	3600	6.4	5.0	4.2	3.5	2.9	2.2	1.5
	4000	8.5	6.7	5.5	4.7	3.8	2.9	2.0
	4400		8.7	7.1	6.1	5.0	3.8	2.6
	4800			9.0	7.7	6.3	4.8	3.3
	5200				9.6	7.8	6.0	4.1
	5600					9.6	7.3	5.0

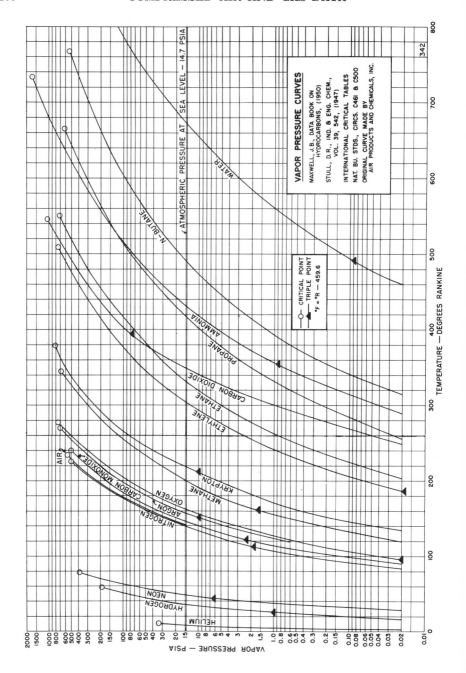

TEMPERATURE CONVERSION CHART

Centigrade—Fahrenheit

NOTE: The center column of numbers in boldface refers to the temperature in degrees, either Centigrade or Fahrenheit, which it is desired to convert into the other scale. If converting from Fahrenheit to Centigrade degrees, the equivalent temperature will be found in the left column, while if converting from degrees Centigrade to degrees Fahrenheit, the answer will be found in the column on the right.

Centigrade		Fahrenheit	Centigrade		Fahrenheit
−273.17	−459.7		−59.4	−75	−103.0
−268	−450		−56.7	−70	−94.0
−262	−440		−53.9	−65	−85.0
−257	−430		−51.1	−60	−76.0
−251	−420		−48.3	−55	−67.0
−246	−410		−45.6	−50	−58.0
−240	−400		−42.8	−45	−49.0
−234	−390		−40.0	−40	−40.0
−229	−380		−37.2	−35	−31.0
−223	−370		−34.4	−30	−22.0
−218	−360		−31.7	−25	−13.0
−212	−350		−28.9	−20	−4.0
−207	−340		−26.1	−15	5.0
−201	−330		−23.3	−10	14.0
−196	−320		−20.6	−5	23.0
−190	−310		−17.8	0	32.0
−184	−300		−17.2	1	33.8
−179	−290		−16.7	2	35.6
−173	−280		−16.1	3	37.4
−169	−273	−459.4	−15.6	4	39.2
−168	−270	−454	−15.0	5	41.0
−162	−260	−436	−14.4	6	42.8
−157	−250	−418	−13.9	7	44.6
−151	−240	−400	−13.3	8	46.4
−146	−230	−382	−12.8	9	48.2
−140	−220	−364	−12.2	10	50.0
−134	−210	−346	−11.7	11	51.8
−129	−200	−328	−11.1	12	53.6
−123	−190	−310	−10.6	13	55.4
−118	−180	−292	−10.0	14	57.2
−112	−170	−274	−9.4	15	59.0
−107	−160	−256	−8.9	16	60.8
−101	−150	−238	−8.3	17	62.6
−96	−140	−220	−7.8	18	64.4
−90	−130	−202	−7.2	19	66.2
−84	−120	−184	−6.7	20	68.0
−79	−110	−166	−6.1	21	69.8
−73.3	−100	−148.0	−5.6	22	71.6
−67.8	−90	−130.0	−5.0	23	73.4
−62.2	−80	−112.0	−4.4	24	75.2

Continued on next page.

TEMPERATURE CONVERSION CHART
Centigrade—Fahrenheit

NOTE: The center column of numbers in boldface refers to the temperature in degrees, either Centigrade or Fahrenheit, which it is desired to convert into the other scale. If converting from Fahrenheit to Centigrade degrees, the equivalent temperature will be found in the left column, while if converting from degrees Centigrade to degrees Fahrenheit, the answer will be found in the column on the right.

Centigrade		Fahrenheit	Centigrade		Fahrenheit
−3.9	25	77.0	18.3	65	149.0
−3.3	26	78.8	18.9	66	150.8
−2.8	27	80.6	19.4	67	152.6
−2.2	28	82.4	20.0	68	154.4
−1.7	29	84.2	20.6	69	156.2
−1.1	30	86.0	21.1	70	158.0
−0.6	31	87.8	21.7	71	159.8
0.0	32	89.6	22.2	72	161.6
0.6	33	91.4	22.8	73	163.4
1.1	34	93.2	23.3	74	165.2
1.7	35	95.0	23.9	75	167.0
2.2	36	96.8	24.4	76	168.8
2.8	37	98.6	25.0	77	170.6
3.3	38	100.4	25.6	78	172.4
3.9	39	102.2	26.1	79	174.2
4.4	40	104.0	26.7	80	176.0
5.0	41	105.8	27.2	81	177.8
5.6	42	107.6	27.8	82	179.6
6.1	43	109.4	28.3	83	181.4
6.7	44	111.2	28.9	84	183.2
7.2	45	113.0	29.4	85	185.0
7.8	46	114.8	30.0	86	186.8
8.3	47	116.6	30.6	87	188.6
8.9	48	118.4	31.1	88	190.4
9.4	49	120.2	31.7	89	192.2
10.0	50	122.0	32.2	90	194.0
10.6	51	123.8	32.8	91	195.8
11.1	52	125.6	33.3	92	197.6
11.7	53	127.4	33.9	93	199.4
12.2	54	129.2	34.4	94	201.2
12.8	55	131.0	35.0	95	203.0
13.3	56	132.8	35.6	96	204.8
13.9	57	134.6	36.1	97	206.6
14.4	58	136.4	36.7	98	208.4
15.0	59	138.2	37.2	99	210.2
15.6	60	140.0	37.8	100	212.0
16.1	61	141.8	40.6	105	221
16.7	62	143.6	43.3	110	230
17.2	63	145.4	46.1	115	239
17.8	64	147.2	48.9	120	248

Continued on next page.

TEMPERATURE CONVERSION CHART

Centigrade—Fahrenheit

NOTE: The center column of numbers in boldface refers to the temperature in degrees, either Centigrade or Fahrenheit, which it is desired to convert into the other scale. If converting from Fahrenheit to Centigrade degrees, the equivalent temperature will be found in the left column, while if converting from degrees Centigrade to degrees Fahrenheit, the answer will be found in the column on the right.

Centigrade		Fahrenheit	Centigrade		Fahrenheit
51.7	125	257	129	265	509
54.4	130	266	132	270	518
57.2	135	275	135	275	527
60.0	140	284	138	280	536
62.8	145	293	141	285	545
65.6	150	302	143	290	554
68.3	155	311	146	295	563
71.1	160	320	149	300	572
73.9	165	329	154	310	590
76.7	170	338	160	320	608
79.4	175	347	166	330	626
82.2	180	356	171	340	644
85.0	185	365	177	350	662
87.8	190	374	182	360	680
90.6	195	383	188	370	698
93.3	200	392	193	380	716
96.1	205	401	199	390	734
98.9	210	410	204	400	752
100.0	212	414	210	410	770
102	215	419	216	420	788
104	220	428	221	430	806
107	225	437	227	440	824
110	230	446	232	450	842
113	235	455	238	460	860
116	240	464	243	470	878
118	245	473	249	480	896
121	250	482	254	490	914
124	255	491	260	500	932
127	260	500			

These formulas may also be used for converting Centigrade or Fahrenheit degrees into the other scales.

°C	Decimal Vernier	°F
0.06	0.1	0.18
0.11	0.2	0.36
0.17	0.3	0.54
0.22	0.4	0.72
0.28	0.5	0.90
0.33	0.6	1.08
0.39	0.7	1.26
0.44	0.8	1.44
0.50	0.9	1.62

$$\text{Degrees Cent., } °C = \frac{5}{9}(°F + 40) - 40$$

$$= \frac{5}{9}(°F - 32)$$

$$\text{Degrees Kelvin, } °K = °C + 273.2$$

$$\text{Degrees Fahr., } °F = \frac{9}{5}(°C + 40) - 40$$

$$= \frac{9}{5}°C + 32$$

$$\text{Degrees Rankine, } °R = °F + 459.7$$

AREAS OF CIRCLES

(Diameters in inches, areas in square inches)

Diameters	Area	Diameters	Area	Diameters	Area
1/16	.00307	3/8	8.9462	3/8	69.0293
1/8	.01227	7/16	9.2806	1/2	70.8823
3/16	.02761	1/2	9.6211	5/8	72.7599
1/4	.04909	9/16	9.9678	3/4	74.6621
5/16	.07670	5/8	10.3206	7/8	76.5888
3/8	.1104	11/16	10.6783	10	78.5398
7/16	.1503	3/4	11.0447	1/8	80.5158
1/2	.1964	13/16	11.4158	1/4	82.5161
9/16	.2485	7/8	11.7933	3/8	84.5409
5/8	.3068	15/16	12.1767	1/2	86.5903
11/16	.3712	4	12.5664	5/8	88.6643
3/4	.4418	1/8	13.3641	3/4	90.7628
13/16	.5185	1/4	14.1863	7/8	92.8858
7/8	.6013	3/8	15.0330	11	95.0334
15/16	.6903	1/2	15.9043	1/8	97.2055
1	.7854	5/8	16.8002	1/4	99.4022
1/16	.8866	3/4	17.7206	3/8	101.6234
1/8	.9940	7/8	18.6655	1/2	103.8691
3/16	1.1075	5	19.6349	5/8	106.1394
1/4	1.2272	1/8	20.6289	3/4	108.4343
5/16	1.3530	1/4	21.6476	7/8	110.7537
3/8	1.4849	3/8	22.6907	12	113.098
7/16	1.6230	1/2	23.7583	1/4	117.859
1/2	1.7671	5/8	24.8505	1/2	122.719
9/16	1.9175	3/4	25.9673	3/4	127.677
5/8	2.0739	7/8	27.1086	13	132.733
11/16	2.2365	6	28.2744	1/4	137.887
3/4	2.4053	1/8	29.4648	1/2	143.139
13/16	2.5802	1/4	30.6797	3/4	148.489
7/8	2.7612	3/8	31.9191	14	153.938
15/16	2.9483	1/2	33.1831	1/4	159.485
2	3.1416	5/8	34.4717	1/2	165.122
1/16	3.3410	3/4	35.7848	3/4	170.874
1/8	3.5466	7/8	37.1224	15	176.715
3/16	3.7583	7	38.4846	1/4	182.655
1/4	3.9761	1/8	39.8713	1/2	188.692
5/16	4.2000	1/4	41.2826	3/4	194.828
3/8	4.4301	3/8	42.7184	16	201.062
7/16	4.6664	1/2	44.1787	1/4	207.395
1/2	4.9087	5/8	45.6636	1/2	213.825
9/16	5.1572	3/4	47.1731	3/4	220.354
5/8	5.4119	7/8	48.7071	17	226.981
11/16	5.6727	8	50.2656	1/4	233.706
3/4	5.9396	1/8	51.8487	1/2	240.529
13/16	6.2126	1/4	53.4563	3/4	247.447
7/8	6.4918	3/8	55.0884	18	254.469
15/16	6.7771	1/2	56.7451	1/4	261.587
3	7.0686	5/8	58.4264	1/2	268.803
1/16	7.3662	3/4	60.1322	3/4	276.117
1/8	7.6699	7/8	61.8625	19	283.529
3/16	7.9798	9	63.6174	1/4	291.040
1/4	8.2958	1/8	65.3968	1/2	298.648
5/16	8.6179	1/4	67.2008	3/4	306.355

Continued on next page.

AREAS OF CIRCLES

(Diameters in inches, areas in square inches)

Diameters	Area	Diameters	Area	Diameters	Area
20	314.159	½	730.618	41	1320.25
¼	322.063	¾	742.645	¼	1336.40
½	330.064	31	754.769	½	1352.65
¾	338.164	¼	766.992	¾	1369.00
21	346.361	½	779.313	42	1385.45
¼	354.657	¾	791.732	¼	1401.99
½	363.051	32	804.247	½	1418.63
¾	371.543	¼	816.865	¾	1435.37
22	380.134	½	829.579	43	1452.20
¼	388.822	¾	842.391	¼	1469.14
½	397.609	33	855.301	½	1486.17
¾	406.494	¼	868.309	¾	1503.30
23	415.477	½	881.415	44	1520.53
¼	424.558	¾	894.618	¼	1537.86
½	433.737	34	907.922	½	1555.29
¾	443.015	¼	921.323	¾	1572.81
24	452.389	½	934.822	45	1590.43
¼	461.864	¾	948.418	¼	1608.16
½	471.436	35	962.115	½	1625.97
¾	481.107	¼	975.909	¾	1643.89
25	490.875	½	989.789	46	1661.91
¼	500.742	¾	1003.788	¼	1680.02
½	510.706	36	1017.878	½	1698.23
¾	520.769	¼	1032.065	¾	1716.54
26	530.929	½	1046.349	47	1734.95
¼	541.189	¾	1060.732	¼	1753.45
½	551.547	37	1075.213	½	1772.06
¾	562.003	¼	1089.792	¾	1790.76
27	572.557	½	1104.469	48	1809.56
¼	583.209	¾	1119.244	¼	1828.46
½	593.959	38	1134.118	½	1847.46
¾	604.807	¼	1149.089	¾	1866.55
28	615.754	½	1164.159	49	1885.75
¼	626.798	¾	1179.327	¼	1905.04
½	637.941	39	1194.593	½	1924.43
¾	649.182	¼	1209.95	¾	1943.91
29	660.521	½	1225.42	50	1963.49
¼	671.959	¾	1240.98	¼	1983.18
½	683.494	40	1256.64	½	2002.97
¾	695.128	¼	1272.39	¾	2022.85
30	706.858	½	1288.25		
¼	718.689	¾	1304.20		

INDEX

This index supplements the Caption Indexes found on the first pages of each chapter. It does not generally duplicate these items. Caption Indexes are referred to herein under appropriate references. Cross-indexing has been used where it seemed desirable.

A

Accuracy of calculations, 2-2
  of piping pressure loss calculations, 26-2
Acid number of lubricants (def), 13-4
Acoustics (see Sound), 33-1
Adiabatic compression (def) (formula), 3-14
  theoretical power, positive-displacement, 3-19
Adiabatic process (def), 2-10
Affinity laws, applied to centrifugal, 4-25
Aftercooling (def), 2-5
Agitation by compressed air, 32-6
Air - compressibility and temperature-entropy charts, 34-12, 13
Air-cooled reciprocating (def), 6-2, 6-5
Air lift, *see caption index*, 31-1
Air speed through valves, 6-20, 21
Air power, compressor selection, 16-2 to 4
  systems for, *see caption index*, 27-1
Air piping, pressure losses (tables), 34-77 to 87
  correction to above tables, 26-10
  equivalent loss in fittings, 34-78
Air requirements, for sand blast, 27-4
  for typical pneumatic tools, 27-5
Air-vapor mixture, properties of (chart), 34-117
  relations-specific humidity, total pressure, saturation temperature (chart), 34-114
  relations-specific volume, total pressure, percent air by weight (chart), 34-115
  relations-temperature, dew point, relative humidity, pressure, specific humidity (chart), 34-118
  saturated (def), 2-11
    specific gravity of vs temperature and relative humidity (chart), 34-116
  superheated (def), 2-12
  weight of water vs temperature and percent saturation (table), 34-119

Air weight vs temperature and pressure (table)' 34-121
Altitude (def), 2-5
  and atmospheric pressure, 34-158, 159
  correction to bhp/100 for reciprocating units (chart), 34-122
  effect on air consumption of rock drills and tools (table), 34-153
  effect on capacity of reciprocating unit (chart), 34-154
  effect on dynamic unit, 4-26
  effect on positive-displacement unit, 4-17
  effect on helical-lobe rotary, 4-21
Amagat's law, 3-3
Ammonia - compressibility and temperature-entropy charts, 34-14, 15
Ammonia feed gas - compressibility and temperature-entropy charts
  five component mixture, 34-43 to 45
  76/24 mixture, 34-46 to 49
Amonton's law, 3-3
Angle-type reciprocating, 6-8, 11
Application
  air agitation in tanks, 32-6
  of axial-flow dynamic, 9-33
  of boosters, 12-2
  of centrifugal, 9-15, 17
  of compressed air - typical, 32-1
  of control systems, 25-1, 9, 11
  of cryogenics, 23-2, 3
  of ejectors as thermal compressors 10-1
  of expanders, 21-1, 2
  of gas turbine, 15-31
  of NL units, 14-2, 3
  of orifices and jets, 5-17
  of portables, 11-2
Area of circles, 34-170, 171
Atmospheric pressure and altitude, 34-158, 159
Auto-ignition of lubricants (def), 13-4